Theodore J. GLEASON

International Commercial Law for Managers

Éditions « Campus Ouvert »

2016

Dans la même collection
(distribuée par L'Harmattan)

BLOCH Monique et SADI Nacer-Eddine : *Droit de l'entreprise pour le manager*
ISBN : 979-10-90293-04-5, 188 pages, 18 €

DAMIAN Michel : *Les chemins infinis de la décarbonisation – Neuf questions-clé pour la COP 21* - ISBN : 979-10-90293-20-5, 133 pages, 12 €

FERGUENE Améziane : *Croissance économique et développement : nouvelles approches*
ISBN : 979-10-90293-01-4, 155 pages, 15 €

FERGUENE Améziane : *Économie territoriale et développement local : concepts et expériences* - ISBN : 979-10-90293-05-2, 180 pages, 18 €

FERGUENE A. et CHANEL A. : *Analyse sociologique des organisations – Eléments pour le diagnostic organisationnel* - ISBN : 979-10-90293-21-2, 162 pages, 18 €

GAULARD Mylène *: Économie politique de l'émergence*

ISBN : 979-10-90293-16-8, 121 pages, 14 €

MORISET Claire : *Com'une histoire – Emergence et structuration de la communication dans les organisations* - ISBN : 979-10-90293 18-1, 177 pages, 18 €

PÉCHOUX M. et PLAUCHU V. *Maitriser les difficultés du français pour réussir ses études de Droit-Économie-Gestion* - ISBN : 979-10-90293-23-6, 182 pages : 18 €

PLAUCHU Vincent : *Socio-Économie de l'environnement : problèmes, analyses, stratégies d'acteurs* - ISBN : 979-10-90293-02-1, 265 pages, 24 €

PLAUCHU Vincent : *Mesure et amélioration des performances des entreprises*
ISBN : 979-10-90293-19-9, 184 pages, 18 €, Nouvelle édition augmentée 2015

PLAUCHU Vincent : *Management environnemental : analyses, stratégies et mise en œuvre*
ISBN : 979-10-90293-00-7, 172 pages, 18 €

PLAUCHU Vincent : *Mettre en place une démarche qualité. Avec quatre études de cas*
ISBN : 979-10-90293-11-3, 171 pages, 18 €

PLAUCHU Vincent : *Invitation à la lecture – Recueil de textes de culture générale*
ISBN : 979-10-90293-14-4, 185 pages, 18 €

SADI Nacer-Eddine : *Introduction aux marchés financiers : fonctions, institutions, opérations, méthodes d'analyse* - ISBN : 979-10-90293-17-5, 161 pages, 18 €

SADI Nacer-Eddine : *Introduction au management : des sciences de gestion aux pratiques managériales* - ISBN : 979-10-902931-15-1, 199 pages, 18 €

SIORAK Richard : *L'analyse stratégique de trois groupes : McDonalds, Danone et Salomon* - ISBN : 979-10-90293-13-7, 209 pages, 18 €

Acknowledgements

I would like to thank Nacer Eddine Sadi for his encouragement as well as Vincent Plauchu and Campus Ouvert for the support and opportunity. Additionally, special thanks go out to Jean-Michel do Carmo Silva, Alexandru Zgardan, and Todd Wells for their review of my drafts as well as for their very useful edits and commentary. Finally, I'd like to thank Lisa Devy for her support.

Table of Contents

Timeline

Throughout history merchants have engaged in trade over long distances. Over time legal systems have developed to regulate such trade, eventually developing into a system of international commercial and trade law. Today's international legal framework in the context of commerce and trade takes its shape mostly from post-World War II multilateral trade agreements between nation states. Nevertheless, the law is ever changing, and in the face of rapid globalization, future development of and changes to the current legal regime are to be expected. Some important past developments related to international commercial and trade law are highlighted below:

- Roman Times – Development of Roman Law; beginnings of code based (Civil Law) legal systems
- Medieval Times – Development of *lex mercatoria*
- 1066 – Norman Conquest; beginnings of Common Law legal system
- 1804 – French Civil Code (Napoleonic Code) established, beginnings of modern Civil Law legal systems
- 1807 – Development of French Commercial Code
- 1883 – Paris Convention for the Protection of Industrial Property becomes effective
- 1887 – Berne Convention for the Protection of Literary and Artistic Works becomes effective
- 1945 – Establishment of the United Nations; Statute of International Court of Justice
- 1947 – General Agreement on Tariffs and Trade (GATT) signed by 23 nations
- 1952 – Creation of European Coal and Steel Community (Belgium, France, Italy, Luxembourg, The Netherlands, West Germany); beginnings of European economic integration
- 1958 – Treaty of Rome comes into force; creation of European Economic Community
- 1959 – New York Convention on the Recognition and Enforcement of Foreign Arbitral Awards becomes effective
- 1966 – Establishment of International Center for the Settlement of Investment Disputes (ICSID)

- 1967 – Inauguration of Association of Southeast Asian Nations (ASEAN)
- 1980 – Vienna Convention on the Law of Treaties comes into force
- 1988 – Convention on the International Sale of Goods (CISG) comes into force
- 1991 – Southern Common Market (Mercosur) becomes effective
- 1994 – North American Free Trade Agreement (NAFTA) comes into force
- 1995 – Marrakesh Agreement comes into force (beginning of the WTO)
- 2009 – Lisbon Treaty comes into force; Most recent reforms to legal framework of EU
- 2015 – Trans-Pacific Partnership negotiations concluded. Agreement up for ratification by domestic legislatures of signatory countries

Introduction
(Why Should Non-Lawyers Study the Law?)

It is pertinent to begin this work with a discussion about why non-lawyers should be interested in learning about the law. Both management students and professionals should care about the law because, simply put, the law is omnipresent. The law covers and regulates almost all areas of business activity from the day a business is formed to the day it is wound up and even beyond. Perhaps the first thing one thinks of when considering business law is the law of contracts. Contracts determine the rights and obligations of parties in the majority of their business relationships. Naturally, contracts are an extremely important area of law for any business to master in order to effectively manage the risk associated with its activities.

Nevertheless, business law goes far beyond "just" contract law. For example, corporate (using US terminology) or company (using UK terminology) law governs business formation, governance issues, securities laws, and other areas related to the functioning of companies. Any business with employees must comply with the relevant employment and labor laws and regulations in the jurisdictions where they have operations. Sales law is a particular area of contract law which governs the sale of goods between two parties. Some businesses might find themselves dealing with matters of criminal law although we all hope to avoid those situations in the first place. Property law gives businesses rights in tangible, intangible, and real property. Intellectual property law gives individuals and businesses the ability to protect their valuable ideas. Legal regimes for insolvency and bankruptcy set rules and provide protections for businesses that are unable to meet their obligations. Of course, like it or not, disputes are likely to arise between a business and its business partners, employees, customers, or even with the government. A dispute resolution strategy needs to be in place to effectively navigate such undesirable situations. To further complicate matters, each of these issues may be regulated differently from country to country!

To say that the short summary in the preceding paragraph is nonexhaustive is an understatement. For the non-lawyer, law can be very intimidating, and many students and even some seasoned professionals may be inclined to forego any serious attempt to understand the law since they believe that if they have legal problems in the future they will just be able to consult with a legal expert. For most, that is wishful thinking. Many companies, especially small and medium sized businesses do not have legal professionals on staff and may not have the ability to incur legal fees every time a legal question arises, reserving the use of outside counsel to the most complex and serious of matters. It is highly important for managers to be able to recognize when they need to ultimately consult with a lawyer, and when they can handle certain issues, i.e., the negotiation of a simple sales contract, without referring to outside help. If professional legal help is available, that is ideal in many situations, but again, this is quite often not the case.

Matters become even more complex when a business moves into the international sphere since doing business internationally carries inherent risks which are not necessarily present domestically. For example, in a domestic sale of goods transaction both parties know that even if the contract contains neither a clause pertaining to the applicable law nor determining how disputes should be resolved, domestic law and court procedures will nonetheless be available to resolve any disputes between those parties. Similarly, the parties understand domestic trade usages and practices. They will use the same vocabulary and jargon. Language and cultural issues generally won't be an issue as it is less likely that something will be "lost in translation." The same sale of goods transaction becomes much more complicated in an international context. The law may be very different concerning relevant issues related to the contract. The court procedures found in the countries where the parties to the contract are located may be completely different. Even if the parties use the same language there may be different understandings of definitions, jargon, or other vocabulary related to the contract. The difficulties that arise when the parties come from two countries with very different languages become even more significant. Add cultural differences to the mix and it is very easy for misunderstandings to arise.

The difficulties do not end there. In the simple example of a contract for the sale of goods additional concerns need to be taken into consideration in an international context which do not necessarily exist in the domestic context. Meeting deadlines may be complicated as communications, even with modern technology, are more difficult due to time zone differences. Distances are greater, requiring the parties to incur higher costs and more risk related to shipping and transport of the goods. Currency rates fluctuate. Unexpected events such as natural disasters or political revolutions take place. In short, while the business law of a particular country is by no means a simple area of law, international business has inherent features which cause the law to become even more complex.

Despite the complexity of business law in an international context the purpose of this work is to focus on international commercial law in an effort to simplify some of the basic concepts which are essential to any party which may engage in international commerce in the future. An important element of management is managing risk; managing legal risk in the international commercial context first requires a basic and subsequently an in-depth understanding of the law related to international commercial work. Legal risk can be managed by first engaging to understand the risks which are present. It may seem obvious, but parties to commercial relationships must strive to use a well-structured contract to manage risk wherever possible. Even somewhat sophisticated entities may at times enter into contracts which are woefully insufficient or lacking in relevant terms. It is also very important to stay up to date since laws can and do change on a regular basis.

Finally, the purpose of this work is not to substitute for the need to consult with an expert. The scope of this work is limited, non-exhaustive, and is merely intended to introduce the reader to some common issues which arise in the context of international commercial and trade law. One of the problems for the non-legally trained professional is that there is a lack of simplified works which can act as a starting point on this vast topic. Therefore, the goal is that through this work the reader, who presumably has little to no formal legal training, will become conversant in the topics covered herein and be able to continue towards more detailed, technical understanding either independently or through following a defined course of studies. Even if the reader continues towards more detailed understanding of these topics, it is nevertheless important to keep in mind that situations will generally arise where one requires an attorney not only licensed in their jurisdiction, but also competent in issues of international commercial law. This work intends merely to provide a basic understanding of the framework of international commercial law so that the current and future managers can confidently move forward when engaging in international commerce.

Legal Systems

Before beginning the discussion of international commercial and trade law it is necessary to have a basic understanding of what legal systems exist around the world[1]. Naturally, each country has its own legal system. There are the French, German, Chinese, UK, US, Indian, Australian and many other legal systems each with their own unique attributes and peculiarities. Some countries, for example a federal country like the United States of America, have multiple legal systems. This means that there is one federal legal system for the country as a whole alongside legal systems unique to each state of the federal system. Additionally, in Europe, all countries which are member states of the European Union have their own domestic legal systems but are also part of and subject to the EU legal system, although European integration does not rise to the level of US federalism. In short, examining and comparing similarities and differences between different legal systems can be a complex endeavor. Since the focus of this work is **international** commercial law there will be no focus on the commercial law of any one particular domestic legal system. Nevertheless, the legal systems found around the world many times do contain a multitude of similarities, which is where we will begin.

Some generalizations must be made in order to gain the required basic understanding of the similarities and differences between domestic legal systems around the world. Fortunately legal systems found around the world can generally be classified into families. Families of legal systems consist of domestic legal systems which share certain characteristics. (De Cruz, 2007) There are two main families of legal systems, the Civil Law[2] legal system and the Common Law legal system. There are

---

[1]It is important to understand that this work and particularly this chapter, being written in English by an attorney with principally Common Law Legal System training, approaches this topic using English terminology heavily influenced by Common Law concepts. Terms used herein may not be directly translatable to other languages and legal systems. This work attempts to simplify and generalize, and when looking at specific legal systems, additional verification of concepts discussed in this chapter is necessary.

[2] Civil Law (capital C, capital L) should be differentiated from civil law (lowercase c, lowercase l). Civil Law refers to a type of legal system found in many parts of the world; civil law refers to a branch of law dealing with private relationships, and is

many other relevant legal systems beyond these two legal systems, for example the Socialist[3] Law legal system, which has diminished in importance since the demise of the Soviet Union. Religious law such as Islamic or Hindu law is quite relevant in certain parts of the world. Some countries mix characteristics of the main legal systems and are not easy to categorize. China has unique characteristics which may not be found outside of China, leading some to classify it as having its own legal system, while others recognize that China has code-based laws and classify it as a Civil Law legal system (although there is some debate to the accuracy of this classification since it also maintains Socialist Law influence). (CIA World Fact Book, 2016) Many other countries have their own customary law unique to their own culture and development. There is also regional law such as that which is applicable in the member states of the European Union. International law exists on top of all these domestic and regional legal systems. Despite the existence of all of these legal systems, when one looks at the world as a whole it becomes clear that the most commonly used systems are the Civil Law and Common Law legal systems. This is in large part a byproduct of European colonization.

The Civil Law legal system is the most widely used legal system in the world in terms of number of countries which use the system. The Common Law legal system is not as widely used as the Civil Law legal system, however in the context of international commerce it is very important since the amount of trade flowing out of Common Law legal systems is almost equal the amount of trade flowing out of Civil Law legal systems (excluding China from the equation since as previously mentioned there is some debate concerning whether China is truly a Civil Law legal system). (Juriglobe, 2007) So what are the differences between the Civil Law and the Common Law legal systems?

1. Civil Law

Let's begin with the Civil Law legal system. The Civil Law legal system is used in countries such as France, Germany, Switzerland, Brazil, Turkey, most of Latin America, various Arab states, North African countries, Indonesia and many other places around the world. Influences of the Civil Law system can be said to begin with Roman law origins, however, modern Civil Law was heavily influenced by the 1804 French Civil

---

found in many different legal systems, including Civil Law and Common Law systems.

[3] In this context Socialist Law legal systems refers to old Soviet style socialism, not the democratic socialism found in Western Europe and elsewhere.

Code (*Code civil*) also known as the Napoleonic Code. The German Civil Code (*Bürgerliches Gesetchbuch*) has also played an important role in development of Civil Law legal systems in various countries. In fact there are two main sub-categories of Civil Law legal systems: 1) countries which follow the French style of Civil Law (Napoleonic), and 2) countries which follow the German style of Civil Law. (Moussakis, 2014) The key characteristic of Civil Law legal systems is that the primary sources of law are statutes, codes, and other legislative instruments. Statutes and codes are laws typically created by a legislative body (e.g., Parliament). In general this is the only branch of government that has the power to create primary sources of law in a Civil Law country.

Hierarchy of Law in Civil Law Legal Systems

It is important to have an understanding of the hierarchy of sources of law in any legal system. In most legal systems there is the highest or **supreme source** of domestic law, which is generally the Constitution. This is the case in typical Civil Law legal systems. The Constitution provides a legal framework for a country, sets basic principles related to the structure and functioning of government, and in many cases also provides basic rights to citizens living in the territory governed by the particular Constitution.

Underneath the Constitution exist **primary sources** of law which set the main rules of law governing a country[4]. In a Civil Law system these primary sources of law generally consist of legislative instruments (laws, codes in various contexts). This is necessary because the Constitution is generally not a document which is detailed enough to provide all the rules necessary to govern the functioning of an efficient society. Nor is that the role of the Constitution. These additional rules are therefore created by the legislature to do the work required to truly govern the citizens of the particular country. It is important to recognize that while statutes, codes, and other legislative instruments are primary sources of law, they are lower on the hierarchy than the Constitution, and therefore

---

[4] Classifying sources of law as "primary" and "secondary" is an approach used in Common Law systems as well as the EU system, but may seem strange to certain Civil Law legal professionals. For example, this classification may strike a francophone legal professional trained in France as being odd since while the French legal system has a hierarchy of sources of law, the terms primary and secondary are not used. For purposes of comparison this work compares primary and secondary sources of law in Common Law systems to their closest equivalents in Civil Law systems.

cannot be in conflict with the principles found in the Constitution. There may also be various forms of legislative instruments in a particular Civil Law country which have a hierarchy among themselves; however such details which may vary greatly from country to country will not be examined in detail in this work.

EXAMPLE

If the Constitution of the hypothetical country of Urbania states that the citizens of Urbania shall never be allowed to wear purple shirts, the Urbanian legislature would not be able to create a law allowing purple shirts to be worn by Urbanian citizens on Fridays. Should the legislature nonetheless attempt to create such a law, the law could be challenged and ultimately be deemed unconstitutional and inapplicable by the judicial or other relevant procedures in Urbania. While this example may be silly (so as to be easier to remember!) this is the general idea of hierarchy of laws. All laws must be in conformity with all other sources which are superior on the hierarchy.

Even in a Civil Law system where the legislature creates comprehensive codes which are drafted and designed to cover as many eventualities as possible, such codes will not be sufficient to regulate the needs of everyday society. Therefore **secondary sources** of law are required in order to provide additional law to fill in the gaps which exist in the higher sources of any given legal system. They can also, under certain circumstances, be developed on their own (such as an executive decree) as long as they do not conflict with higher sources on the hierarchy. Secondary sources of law can take many forms, and in most countries there is a sub-hierarchy within this very large category of sources of law; however such sub-hierarchies are beyond the scope of this work.

Secondary sources of law can be executive decrees or orders created by the executive branch of government (President, e.g.) as well as rules and regulations issued by government agencies or ministries. Importantly, in Civil Law jurisdictions, case law or jurisprudence is considered to be a secondary "source" of law. Judges in Civil Law countries do not create binding, primary sources of law; they merely apply the law as it exists to the case in front of their court. Their reasoning can be used by lawyers in future cases as persuasive authority in an attempt to convince a Court to rule in their favor, but case law simply does not "create law" in Civil Law countries. Additionally, doctrinal or scholarly writings commenting on interpretation of the law as well as discussing any gaps that exist in the primary sources of law, while not technically sources of hard law, can be influential in influencing lawmakers as well as judges (perhaps more so than in Common Law systems). Keep in mind, once more, that the specific hierarchies will differ from country to country, and this is merely a simplified overview of a general hierarchy of laws that will exist in a "typical" Civil Law country.

The Code in Civil Law Legal Systems

Understanding that code is a primary source of law in Civil Law systems, the next step is to understand how code is created. As previously explained, code is generally created by legislative bodies. Each country's legislature has its own domestic procedures for creating laws. Nonetheless, in a Civil Law country the purpose of code is to provide general rules which are developed in the abstract. In other words, the rules are not developed in response to any specific case between two parties rather they are developed in an effort to govern all future possible cases and to solve any future problem in a particular area of law. Code is generally structured in a logical fashion whereby at the very least a general principle will be concisely stated in the code. This general principle may be followed by additional detailed rules until the initial general principle is fully developed. The code will then move to the next general principle.

Even if an article of code by itself seems to be quite detailed it does not exist in a vacuum. It will often contain cross references to other sections of the same code or even articles contained in other legal instruments from the same legal system. The code will also be complemented by secondary sources of law such as executive decrees and orders. Even still, there may be gaps in the law which need to be complemented by understanding doctrinal writing or jurisprudence. In short, it is not necessarily possible to simply read the code and have a full understanding of what the law governing a particular matter in a Civil Law country may be; however the code is where one must begin when trying to determine what the law is.

So far the only code that has been generally referenced in this work has been the Civil Code. However, in Civil Law legal systems specialized codes exist for various areas of the law. Typically there will be specialized codes such as the Tax Code, the Intellectual Property Code, the Penal Code, the Commercial Code, etc.

Commercial Law

Commercial law in Civil Law legal systems is a generally governed by its own special set of rules, the Commercial Code. There is a very important distinction between general civil law matters and commercial law matters in Civil Law jurisdictions. Such distinctions are not normally as apparent in Common Law jurisdictions. For example, in many Civil Law countries there are separate courts for commercial matters with court procedures for disputes designed with commercial parties in mind. Additionally, the specific rules governing commercial contracts might be different than the rules governing general civil contracts.

A relevant example could be a contract for the sale of a car. If one individual, a natural person, sells his car in his individual capacity to another individual, natural person, in her individual capacity for 15,000€, the contract is a general civil contract. The parties are not merchants or traders, are not acting in a commercial context, and therefore the commercial code would not apply. If the parties have a dispute about the contract, it will go to a court of general civil jurisdiction and not a commercial court. However, if we change the example, and both parties are merchants, but the subject matter of the contract is the same (e.g., sale of the same car for 15,000€) this transaction will be nevertheless considered as commercial. This means that the law governing the contract will be commercial law in addition to the general civil law related to contracts, and these laws might be substantively different. Where they are different the commercial law will apply. If there is a dispute between the parties, they will not go to the court of general civil jurisdiction; rather they will go to a commercial court, which will have different procedures designed for use by commercial parties (e.g., the type of evidence allowed to be used in the case may be different). The judges will also be different and will likely have a commercial background.

Public v. Private

In Civil Law legal systems there is also an important fundamental difference between the branches of public and private law. Simply defined, public law is the branch of law dealing with relations concerning the government. Government is broadly defined and generally can mean any subdivision of the government, or even a state owned enterprise. Private law simply defined is the branch of law dealing with the rights and duties between private persons. (Rosenfeld, 2013) Private persons can be broadly defined as anyone from a natural person (individual), to a corporation, to an association or non-profit organization, to any other non-government organization. So if the government is involved in the matter it is a matter of public law. If the government is not involved in the matter it is a matter of private law. While there are some different rules in Common Law systems for public and private law matters, when comparing Common Law systems to Civil Law systems the differences between public and private law are not nearly as significant.

The substance of public law rules can be different than the substance of rules governing relationships between private parties. There are separate courts for public (e.g., an administrative court) and private law (e.g., a civil court of first instance) matters. There may be different court hierarchies. For example, in France there is a "Cour de Cassation" which operates as the highest court for French private law matters and the "Conseil d'État" which is the highest court for French public law matters. In Civil Law legal systems, the difference between public and private law is important enough that law students many times decide to focus their studies and legal professionals focus their practice on one branch or the other.

EXAMPLE

An example of how the public and private law distinction is relevant to business and commerce can be illustrated by the following example which takes place in Agriculturaneo, a hypothetical Civil Law country:

- If Company A in Agriculturaneo contracts to sell goods to Company B in exchange for payment, this is clearly a matter of Agriculturanean private law, governed by private rules of contracts, and if there is a dispute, the court system in place for matters of private law (likely a commercial court) will be used to resolve the dispute.

- If instead Company A sells the same goods to the Government of Agriculturaneo for the same price that they sold the goods to Company B, the contract will be governed by different laws and rules applying to public contracts. Even though the contract concerns the same goods for the same price as the previous example, if there is a dispute between Company A and the Agricultaranean government, the courts and procedures used to resolve the dispute will be those available for public law matters (and in reality, depending on the country, may take much longer than commercial court, e.g.).

Court Procedures

Another characteristic of note is that, while no country's trial system functions as a pure prototype model, Civil Law countries use an inquisitorial system of trial proceedings for civil and commercial matters. (Australian Law Reform Commission, 1999) Trials in Civil Law legal systems bear little resemblance to what one may see in Hollywood movies and television series, which are generally based on Common Law court procedures (although even then, in many cases it is not fair to say that Hollywood fairly represents what Common Law trial procedures look like...directors many times do not let accuracy get in the way of compelling storytelling!). This is because the Common Law system uses the adversarial trial system, which is quite different than the inquisitorial system found in civil law countries.

The principal characteristic of the inquisitorial trial system is that the judge is an active participant in the trial, and engages directly with the parties. This means that the judge may ask for certain evidence to be produced by the parties, engage experts to assist the court, and examine witnesses directly. It is also important to note that in Civil Law legal systems, the procedures are mostly written, and courts rely much less on oral witness testimony than the Common Law systems, preferring written witness statements to oral witness testimony.

2. Common Law

Now that the basics of the Civil Law system have been covered, it is pertinent to look at the basic characteristics of the Common Law legal system. The historical origins of the Common Law legal system begin with the Norman Conquest of England in 1066. At this time the laws and customs found throughout the English territory were local in nature, and every village, town and city had its own customary law. Written laws were the exception, not the rule. The Norman Kings used a system of training itinerant justices (traveling judges) in the royal court system and sending those justices to all corners of the country to make royal justice more accessible (as well as to impose the royal law). This had the effect, over the course of centuries, of consolidating English law, moving from a system where each village, town and city had its own different law to a system where a common law, in other words the royal law, was applied throughout the territory. (Servidio-Delabre, 2004)

The English Common Law system has been in continuous development since, and was spread throughout the world via colonialism.

Today legal systems based on Common Law can be found all over the world, and in particular are used by many large trading nations. The Common Law system is in place in England and Wales, the United States, Australia, Canada, Hong Kong, Singapore, India, Nigeria, Kenya, Malaysia, and many other countries.

Hierarchy of Laws

Just as in Civil Law legal systems, the **supreme** or highest source of law in Common Law legal systems is the constitution. Again, the constitution of a country provides a government framework, defines and limits the powers of respective branches of governments, and often provides basic rights to citizens. Notably, the United Kingdom does not have a written constitution (although it does have "Constitutional Law" which is pieced together from various sources of law such as Acts of Parliament, conventions, and case law), however the UK is an outlier and the grand majority of Common Law legal systems have written constitutions.

The main difference between the hierarchy of laws in Civil and Common Law legal systems is found at the level of **primary** sources of law. Just as in Civil Law legal systems codes, statutes and other legislative instruments are primary sources of law. Yet, in Common Law systems case law (a.k.a. jurisprudence) is also a primary source of law. **Secondary** sources of law in Common Law jurisdictions take the form of executive orders and decrees, administrative or ministerial rules and regulations, doctrinal and scholarly writings, and all other sources of law. Please keep in mind that the specific hierarchy for any given country is more complex than the basic description given here, and there may be additional sub-levels of the hierarchy within the category of secondary sources of law, e.g., an executive order is a higher source of law than an academic article, which is a soft form of law.

When comparing the hierarchies of laws between Civil and Common Law systems it becomes clear that the main difference lies in the systems' respective approaches to case law. In Common Law systems judges have the power to "create" primary sources of law through their interpretation of law based on specific facts in front of the courts. As a general matter, Civil Law system judges do not have this power as only the legislature can create primary sources of law. On paper this may not seem like a very big difference. In reality this causes many differences in how these legal systems function.

For example, while both systems use code, statutes and other legislative instruments as primary sources of law, the nature of these legislative instruments are quite different between the legal systems. Civil Law codes can be quite extensive and attempt to provide a comprehensive set of rules to govern any given situation. To the contrary, while specific articles of codes or statutes found in Common Law legal systems may be very precise and detailed, as a body of law these codes and statutes tend to be less comprehensive, leaving room for the judicial branch to fill in any gaps through interpretation of the law in specific factual situations which come before the court.

For the commercial party it is important to note that the comprehensive nature of code in Civil Law systems can lead to contracts which contain less detailed provisions. This is because the Civil Law system code contains default articles (*dispositions suppletives*) which can be applied to a contract when the contract is silent on a particular issue. (Mousseron, 2010) Apart from certain mandatory provisions of statutory law, such default articles are not required to be used between the parties, but again, if the contract says nothing, these provisions will fill in the gaps of the contract. So if a party in a Civil Law system knows and is comfortable with the law, they need not write every detail in the contract since the Code may be able to fill in the gaps for them. In Common Law legal systems parties generally do not have this option. In most circumstances in a Common Law legal system if the parties wish to have something in their contract they must put it in their contract. This means that contracts in Common Law legal systems tend to be lengthier and more detailed than their Civil Law system counterparts.

This can lead to difficulties during contractual negotiations between parties coming from the different legal traditions. For example a party from a Civil Law legal system might take offense when their counterpart from a Common Law legal system proposes a 35 page long contract for a relatively simple and routine transaction. The party from the Civil Law legal system if given the chance to propose a similar contract may have proposed a much shorter version of the contract with references to the code provisions which govern the rights, duties and obligations of the parties to the contract along with any deviations therefrom. However, the party from the Common Law legal system does not have this option and therefore attempts to include as many potential situations in the contract as possible, even if it is unlikely that certain situations would ever occur. The party from the Civil Law system might not feel comfortable with the detailed contract and may even take offense at the fact that the contract includes provisions which it thinks are unnecessary or unwarranted. The party from the Civil Law system might even interpret the contract an insult or a commentary on their credibility or trustworthiness! Nonetheless the party from the Common Law legal system may simply be attempting to protect its own interests based on its local legal culture. This difference in legal culture is a direct result of the different hierarchies of sources of law found in the systems, and must be overcome if parties from the different legal systems wish to work together.

Jurisprudence

The key defining characteristic of the Common Law legal system is the role of jurisprudence or case law. Judges have the ability to create primary sources of law alongside the legislature in Common Law legal systems. The importance of this difference between the two systems cannot be understated. In Civil Law systems it is generally the legislature alone which has this power. In Common Law countries this role is shared between the legislature and the judiciary.

Cases in Common Law systems set **precedent**. Precedent simply refers to binding jurisprudence. In other words, when the courts decide a specific case in a certain way, future similar cases must follow the same reasoning as the previous case and arrive at a similar result. The logic behind the idea of precedent is that using previous cases to set the law will give parties the power to predict how the law will be applied in future cases, providing consistency and clarity in the application of law, thereby avoiding chaos. Nonetheless, in many cases the parties (via their lawyers) are arguing about whether the case in front of the court is in fact similar to a previous case or cases. This is because a judge in a Common Law system has the power to distinguish the case in front of his/her court and not apply the law from a previous case if the facts between the two cases are not similar enough. There is an inherent amount of flexibility for courts in Common Law systems to make their own interpretations.

That being said, it would be a misnomer to state that **all** courts in the Common Law legal system have the power to create law. (Perell, 1987) As a general matter, the power to create law begins at an appellate level and continues to a top (supreme) level. In order to better understand how this works, one must first understand that each legal system (whether Common Law or Civil Law), has a hierarchy of courts. Typically a court hierarchy will consist of three levels. At the bottom of the hierarchy will be a first instance or trial court, in the middle there will be an intermediate court of appeals to review court decisions from the first instance/trial level, and at the top there will be a supreme or highest level court, which makes the final decisions for a particular legal system. Again, this typical hierarchy can be found in both Common and Civil Law legal systems, but the role of the intermediate and highest level courts is distinct in Common Law legal systems as these courts have the power to create binding law. In other words, their decisions must be followed by future courts in similar cases.

Court Hierarchy	Power to Create Binding Jurisprudence in Common Law Legal Systems
Highest Level Court	The decisions and jurisprudence of the highest court in a Common Law legal system create law which must be followed by all lower courts in that legal system, and will typically be followed by the highest court itself in the future, unless the court itself is convinced in a future case that it should overrule its previous jurisprudence.
Intermediate Appellate Court	In general, the decisions and jurisprudence of intermediate appellate courts in a Common Law legal system create law which must be followed by all lower courts within that appellate court's geographic jurisdiction, and also followed by that future intermediate appellate court, unless the court itself is convinced in a future case that it should overrule its previous jurisprudence. The highest level court in a Common Law legal system is not bound by the previous decisions of intermediate appellate courts.
First Instance/Trial Court	The First Instance/Trial Court in general does not create law. It is not bound by its own previous decisions, and future courts are under no obligation to refer to previous First Instance/Trial Court decisions. A decision written by a court at this level can be persuasive in future cases, but is not binding. Reasoning for this lies in the fact that the principal role of the courts at this level is to make sure that the rules of procedure and evidence are appropriately applied, and ultimately make a solid decision grounded in law. Creating law would be an additional task which is beyond the scope of these courts' duties. Also, as a practical matter, it would lead to chaos as there are many of these courts in any given legal system, which could lead to conflicting decisions creating conflicting law throughout a particular jurisdiction. The purpose of precedent is to avoid chaos.

It is worth noting that in the previous paragraph only very general names are used to describe each court in the hierarchy. This is intentional since court names can be confusing and do not in reality tell us very much about the functions of a particular court. For example, in the United States, the Federal court system designates the first instance/trial court as the District Court, the intermediate court as the United States Court of Appeals, divided into regional "Circuits", and the highest court as the United States Supreme Court. A typical state such as Colorado, follows a similar structure and designates the first instance/trial court as the District Court, the intermediate court as the Colorado Court of Appeals, and the highest court as the Colorado Supreme Court. However, if you go to New York you will find that the first instance/trial court is called the Supreme Court, the intermediate court as the Appellate Division of the Supreme Court, and the highest court as the Court of Appeals. Similarly, in England (as well as many other Common Law countries), the first instance/trial court for certain matters is misleadingly called the High Court, the intermediate court is Court of Appeal, and the highest court is the Supreme Court of the United Kindgom.[5]

Code in Common Law Legal Systems

It is also imperative not to underestimate the importance of the Common Law equivalent of code. Legislatures in Common Law legal systems have the essential function of creating written, primary sources of law, just as in their Civil Law legal system counterparts. Nevertheless, the nature of these legislative instruments is different between the two systems. The Common Law equivalent of code (whether called, acts, statutes, codes, or anything else; what it is called will depend on the legal system) will generally be less comprehensive than its Civil Law counterpart. Again, this reverts back to the fact that the courts, alongside the legislature have the shared power to create primary sources of law in Common Law legal systems, whereas this function is reserved to the legislature in Civil Law legal systems. Despite this, when presented with a question for legal research, typically a Common Law lawyer will first resort to the legislative materials of his jurisdiction before diving into additional research (i.e., looking at jurisprudence). This is not to say that specific Common Law statutes will not be detailed, and in fact they are

---

[5] The UK court system underwent reform in 2005, which created the Supreme Court of the United Kingdom. Prior to this reform, the House of Lords (the upper branch of UK Parliament) had a judicial function in addition to its other roles, and had 12 'Law Lords' who acted as the highest court in the UK.

normally drafted in a detailed, precise manner. The caveat is that it is more likely that the legislative materials in the Common Law jurisdiction, being less comprehensive than their Civil Law counterparts overall, may not cover the particular questions at issue, meaning that often Common Law lawyers must begin their research by going directly to the case law. This would be comparatively rare for the Civil Law lawyer.

Court Procedures

As previously discussed, the Common Law system follows an adversarial approach to trial. This means that the role of the judge is to sit back and act as an inactive referee. This gives a lot of control to the lawyers in Common Law legal system court proceedings. While some judges are more active than others during court proceedings, and may ask occasional question, most judges in the Common Law system are passive in comparison to their Civil Law system counterparts. At the trial court level the judge is there to manage the proceedings to make sure that the rules of procedure and the rules of evidence are properly followed by the parties.

As anyone who has ever seen a Hollywood lawyer movie or television series can attest to, significant use is made of oral witness testimony in Common Law legal systems, even in civil and commercial cases. Many Civil Law systems do not rely as heavily on oral witness testimony, giving greater weight to written evidence, which renders witness testimony in Civil Law systems comparatively rare. The heavy use of witness testimony in Common Law systems is derived from the nature of the adversarial system. The idea, whether correct or not, is that through confrontation the truth shall prevail. That means that if a person has something to testify about which is relevant to a case, they are permitted to do so subject to evidentiary rules, with the very important caveat that they will be subject to cross-examination. Cross-examination is simply the procedure where the party offering testimony is examined by the lawyer for the party who is hostile to that witness's testimony. This leads to many heated courtroom exchanges, and such exchanges are comparatively harder to find in a Civil Law courtroom.

The adversarial system also allows each party to maintain significant control over gathering evidence, deciding which witnesses to present, and generally preparing their respective cases. This is especially interesting in the context of expert witnesses. Here, Common Law and Civil Law approaches diverge once more. In the Common Law, adversarial system, the parties commonly appoint their own (much of the time remunerated) experts. This many times can lead to a situation where both sides find an expert who opines in favor of each respective party. Often a case will turn on which expert is more credible, and this is sometimes referred to as the battle of the experts. Such battles are less common in Civil Law systems as judges in those systems will often appoint one expert for the case. In other words, there is simply a court-appointed expert and the parties do not find their own respective experts to support their positions. This avoids the battle of the experts, and appears to be more neutral at first glance, but any perceived benefits will always depend on the quality of the court-appointed expert!

Another Common Law system approach that would be foreign to a party from a Civil Law system is that prior to a trial the parties generally have the right to receive information from each other (e.g., Disclosure in the UK; the dreaded Discovery in the US where the parties not only receive information, but can demand information from each other, etc.). The rules can be quite different from country to country, but in general, parties must exchange information related to their case, even if it is adverse to their position, or be subject to penalties assessed by the Court. Of course there are limitations on this obligation to disclose, and in some cases right to demand, information from another party. At a basic level, such requests must be reasonable. Unlike in Civil Law systems, the Disclosure/Discovery procedures allow parties to file lawsuits even before they have collected all of the evidence required to prove their case, especially in North American jurisdictions. Parties to disputes do this knowing that procedures exist to obtain this information after the suit has been filed. To the contrary, for the most part a Civil Law lawyer will need to gather and compile all of the evidence required to prove their client's claim (to the extent possible), prior to filing the lawsuit, since no directly equivalent procedures are available.

Bibliography

AUSTRALIAN LAW REFORM COMMISSION. 1999. "The Adversarial-Non Adversarial Debate." *Siteresources.worldbank.org.* http://siteresources.worldbank.org/INTLAWJUSTINST/Resources /AdversarialNonAdversarialDebate.pdf.

CENTRAL INTELLIGENCE AGENCY. 2016. "The World Factbook; Field Listing::Legal System." *Www.cia.gov.* Accessed March 22. https://www.cia.gov/library/publications/the-world-factbook/fields /2100.html.

DE CRUZ, Peter. 2007. *Comparative Law in a Changing World*. 3rd ed. New York, NY: Routledge-Cavendish.

JURIGLOBE - World Legal Systems Research Group - University of Ottawa. 2016. "Tables of Distribution of the World GDP and GNI per Capita (in US $) per Legal Systems and Their Various Components."Accessed March 22. http://www.juriglobe.ca/eng/pib-rnb/entite-poli-pib-rnb.php.

MOUSOURAKIS, George. 2014. *Roman Law and the Origins of the Civil Law Tradition*. New York, NY: Springer Berlin Heidelberg.

MOUSSERON, Jean Marc, and Pierre Mousseron, eds. 2010. *Technique contractuelle*. 4. éd. par: Pierre Mousseron. Paris: Éditions Francis Lefebvre.

PERELL, Paul M. 1987. "Stare Decisis and Techniques of Legal Reasoning and Legal Argument – Best Guide to Canadian Legal Research." *Legal Research Update* 3 (11). http://legalresearch.org/writing-analysis/stare-decisis-techniques/.

ROSENFELD, Michel. 2013. "Rethinking the Boundaries between Public Law and Private Law for the Twenty First Century: An Introduction." *International Journal of Constitutional Law* 11 (1): 125–28. http://icon.oxfordjournals.org/content/11/1/125.full.

SERVIDIO-DELABRE, Eileen. 2004. *Common Law: Introduction to the English and American Legal Systems*. Hypercours Dalloz. Paris: Dalloz.

International Law

After gaining an understanding of what domestic legal systems look like around the world, it is appropriate to begin discussing international law. International law clearly exists, however its features are inherently different than traditional domestic law. Cynics who lack an understanding of the nature of international law may comment that 'there is no such thing as international law'. This is misguided. The cynic's comment is perhaps understandable when making the comparison of domestic law to international law. For example, as a very general matter when a law is passed in a domestic legal system, generally all persons within that legal system's jurisdiction are required to comply with that law, even if they do not agree with the law. This is not the case in international law.

EXAMPLE

The fictional country of Suburbanada passes a law, the Tuesday Green T-shirt Act, stating that green t-shirts must be worn by all citizens on Tuesdays (assume that this is constitutional in Suburbanada). A large and vocal minority, perhaps 40% of the citizens of Suburbanada object to this law and do not want to wear green t-shirts on Tuesdays. Nonetheless, assuming that the Tuesday Green T-shirt Act was validly passed by the Suburbanadian government, then those objectors are nonetheless subject to the law and if they do not comply they are subject to the penalties set forth by the law.

International law on the other hand is based on the simple idea that it only exists for and applies to those who agree. The basic fundamental principle is consent, in a way similar to contract law. Additionally, from a traditional viewpoint, it is nation-states that have the power to agree to international law, and it is nation-states to which international law applies. (August, 2004) Of course, in practice international law affects many private parties, the details of which will be further explored later in this work. In sum, international law is applied selectively to those state parties who want it to apply to them. Therefore if a state does not agree to a widely accepted international legal text, they are not bound by that text. In other words, unlike in a domestic legal context, if an objecting party (which would be a state in an international context) does not agree with an international legal text, they are not required to follow that law. This is fundamentally different than domestic law. There are many real life examples of this.

EXAMPLE

One example which is clearly relevant concerns the Convention on Contracts for the International Sale of Goods ("CISG"). This is a treaty (discussed *infra*) which creates a uniform law for contracts related to the international commercial sale of goods. Over 80 countries, including the USA, France, China, Brazil, Russia, Germany, and many other major trading nations have signed and ratified this treaty. That is to say that they have agreed and consented to this international law being applicable to their respective countries, as well as the private parties doing business in those countries. Nonetheless, not everyone has adopted the CISG. Notably, the UK, India, Taiwan, Indonesia, and South Africa among other countries have not consented to the CISG being the law applicable to these transactions in their countries. Therefore, this international law does not apply to them.

---

1. Sources of International Law

It is absolutely imperative to understand that there is no international legislature that has a general power to create laws that are automatically binding all around the world. This simply does not exist. The UN General Assembly may look like a legislature in the sense that they will debate proposals for resolutions and then vote on such proposals, but such resolutions are ultimately non-binding (with some exceptions, e.g., UN budgetary matters). If a country disagrees with the resolution of the UN General Assembly, they are not required to follow it. A legislature does exist in the European regional context as the EU has its own Parliament, which has the power to create binding laws. Nonetheless, the areas in which the EU can make law are limited and such laws only need to be followed by countries who are members of the EU. If a member state of the EU disagrees with EU legislation, they are still bound by such laws despite their objection. This is the result of the EU Treaties (the Treaty of Rome through the Treaty of Lisbon) wherein the EU Member States conferred this power on the EU. EU law is far reaching since it not only affects businesses based in the Member States but also parties from outside the EU who wish to do business in the EU.

The important point to take away from the above paragraph is that there is no uniform method of creating international law similar to what one would find in a domestic legal system. Again, the mechanism for creating international law is the consent of states that wish to be bound by a specific international law. Article 38(1) of the Statute of the International Court of Justice[6] lists the sources of international law from which in practice a hierarchy has been implied. (Zimmerman, 2012; August, 2004) At the top of the list are international conventions, followed by international custom, the general principles of law recognized by civilized nations, and finally subsidiary means for the determination of international law consisting of judicial decisions and the teachings of publicists (highly qualified experts in international law).

Statute of the International Court of Justice – Article 38(1)

1. The Court, whose function is to decide in accordance with international law such disputes as are submitted to it, shall apply:

    a. international conventions, whether general or particular, establishing rules expressly recognized by the contesting states;

    b. international custom, as evidence of a general practice accepted as law;

    c. the general principles of law recognized by civilized nations;

    d. subject to the provisions of Article 59, judicial decisions and the teachings of the most highly qualified publicists of the various nations, as subsidiary means for the determination of rules of law.

Conventions

The generic meaning of the word convention has been clarified by the UN to mean all international agreements. So any treaty or convention is seen as being the highest source of international law. Treaty can refer to any binding international legal agreement between international entities such as sovereign nations as well as international organizations. Convention in its modern usage is commonly used to refer to multilateral treaties which are open to participation by a large number of countries, often sponsored by the UN. (UN Treaty Collection Database, 2016) Treaties and Conventions are the most effective sources of international since such legal instruments constitute a written expression of rules expressly recognized by states which have accepted such instruments.

Furthermore, as a practical matter, treaties must be ratified in order to be applied on the national level. **Ratification**, while procedurally different from country to country is the process by which each state that has signed the treaty formally approves the treaty, most commonly through legislative procedures. In most countries, simple signature of a treaty, even by the head of state, is not enough to make it the law of the

---

[6] The Statute of the International Court of Justice is an annex to the Charter of the United Nations which forms the International Court of Justice, which is the judicial branch of the United Nations.

country. Domestic legislative approval, or ratification, is required. In many countries this ratification gives the treaty at least the same effect as domestic legislation.

Finally, normally a country will sign and ratify a treaty because there is some perceived benefit to being a party to the agreement. A country will most often follow comply with its obligations commitments under a treaty due in an effort to maintain that perceived benefit. A country may fear that if it does not comply with its treaty obligations, other parties will retaliate, and the perceived benefits under the treaty will be lost. The international image of the country may suffer as well, resulting in the potential loss of investments and trade relations, even with states that are not parties to the treaty.

Custom

Customary international law is composed of rules that are not written in treaties, but that have been consistently observed and followed by the practice of states for a long period of time. Generally a rule is considered to be customary if two elements can be shown, state practice and *opinio juris*. (Shaw, 2003) The first element, referred to as state practice (*usus*), simply means that states have consistently and recurrently followed the particular rule. (August, 2004) The second element is a belief by the state that the rule is binding (*opinio juris sive necessitatis*). In other words, for a rule to be customary international law, the states following the rule must believe they are required to follow the rule. (Restatement 3d., 1987)

A state may be exempted from a rule of customary international law if they persistently object to the application of such rule, from the beginning. Examples of customary international law include the criminal immunity of foreign diplomats, and the protection of non-combatants during armed conflict. Also relevant to the discussion of customary international law is the doctrine of *jus cogens. Jus cogens* refers to the principle that some rules of international law are pre-emptory, meaning that no state can derogate or decide not to apply them. A clear example of *jus cogens* would be the prohibition of genocide. (Notar, 2006)

General Principles of Law

When there is neither a clear treaty provision nor a rule of customary international law available to resolve an international legal issue, an international legal issue can also be resolved by general principles of law recognized by civilized nations. (Apple, 2007) This simply refers to general principles of law which are applied and followed universally in countries around the world. Some examples may be the general principle that judges must act impartially, or the principle of good faith.

Subsidiary Means for the Determination of International Law

Subsidiary means refers not to direct sources of international law, but rather to other sources of law which can be used to prove the existence of either customary international law or a general principle of law. (Bederman, 2003) Art. 38(1) states that these subsidiary means can consist of judicial decisions and teachings of publicists/experts in international law. Judicial decisions refers not only to the judicial decisions of an international court such as the International Court of Justice, but also to national courts if such courts are ruling on issues of international law. Teachings of publicists/experts in international law refers to the scholarly writing of the most highly qualified experts in the field of international law.

2. Public International Law

Furthermore, international law can be divided into the branches of public and private international law. Public international law refers to the law between sovereign nations, those international legal relations to which states are parties. This has traditionally been determined to cover issues such as state territory, law of the sea, law of war, the law of treaties (and other sources of international law), etc. A good example of public international law is when a group of countries come together to negotiate a treaty. The treaty that is the result of these negotiations is an instrument of public international law. Only nation-states have the right to participate in this type of negotiation and it is fair to say that only states, as well as certain international organizations that derive their powers through nation-state membership, participate in the creation of public international law. That is not to say however that public international law has no effect on private parties.

EXAMPLE
Perhaps a simple example is this idea is found by looking at the WTO Agreements. The WTO Agreements apply to the nation-states who have agreed to them. The Agreements require each of these countries to modify their own laws regarding international trade. The obligations apply to subjects of public international law, in other words, countries. Nevertheless, this clearly has an effect on private parties. Any party who engages in international trade in one of these WTO member states is required to comply with that state's trade law regime. Of course, WTO member states' trade law regimes must comply with the WTO Agreements, so the Agreements indirectly apply to, but directly and significantly affect the practices of private parties.

3.   Private International Law

Private international law refers to transnational legal relationships between private parties. This can be found in myriad contexts, for example, a commercial transaction, an international adoption of a child, infringement of intellectual property rights of one party by a person based in a different country, etc. Some treaties have been developed specifically to regulate private international relationships, for example the aforementioned CISG, or the New York Convention on the Recognition and Enforcement of Foreign Arbitral Awards (both to be discussed in more detail later in this text). These treaties present an interesting cross between public and private international law. In these contexts a treaty, which is an instrument of public international law, has been designed to regulate a private international relationship. This is entirely possible, but one must keep in mind that in general a private relationship is only covered by such treaties if the private parties are subject to the legal systems of countries who have adopted these treaties.

Despite the existence of certain treaties governing private international legal relationships in certain contexts, in many other situations there is not a treaty to help determine what law governs such relationships. In this private international law context the principle question that needs to be resolved is: "What law applies to this relationship?" In essence, issues of private international come down to a conflict of laws analysis.

EXAMPLE

A consulting firm in France provides its services to Californian company. They decide to keep things simple and do not involve any lawyers. They use a very simple contract, which is silent on what law applies to the contract, as well as concerning what court or other method of dispute resolution should be used if a dispute arises.

If something goes wrong during performance of the consulting services contract, a very important question arises about what law applies to this contract. It is very possible that each party will want the law of their home jurisdiction to apply to the contract. The French consulting firm is most comfortable with French law, and the Californian company is happy with the federal law of the United States and the state law of California. So prior to resolving the underlying dispute about performance of the consulting services contract, the parties must resolve a preliminary jurisdictional dispute about what law applies to the contract. This will take time and cost money.

In addition to fighting about what law should apply to their relationship, the parties will also fight about what court (or other dispute resolution technique) to use in resolving their dispute. Naturally, the French party is partial to the Civil Law, inquisitorial trial system found in France and has no desire to be caught in a Common Law, adversarial, trial proceeding, especially in a US state such as California where the use of Discovery procedures is standard and there is also the potential to have the case heard in front of a jury of local Californians. Of course, the Californians are right at home in this system, but would feel uncomfortable in the unfamiliar French court proceedings.

What is the solution to the above private international law problem? The easiest solution in a contractual context is for the parties to choose the law that governs the relationship between the parties and the forum to be used if a dispute arises. The term "forum" simply refers to the Court or other place for dispute resolution, such as an arbitration tribunal. The problem becomes more difficult when the parties either (a) have not chosen an applicable law or forum, or (b) are engaged in a non-contractual dispute (e.g., torts or intellectual property). Over time principles of private international law have developed to help parties resolve these complicated and controversial problems.

The principles of private international law will not be explored in great detail here since such detailed analysis is beyond the scope of this work, but an example of a commonly used principle is the **closest connection** test. (Trans-Lex, 2016) The closest connection test can be used, for example, to determine what legal system's laws should be applied to a contract which did not contain a choice of law provision. This situation will require a court to examine the contract, hear arguments from the parties to the dispute, and use its discretion to make this determination. If the court uses the 'closest connection' test it will attempt to determine which of the disputing parties' legal system is more closely connected to the performance of the contract and apply that legal system's laws to the dispute. The outcome of this determination may determine who wins and who loses the underlying dispute since matters can be handled differently under different legal systems. This is a problem to be avoided if possible, and the concept of party autonomy, which allows parties in a commercial context to determine what law will apply and where their legal disputes will be resolved will be discussed later in this work (*see infra*, Dispute Resolution).

Bibliography

AMERICAN LAW INSTITUTE. 1987. *Restatement of the Law (3d) of Foreign Relations Law of the United States, § 102.*

APPLE, James G. 2007. "General Principles of International Law." *International Judicial Monitor* 2 (2). http://www.judicialmonitor.org/archive_0707/generalprinciples.html

AUGUST, Ray. 2004. *International Business Law: Text, Cases, and Readings.* Upper Saddle River, N.J.: Prentice Hall.

BEDERMAN, David J., Christopher J. BORGEN, and David A. MARTIN. 2003. *International Law: A Handbook for Judges.* Studies in Transnational Legal Policy, no. 35. Washington, DC: American Society of International Law.

NOTAR, Susan. 2006. "Customary International LAw." *International Judicial Monitor* 1 (5). http://www.judicialmonitor.org/archive_1206/generalprinciples.html

SHAW, Malcolm N. 2003. *International Law.* 5th ed. Cambridge, U.K. ; New York: Cambridge University Press.

TRANS-LEX. 2016. *Principle No. No. XIV.2 - Law Applicable to International Contracts.* Accessed March 22. http://www.trans-lex.org/971000.

UNITED NATIONS. 2016. "United Nations Treaty Collection - Definitions." *Treaties.un.org.* https://treaties.un.org/Pages/overview.aspx?path=overview/definition/page1_en.xml#conventions.

ZIMMERMANN, ANDREAS, Karin OELLERS-FRAHM, and Christian J. TAMS, eds. 2012. *The Statute of the International Court of Justice: A Commentary.* Second edition. Oxford Commentaries on International Law. Oxford, United Kingdom: Oxford University Press.

Organizations Affecting International Commercial Law
(The Public Side of International Trade Law)

In looking more specifically at international commercial and trade law, it is perhaps logical to begin by examining the international organizations which help to shape law in the field. This can be considered to be the public side of international commercial law since it is sovereign states, not natural or legal persons[7] who are members of such organizations. Nonetheless, despite the public nature of these international organizations, their influence on international trade and commerce cannot be understated, and private parties are significantly affected by their work.

1. The World Trade Organization

The free trade organization now known as the World Trade Organization ("WTO") was preceded by the 1947 General Agreement on Tariffs and Trade ("GATT 1947"). The GATT 1947 was a multilateral agreement originally negotiated between 23 developed market economies. Between the GATT 1947 and the formation of the WTO in 1995, membership greatly expanded to include 123 countries, many of which had developing economies. The basic foundational principle behind these organizations, first the GATT 1947, and subsequently the WTO, is trade liberalization. Trade liberalization is perceived as a driving force of globalization and can be summarized as a philosophy which advocates that barriers to trade should be reduced. (ILO, 2001) This philosophy has prevailed over competing theories since World War II, and continues its march forward, despite many criticisms (sometimes legitimate, other times less so). The WTO currently has more than 160 member states[8].

The WTO's member states consist of the major trading nations of the world, including, but not limited to, the USA, China, The European

---

[7] To be clear, the word person has a broad legal definition. It includes living, breathing individuals, what laymen might consider to be a person, and what the law calls **natural persons**. It also includes **legal persons** which can be corporations, partnerships and other organizations (e.g., NGO's).

[8] 162 member states as of 30 November 2015 with the accession of Kazakhstan

Union (each EU member state individually, as well as the EU itself) Russia, India, Japan, Australia, Canada, Brazil, and many others. Additional states such as Afghanistan, Algeria, Belarus, Ethiopia, Iran, Iraq, and Serbia have observer status at the WTO, meaning that they are not members but have decided to become more familiar with the WTO. Typically an observer state must begin the process of becoming a WTO member within five years of obtaining observer status. Only a small number of countries do not participate in the WTO's activities, e.g., North Korea, South Sudan, Eritrea, Somalia, Turkmenistan, and various small island nations. These countries typically do not have large economies. A full and up to date list of WTO member states can be found at: https://www.wto.org/english/thewto_e/whatis_e/tif_e/org6_e.htm.

Prior to the GATT 1947, countries were more prone to engage in trade protectionism. This has been cited as one of the (many) causes of World War II. Prior to World War II, when the world was mired in serious economic depression, beginning with the passage of the protectionist Smoot-Hawley Tariff Act in the United States, countries engaged in trade protectionism in an effort to lift their economies out of depression. In short, the U.S. raised its tariffs on imports believing that it would cause U.S. based businesses to have an advantage on their home market. This rationale failed when other countries responded by engaging in the same type of protectionist behavior, causing international trade to diminish and come to a standstill. This standstill caused economic conditions to further deteriorate rather than improve, which in turn contributed to political phenomena leading to World War II which will not be examined further here. The GATT 1947 was designed to prevent trade protectionism from rearing its head again. The basic fundamental legal principle found in the GATT 1947 (and subsequently incorporated into the WTO) is Non-Discrimination, which can be further broken down into the i) Most Favored Nation, and ii) National Treatment principles. (Schaffer, Agusti, Dhooge, and Earle, 2012) These principles will be discussed herein.

From the GATT to the WTO

Between the 1947 development of the GATT to the conclusion of the Uruguay Round of trade negotiations in 1994, the GATT principles were continuously expanded, amended and modified during various "rounds" of multilateral negotiations. The early rounds focused on reducing tariff barriers to trade. By the time the Uruguay Round had concluded, the scope of the multilateral trade negotiations had expanded far beyond a simple discussion of tariffs and trade in goods, therefore, a more comprehensive set of trade agreements and an organization to administer these agreements were put in place. The result of the Uruguay Round of multilateral trade negotiations was the formation of the WTO. The GATT was updated and included in the much larger set of WTO Agreements. The *ad hoc* international organization that administered the GATT was turned into the permanent international organization known as the World Trade Organization.

Most Favored Nation

The Most Favored Nation principle has what today may seem like a funny name. Some context will help to understand the name, and subsequently the rule. As previously described, when the GATT 1947 was negotiated, it was accepted by a small group of 23 nations. It was kind of like a small trading club. Members of the club were part of a special group, and each member of this group was equally favored over all non-members. Specifically, the GATT 1947 Most Favored Nation rule requires each member to apply its tariff rules (imposition of customs duties and other charges) equally to all members. (GATT 1947, Art. I) For example, if countries A, B, and C are all signatories to the GATT, when A is developing its tariff scheme for the importation of automobiles, it cannot give B a more favorable tariff rate than C. Both B and C are part of the "club", and must be treated the same. In other words, each member has Most Favored Nation status with the other members. In the context of the WTO the "club" has expanded to the point where the name of the rule perhaps does not fit its application, but this is the basic principle.

Unfortunately in practice, application of the Most Favored Nation rule is not as simple as the above example would seem to indicate. Simple extrapolation of the above rule would lead one to believe that once a country sets a tariff rate for certain types of goods that tariff rate is applied exactly the same to goods imported from all WTO countries. Such simplicity in international trade law is rare. In fact, there are various exceptions to the Most Favored Nation rule, and the customs duties and other charges that A applies to automobiles from B in reality may be different than the customs duties and other charges that A applies to automobiles from C.

An important exception to the Most Favored Nation rule allows for the creation of customs unions and free trade zones. This allows for groups of countries to give each other even more preferential treatment than general WTO members receive. (GATT 1947, Art. XXIV; GATT 1994, Understanding on Art. XXIV) A very important example of this is the European Union. Members of the EU have agreed to form an internal market and customs union, meaning that they do not allow for tariffs to be applied to goods traded between them; in addition to many other things. This does not violate the Most Favored Nation rule, it is an explicit exception allowed for by it. The world has seen, and continues to see a proliferation of such regional trade arrangements (e.g., NAFTA, Mercosur, ASEAN, TPP etc.).

There is also a scheme allowing for preferential treatment of developing states. This allows developing states to give each other more favorable treatment (e.g., charge lower tariffs) than they give to developed nations. It also allows for developed nations to give favorable treatment to developing nations without reciprocity. (GATT Decision of 28 November 1979)

In addition, tariffs on goods from one country may be raised when another country determines that the exporting country is not properly following the rules. This is commonly seen when countries levy anti-dumping duties or countervailing measures. Such decisions are taken unilaterally by the country imposing such additional charges, and often lead to disputes between countries.

Anti-dumping Duties

Dumping occurs when a product is "introduced into the commerce of another country at less than its normal value". (Anti-dumping Agreement, Art. 2) Dumping in and of itself is not necessarily a prohibited practice, but many countries have rules to protect their domestic industries when they are threatened by dumping. The country where the dumping is occurring may put an additional tax, called an anti-dumping duty, on the goods which are being dumped. The WTO Agreements allow for a country to take action against dumping as long as there is genuine injury to a domestic industry in the country where the goods are being dumped. For the country that wishes to impose such duties, it is important that it is able to prove the existence and extent of the dumping and injury. Normally, this takes place unilaterally via domestic anti-dumping proceedings through governmental trade authorities which regulate international trade. (Understanding the WTO, 2016) Every country has its own internal procedure and is required to conduct a detailed investigation before imposing anti-dumping duties. In WTO Member States anti-dumping procedures are subject to the WTO

Agreements. If a country of import imposes anti-dumping duties, the country of export may object and initiate WTO dispute resolution proceedings to determine whether the anti-dumping duties are permissible according to the WTO Anti-dumping Agreement. (Anti-dumping Agreement, Art. 17)

Countervailing Measures

Countervailing Measures can be imposed by an importing countries where there improper use of subsidies by WTO Member States. Like dumping, subsidies are not inherently prohibited. Nonetheless, certain types of subsidies are not allowed, e.g., those that distort international trade. (CVD Agreement, Art. 3; Understanding the WTO, 2016) If a country provides domestic industries with subsidies that adversely affect trade in another WTO Member State, the affected Member State may conduct a detailed investigation, normally through its domestic trade authority in a fashion similar to the investigation described above in the context of anti-dumping duties. If injury is found, the WTO Agreement on Subsidies and Countervailing Measures permits the affected state to impose an additional import tax on the improperly subsidized goods, called a countervailing measure. As in the context of anti-dumping duties, if a country imposes countervailing measures, the country of export may object and initiate WTO dispute resolution proceedings. (CVD Agreement, Art. 30)

National Treatment

The other part of the legal principle of non-discrimination is the National Treatment principle. This principle simply requires a WTO member state to treat imported, foreign goods equal to domestic, national goods once the imported goods have passed through customs. Customs tariffs are allowed to be levied at the border, but once such duties are paid, there cannot be discrimination against imported goods based on their origin. (GATT 1947, Art. III)

For example, if Country A manufactures cars, it can impose tariffs on the importation of cars from Countries B and C, but once those cars from B and C pass customs and the tariffs are paid, no additional taxes can be levied based on origin. Therefore, if A had a "foreign car sales tax" that was not applied to car manufactured in A, such policy would violate the national treatment principle and would be subject to challenge via WTO dispute resolution procedures. If A had a "car sales tax" that was applied equally to all cars, no matter their origin, such policy would not violate the national treatment principle. As with the Most Favored Nation Rule (and pretty much every other legal rule, both in the context of the WTO and otherwise) exceptions are plentiful. For example, Member State governments are allowed to discriminate when they procure goods. In other words, they can set up government programs where they only purchase materials and goods which produced in their own country thereby discriminating against foreign goods, when such procurement is for government purposes. (GATT 1947 Art.III(8)) There are various other exceptions to the National Treatment rule.

Other WTO principles

The WTO Agreements are quite complex and the details of each one are beyond the scope of a simple overview of the organization. Nonetheless, some of the additional principles will be briefly discussed herein.

Protection through Tariffs Only

Recall that the philosophy underlying the WTO is trade liberalization; in other words, reducing barriers to trade. This does not mean total elimination of barriers to trade. Nonetheless, under the WTO Agreements, as a general matter, the only acceptable barriers to trade are tariffs. This is the principle of protection through tariffs only. The WTO provides some basic rules for imposing tariffs. For example, when a WTO Member State is calculating tariff rates to apply to goods coming from other WTO countries it must comply with the "bound" tariff rates. The bound tariff rates indicate the highest tariff rates that a given WTO Member State can apply to imports from other WTO countries. These rates act as ceilings, and Member States can, and typically do set lower tariff rates. Additionally, bound tariff rates will depend on the types of goods at issue. Goods are classified pursuant to the World Customs Organization's "Harmonized System". Each classification of goods has its own bound tariff rate, and the bound tariff rates are available using online databases published by the WTO (*see* https://www.wto.org/english/tratop_e/tariffs_e/tariff_data_e.htm).

All other barriers such as quotas or quantitative restrictions are forbidden subject to various exceptions. (Hoekman and Mavroidis, 2015) An example of a valid exception would be in circumstances of an agricultural crisis where the basic principle of protection through tariffs could be suspended in order to allow quantitative restrictions in an effort to protect an agricultural sector from failure. (GATT 1947, Art. XI) Finally, in addition to the general WTO rules applying to all member states, each WTO Member State makes specific commitments in the context of WTO negotiations, called concessions. These concessions are indexed in the Schedules of Concessions annexed to the GATT 1994. A concession in the context of goods may be a bound tariff rate for a specific classification of goods. The concessions given by a particular WTO Member State will change over time, and like the bound tariff rates, can be consulted online using various internet resources, including those published by the WTO (*see* https://www.wto.org/english/tratop_e/schedules_e/goods_schedules_ e.htm), although as a practical matter specialized knowledge will be required to search for and use such information.

Decreasing "red tape"

Another important goal that the WTO has been working towards is trade facilitation. The goal of trade facilitation is to decrease excessively burdensome governmental procedures for international trade, commonly referred to as "red tape". The WTO Agreements attempt to achieve this in part by increasing transparency. This requires WTO Member State governments are to make their trade rules, regulations, and practices available and accessible. (Understanding the WTO, 2016) An opaque trade policy in one country can act as a barrier to trade. An example of an opaque trade policy would be one that is short on details, and difficult to obtain (e.g., only available in person at a central government office from the hours of 2pm to 4pm on the second Tuesday of each month).

As an example, if an exporter of consumer electronics in Country A wishes to export its goods to country B, they would naturally need to know what the requirements for importation of consumer electronics are in Country B. This needs to be determined before a valuable shipment is sent across the ocean. If the goods do not meet the requirements when they arrive in Country B, they cannot enter into B's market and need to be taken, stored, and disposed of elsewhere, which will cause significant expense, delay and headache. A potentially profitable venture can easily turn into a loss. If the exporter is able to ascertain what is required prior to importation of consumer electronics in Country B, then the exporter can significantly reduce this risk and is much more likely to engage in the transaction.

Additionally, WTO states are committed to simplification. This means simplifying import and export formalities. (WTO 10 Benefits, 2008) Forms should be simple. Traders should only have to deal with one government office, etc. For example, an importer should not be required to obtain an "importation form" from government office X, submit the form to government office Y, and receive import clearance from government office Z.

Expansion beyond Trade in Goods (Services, Intellectual Property)

As previously discussed, the creation of the WTO expanded multilateral trade agreements far beyond trade in goods. In addition to goods, the WTO Agreements cover trade in services (General Agreement on Trade in Services, or GATS), and intellectual property (Agreement on Trade Related Aspects of Intellectual Property, or TRIPS). At the time the WTO was negotiated this was determined to be a necessary expansion to the global trade regime since each of these areas has a significant impact on the total volume of global trade and the functioning of the global economy.

General Agreement on Trade in Services ('GATS')

Services represent over 60% of global production and employment (CIA World Factbook, 2014), and 20% of global trade (UNCTAD, 2014). Many developed market economies have moved from goods manufacturing economies to service providing economies. One of the principal achievements of the Uruguay Round was bringing services into the scope of multilateral trade agreements and the WTO through the General Agreement on Trade in Services ("GATS"). The above referenced principles found in the GATT, most notably the principle of non-discrimination, are found in the GATS as well. The GATS applies to all service sectors with the exceptions of "services supplied in the exercise of governmental authority", e.g., public health services (GATS, Art. 1), and air transport services (Annex on Air Transport Services).

The GATS seeks to establish a framework of rules to ensure that services are not regulated in a way constituting unnecessary barriers to trade. Nonetheless, members maintain autonomy to pursue their own policy objectives. For example, a WTO Member State can regulate who is able to provide legal services within its jurisdiction, and the GATS does not change that as long as the regulation is reasonable, objective, and impartial and at the same time does not constitute an unnecessary barrier to trade.

Agreement on Trade Related Aspects of Intellectual Property Rights ('TRIPS')

The WTO also contains the Agreement on Trade Related Aspects of Intellectual Property Rights, or TRIPS. Intellectual property was rightly included in the comprehensive trade agreements. Failure to protect intellectual property by one country can act as a barrier to trade in that country.

EXAMPLE
Pumpkin, Inc. develops smartphones. Pumpkin, Inc. would like to export its smartphones all over the world. The company has obtained patents to protect its technology in its home country of Siliconia. However, patent protection as with other forms of intellectual property protection is national, or in some cases regional (e.g. European Patent Office), but never truly international. Pumpkin, Inc. may decide not to export its phones to a country which does not offer the same, or at least similar, protections that it is able to enjoy in Siliconia. They are afraid that if they send their phones to a country that lacks proper protection, the patented technology will be copied and there will be nothing that they can do to prevent infringement. If the country of Ludditia has no legal framework for the protection of intellectual property, then Pumpkin, Inc. might refrain from exporting there.

TRIPS attempts to resolve the above referenced problem. It sets basic minimum standards that countries must apply to protect intellectual property, as well as providing for enforcement mechanisms for cases of intellectual property infringement. (TRIPS Agreement, 1994) WTO Member States still have a certain amount of autonomy in setting their intellectual property legal regimes. For example, many states provide more protection to intellectual property than that which is called for by TRIPS. TRIPS is a floor, not a ceiling. Nonetheless, it has achieved significant harmonization between WTO Member States in the field of intellectual property law. Some of the specific provisions found in TRIPS will be examined later in this work in the section on intellectual property law.

Disputes

It is important to keep in mind that the parties directly subject to WTO regulation are state parties, and not private enterprises. This means that if a business believes that a country to where it exports has adopted a policy that discriminates against the goods that they are exporting, that business has no direct recourse, at least through the WTO. Therefore, a business who is negatively affected by a trade policy in another country must work through its own government, usually through a trade authority, in an attempt to resolve the trade dispute. If their home country government decides to take up their cause, the WTO dispute settlement procedures may be implicated.

When one WTO Member State alleges that another WTO Member State is not complying with their obligations under the WTO Agreements, the disputing states are encouraged to resolve the matter via consultation (confidential negotiations). Should the consultation fail, a Member State may request that the WTO Dispute Settlement Body ("DSB") establish a Dispute Settlement Panel ("Panel"). (DSU, Art. 4) The DSB is a permanent organ of the WTO consisting of representatives from all WTO Member States which manages the WTO dispute settlement procedures.

A separate Panel is set up by the DSB for each dispute brought in front of it. This allows the DSB to compose a Panel consisting of experts in the field to which the dispute relates. (DSU, Art. 8) For example, if Country A alleges that Country B has been impermissibly dumping goods, the DSB can set up a Panel composed of experts in anti-dumping duties. The members of the Panel will have nationalities different from those of the Parties involved in the Dispute. The Panel will hear the dispute and make a report ruling on the dispute. The report will be adopted by the DSB (or rejected by consensus)

The Panel is the equivalent to the level of first instance in the context of the WTO. Should a party lose their case in front of a Panel, they may appeal to the WTO Appellate Body. Unlike the Panel, and like the DSB, the Appellate Body is a permanent organ of the WTO, consisting of 7 members appointed for terms of 4 years. The members are individuals, unaffiliated with any government, with recognized expertise in international trade law. Each appeal is heard by three of the seven members. (DSU, Art. 17) When an appeal is made to the Appellate Body, this is the final level of appeal. The report ruling on the dispute made by the Appellate Body is adopted by the DSB (it can also be rejected by consensus of the DSB).

Once an unchallenged Panel decision or Appellate Body decision is made, the DSB then monitors the implementation of the rulings and recommendations made therein. (DSU, Art. 21) Should a Member State who lost a dispute fail to comply with the ruling in a Panel or Appellate

Body report, the DSB is tasked with enforcing the decision. The DSB may force the non-complying party to pay compensation or even authorize an injured party to retaliate. Retaliation could take the form suspension of trade concessions and WTO obligations of WTO Member States towards the non-complying state. (DSU, Art. 22)

EXAMPLE

If the country of Railtopia, which is a WTO Member State, imposes high tariffs on rail cars imported from the country of Manufacturia, which is also a WTO Member State, but does not apply the same high tariffs to rail cars imported from other WTO Member States, then Railtopia is violating the principle of Non-Discrimination, and in particular the Most Favored Nation Rule. Rail car manufacturers in Manufacturia complain to the International Trade Bureau of Manufacturia, who decides to take up their cause. Rail cars manufactured in Manufacturia are of high quality and priced very competitively. Thereafter, the government of Manufacturia, following WTO procedures, attempts to consult with Railtopia to resolve the dispute concerning Railtopia's trade policy towards rail cars made in Manufacturia, but unfortunately, consultations fail. At this point Manufacturia initiates a dispute settlement proceeding at the WTO. The DSB constitutes a Dispute Settlement Panel for this particular dispute consisting of neutral experts in non-discrimination. Manufacturia wins the case in front of the Panel. Railtopia Appeals. Manufacturia wins again. The Appellate Body report confirms that Railtopia should modify its trade policy to be in line with the WTO Agreements. Railtopia fails to do so. At this point the DSB can order Railtopia to pay compensation to the injured party, and perhaps even authorize limited trade sanctions on Railtopia suspending any trade concessions and obligations towards Railtopia in the same sector as the dispute if possible.

The effects of the hypothetical trade dispute in the above example would be felt in both Manufacturia and Railtopia. In the short term rail car manufacturers in Manufacturia, their employees, component part manufacturers and suppliers, some of whom may even be in Railtopia, will suffer since fewer rail cars from Manufacturia will be able to access the Railtopia market. The Railtopian consumers of rail cars, presumably railroad companies and eventually even passenger on trains in Railtopia will also suffer since the price the high quality rail cars from Railtopia will be increased. In the long term, when Manufacturia is permitted by the DSB to retaliate, similar effects will be felt in the opposite direction.

Trade Policy Review

The goal of transparency is achieved in part through surveillance of the trade policies of the Member States. Annex 3 of the WTO

Agreements is the Trade Policy Review Mechanism which in essence provides for regular peer review of Member State trade policies and practices by the WTO. The purpose is to increase transparency and foster understanding of countries' trade policies and practices as well as to encourage countries to comply with their WTO obligations and commitments. All WTO Member States face this periodic review. The largest four traders (EU, USA, Japan and China) face the review every two years, the next 16 largest traders every four years, and for all other countries the general timeframe is once every six years. (TPRM)

Criticisms of the WTO

There are many criticisms levied against the WTO, some valid, some less so. The purpose of this work is not to take a position on the validity of such criticism, nor to take a position concerning WTO policies, etc. Nonetheless, some of the criticisms will be briefly addressed herein.

The WTO maintains its principle of decision making by consensus. This means that for major decisions to be made, including any changes to the WTO Agreements, everybody must agree to such changes. With over 160 Member States, this is exceedingly difficult to achieve. (Walker, 2011) Also, allegations are made that more powerful countries coerce less powerful countries (sometimes by offering incentives), prevent them from fully participating by not inviting them to informal negotiations, and that poorer countries are understaffed and do not have enough personnel to participate in all of the ongoing trade negotiations. (Oxford Analytica, 2010) Additionally, critics often state that corporate interests are over-represented by governments who negotiate trade agreements, and other groups such as labor or environmental groups are ignored by countries' trade representatives when negotiating trade agreements. These groups believe that the WTO is so focused on trade liberalization that it ignores labor, environmental and other issues.

Additionally, the latest round of WTO multilateral trade negotiations have been unsuccessful. The Doha Development Round of negotiations was launched in 2001 with a highly ambitious agenda intending to further lower barriers to trade and expand negotiations and further open markets in agriculture, manufacturing, services, and other areas. It also intended to address problems faced by developing economies in implementing their WTO obligations. Nonetheless, a North-South divide quickly developed pitting developed economies against developing economies. Furthermore, disagreement on agricultural issues, particularly between the US, China and India, caused further collapse of the negotiations. The negotiations remained stalled and the future is uncertain. In the meantime, global trade continues to evolve, and the WTO Agreements are more than 20 years old. This is leading in part to a proliferation of regional trade agreements (which is permitted under the WTO Agreements), including major ongoing negotiations such as the Trans-Pacific Partnership (TPP) and the Transatlantic Trade and Investment Partnership (TTIP). This failure to evolve may lead to a less influential WTO over time.

2. The European Union

While the WTO attempts to regulate and liberalize trade on a global scale, there are various organizations which attempt to do the same, on a regional scale. Foremost among these organizations is the European Union ("EU"). While the current activities of the EU go beyond simply regulating trade, at its heart the EU is an economic union.

Historical Development

The full origins of the EU will not be discussed in this work; however, some historical context concerning the development of the European Union is relevant. The beginnings of the EU can be traced to the 1950s. During this period, the scars of World War II were still fresh in the mind of many leaders, and an effort was made to create closer relations between various states. Six member states (France, Italy, the Netherlands, Belgium, Luxembourg, and West Germany) agreed to form the European Coal and Steel Community (agreement signed in 1951, came into force in 1952), The European Atomic Energy Community (signed in 1957, in force in 1958) and the Treaty of Rome forming the European Economic Community (also 1957, 1958). The latter agreement is considered to be the true starting point of the current European economic integration. (EU History, 2015)

The Treaty of Rome strived to develop harmony in economic activities between member states by creating a common market which would initially allow people, goods and services to flow freely across national borders. Nevertheless, despite the establishment of the common market trade did not immediately begin to flow entirely freely across borders due in large part to many different national regulations and laws between the Member States. For example, even though quotas and tariffs between the Member States were eliminated, many non-tariff barriers remained. An example of a non-tariff barrier would be different labeling requirements for goods, or different government administrative approval procedures for a product or service. This lead to the Single European Act (signed in 1986, in force in 1987) which created the more integrated internal market, discussed below. (Moussis, 2011)

Over the years, the 1958 Treaty of Rome, which is the original foundational treaty of the European Union, has been modified on various occasions, and many additional countries have achieved EU membership. There are currently 28 Member States. Each major modification is agreed to by consensus, meaning that all member states must agree, and a new treaty is signed and comes into force (e.g. European Single Act in 1987, Treaty of Maastricht in 1993 leading to the Euro currency among other things, etc.). The most recent major modifications are found in the Treaty of Lisbon which was signed in 2007 and came into force in 2009. More specifically the Treaty of Lisbon consists of modifications to the Treaty on European Union ("TEU" aka the Maastricht Treaty) and the Treaty on the Functioning of the European Union ("TFEU"). Nevertheless, the 1958 Treaty of Rome and its subsequent versions continue to form the original basis of the Lisbon Treaty, and in particular the TFEU. In other words, some of the treaty provisions found in the Treaty of Lisbon are the same provisions which originally appeared in the 1958 Treaty of Rome and have been maintained in each subsequent treaty modification.

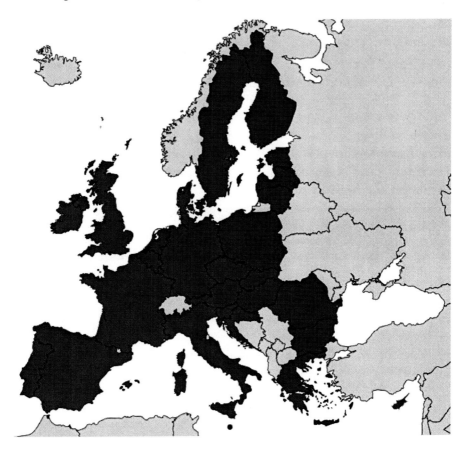

The Treaty of Lisbon represented a significant change to the functioning of the EU. In particular, it attempted to give a clearer definition of the areas in which the EU has the competence to govern, and those areas in which the Member States retain the competence to govern. It clarified that there are three types of competence, exclusive, shared, and supporting. Exclusive competence means that the EU has the exclusive ability to create laws in a specific area. Shared competence means that the ability to create laws in specific areas is shared between the EU and the Member States, however Member States can only act if the EU has not chosen to do so. Supporting competence simply means the EU does not have competence in a specific area of law, and can merely provide support to the Member States in creating their own laws. (TFEU, Arts.3 – 6)

It is important to understand that the EU only has the powers given to it by the Member States. This is quite different than the powers inherent to a nation-state. Most nation-states have inherent power to create laws subject to certain limitations, usually found in a constitution or other source of law. The EU does not have this inherent power to create law. It is limited by the conferral of power given to it by its Member States. When Member States confer power to the EU, they in essence decide to give a piece of their sovereignty to govern themselves to the EU. This simply means that they grant the EU competence to create laws in certain areas. The EU therefore cannot just make whatever laws it wants. For example, the EU has not been granted the competence to make European divorce laws. To determine whether the EU has competence, one must look at the foundational treaty (currently Lisbon), as well as interpretations of EU law.

Exclusive competence (*see* Art. 3 TFEU)	Shared competence (*see* Art. 4 TFEU)	Supporting competence (*see* Art. 6 TFEU)
• Customs Union • Competition Law • Monetary policy for states using the Euro • Common Fisheries Policy for the conservation of marine biological resources • Common Commercial Policy • Concluding International Agreements	• Internal Market • Social Policy • Economic, Social, and Territorial Cohesion • Agriculture • Fisheries (excluding for the conservation of marine biological resources) • Environment • Consumer Protection • Transport • Trans-European Networks • Energy • Area of Freedom, Security and Justice • Public Health (common safety concerns limited by the Lisbon Treaty) • Research, Technological Development, and Space • Development Cooperation and Humanitarian Aid	• Protection and Improvement of Human Health • Industry • Culture • Tourism • Education, vocational training, youth and sport • Civil Protection • Administrative Cooperation
Chart taken and partly modified from: http://ec.europa.eu/citizens-initiative/public/competences/faq?lg=en#q2		

Role in Regulating Trade

One area of EU competence is in the regulation of trade. The European Union is both a customs union and an internal market. The EU has exclusive competence over the customs union. (TFEU, Art. 3) This means that there is uniform EU policy for import into and export out of the EU Member States. Member States do not have the ability to create their own customs laws since they have given this part of their lawmaking ability to the EU. Again, they have given this piece of their sovereignty to the EU. For example, Italy cannot unilaterally decide to put a tariff on the importation of Japanese cars, nor can any other EU country. There will be one tariff policy for the importation of Japanese cars into the EU, no matter whether the point of importation is France, Italy, Germany, or any other Member State. Being a customs union also means that there should be no tariffs between the Member States themselves. For example, Italy cannot decide to put a tariff on French and German cars. Such cars produced in France and Germany must be able to move freely between the EU Member States.

Regulation of the internal market is within the shared competences of the EU, meaning that both the EU and the Member States can regulate the internal market, however, the Member States can only act on a particular issue if the EU has not. (TFEU, Art. 4) As briefly stated above, the internal market was developed to further increase the free flow of trade between the Member States. For example, when there are ever-changing technical regulations between all of the different Member States, which could be as simple as labeling, packaging or inspection requirements, it becomes more difficult for private parties to engage in trade in other Member States. The effective creation of an internal market requires allowing for free movement, often referred to as the four freedoms in the context of the EU. The four freedoms attempt to eliminate barriers to trade and ensure the free movement of people, services, goods, and capital between Member States.

The EU undertakes significant efforts to harmonize the laws of the Member States when it comes to trade as well as other areas in which it has competence. Many sectors of trade have been harmonized (e.g., medical devices, automotive, chemicals, electronics, etc.). This means that the EU has set common rules for Member States to follow across the internal market. Keep in mind that harmonization does not mean that each Member State has the same exact laws. Rather it means that the laws of the Member States shall not be incompatible with, and in fact will follow the rules set by the EU. Nevertheless, the EU has not harmonized all areas of trade. This however, does not give Member States the right to then discriminate against products coming from other Member States. The principle of mutual recognition states that a product lawfully produced and marketed in one Member State shall not be prevented from being marketed in another Member State, even if the technical regulations in the Member State where the product is marketed are different than in the Member State of origin. (Regulation (EC) No 764/2008) There are exceptions for public safety, health, or environmental concerns. This is a principle originally stated by the European Court of Justice in the famous *Cassis de Dijon* case and illustrates the EU's commitment to eliminating barriers to trade between the Member States.

Laws Used to Harmonize Trade

The EU takes on various roles in effectuating the internal market. The first is through making laws. As discussed above, the EU has the power to make laws in areas in which it has competence. The body of EU law in its entirety is referred to as the *acquis communautaire* and is comprised of the primary legislation of the EU (consisting of the treaties), secondary legislation (which takes the form of regulations, directives, decisions, recommendations, and opinions), and case law of the European Court of Justice.

The legislative instruments commonly used by the EU to ensure that Member States are complying with their treaty obligations are regulations and directives. Regulations have a general application and directly apply to all Member States. Regulations can be compared to laws in a domestic context in the sense that once the Regulation is passed, it is the law for everyone, and applies the same to all persons. Directives on the other hand do not have a general application. They can be addressed to all of the Member States or can be specifically addressed to only one or some of the Member States. Directives are binding as to the result; however, the Member States to whom a Directive is addressed have the ability to choose the form and methods of achieving the goals stated in the Directive. (TFEU, Art. 288)

Since Directives are not directly applicable in Member States, when a Directive is addressed to a Member State, the domestic legislature must then consider the Directive and pass implementing legislation called a "national transposition measure" in order to achieve the goals of the Directive by incorporating the goals into national law. This is the often used method of harmonizing laws between Member States. When Member States are subject to a Directive, they have a stated time period to meet those goals, often three years. The Directive is a useful tool for harmonization since while it sets goals for the Member States to meet it also allows for flexibility in meeting the goals. This flexibility can be beneficial since the situation on the ground might be different in each Member State and they each may need to take different steps to achieve the goals.

In addition to legislation, the functioning of the internal market must be monitored by the EU. This role falls principally to the European Commission. The Commission will ensure the implementation of EU laws in the context of trade and the internal market, as well as take decisions penalizing Member States who do not comply with EU Law. When a Member State is perceived not to be following EU Law, the Commission will investigate either based on its own initiative, based on a complaint from one Member State against another, or even based on a complaint from a private party. For example, the car service Uber, an American firm, has filed a complaint with the Commission against France asking the Commission to determine whether a French law which protects traditional taxis by putting restrictions on private car services (by for example, restricting the use of geolocation to show car availability on smartphones) was contrary to various EU Laws. It has filed similar cases against laws in Germany and Spain. The outcome of the Commission's investigation is pending at the date of this writing.

In addition to the Commission, the European Court of Justice plays an important role in interpreting EU Law and determining whether Member States national laws are in compliance therewith. The ECJ will strike down Member State laws which it deems to be in conflict with EU Law (where the EU has competence of course). National courts of Member States frequently refer cases from their judicial systems to the European Courts for preliminary rulings on the interpretation of EU law in a national court case. The ECJ will also review decisions taken by the Commission to make sure that they do not conflict with EU legal principles.

Keep in mind that this is a mere overview of the functioning of the EU in the context of trade. Significant details can be found in myriad sources, not the least of which is the EU's own, comprehensive website found at: europa.eu.

3. Other Regional Trade Agreements and Organizations

Other parts of the world have also developed regional trade organizations. Often times this is done using a Free Trade Agreement. In addition to regional multilateral agreements concerning trade, countries regularly enter into bilateral trade and investment agreements. None are quite as comprehensive as the EU, but some of the major ones will be briefly discussed in this section. Free Trade Agreements, while often controversial, are generally intended to open up markets between countries. This is usually done through reducing trade barriers using the techniques discussed in the preceding sections. In theory this makes it easier and cheaper for companies to export goods and services to other countries who are parties to Free Trade Agreements.

Nevertheless, these agreements are generally entered into in the face of opposition from various groups. Environmental organizations are (often times justifiably) concerned about the impact of increased trade on the environment. Labor groups are concerned about the loss of jobs when a Free Trade Agreement allows companies to move production facilities from one country where labor is expensive to another where it is less so. Political groups may be worried about the tide of privatization, a focus on corporate interests, and a rise of income inequality that often accompanies such agreements in some parts of the world. Pro free trade arguments abound as well. Global poverty has been reduced since the implementation of free trade policies. (Economist, 2013) Prices of consumer goods have plummeted. Economies theoretically become more efficient. These are interesting debates in which the citizenry of countries negotiating such agreements should actively engage. Nonetheless, Free Trade Agreements are the tools of trade liberalization as well as the *status quo*.

Free Trade Agreements between two or more countries lower tariff and non-tariff barriers to the free movement of people, goods, and services. Often they go beyond the minimum which is required by a country's WTO obligations. Even though this seems to contradict the Most Favored Nation principle of the WTO, it does not since the WTO Agreements allow for additional trade concessions through free trade areas or customs unions.

Definitions	
Free Trade Area	A Free Trade Area ("FTA") broadly refers to a situation where states agree to reduce, and in some cases eliminate tariffs and quotas on trade between themselves. They can be bilateral (between two states) or multilateral (between a group of states). Often they are concluded on a regional basis (e.g., NAFTA, ASEAN). FTAs can be limited to goods, or can be broader and cover trade in services, intellectual property protections, labor issues, environmental issues, and more. The members of a FTA retain the ability to negotiate their own trade policies with non-members.
Customs Union	A Customs Union ("CU") indicates a higher level of integration between the members when compared to a FTA. Like the FTA, members of a CU agree to reduce or eliminate tariffs and quotas on trade, but in addition agree to have a common external policy which applies to non-members. For example, the CU sets tariffs on goods imported to any member from outside the CU, referred to as a common external tariff. The members do not have the ability to set their own tariffs on such goods. Trade negotiations with non-members are conducted not by the individual members, but by the CU as a single entity.
Common Market (Single/Internal Market)	A Common Market (CM) refers to a group of countries who have achieved a higher level of integration than a CU. Like the FTA, tariffs and quotas have been eliminated. Like the CU, the trade bloc has a common external tariff and common trade policy towards nonmembers. But the CM goes further since the freedom of movement of factors of production (the four freedoms; goods, people, capital, and services) is guaranteed between members. All obstacles to trade between the national markets of the members should be removed. For example, labeling requirements between members in a CM (a technical barrier to trade) would need to be harmonized, whereas this is not necessarily the case in a CU.

North American Free Trade Agreement ("NAFTA")

The North American Free Trade Agreement was created in 1994 between the United States, Canada, and Mexico. NAFTA is neither a customs union nor a common market. It is, as its name would indicate, a Free Trade Area. In fact, long before NAFTA, the GATT 1947 allowed for free trade among these three countries. The 1994 NAFTA simply went much further than the pre-existing GATT 1947 obligations and attempted to further lower and eliminate tariffs and barriers to trade between the three countries. Therefore, goods produced in one of the NAFTA countries receive preferential treatment in the other NAFTA countries. Additionally, NAFTA provides a forum for trade disputes between the NAFTA Member States. Similar to the WTO, NAFTA has a non-discrimination rule meaning goods produced in one NAFTA country should be treated no differently than domestic goods. (NAFTA, Chapter 3). NAFTA also attempted to increase investment and liberalize trade in services. (NAFTA, Chapters 11 and 12).

Association of Southeast Asian Nations ("ASEAN")

The Association of Southeast Asian Nations was formed between Indonesia, Malaysia, the Phillipines, Singapore, and Thailand with the ASEAN Declaration in 1967. Since that time, Brunei, Vietnam, Laos, Burma, and Cambodia have all become members. The ASEAN Declaration, which is the founding document of ASEAN, intended to form an organization which promotes political and economic cooperation. These goals have been further strengthened by the ASEAN Charter, signed and ratified by all 10 nations and effective in 2008. ASEAN nations tend to have dynamic, growing economies and ASEAN is an important regional organization in the context of trade since its combined GDP is over US $2.4 trillion. (ADB, 2016)

Currently, the economic element of ASEAN operates under a Free Trade Agreement. It is not a customs union or internal market. There is no common external tariff, currency union, or four freedoms as in the EU. Nonetheless, proposals to move in this direction have been made, so this is a development to monitor in the future. For the time being it has a "Common Effective Preferential Tariff Scheme" in place which significantly reduces tariffs between all of the Member States. (CEPT, 1992) It also has a treaty in effect with China which reduces tariffs. This latter trade agreement is the largest in the world in terms of population coverage. (Walker, 2010)

Mercosur

Mercosur is the 'common market of the South' and is a trading bloc and customs union comprised of Argentina, Brazil, Paraguay, Uruguay, and most recently, Venezuela. At the time of writing, Bolivia is also in the process of becoming a full member. Mercosur allows for free movement of goods and services between the Member States. Additionally, there is a common external tariff in place. There are also associate members, Chile, Colombia, Ecuador, and Peru who do not have full voting rights in Mercosur, but receive tariff reductions. Associate members are not subject to the common external tariff as they are not members of the customs union. (CFR, 2012) Bolivia has engaged in efforts to become a full Member State and is in the process obtaining full membership. (Mercosur, 2016)

Mercosur Members

■ Mercosur Members

▨ In process of becoming Mercosur Member

Proliferation of larger regional trade agreements: CETA, TTIP, TPP

While the WTO has successfully created a basic regime for the regulation of international trade between its Member States and regional trading blocs have taken shape around the world wielding significant local and regional influence, recent years have seen a proliferation of even larger scale 'regional' trade agreements, such as the aforementioned China-ASEAN Free Trade Area. These mega trade agreements have begun to take shape whilst the WTO Doha Round made little progress. Despite the lack of progress at the WTO, world trade continues to develop, and countries who wish that their trade regimes progress alongside such developments are left with few options but to seek alternatives. Some of these alternatives are very ambitious.

Comprehensive Trade and Economic Agreement ("CETA")

These ambitious alternatives include the Comprehensive Trade and Economic Agreement ("CETA"), which is the recent agreement entered into between Canada and the EU in 2014. CETA is a broad agreement covering not only trade in goods and services, but a wide array of other areas including but not limited to investment, telecommunications, financial services, intellectual property, work visas, and many other areas. CETA is currently subject to ratification procedures in the EU and Canada. (EU, 2016)

Trans-Pacific Partnership ("TPP")

Perhaps even more ambitious is the Trans-Pacific Partnership ("TPP"), which is a broad trade agreement intended not only to lower barriers to trade in goods and services, but which also contains provisions concerning intellectual property, environmental standards, labor standards, and resolve disputes via investor state dispute settlement mechanisms (investment arbitration, *see infra*). The TPP is has been negotiated between Australia, Brunei Darussalam, Canada, Chile, Japan, Malaysia, Mexico, New Zealand, Peru, Singapore, the United States and Vietnam. In October of 2015 these countries agreed on the terms of the TPP, which was signed by trade ministers in February of 2016. The agreement is currently subject to ratification in the above referenced countries. (ICTSD, 2016)

The TPP has faced many hurdles since negotiations began in 2008, in large part due to the fact that the proposed text of treaty was not made public (although much of it was leaked during negotiations) raising various concerns and significant opposition. The negotiations were laborious and delayed on various occasions. A major step towards possible success of the TPP was achieved in 2015 when the United States Congress granted the Obama administration fast track negotiation authority (aka Trade Promotion Authority) to negotiate the content of the TPP without the possibility of the US Congress making unilateral amendments thereto. This was previously seen as a large hurdle in the way of potential success of the TPP. Whether the TPP will be ratified by all of the negotiating states remains to be seen, but is another important international trade issue to monitor.

As China did not participate in the TPP negotiations, an alternative regional trade agreement in the Asia Pacific region has been proposed. This agreement, called the Regional Comprehensive Economic Partnership ("RCEP") is being negotiated between China, the 10 member states of ASEAN, Japan, South Korea, India, Australia, and New Zealand. The RCEP is not as advanced in negotiations as the TPP, and the agreement on the latter is increasing pressure on the RCEP to move forward. There are interesting geo-political factors at play here, which will not be discussed in detail in this work; however this is another interesting development to be monitored by those engaging in international trade and commerce.

Transatlantic Trade and Investment Partnership ("TTIP")

The Transatlantic Trade and Investment Partnership ("TTIP") is an additional mega-trade agreement in the process of being negotiated. This is the proposed agreement between the EU and the US, which will create the largest free trade area in the world if successful. Similar to the TPP, the agreement will be broad in scope covering not only trade in goods and services, but cover other areas including, but not limited to environmental, labor, agricultural, consumer goods, and investor state dispute settlement via arbitration. The TTIP is not as far along in the negotiation stage as the TPP and faces many barriers that may prevent agreement. Not the least of these revolves around EU concerns about US agricultural standards, and other doubts about issues such as investor state arbitration. (EU, 2016)

To conclude, larger regional trade agreements have been proliferating in recent years, and likely will continue to do so. It remains to be seen whether such mega trade agreements such as CETA, TPP and TTIP, among others, will come into force and change the landscape of world trade, including the rules and regulations which govern. It also remains to be seen whether the WTO as well as currently existing regional trade organizations will be able to make the necessary modifications to their legal regimes to stay relevant. Like most areas of the law, international trade law is a continuously changing area which necessitates close attention to detail when engaging therein. Changes should be closely monitored by parties engaging in international commerce and trade.

FDI, BITs, and ICSID

In addition to bilateral and multilateral trade agreements, countries often enter in to investment treaties which protect foreign parties who decide to set up a business in a particular country. This can be seen as useful since when deciding to enter into new, foreign markets, some companies may determine that there is a strategic advantage to actually setting up a new business entity in the new market. Such a strategy is referred to as foreign direct investment ('FDI'). FDI takes myriad forms, and could be setting up agricultural operations, constructing and operating a manufacturing facility, opening a call center, operating a mine, or a multitude of other possibilities. When a company decides to do this it is a much bigger commitment to doing business in the foreign market as compared to trading goods or services. The company engaging in FDI is subjecting itself to the legal, political, and financial risks associated with doing business in the country. They must comply with the host-country's laws, pay taxes, etc. In some countries, the environment for foreign direct investment is seen to be stable, and foreign companies have little trepidation when it comes to engaging in FDI and starting business operations there. In other countries companies may, often times justifiably, feel that the environment is too uncertain for large scale direct investments. This could be due to the risk of war, political risk (e.g., nationalization of private interests), hostility to foreigners, or economic instability. Over the last decades there has been a large scale proliferation of treaties which are intended to protect investors who wish to invest in foreign countries, many times between two countries. These are referred to as Bilateral Investment Treaties ('BITs').

BITs

Bilateral Investment Treaties ('BITs') are treaties which establish the terms by which countries agree to protect private investment originating from outside of their borders. While the number is constantly in flux, there are currently over 2200 BITs in force, along with various other international agreements which protect foreign investors (often between more than two countries). (Investment Policy Hub, 2016) Typically a BIT will define its coverage and scope by clarifying who and what types of private investors are covered by the treaty. It will provide for limitations on expropriation of private property owned by foreign investors and require compensation to be paid when expropriation occurs. Additionally, a typical BIT will call for fair and equitable treatment of the investor and require that the investor be given full protection and security in the host country. If the host state breaches its obligations towards an investor, then the investor may bring a claim against the host state in arbitration, generally to recover damages. Since the scale of FDI is often times quite large, these claims for damages can reach very high totals (even in the billions). This allows private companies to essentially sue countries, which is currently a controversial and hotly debated topic in both trade and law circles. Investment arbitration is also found in various multi-lateral trade agreements, and as referenced above, has been proposed for inclusion in both the TPP and the TTIP. Interestingly, in the TTIP negotiations the EU has proposed the creation of an investment court system to replace the current system of investment arbitration in the context of the TTIP, and perhaps beyond. (EU, 2016) It remains to be seen whether this proposal will be adopted.

ICSID

Typically, as mentioned above, investor-state disputes go to international arbitration. These cases are often handles by the International Center for the Settlement of Investment Disputes ("ICSID"). ICSID was established in 1966 and is a part of the World Bank Group, and has 151 contracting states. Over 500 such cases have been filed, and the amount of cases filed has been increasing in recent years. Critics of investor state arbitration will state that it allows corporations to use "secret tribunals" where "corporate lawyers" make decisions behind closed doors. The rhetoric is overblown. The ICSID procedure typically uses a panel of three arbitrators which allows for both the investor and the state to each choose one arbitrator, and then seek joint agreement on the third arbitrator. (ICSID Arbitration Rules, 2003) ICSID awards (or at least excerpts therefrom), are generally made available to the public, as well as many other filings in the cases. Supporters of investor state arbitration would argue that it makes foreign direct investment more secure and increases capital inflows in places that need it. Nonetheless, the costs associated with investor state arbitrations can be extremely high, and total into the millions. Claims alleged against states can reach into the billions. Shrewd corporations have been accused of using the threat of costs associated with investor state arbitration to bend governments to their will, and this has happened. At the same time there are a multitude of examples where an honest investor had its investment taken away, perhaps by local government officials for nefarious reasons, and was forced to leave the country. Those companies surely need some form of protection. The debate concerning investor-state arbitration and ICSID is a very interesting and current topic, which is gaining more importance since such mechanisms have been proposed to be included in the TPP and TTIP. This is an issue to be understood and monitored by all those who are interested.

The United Nations ("UN") and the Commission on International Trade Law ("UNCITRAL")

The United Nations ("UN") also plays a role in the development of international commercial and trade law. As previously mentioned, there is no international legislature that has the ability to create law that is binding on all countries of the world. The UN General Assembly does not have this power. Additionally, while the UN Security Council has the power to issue binding resolutions, the subject matter of such resolutions is limited in scope to peace and security matters, which can include economic sanctions. (Chapter VII, UN Charter) Therefore, the UN is not an organization which creates directly enforceable laws affecting commercial relationships and trade. Nevertheless, multiple UN entities play an important role in shaping international commercial law in both a public and private context.

Not least among the UN entities which shape international commercial and trade law is the United Nations Commission on International Trade Law ("UNCITRAL"). UNCITRAL was established by the UN General Assembly 1966 and is based in Vienna, Austria. It endeavors to achieve harmonization and modernization of international trade and commercial law. It works towards these goals using various legal texts such as conventions, model laws, legislative guides, contractual rules, and legal guides. UNCITRAL does not have the authority to force UN Member States to follow the rules that they develop, but they have been largely successful in achieving harmonization in certain areas of international commercial and trade law. UNCITRAL texts address both States (legislative texts such as conventions, model laws, and legislative guides) and private parties (contractual rules and legal guides).

Types of Legal Texts Developed by UNCITRAL	Description
Convention	As previously discussed, a Convention is an agreement between States (a treaty). UNCITRAL develops treaty proposals, which it then recommends to UN Member States. UN Member States are then free to adopt the treaty (generally through signature and ratification), but they are not obligated to accept a UNCITRAL proposed Convention.
Model Law	A Model Law is a set of proposed legislative provisions (e.g., a code), which States can choose to adopt as their domestic law covering a specific area of the law if they so desire (e.g, international commercial arbitration). It is a proposal of law, much like a Bill in a domestic legislature. While a Model Law is directed to states and not private parties, it is different than a Convention because it does not require agreement between two or more countries to be effective. Also, countries can unilaterally make modifications to a Model Law as they see fit.
Legislative Guide	A legislative guide provides suggestions and guidance for countries who wish to further develop their trade laws. A country wishing to modernize its law in a particular area may refer to a UNCITRAL Legislative Guide (such as the Legislative Guide on Insolvency Law). The legislative guide does not contain proposed articles of law, but instead contains detailed analysis and recommendations.
Rules	Rules can refer to either standard clauses to be used in contracts, generally between private parties, or rules governing the relationship between private parties. For example, two parties who have a legal dispute can contractually agree to use arbitration following the UNCITRAL Arbitration Rules.
Legal Guide	On occasion, UNCITRAL has prepared legal guides to assist parties with various issues in an international commercial context, for example, the Legal Guide on Electronic Funds Transfers.

Modified from: http://www.uncitral.org/pdf/english/uncitral-leaflet-e.pdf

UNCITRAL has found success in various areas of the law; two pertinent examples are in the context of the sale of goods, as well as international commercial arbitration. Over 80 countries have adopted the **Convention** on the International Sale of Goods ("CISG"), meaning that the default law governing sale of goods transactions between most major trading nations is harmonized. The same principle text, with minor possible variations, has been adopted by all of these countries; keep in mind that case law interpretations may nonetheless vary. The CISG will be further addressed herein. Additionally, UNCITRAL has developed a successful **Model Law** for international commercial arbitration (the UNCITRAL Model Law on International Commercial Arbitration). Legislation based on this model law has been adopted in a total of 102 jurisdictions, meaning that the law governing certain types of arbitration procedures (international and commercial) is harmonized to a certain extent. (UNCITRAL, 2016) It may not be the exact same text in each jurisdiction as each state has autonomy to make certain modifications, but the legislation is based on the model law, so the basic principles will be generally shared between these countries. Again, case law interpretations may vary greatly between countries.

In addition to developing legal texts used by states and private parties, UNCITRAL provides additional services. It attempts to coordinate work of organizations involved in international trade law within as well as outside of the UN system and provides technical assistance to parties interested in reforming trade law. It also maintains a trade law library in Vienna and has established an online database of case law from around the world related to its work (court decisions and arbitral awards interpreting UNCITRAL legal texts). In short, even though UNCITRAL has no 'hard' power to bind countries to follow its laws; it has been a successful and influential organization which has played an important role in shaping international commercial and trade law.

The United Nations Conference on Trade and Development ("UNCTAD") influences international trade law as well. UNCTAD principally works with developing countries providing technical assistance. The aim is to assist countries with integrating into the global economy. UNCTAD also develops reports on various topics related to trade, compiles statistics, and works with the WTO through the International Trade Center ("ITC"). The ITC further assists small and medium size businesses to achieve internationalization providing various forms of assistance (see, e.g., Model Contracts for Small Firms).

UNIDROIT

Not to be confused with a UN entity, UNIDROIT is nonetheless a highly influential organization in the field of private international law. UNIDROIT is the International Institute for the Unification of Private Law, and is an independent intergovernmental organization. UNIDROIT actually pre-dates the UN as it was originally set up by the League of Nations in 1926, and re-established in 1940. There are 63 Member States.

UNIDROIT's activities are similar to those of UNCITRAL in the sense that they draft proposed conventions, model laws and other uniform law instruments with a goal of unifying, harmonizing and modernizing private law around the world. It has worked in a wide array of legal fields, including, but not limited to agency, commercial contracts, international sales, transport, franchising, leasing, and more. Just as with conventions and model laws drafted by UNCITRAL, those drafted by UNIDROIT are merely suggestions to states wishing to modernize their laws in various fields. States must decide to adopt any convention or model law drafted by UNIDROIT.

UNIDROIT also has developed various principles to be used in a private law context. Importantly, the UNIDROIT Principles of International Commercial Contracts can be agreed upon to govern commercial contracts between private parties in an international context. This may be a useful solution to parties from different countries that are unable to agree on the appropriate law to govern their relationship, or to act as gap filler if the principal chosen law is incomplete. These principles will be further addressed in subsequent sections.

The Hague Conference

The Hague Conference on Private International Law is a third organization which operates in a context similar to UNCITRAL and UNIDROIT. These three organizations are sometimes referred to as the "three sisters" since their work is inter-related. (UNIDROIT, 2016) The Hague Conference is an organization which focuses on unifying private law not only in the context of international commercial law, but also in finance law, international legal co-operation and litigation, and even in the international protection of children, family and property relations.

The work of the Hague Conference comes in particularly handy when dealing with international procedural issues in the context of court litigation, whether in a commercial context or otherwise. Successful conventions from the Hague Conference include the Convention Abolishing the Requirement of Legalisation for Foreign Public Documents (aka the Apostille Convention), Convention on the Taking of Evidence Abroad in Civil or Commercial Matters, and the Convention on the Service Abroad of Judicial and Extrajudicial Documents in Civil and Commercial Matters. (HCPIL, 2016) Parties engaged in disputes with uncooperative adversaries in foreign countries may be forced to resort to these international conventions to help the judicial process proceed in a meaningful fashion.

Bibliography

ASEAN. 1967. *The Asean Declaration.* http://www.asean.org/the-asean-declaration-bangkok-declaration-bangkok-8-august-1967/.

————. 1992. *Agreement on the Common Effective Preferential Tariff Scheme for the ASEAN Free Trade Area.* http://www.asean.org/storage/images/2012/Economic/AFTA/Co mmon_Effective_Preferential_Tariff/Agreement%20on%20the%20 Common%20Effective%20Preferential%20Tariff%20Scheme%20for %20the%20ASEAN%20Free%20Trade%20Area.pdf.

ASIAN DEVELOPMENT BANK. 2015. "ASEAN Economic Community: 12 Things to Know." *Www.adb.org,* December 29. http://www.adb.org/ features/asean-economic-community-12-things-know.

BLANKMAP-WORLD6.SVG: Happenstance et al.; Derivative work: Danlaycock. 2014. *WTO Members and Observers.* https://commons.wikimedia.org/ wiki/File:WTO_members_and_observers.svg.

CENTRAL INTELLIGENCE AGENCY. 2016. "The World Factbook; Field Listing::GDP - Composition, by Sector of Origin." *Www.cia.gov.* Accessed March 22. https://www.cia.gov/library/publications/the-world-factbook/fields/2012.html.

COUNCIL ON FOREIGN RELATIONS. 2012. "Mercosur: South America's Fractious Trade Bloc." *Council on Foreign Relations.* July 31. http://www.cfr.org/trade/mercosur-south-americas-fractious-trade-bloc/p12762.

EUROPEAN COMMISSION. 2015. "Commission Proposes New Investment Court System for TTIP and Other EU Trade and Investment Negotiations." *Trade.ec.europa.eu.* September 16. http://trade.ec.europa.eu/ doclib/press/index.cfm?id=1364.

———. 2016. "EU-Canada Comprehensive Economic and Trade Agreement (CETA)." *Ec.europa.eu.* March 3. http://ec.europa.eu/trade/policy/in-focus/ceta/.

———. 2016. "Transatlantic Trade and Investment Partnership (TTIP)." *Ec.europa.edu.* Accessed March 22. http://ec.europa.eu/trade/policy/in-focus/ttip/.

EUROPEAN COURT OF JUSTICE. 1979. *Cassis de Dijon Case.* http://eur-lex.europa.eu/legal-content/EN/TXT/PDF/?uri=CELEX:61978CJ0120&from=EN.

EUROPEAN UNION. 2016. "EUROPA - The History of the European Union." Accessed March 22. http://europa.eu/about-eu/eu-history/.

HAGUE CONFERENCE ON PRIVATE INTERNATIONAL LAW. 2016. "The Hague Conventions: Signatures, Ratifications, Approvals and Accessions: Status on 21 March 2016." https://assets.hcch.net/docs/ccf77ba4-af95-4e9c-84a3-e94dc8a3c4ec.pdf.

HOEKMAN, BERNARD M., and PETROS C. MAVROIDIS. 2016. *The World Trade Organization: Law, Economics, and Politics.* Second edition. Global Institutions 108. London: Routledge.

INTERNATIONAL CENTRE FOR SETTLEMENT OF INVESTMENT DISPUTES. 2006. *ICSID Convention, Regulations and Rules.* https://icsid.worldbank.org/ICSID/StaticFiles/basicdoc/main-eng.htm.

INTERNATIONAL CENTRE FOR TRADE AND SUSTAINABLE DEVELOPMENT. 2016. "TPP Countries Gear Up for Ratification Push After Auckland Signing Ceremony." *Www.ictsd.org.* Accessed March 22. http://www.ictsd.org/bridges-news/bridges/news/tpp-countries-gear-up-for-ratification-push-after-auckland-signing.

INTERNATIONAL LABOUR OFFICE GOVERNING BODY: Working Party on the Social Dimension of Globalization. 2001. *Trade Liberalization and Employment.* https://www.google.fr/?gws_rd=ssl#q=GB282-WP-SDG-2-2001-10-0224-1-EN.Docv2+1+INTERNATIONAL+LABOUR+OFFICE+GB.282%2FWP%2FSDG%2F2+282nd+Session+Governing+Body+Geneva%2C+November+2001+Working+Party+on+the+Social+Dimension+of+Globalization+WP%2FSDG+SECOND+ITEM+ON+THE+AGENDA+Trade+liberalization+and+employment.

MERCOSUR. 2016. "Mercosur." Accessed March 22. http://www.mercosur.int/.

NAFTA. 1994. *North American Free Trade Agreement.* https://www.nafta-sec-alena.org/Home/Legal-Texts/North-American-Free-Trade-Agreement.

OFFICIAL JOURNAL OF THE EUROPEAN UNION. 2012. *Consolidated Versions of the Treaty on European Union and the Treaty on the Functioning of the European Union.* http://eur-lex.europa.eu/legal-content/EN/TXT/PDF/?uri=OJ:C:2012:326:FULL&from=EN.

OXFORD ANALYTICA. 2010. "Small Developing Countries Struggle In WTO - Forbes." *Forbes,* May 19. http://www.forbes.com/2010/05/18/wto-gatt-trade-business-oxford-analytica.html.

SCHAFFER, RICHARD, FILIBERTO AGUSTIT, LUCIEN J. DHOOGE, and BEVERLEY EARLE. 2012. *International Business Law and Its Environment.* 8th ed. Mason, OH: South-Western Cengage Learning.

THE ECONOMIST. 2013. "Towards the End of Poverty." *The Economist,* June 1. http://www.economist.com/news/leaders/21578665-nearly-1-billion-people-have-been-taken-out-extreme-poverty-20-years-world-should-aim.

THE EUROPEAN PARLIAMENT AND THE COUNCIL. 2008. *Regulation (EC) No. 764/2008.* http://eur-lex.europa.eu/legal-content/EN/TXT/PDF/?uri=CELEX:32008R0764&from=EN.

UNCITRAL. 2004. "Facts about UNCITRAL." http://www.uncitral.org/pdf/english/uncitral-leaflet-e.pdf.

———. 2016. "Status -UNCITRAL Model Law on International Commercial Arbitration (1985), with Amendments as Adopted in 2006." *Www.uncitral.org.* http://www.uncitral.org/uncitral/en/uncitral_texts/arbitration/1985Model_arbitration_status.html.

UNCTAD. 2015. "Key Statistics and Trends in International Trade 2014." UNCTAD/DITC/TAB/2014/2. unc. http://unctad.org/en/PublicationsLibrary/ditctab2014d2_en.pdf.

———. 2016. "International Investment Agreements Navigator." *investmentpolicyhub.unctad.org/IIA.* Accessed March 22. http://investmentpolicyhub.unctad.org/IIA.

UNIDROIT. 2016. "UNIDROIT - HISTORY AND Overview." *Www.unidroit.org.* January 13. http://www.unidroit.org/about-unidroit/overview.

UNITED NATIONS. 1945. *Charter of the United Nations - Chapter VII.* http://www.un.org/en/sections/un-charter/chapter-vii/.

WALKER, Andrew. 2010. "China and Asean Free Trade Deal Begins." *BBC News*, January 1. http://news.bbc.co.uk/2/hi/business/ 8436772.stm.

WALKER, Aurelie. 2011. "The WTO Has Failed Developing Nations." *The Guardian*, November 14. http://www.theguardian.com/global-development/poverty-matters/2011/nov/14/wto-fails-developing-countries.

WORLD INTEGRATED TRADE SOLUTION. 2016. "WITS - Glossary." *Wits.worldbank.org*. Accessed March 22. http://wits.worldbank.org/ glossary.html.

WORLD TRADE ORGANIZATION. 1948. "The General Agreement on Tariffs and Trade (GATT 1947)." January 1. https://www.wto.org/ english/docs_e/legal_e/gatt47_01_e.htm.

———. 1979. *Decision of 28 November 1979 (L/4903)*. https://www.wto.org/english/docs_e/legal_e/enabling1979_e.htm.

———. 1995a. *Agreement on Implementation of Article VI of the General Agreement on Tariffs and Trade 1994*. https://www.wto.org/english/ docs_e/legal_e/19-adp.pdf.

———. 1995b. *Agreement on Subsidies and Countervailing Measures*. https://www.wto.org/english/docs_e/legal_e/24-scm.pdf.

———. 1995c. *Annex 1C - Agreement on Trade-Related Aspects of Intellectual Property Rights*. https://www.wto.org/english/docs_e/legal_e/27-trips.pdf.

———. 1995d. *Annex 2 - Understanding on Rules and Procedures Governing the Settlement of Disputes*. https://www.wto.org/english/tratop_e/ dispu_e/dsu_e.htm.

———. 1995e. *Annex 3 - Trade Policy Review Mechanism*. https://www.wto.org/english/docs_e/legal_e/29-tprm.pdf.

———. 1995f. *Annex on Air Transport Services*. https://www.wto.org/english/docs_e/legal_e/26-gats_02_e.htm#annats.

———. 1995g. *General Agreement on Trade in Services*. https://www.wto.org/english/docs_e/legal_e/26-gats_01_e.htm.

———. 1995h. *Understanding on the Interpretation of Article XXIV of the General Agreement on Tariffs and Trade 1994*. https://www.wto.org/english/tratop_e/region_e/regatt_e.htm#und erstanding.

———. 2009. *10 Benefits of the WTO Trading System.* Genève: WTO.

———. 2016. "Understanding the WTO - Anti-Dumping, Subsidies, Safe-guards: Contingencies, Etc." Accessed March 22. https://www.wto.org/english/thewto_e/whatis_e/tif_e/agrm8_e.htm.

Laws and Rules affecting private international commercial relationships
(the private side of international trade law)

So far, this work has examined the public side of international trade law. As discussed it is international organizations, whose memberships consist of state parties and not private parties such as businesses, which create the general legal framework in which international trade and commerce exists. Nevertheless, it is private parties who most often directly engage in international trade and commerce. So how are relationships between private parties affected by international commercial and trade law? Of course, private parties must follow the laws of the countries where they operate. Such countries are (in theory) following the rules set by the international organizations and agreements to which they are parties. This sets basic rules for things like import and export, labeling, etc. So while private parties do not directly participate in the negotiation of international agreements affecting trade law (like the WTO Agreements), they are affected by the results since they will be required to follow the rules set by such agreements. Of course, private parties influence their governments when negotiations of international trade law agreements are taking place, sometimes making significant contributions to the final texts thereof. At the end of the day though, it is public, state parties who negotiate and sign such agreements, thereby creating the framework of international trade law.

The above explanation does not take into consideration the fact that private parties also enter into relationships with each other which are beyond the scope of the rules that they must follow when engaging in international trade. This could take the form of an agreement to buy or sell goods, or licensing of intellectual property, or entering into a joint venture, etc. These private international relationships are also governed by a legal framework, based principally on contract law. Therefore, this work will focus on basic legal issues surrounding typical international commercial transactions, mostly in a contractual context. The first question that must be resolved in this context is: "What law applies to this private international commercial relationship?"

1. Choice of Law

The problem of what law applies to a private international relationship was briefly explored in the previous section concerning private international law. Private parties in an international commercial context are not required to choose the law which applies to their relationship; however they are strongly advised to do so. Failure to do so could give the parties significant headaches if, for example, a term of the contract or relationship needs to be interpreted, or even more importantly if a dispute arises which must be resolved in front of a court or some alternative forum for dispute resolution. In these situations, before the parties can even discuss the substance of the contractual terms that need to be interpreted or the nature of the dispute which needs to be resolved, they must determine what law applies. It is possible, and perhaps even likely that they will not agree on the law that applies since each party may prefer the law of their home jurisdiction. Therefore there will be a dispute about what law applies that needs to be resolved before anything else can be addressed. This will take time and cost money (in general, lawyers do not work for free!).

Fortunately, the parties can resolve this problem quite simply by choosing the law which applies to their private international commercial relationship. This is an easy, straightforward solution to the above referenced problems, but it is not to be taken lightly. Choice of law is crucial, and should be given careful thought prior to the conclusion of any contract.

In the international commercial context parties' choice of law will generally be honored. (*See e.g.,* UNCITRAL Model Law on International Commercial Arbitration, Art. 28). However, different countries follow different rules on determining the validity of a choice. In some countries, and in various US States, the law chosen must have some substantial relationship with the parties, or at the least there must be a reasonable basis for the choice. (*See e.g.,* RST 2d Conflict of Laws §187, *et seq.*) Other jurisdictions may be more liberal in honoring parties' choice of law. For example, New York wishes to be recognized as the leading jurisdiction for international commercial matters, and does not require any relationship between the parties and the state for New York law to apply, at least for contracts whose value is above a certain threshold, US$250,000. (New York General Obligations Law, § 5-1401) New York also allows access to its state courts for disputes involving contracts valued at greater than US$1,000,000, even where the contract was unrelated to state. (New York General Obligations Law, § 5-1402) Switzerland follows a similar policy. (Born, 2001) Significantly, in the EU, the parties have freedom of choice and are not required to choose a law most closely related to the contract, nor are they required to choose the law of a Member State. (Rome I Regulation, 2008)

The doctrine of party autonomy generally prevails in the international commercial context. This simply refers to the idea that parties have the right to choose how to handle and resolve their disputes not only by choosing the law but as well as by choosing the procedure and the forum (place where the dispute will be resolved, e.g., court, arbitration tribunal, etc.). (Redfern & Hunter, 2004) The basic rational is that allowing parties to choose law and forum creates certainty and efficiency in the event that rights, duties and obligations need to be interpreted and disputes need to be resolved. Another theory is that this doctrine leads to competition between legal systems as leading jurisdictions will strive to innovate by having more efficient and party friendly laws and procedures.

The most common way that party choice of law is effectuated is through a choice of law clause in a contract. This is simply a clause in a contract that states which law will apply in interpreting a contract and enforcing its terms. It is important that the choice of law clause is clear and unambiguous. For example, a choice of law clause choosing the "law of the United States" may lead to problems since the US is highly federalized and the laws of each state can be significantly different. Most contract law in the US derives from individual state law, increasing the complexity of choice of law in that country. A better choice might be "the laws of the State of California" which would include both state and federal laws. This would reduce ambiguity and is more likely to be a valid choice of law.

Keep in mind that the choice of law principles addressed herein apply in a commercial context. Countries generally apply the doctrine of party autonomy allowing parties to choose law in a commercial context, but may be less likely to do so in other contexts. For example, the ability to make a choice of law may be limited in consumer, employment, and various other types of contracts, but this will depend on the specific rules of each jurisdiction. (*See, e.g.*, Rome I Regulation, 2008)

In the EU, the rules for determining the applicable law in an international context have been harmonized for both contractual and non-contractual obligations between parties based in EU Member States through the Rome Regulations. The Rome I Regulation provides rules for determining applicable law for contractual obligations in civil and commercial contracts with various exceptions such as for contracts related to family relationships, negotiable instruments, or arbitration clauses. Rome II provides rules for non-contractual obligations. Under both Rome I and II a choice of law made by parties will generally be valid (although choosing law in a non-contractual context, for example in a tort case involving negligence, may be impractical). The importance of the Rome Regulations is that they provide rules for determining what law applies between private parties in an international context when no choice is made. Some of these rules are summarized in the following, non-exhaustive chart:

Rome I – Contractual Obligations	Rome II – Non-Contractual Obligations
• a contract for sale of goods, is governed by law of country where seller has his habitual residence • a contract for provision of services, is governed by law of country where service provider has his habitual residence • a contract relating to a right in immovable property shall be governed by the law of the country where the property is situated (this applies to real property such as land, apartments, houses, etc.) • a franchise contract shall be governed by the law of the country where the franchisee has his habitual residence • a distribution contract shall be governed by the law of the country where the distributor has his habitual residence	• The law that will apply to a non-contractual obligation arising out of a tort will generally be the law of the country in which the damage occurs • The law applicable to a non-contractual obligation arising out of damage caused by a product (product liability) shall be the law of the country in which the person sustaining the damage had his or her habitual residence when the damage occurred, if the product was marketed in that country (if this is not possible the Regulation provides various additional possibilities) • The law applicable to a non-contractual obligation arising from an infringement of an intellectual property right shall be the law of the country for which protection is claimed • The law applicable to a non-contractual obligation arising out of an act of unfair competition shall be the law of the country where competitive relations or the collective interests of consumers are, or are likely to be, affected
Source: REGULATION (EC) No 593/2008 (Rome I)	**Source:** REGULATION (EC) No 864/2007 (Rome II)

Despite the existence of the Rome Regulations in the EU, as well as more general conflict of law principles internationally, it is nonetheless advisable to make an informed choice of law whenever possible. This avoids messy situations where expensive lawyers need to be engaged to resolve a question of applicable law that in many cases could have easily been taken care of by the parties themselves long before a problem arose while they still had a healthy working relationship. When negotiating contracts it is useful to keep in mind the words of Benjamin Franklin who once said, "[a]n ounce of prevention is worth a pound of cure."

2. Lex Mercatoria

While parties are generally free to choose the law that they wish to apply to their contracts, the question remains whether there are any general legal principles which are common to international commercial contracts. This is a relevant question since throughout history merchants engaging in commerce have had a tendency to develop rules governing their interactions. This goes back at least to the Middle Ages, with the development of the *lex mercatoria*, or merchant law. The *lex mercatoria* of the Middle Ages developed between merchants via custom and practice outside the scope of territorial laws and boundaries. There were differences between local trade practices from place to place. Merchants, being naturally pragmatic, recognized the need for a body of rules to regulate trade and to enforce these principles to resolve disputes among themselves.

In modern times there is much debate among legal scholars concerning the existence and makeup of the modern *lex mercatoria*. The debate recognizes the need of uniform principles to be applied between private parties coming from different legal backgrounds, a necessity that continuously becomes more important in the face of ever expanding globalization. Nonetheless, there is no agreed upon definition of a modern merchant law in an international context. While there is no uniform definition, the modern *lex mercatoria* consists of transnational legal principles which can be found in various sources such as Conventions and Treaties, international custom, trade practice, and other possible sources. (Redfern & Hunter, 2004) *Lex mercatoria* is not national law; rather it is made up of international rules not based on any particular legal system, and remains quite general. Commentators point to legal texts such as the UNIDROIT Principles of International Commercial Contracts (some would say that these principles are not a source of *lex mercatoria*, but simply embody the concepts found in the *lex mercatoria*) or the International Chamber of Commerce's Incoterms®, among other sources, as examples of sources of the modern *lex mercatoria.* (Moses, 2012)

Parties to an international commercial contract could theoretically choose the *lex mercatoria* to be the law governing their relationship, however this choice would not be advisable since it is not necessarily clear to what exact sources of law the general term *lex mercatoria* refers. It is important to recall that clarity is essential in making a choice of law since uncertainty causes fights; therefore such a choice would be unlikely in practice. So how is *lex mercatoria* important in the context of modern commercial practice? It is often used to supplement a choice of law made by the parties. For example, a contract may incorporate an FOB Incoterm. The Incoterms® are private rules developed by the International Chamber of Commerce, *see infra*, but may also be considered as *lex mercatoria* by some, and are used to clearly stipulate to transport obligations. Or if parties choose the Convention on Contracts for the International Sale of Goods, *see infra*, to govern their sales contract, they recognize that this convention does not cover all possible contract law issues. They may then supplement their choice using the UNIDROIT Principles of International Commercial Contracts. In short, the modern *lex mercatoria* exists to facilitate trade in an international context, and instruments thereof can be used to achieve clarity and consistency in contractual negotiations as well as provide uniform rules for dispute resolution.

3. UNIDROIT Principles

A good source of basic contractual principles and rules for international commercial contracts can be found in the UNIDROIT Principles of International Commercial Contracts ("UNIDROIT Principles" or "Principles"). In 1994 UNIDROIT (*see supra*) drafted the first version of the Principles, with subsequent revised versions being released in 2004 and 2010. The intent of the Principles is to create general rules for international commercial contracts. The Principles can be adopted by international parties as the law governing their commercial relationship through a choice of law provision in a contract, or as a supplement to the law governing their contractual relationship. The Principles can also be referred to by courts and arbitration tribunals when the parties have not made a specific choice of law. (Preamble, UNIDROIT Principles 2010) As discussed above, while there is some scholarly debate on the point, the Principles have been said to embody concepts within the *lex mercatoria.*

The UNIDROIT Principles are simply a statement of general contract principles with 11 Chapters covering basic contract law concepts such as the formation of a contract and the performance obligations of the parties to a contract. Contract law principles can be quite different from country to country, and the UNIDROIT Principles provide users with a solid neutral legal framework for contracts in an international commercial context. The Principles are not law since they were not created by a domestic legislature, and should not be relied upon as such. Nor are the Principles a Treaty or Convention which have been accepted and incorporated into domestic legal regimes by state parties. If a party needs to understand contract law in a particular jurisdiction, they need to look directly at the law of said jurisdiction, as well as any international law which may apply such as the Convention on Contracts for the International Sale of Goods (*infra*). It is therefore important to understand that the Principles are private rules, which when adopted by private parties operate to govern the private relationship between those parties. As previously discussed, when parties enter into a contract, they are free to determine the content of that contract and create the rules that will govern their relationship.

Although they are not hard law, the Principles nevertheless provide a welcome opportunity to talk about some basic contract law principles in an international commercial context. This is a generally difficult task since the law of each country is different. This work will take advantage of the UNIDROIT Principles to engage in a general discussion of contract law through study of selected articles. Again, keep in mind that these principles are not the law of any particular country, but are nonetheless important as they can be seen as general international commercial contract law principles (*lex mercatoria*) and are especially important if parties choose the principles to govern their relationship or supplement the law governing their relationship. However, the disclaimer remains in place: *Unless parties to a contractual relationship have chosen the UNIDROIT Principles to govern, the relevant contract law will be found in either the domestic legal regimes of the parties or the legal regime chosen by such parties.* With that understanding readers may proceed with caution in an effort to understand basic international commercial contract law using the Principles as a guide.

Selected provisions of the Principles will be examined herein, beginning with the freedom of contract. The principle of freedom of contract is a widely accepted legal principle, and is found in Art. 1.1 of the UNIDROIT Principles:

| **Art. 1.1 (Freedom of Contract)** |
| The parties are free to enter into a contract and to determine its content. |

While this freedom extends quite far, it is still subject to mandatory rules of law of domestic legal systems. For example, if two commercial parties from countries A and B enter into an international joint venture in country C, they cannot agree that the individuals employed by the joint venture in country C will be paid less than the minimum wage in that country. The minimum wage law in country C would be a mandatory rule of law that they parties are not allowed to derogate from.

With regard to contract formation, the Principles provide basic guidance on what is required to form a valid contract. While this text will not examine the entirety of the UNIDROIT Principles, this is an interesting area to focus on since it highlights the need to have uniformity in an international setting. This is because the requirements to form a valid contract can vary significantly from country to country. Some countries require contracts to be in writing, while others are perfectly fine with oral contracts. While it is universally accepted that a contract requires agreement, or consent to contract (offer and acceptance), in most legal systems something more than mere agreement is required to form a valid contract. Not every promise gives rise to a contract.

For example, in addition to offer and acceptance, Common Law legal systems require that there be "consideration" for a valid contract to be formed. Consideration simply refers to the idea that there must be an exchange of something of legal value between each of the parties when making a contract, in other words each party must give something. This could be money, property, abstaining from exercising a validly legal right, or many other things. Without consideration, a valid contract is not formed in Common Law legal systems.

The concept of consideration is foreign to Civil Law legal systems since they do not have the same rule. Nonetheless, Civil Law systems also generally require something more than mere agreement for valid contract formation. A validly formed bilateral contract in Civil Law systems following the traditional French model requires "cause" in addition to offer and acceptance. (French Civil Code, Art. 1108) In short, in determining whether cause exists one can typically look at the "end pursued" by each party. (Nayler, 2006) For example, the purchaser of a car agrees to pay money to the seller in order to receive the car. The seller agrees to give the car to the purchaser in order to receive the money. Each party's obligation benefits the other party and causes the other party's obligation. The cause must exist and be legal. While this clearly a different theoretical approach, often it is functionally equivalent to consideration in Common Law legal systems. (Steiner, 2010; Art. 3.1.2 Commentary, UNIDROIT Principles 2010) The requirement in a Civil Law system following the German model is conceptually simpler as it requires neither cause nor consideration; rather it merely requires corresponding declarations of intent between the parties to enter into a contract.

Consequently, the international setting is rife with potential confusion between parties who come from different legal backgrounds. Thus, the French business negotiating with the American business will need to be cognizant of the difference between the legal principles from these countries in order to effectively negotiate a contract since even something as basic as the legal principles related to contract formation might be significantly different. This is a good example where neutral rules such as the UNIDROIT Principles could come in handy. Below is a chart containing selected the UNIDROIT Principles related to contract formation:

Selected Articles re: Formation Requirements under the UNIDROIT Principles:
Art. 1.2 (No form required)
Nothing in these Principles requires a contract, statement or any other act to be made in or evidenced by a particular form. It may be proved by any means, including witnesses.
Art. 2.1.1 (Manner of formation)
A contract may be concluded either by the acceptance of an offer or by conduct of the parties that is sufficient to show agreement.
Art. 2.1.2 (Definition of offer)
A proposal for concluding a contract constitutes an offer if it is sufficiently definite and indicates the intention of the offer or to be bound in case of acceptance.
Art. 2.1.6 (Mode of acceptance)
(1) A statement made by or other conduct of the offeree indicating assent to an offer is an acceptance. Silence or inactivity does not in itself amount to acceptance.
(2) An acceptance of an offer becomes effective when the indication of assent reaches the offeror.
(3) However, if, by virtue of the offer or as a result of practices which the parties have established between themselves or of usage, the offeree may indicate assent by performing an act without notice to the offeror, the acceptance is effective when the act is performed.
Art. 3.1.2 (Validity of mere agreement)
A contract is concluded, modified or terminated by the mere agreement of the parties, without any further requirement.

In examining these selected principles on forming a valid contract, it is interesting to begin with Art. 1.2 which states that there is no need to follow a particular form when forming a valid contract in an international commercial context. In other words, oral, non-written contracts can be valid under the UNIDROIT Principles. Many countries follow rules similar to Art. 1.2, however such flexible formation requirements may be contrary to domestic legal rules in other jurisdictions. Some domestic legal systems may require a written contract, signatures, witnesses, notarization, written forms of proof (not witness testimony), or other formalities to form a valid contract. The official comment to Art. 1.2 states that "[t]he principle…seems particularly appropriate in the context of international trade relationships where, thanks to modern means of communication, many transactions are concluded at great speed and by a mixture of conversations, telefaxes, paper contracts, e-mail and web communication."

In short, it is quite simple to form a contract under the UNIDROIT Principles. A phone conversation, e-mail, formal letter, SMS, or even a handshake over dinner is sufficient to meet the form requirements. Of course, proving the existence of the contract is of the utmost importance, so certain forms are clearly more advisable than others. People forget things, remember the facts differently, or sometimes lie, even while under oath in court. Nevertheless, a prudent company which operates internationally should train their representatives to state over and over that a final written contract will need to be negotiated and signed. The more formalities undertaken by the parties (e.g., putting the agreement in writing), the less likely they are to have evidentiary problems further down the road.

While form requirements are highly flexible, an offer and an acceptance are nonetheless basic minimum requirements. Art. 2.1.1 envisions express acceptance of an offer through words (written or oral), which is what typically occurs in a commercial context. If one party sends an email offering to buy certain goods from another party, the contract is typically concluded through a return communication indicating acceptance. Art. 2.1.1 also provides for the possibility of accepting through conduct. For example, if after various rounds of negotiations one party sends an email offering to purchase goods from another party, the other party responds by simply shipping the goods. This conduct could be sufficient to show agreement.

Should there be questions between the parties as to whether there was a valid offer or acceptance, the Principles go further and provide guidance to help determine whether an offer or acceptance is valid. For example, Art. 2.1.2 defines an offer and clarifies that the proposal needs to be sufficiently definite in addition to containing the intention to be bound by the terms of the offer if it is accepted. For example, if ABC, Inc. sends an email to XYZ, S.A. which simply says "I am interested in your widgets, what is the price per unit?" is this communication a valid offer under the UNIDROIT Principles? Based on the plain language of Art. 2.1.2 it is not. It is neither sufficiently definite nor does it indicate an intention to be bound. All we know from this language is that ABC, Inc. is interested in widgets, but we do not know the quantity desired, the delivery terms proposed, or anything else. This does not meet the threshold of being sufficiently definite. Additionally, the language does not indicate an intention to be bound as ABC, Inc. is merely shopping and looking for price information and could find the response from XYZ, S.A. concerning price to be unsatisfactory at which point ABC, Inc. would go elsewhere in search of widgets. It simply appears to be a communication intended to begin the process of negotiation and invite responses from the counterparty.

Art. 2.1.6 gives guidance as to the validity of acceptances and provides a few basic principles concerning acceptances. As previously discussed, offers can be accepted expressly through words or impliedly through conduct, but silence or inactivity by itself cannot be acceptance. When conduct is the means of acceptance, such conduct does not need to be communicated in advance to the other party if such accepting conduct is foreseen by a previous practice or trade usage. For example, a party sends an offer saying "if I don't hear back from you within 1 week I will consider that you have accepted the offer." Such language by itself does not create acceptance 1 week later if there is no response. It could create a valid acceptance if there was a previously established practice between those parties or perhaps if it was based on a well-known industry practice. Absent such circumstances, silence is not acceptance. Art. 2.1.6 also explains that acceptance becomes effective once the offeror receives it, and no earlier. So if the offeree sends an acceptance for the purchase of goods by traditional mail, but between the time that the acceptance was sent and received the offeror decides to sell the goods to a third party, there was no valid acceptance in time.

Finally, under the UNIDROIT Principles, the previously mentioned dilemma of differing national law contract formation rules requiring something more in addition to mere agreement (e.g. consideration, cause) are eliminated. There is no requirement of consideration, cause, intent or anything else. Pursuant to Art. 3.1.2 a mere agreement of the parties is all that is required. This is a simple rule, however, as the commentary to the article aptly points out, it is perhaps of little practical significance since in a commercial context there normally are few questions of consideration, cause or intent given that these elements are normally satisfied by the very nature of commercial transactions. In other words, parties to commercial transactions are by their inherent nature serious in their intent to enter into business with other parties, their actions are caused by the counter promises of the other party, and some exchange of legal value is generally made (e.g., goods for money).

Whether it is oral or written, once a contract is formed, the contractual obligations must be honored. This is based on the widely accepted principle of contract law that once a contract is formed, it is binding, and agreements must be kept. The UNIDROIT Principles follow this principle, which is also referred to as the principle of *pacta sunt servanda*. Yet, although contracts are generally binding, they are not written in stone and can be modified. Under the UNIDROIT Principles, all that is required to modify a contract is the agreement of the parties. This is all found in Art. 1.3 of the Principles:

| **Art. 1.3 (Binding Character of Contract)** |
| A contract validly entered into is binding upon the parties. It can only be modified or terminated in accordance with its terms or by agreement or as otherwise provided in these Principles. |

Not only is the international commercial contract binding under the UNIDROIT Principals, but the parties are also required to act in accordance with principles of good faith and fair dealing. This is a mandatory rule under the UNIDROIT Principles. The principle of good faith and fair dealing generally refers to the idea that contracting parties enter into contracts with the presumed intention of honoring the contract, and treating the other party in a fair and honest fashion. One of the difficult elements of entering into a contract with a party from another country is that there may be significant cultural and/or linguistic differences between the contracting parties. This can lead to various misunderstandings between parties concerning what behavior is considered to be honest and fair. UNIDROIT attempts to resolve this issue by stating that good faith and fair dealing should be measured not by any particular domestic standard, but rather examined in the context of international trade.

> **Art. 1.7 (Good Faith and Fair Dealing)**
> (1) Each party must act in accordance with good faith and fair dealing in international trade.
> (2) The parties may not exclude or limit this duty.

Not only must parties act in good faith once the contract has been concluded, but they must also refrain from acting in bad faith during the pre-contractual negotiations. Beginning negotiations does not mean that a contract will be necessarily concluded as negotiations can fail. However, in the international context under the UNIDROIT Principles it is not permissible to enter into negotiations with no intention of entering into a contract:

> **Art. 2.1.15 (Negotiations in bad faith)**
> (1) A party is free to negotiate and is not liable for failure to reach an agreement.
> (2) However, a party who negotiates or breaks off negotiations in bad faith is liable for the losses caused to the other party.
> (3) It is bad faith, in particular, for a party to enter into or continue negotiations when intending not to reach an agreement with the other party.

For example, ABC, Inc. contacts XYZ, S.A. to negotiate the sale of widgets, but ABC, Inc.'s intention is not to conclude a contract. Perhaps ABC, Inc.'s intention is to merely find out information about its competitors with whom XYZ, S.A. also does business. Or maybe ABC, Inc.'s motive is to gain knowledge about XYZ, S.A.'s trade secrets or proprietary information in order for ABC to cut into XYZ, S.A's competitive advantage. Or perhaps ABC, Inc. wishes to enter into lengthy negotiations for large quantities simply to prevent XYZ, S.A. from selling to ABC, Inc.'s competitors. In these instances of bad faith negotiations ABC, Inc. may be liable for XYZ, S.A.'s expenses incurred during the negotiations as well as lost opportunity as a result of the bad faith negotiations. (*See* Art. 2.1.15 Commentary, UNIDROIT Principles 2010) Even if such tactics were acceptable and standard in ABC, Inc.'s home market, the UNIDROIT Principles prevent the use of such bad faith negotiating tactics in an international context.

Another interesting issue that can arise as a result of cultural and linguistic differences can be related to trade usages and practices. When parties form a contract, they do not necessarily fully define every term in the contract, and in the international setting, under the UNIDROIT Principles we can turn to trade usages and practices to help determine what the parties mean when they use undefined terms. For example, if ABC, Inc. sells widgets both domestically and internationally, the trade usages and practices may differ between the two markets. Perhaps the standard quality terms for widgets on ABC, Inc.'s domestic market (e.g., a minimum quality standard which is relatively low) are different than the widely recognized standard quality terms for widgets sold on the international market (e.g., a higher quality standard). If ABC, Inc. contracts with a XYZ, S.A., who is from another country and has never dealt with parties in ABC, Inc.'s home jurisdiction, and the contract merely calls for "standard quality widgets" without further definition, what does the term "standard quality widgets" mean? This is addressed by Art. 1.9 of the UNIDROIT Principles:

Art. 1.9 (Usages and Practices)
(1) The parties are bound by any usage to which they have agreed and by any practices which they have established between themselves.
(2) The parties are bound by a usage that is widely known to and regularly observed in international trade by parties in the particular trade concerned except where the application of such a usage would be unreasonable.

Applying this principle to the above example, if the contract between ABC, Inc. and XYZ, S.A. does not agree to any particular usage or practices concerning the quality terms for widgets, then they are bound by the international usage which is widely known and regularly observed. Even though the contract did not specifically define the term "standard quality widgets", the quality terms for the widgets must meet the international standard, not the domestic standard.

Once the contract has been formed, the UNIDROIT Principles naturally provide additional rules that are available to help parties interpret their contractual relationship. A table of selected articles is found below:

Selected Articles re: Contract Interpretation under the UNIDROIT Principles:

Art. 4.1 (Intention of the parties)

(1) A contract shall be interpreted according to the common intention of the parties.

(2) If such an intention cannot be established, the contract shall be interpreted according to the meaning that reasonable persons of the same kind as the parties would give to it in the same circumstances.

Art. 4.2 (Interpretation of statements and other conduct)

(1) The statements and other conduct of a party shall be interpreted according to that party's intention if the other party knew or could not have been unaware of that intention.

(2) If the preceding paragraph is not applicable, such statements and other conduct shall be interpreted according to the meaning that a reasonable person of the same kind as the other party would give to it in the same circumstances.

Art. 4.3 (Relevant circumstances)

In applying Articles 4.1 and 4.2, regard shall be had to all the circumstances, including

(a) preliminary negotiations between the parties;

(b) practices which the parties have established between themselves;

(c) the conduct of the parties subsequent to the conclusion of the contract;

(d) the nature and purpose of the contract;

(e) the meaning commonly given to terms and expressions in the trade concerned;

(d) usages.

Art. 4.6 (Contra proferentem rule)

If contract terms supplied by one party are unclear, an interpretation against that party is preferred.

Art. 4.7 (Linguistic discrepancies)

Where a contract is drawn up in two or more language versions which are equally authoritative there is, in case of discrepancy between the versions, a preference for the interpretation according to a version in which the contract was originally drawn up.

First and foremost, when a contract needs to be interpreted, pursuant to Art. 4.1 of the UNIDROIT Principles it should be interpreted in a way that will achieve the common intention of the parties, or in other words, the shared subjective intent of the parties. Interpretation may be necessary in situations where the contract terms are ambiguous and susceptible to two or more meanings. If it is not possible to establish the common intention of the parties, then the contract should be interpreted using a standard of reasonableness. This is an objective standard which asks: "What would be the intention of the hypothetically reasonable person in the same position as the parties to the contract?" The answer to this question needs to be determined on a case by case basis. Similarly, pursuant to Art. 4.2, in interpreting statements or conduct of a party one first looks to a party's ascertainable subjective intent in making such interpretations. If the subjective intent is known and can be proven, this is the intent interpretation that prevails. If such subjective intent is unknown to the other party, its statements and conduct will then be interpreted using an objective standard of reasonableness.

For example, George from the USA intends to sell "standard widgets" to Pierre from France. The domestic USA standard is different from the international standard. George intends to sell widgets based on the USA standard. The contract drafted by George merely says "standard widgets", and no statements or conduct to the contrary are given to Pierre. Even though George subjectively intends to sell USA standard widgets to Pierre, this intention was unknown, and based on the international nature of this transaction, a reasonable, objective interpretation would be that "standard widgets" in an international context refers to the international, and not the USA standard. Art. 4.3 would allow the parties to look at the relevant circumstances surrounding the transaction in order to make this determination, such as the nature of the negotiations, overall context (one party from USA, other from France), industry standards (different standards in USA and Internationally), etc. Additionally, since George drafted the ambiguous term "standard widgets", the interpretation of the ambiguous term will be against him and in favor of Pierre, the non-drafting party, pursuant to the rule of *contra proferentem*. This rule stands for the proposition that ambiguous terms found in a contract are to be construed against the party who drafted them. This principle is embodied by Art. 4.6 of the UNIDROIT Principles and likewise found in many domestic legal systems around the world.

Moreover, international commercial contracts are often drafted in multiple languages. Normally parties will choose one version to be the official version in case of a discrepancy between the versions based on linguistic differences. This is an advisable practice. As most anyone who has ever dealt with parties from other countries can attest to, sometimes things can get "lost in translation". Nevertheless, if the parties fail to designate one version as the authoritative version in their contract, UNIDROIT Principle 4.7 designates a preference for the language in which the contract was originally drawn up if such is able to be ascertained.

In addition to formation and interpretation issues, the UNI-DROIT Principles provide guidance in determining the parties' obligations under an international commercial contract. A table of selected articles concerning the obligations of parties to an international commercial contract is found below:

Selected Articles re: Contractual Obligations under the UNIDROIT Principles:
Art. 5.1.1 (Express and implied obligations)
The contractual obligations of the parties may be express or implied.
Art. 5.1.2 (Implied obligations)
Implied obligations stem from:
(a) the nature and purpose of the contract;
(b) practices established between the parties and usages;
(c) good faith and fair dealing;
(d) reasonableness.

Obviously, the obligations of the parties can, and should to the extent possible be expressly stated in the contract. A well drafted contract clearly states the rights, duties and obligations of the parties, and reduces the likelihood of disputes. Of course, we do not reside in a perfect world, and even in highly negotiated, complex contractual scenarios there still may be gaps in a contract. Art. 5.1.1 of the UNIDROIT Principles recognizes this possibility and states that not only may obligations of the parties be expressed, they may also be implied. Art. 5.1.2 goes further and provides guidance as to where the implied obligations can be derived from. In short, just because something is not expressly stated in a contract does not mean that no obligation exists. A totality of the circumstances approach needs to be employed by parties to international commercial contracts when determining the extent of their obligations.

Finally, even the best planned contractual relationships may suffer from a failure of one of the parties to comply with its obligations. Naturally, the UNIDROIT Principles provide some guidance for situations where there is non-performance, when non-performance may be excused (*e.g., force majeure*), and how to calculate damages when there is no valid excuse for non-performance. Selected articles can be found in the chart below:

Selected Articles re: Non-Performance and Damages under the UNI-DROIT Principles:

Art. 7.1.1 (Non-performance defined)

Non-performance is failure by a party to perform any of its obligations under the contract, including defective performance or late performance.

Art. 7.1.7 (Force majeure)

(1) Non-performance by a party is excused if that party proves that the non-performance was due to an impediment beyond its control and that it could not reasonably be expected to have taken the impediment into account at the time of the conclusion of the contract or to have avoided or overcome it or its consequences.

(2) When the impediment is only temporary, the excuse shall have effect for such period as is reasonable having regard to the effect of the impediment on the performance of the contract.

(3) The party who fails to perform must give notice to the other party of the impediment and its effect on its ability to perform. If the notice is not received by the other party within a reasonable time after the party who fails to perform knew or ought to have known of the impediment, it is liable for damages resulting from such non-receipt.

(4) Nothing in this Article prevents a party from exercising a right to terminate the contract or to withhold performance or request interest on money due.

Art. 7.4.1 (Right to damages)

Any non-performance gives the aggrieved party a right to damages either exclusively or in conjunction with any other remedies except where the non-performance is excused under these Principles.

Art. 7.4.2 (Full compensation)

(1) The aggrieved party is entitled to full compensation for harm sustained as a result of the non-performance. Such harm includes both any loss which it suffered and any gain of which it was deprived, taking into account any gain to the aggrieved party resulting from its avoidance of cost or harm.

(2) Such harm may be non-pecuniary and includes, for instance, physical suffering or emotional distress.

Art. 7.4.3 (Certainty of harm)

(1) Compensation is due only for harm, including future harm, that is established with a reasonable degree of certainty.

(2) Compensation may be due for the loss of a chance in proportion to the probability of its occurrence.

(3) Where the amount of damages cannot be established with a sufficient degree of certainty, the assessment is at the discretion of the court.

Art. 7.4.4 (Foreseeability of harm)

The non-performing party is liable only for harm which it foresaw or could reasonably have foreseen at the time of the conclusion of the contract as being likely to result from its non-performance.

Art. 7.1.1 simply defines non-performance (sometimes referred to as breach), and connects to Art. 7.4.1 which gives an aggrieved party the right to claim damages in response to non-performance. An important exception to this right to damages is that no damages are available when there was a valid excuse for the non-performance.

A well-known excuse for non-performance which exists both in the context of many national legal systems as well as the UNIDROIT Principles is that of *force majeure*, found at Art. 7.1.7. As explained by the official commentary to the UNIDROIT Principles, this article provides a general definition of *force majeure* which may be different than the specific concepts of *force majeure* found in various domestic legal systems. In the context of the Principles *force majeure* refers to an impediment beyond the control of the parties where the parties could not reasonably have been expected to have taken the impediment into account at the time that the contract was concluded. The parties must also be unable to overcome the consequences of the impediment. Typical examples of a *force majeure* type impediment beyond the control of the parties could be earthquakes, hurricanes, tsunamis, wars, or riots. Often times, parties to international contracts prefer to have more definite and precise definitions of *force majeure* events excusing performance of contractual obligations which is based on familiar domestic definitions of *force majeure*, or industry practice, or even custom definitions drafted by a party's attorneys. These parties can import their own *force majeure* standards into their contractual relationship by using a more detailed clause in their contract, but should do so understanding that this may in fact limit their ability to raise *force majeure* as an excuse for non-performance.

Should non-performance be unexcused, as previously addressed, the aggrieved party can claim damages. Pursuant to Art. 7.4.2 the UNIDROIT Principles provide the aggrieved party with the right to claim full compensation from the non-performing party. Full compensation is broadly defined by the Principles and goes as far as allowing for damages beyond mere pecuniary (economic or monetary) losses. Non-economic damages for physical damage and emotional distress are available under these principles, which may conflict with domestic legal principles that various parties are familiar with.

Additionally, consequential damages such as lost profits resulting from non-performance of contractual obligations are recoverable under the broad standard of Art. 7.4.2. For example, if ABC, Inc. purchases widgets from XYZ, S.A., and intends on reselling the widgets on its local market, if XYZ, S.A. does not perform its obligations and never provides the widgets to ABC, Inc., ABC, Inc. may then be able to claim the lost resale profits as damages. ABC, Inc. however is not guaranteed that such damages will be recoverable even under the broad standard of Art. 7.4.2 since the harm suffered must be both certain (*see* 7.4.3) and foreseeable (*see* 7.4.4). So if ABC, Inc.'s lost profit calculations are speculative and cannot be established with certainty, the claim for lost profits may be rejected by a court or arbitration tribunal. Similarly, if XYZ, S.A. sold the widgets to ABC, Inc., but never knew that ABC, Inc. intended to resell the widgets, the lost profits would not have been foreseeable to XYZ, S.A. at the time that the parties concluded the contract, and therefore XYZ, S.A. would not responsible for the lost profits. Perhaps XYZ, S.A. would have charged a different price, or somehow performed the contract differently (used different delivery methods, etc.) if they knew that ABC, Inc. planned on resale of the widgets, and they were denied this opportunity.

The above analysis of the UNIDROIT Principles is merely intended as a brief overview, and is far from exhaustive. The intent of this work is merely to introduce the Principles along with selected basic contract law issues to the readers. The Principles along with excellent, more detailed commentary and examples can be found at http://www.unidroit.org/instruments/commercial-contracts/unidroit-principles-2010, which is a great resource for understanding and using the UNIDROIT Principles.

4.   The Sale of Goods between Private Parties

Perhaps the most typical type of international commercial relationship involves the "simple" sale of goods. Trade in goods accounts for roughly 80% of global trade. (WTO, 2014) Much of this trade is between private parties who are unrelated to each other. For example a private party in Country A purchases manufactured goods from a private party in Country B. The law governing this type of relationship is a subset of contract law referred to as sales law. In the lexicon of law, the term sales law has a very specific meaning and refers to the sale of goods. One **sells goods**, and enters in to a sales contract related thereto, but does not, for example, enter into a sales contract for services. To the contrary, a party may **provide services** and enter into a provision of services contract. The sales contract is a well-defined and very typical type of relationship, and this chapter will endeavor to provide an overview of legal issues related to sales of goods. While parties may decide to apply the previously addressed UNIDROIT Principles to a sales contract, the Principles are broadly drafted and can apply to a wide range of international relationships including the sale of goods, the provision of services, and other types of contracts. Parties may instead decide to apply sales law specifically designed for sales contracts (or such laws may apply by default).

The Sales Contract

The sales relationship between private parties is generally, but not necessarily, encompassed in a written sales contract. The sales contract is the document that governs the relationship between two parties involved in a sale of goods. It quite simply attempts to set out the rights, duties, and obligations of the parties to the sales transaction. In a well written sales contract the terms will be clearly defined. Any conditions which need to be fulfilled by the parties will also be clearly delineated. Necessary terms in a sales contract include quantity and price. Even if quantity and price are not yet defined between the parties, the contract needs to have some method for calculating these terms. For example, the quantity can be "the requirements of company A for the month of June, 2015" or the price could be "market price as of September 1, 2015." Neither of these examples contains a specifically defined term, but both contain a method for fixing the required terms.

Written sales contracts do not all look the same as there is no standard sales contract. Some may be quite simple containing only the most essential terms. Others may be highly formal containing myriad terms and conditions covering as many contingencies as possible. International sales law is flexible concerning the formation of sales contracts and allows for highly informal exchanges to become valid sales contracts. A sales contract could be formed through an exchange of communications such as emails. It could even be formed orally between two business associates over dinner. As discussed previously, despite the possibility of having valid oral contracts, this is rarely an advisable practice for reasons related to proof. The purpose of sales contracts, as well as contracts in general, is to increase certainty and clarity in business relationships and the oral contract inherently carries the possibility of creating inconsistencies and conflicting understandings of contractual relationships.

Despite the lack of a uniform, standard, international sales contract, the written sales contract is ubiquitous in the context of international trade. It is highly important that parties engaging in international sales take the time to understand the rights and obligations contained in their sales contracts. They are not "one size fits all" type contracts. It is a risky proposition to simply go on the internet, enter "international sales contract" into your favorite search engine, and take the one that looks to be the most developed. Typically sales contracts are specifically negotiated between the parties, particularly where the parties have relatively equal bargaining positions. On the other hand, they may be drafted in favor of one of the parties in a situation where there is unequal bargaining power. Therefore, any given sales contract may contain terms which are relevant to the circumstances of the parties who negotiated the contract but are not be useful to others. For the small and medium sized business that may not be able to engage a lawyer in negotiating a sales contract, there are useful model sales contracts available. These model contracts provide a sort of "fill in the blank" option to creating a sales contract. Nonetheless, to effectively use one of these model contracts, a basic knowledge of sales law along with the mechanics of a sale of goods is necessary. A good model contract still requires the parties to choose between relevant alternative model contractual clauses when constructing the contract. Also, there are good and bad models in existence. A good example of model contracts has been developed by the International Trade Center (ITC) through their "Model Contracts for Small Firms," found at http://www.intracen.org/model-contracts-for-small-firms/. (ITC, 2010)

Domestic Sales Laws

As stated above, sales law is the body of law that governs the present and future sales of goods. Each country has is its own domestic sales law. For example, in the United States, each state has its own sales law, although the sales law of the individual states has been unified by a Uniform Commercial Code (except for Louisiana). (Magnus, 2012) France's domestic sales law is found in both its Civil and Commercial Codes. (Schwenzer, *et. al.*, 2012) Domestic sales in China are covered by its 1999 Contract Law. In the UK, domestic sales are subject to the UK Sale of Goods Act. These are just a few selected examples; it suffices to say that each country has its own domestic sales law. A detailed comparative analysis of each of these laws is far beyond the scope of this introductory work, but there are often times substantive differences between the domestic sales laws of each country. These differences in domestic sales laws can act as a barrier to trade.

For example, the hypothetical country of Protectonia has a domestic sales law which obliges parties to a sale of goods to comply with many formalities in order to have a valid sales contract. The Protectonia Sales Act requires a valid sales contract not only to be written, but to also be signed, dated, and stamped by the parties to the contract in the upper left hand corner of each page of the document using each company's official state issued stamp. Any sales contract that does not meet this technical requirement is invalid. This works fine in Protectonia where everybody knows the rules and is capable of complying with them. However, in a situation where an outsider wishes to do trade with a party in Protectonia, this rule may put the outsider at a disadvantage.

To expand on the above hypothetical, a mining company in Protectonia who mines highly sought after rare minerals enters into a contract for the sale of rare minerals (goods) with a foreign company. Since the mining company has the rare minerals which are desired by the foreign company, they have much of the bargaining leverage and can impose many of their desired contractual terms on the other party, and their own home country choice of law. Therefore, the expressly chosen law is the law of Protectonia. The foreign company is not aware of the requirement that the sales contract be signed, dated, and stamped in the upper left hand corner of each page. Or perhaps, even if they are aware, they are unable to comply since they do not have an official state issued stamp and cannot obtain one. Therefore, the contract is not validly formed under Protectonia law. After conclusion but prior to performance of the contract the market conditions change causing the price of the minerals to increase well above the price of the contract. Since under the sales law of Protectonia the contract did not meet the required formalities (signed, dated, stamped, etc.), the mining company may have a convenient way out of the contract. This creates serious uncertainty for the foreign company, and in the future they will be wary of doing business in Protectonia, or perhaps any foreign jurisdiction, since they are unfamiliar with the requirements of the domestic sales laws of other countries. This uncertainty can act as a barrier to trade.

In short, it is very important for both parties to be aware of the law which applies to their international sales contract prior to concluding the contract since the differences in national sales laws can create uncertainty in international sales relationships. As already addressed *supra*, the parties are able to choose the law which applies to their sales contract, which should help to reduce the uncertainty. The parties should nevertheless exercise caution when making this crucial choice. If no choice is made, there are two main possibilities. Either the principles of private international law will operate to help the parties (or a court) determine what law applies to the relationship, or the Convention on Contracts for the International Sale of Goods will apply to the contractual relationship.

United Nations Convention on Contracts for the International Sale of Goods

By the late 20th century, countries had recognized that the country specific differences in domestic sales law made it harder to successfully conclude international sales transactions and effectively acted as a barrier to trade. Therefore, in the 1970s the UN through UNCITRAL in Vienna, Austria endeavored to develop an international sales law. This lead to the creation of the Convention on Contracts for the International Sales of Goods ("CISG"), which was originally signed in 1980 by various countries and became effective in 1988. The CISG has now been adopted by over 80 countries (the number continues to increase), including most major trading nations such as the United States, China, Germany, France, Brazil, Russia, Australia, and many others. (UNCITRAL, 2016) Notable absences from the CISG include the UK, India, Taiwan, Indonesia, and South Africa among others.

Countries which have ratified the CISG did not discard their domestic sales laws; rather they decided that they would have two sets of distinct laws for two different types of sales. A domestic sales law for domestic sales and an international sales law for international sales. This approach can be useful since the nature of doing business is often quite different between domestic and international contexts. In the domestic context the parties are less likely to have major cultural, linguistic or other differences which may impede the successful conclusion and performance of sales contracts. Commercial entities will (or at least should) know the rules which apply in their principal place of business, so there is less of a possibility that one party will be adversely affected by a technicality in the local law. In the international context things become more difficult. There may be large linguistic and cultural differences. Trade practices and usages can vary between different countries. Domestic sales laws, as discussed above, can be technical and unfamiliar to outsiders. Distances are greater requiring serious thought to go into transportation and logistical planning. Currencies fluctuate in value and payment methods and practices can vary from place to place. In short, international sales transactions present challenges which do not exist in a domestic context.

In light of these additional difficulties present in international sales, one of the fundamental premises of the CISG is that it is a flexible law which tries to keep parties in their contracts rather than allowing technicalities to invalidate agreements that were otherwise valid in principle. For example, there are no form requirements for the conclusion of a valid sales contract (although a few countries, notably Russia, signed the CISG with the reservation that sales contracts must be in writing). (Art. 96, CISG) Therefore, the hypothetical problem in Protectonia addressed in the preceding section should not occur in a situation where the CISG applies. So when does the CISG apply to international sales contracts?

Application of the CISG

Perhaps the most obvious situation where the CISG applies is when the parties choose the CISG to apply to their contractual relationship through a choice of law clause in their contract. Via the principles of party autonomy and freedom of contract parties can choose the CISG to apply to their sales contract, even when they are not from a country which has adopted the CISG. But when does the CISG apply as the default law to an international commercial sales contract? To answer this question specifically, we must turn to the language of the CISG itself, specifically Arts. 1, 2 , 3, and 6. (Lookofsky, 2008)

Selected Articles re: Application of CISG to International Sales Contracts

Article 1 (excerpt)

(1) This Convention applies to contracts of sale of goods between parties whose places of business are in different States:

    (a) when the States are Contracting States; or

    (b) when the rules of private international law lead to the application of the law of a Contracting State.

Article 2

This Convention does not apply to sales:

    (a) of goods bought for personal, family or household use, unless the seller, at any time before or at the conclusion of the contract, neither knew nor ought to have known that the goods were bought for any such use; (b) by auction; (c) on execution or otherwise by authority of law; (d) of stocks, shares, investment securities, negotiable instruments or money; (e) of ships, vessels, hovercraft or aircraft; (f) of electricity.

Article 3 (excerpt)

(2) This Convention does not apply to contracts in which the preponderant part of the obligations of the party who furnishes the goods consists in the supply of labour or other services.

Article 6

The parties may exclude the application of this Convention or, subject to article 12, derogate from or vary the effect of any of its provisions.

First, Art. 1 of the CISG states that it will apply to a sale of goods when the parties have their places of business in different states, it must be an international sale, and the states where the parties are based have ratified the CISG. This is relatively simple to grasp. If there is a sale between a Chinese seller of goods and a French buyer, and the parties do not choose a law to the contrary, the CISG will automatically apply to that sale since both China and France have ratified the CISG. Alternatively, if only one of the states to an international sale has ratified the CISG, the rules of private international law may still lead to the application of the international sales law of a state which has adopted the CISG. For example, if a Brazilian seller sells goods to a UK buyer and there is no choice of law, a court may be required to determine which law applies to the contract. If the court determines, through the application of private international law principles such as the closest connection test, that Brazilian law and more specifically Brazilian international sales law (which is the CISG) should apply to the contract, then the CISG is the law which applies to the contract even though the buyer was from the UK which has not ratified the CISG. A handful of countries, notably China and the USA, signed the CISG with the reservation that the CISG would only automatically apply when both parties are from contracting states. (CISG Advisory Council Opinion No. 15, 2013)

Art. 2 provides a list of types of sales where the CISG does not apply, even when a sale is international and the parties are both from states that have ratified the CISG. For example, Art. 2(a) makes it clear that the sale of goods needs to be commercial in nature as consumer sales are excluded from the application of the CISG. Rules for sales at auction and by execution of law vary greatly between legal systems, and therefore are outside the scope of the CISG (Arts. 2(b) and (c)). A similar rationale excludes commercial paper (stocks, shares, investment securities, negotiable instruments or money, Art. 2(d)). Interestingly, Art. 2(e) excludes ships, vessels, hovercraft or aircraft, but not other vehicles such as cars, trucks and buses. The Secretariat Commentary to the CISG provides the rationale for this exclusion as being based on the fact that these items are classified as goods in some countries, but as immovables in others. Additionally, different registration requirements for such items in each country further complicate matters. (UNCITRAL Secretariat, 1978) Therefore, the CISG will not apply to sales of the items listed under Art. 2(e) even if they are considered to be goods by some domestic legal regimes. Also, electricity is not a good under the CISG Art. 2(f).

Finally, as previously stated, the CISG only applies to contract for the sale of goods, and does not apply to contracts for the provision of services. In reality though, contracts issues are not necessarily black and white, and parties may desire to have one contract for a complex transaction which includes both the sale of goods and the provision of services. For example, Company A sells a piece of complex industrial machinery to Company B. This is clearly a sale of a good. In addition to the sale, Company A provides training, maintenance and operation services related to the industrial machinery. This is clearly the provision of services. So is this mixed contract a contract for the sale of goods, or the provision of services? Art. 3 of the CISG states that it does not apply to contracts where the preponderant part, generally understood to be greater than 50%, of the obligations of the party providing the goods is in fact the supply services. The next question is related to how the parties determine what the preponderant part of the obligations is. There has been much academic commentary on this issue, but the simplest method is to compare relative values. In other words, what is the value of the goods versus the value of the services? If the value of the services is greater than the value of the goods, the CISG does not apply as it is a provision of services, and not a contract for the sale of goods. (Lookofsky, 2000)

In addition, pursuant to Art 6 the CISG does not apply when the parties to the contract choose to exclude the CISG's application, or in other words, opt out. This is possible even when the parties to the sales contract are all from countries which have ratified the CISG. In fact, this is quite common in practice. Art. 6 also allows the parties to derogate from specific provisions of the CISG only, for example by using a *force majeure* clause which is more limited in scope than the CISG principles.

The CISG is well known and respected in the academic and legislative worlds. In fact, there is even a well-known (at least among international trade lawyers) song about it! *See* http://www.law.pitt.edu/academics/cile/cisgsongpage. In practice however, many lawyers and business people look upon the CISG with suspicion and choose to use laws with which they have more experience and are more familiar which normally consist of the domestic sales laws that they use on a regular basis. Some lawyers who exclude the CISG believe that it is not practical to use because they are unfamiliar with, or lack of experience with the CISG. Others may perceive that there is no advantage for their client to having a uniform law. Lawyers may also cite legal reasons for excluding the CISG. Some may feel that the national sales laws are more advantageous to their clients (even though many academic commentators would disagree). Others might find the law to be more clearly defined in domestic jurisdictions, and that the CISG is too flexible and unpredictable. For more detailed reasons as to why lawyers choose to exclude application, a survey by Martin Koehler is instructive, available at: http://cisgw3.law.pace.edu/cisg/biblio/koehler.html. (Koehler, 2006)

EXAMPLE
Examples of language that may be considered to be too flexible and unpredictable by lawyers can be found throughout the CISG. For example, under the CISG a buyer of goods has an obligation to inspect the goods upon receipt and notify the seller of any non-conformity of the goods (Arts. 38 and 39). However, the language of the CISG defining these obligations requires case by case interpretation as Art. 38 says "The buyer must examine the goods, or cause them to be examined, within as short a period as is practicable in the circumstances." Similarly, Art. 39 states "The buyer loses the right to rely on a lack of conformity of the goods if he does not give notice to the seller specifying the nature of the lack of conformity within a reasonable time after he has discovered it or ought to have discovered it." This leads to some relatively obvious questions that will need to be resolved each time that either of these articles is invoked by a party in an international sales transaction. What is as short a period as is practicable in the circumstances? What is a reasonable time after he has discovered it or ought to have discovered it? Parties may have different interpretations of such language, and may not be comfortable with a law providing such flexibility in the rules applying to their relationship. Such parties are permitted to opt out.

When opting out of the CISG parties need to be explicit in doing so. For example, simply choosing "the law of New York," which may be a relatively standard choice of law clause for a party, to apply to a sales contract is insufficient to definitively exclude application of the CISG. New York is part of the United States, and the United States has ratified the CISG. Therefore, the law of New York includes both the state sales law of New York, and the international sales law of the United States, which is the CISG, a treaty ratified by the federal government. (Drago, 2002; Huber, 2007) If the parties do not wish to use the CISG they should expressly exclude application of the CISG using additional language making their intent clear such as "the parties agree that the 1980 United Nations Convention on Contracts for the International Sale of Goods shall not apply to this contract."

Formation of Contracts under the CISG

Many of the principles concerning formation of contracts under the CISG will appear familiar since they also appear in the UNIDROIT Principles (addressed *supra*). This is especially true for the CISG provisions related to contract formation. In many cases, the language of the CISG and UNIDROIT Principles is the same. Nonetheless, the CISG does in various instances go into more detail than the UNIDROIT Principles. This is easier for the CISG to do since it covers the specific subject matter of international sales whereas the UNIDROIT Principles are of a more general application covering international commercial contracts generally, not just sales contracts. Selected articles will be examined herein.

Selected Articles re: Forming a Valid Contract Pursuant to theCISG

Article 11

A contract of sale need not be concluded in or evidenced by writing and is not subject to any other requirement as to form. It may be proved by any means, including witnesses.

Article 14

(1) A proposal for concluding a contract addressed to one or more specific persons constitutes an offer if it is sufficiently definite and indicates the intention of the offeror to be bound in case of acceptance. A proposal is sufficiently definite if it indicates the goods and expressly or implicitly fixes or makes provision for determining the quantity and the price.

(2) A proposal other than one addressed to one or more specific persons is to be considered merely as an invitation to make offers, unless the contrary is clearly indicated by the person making the proposal.

Article 18

(1) A statement made by or other conduct of the offeree indicating assent to an offer is an acceptance. Silence or inactivity does not in itself amount to acceptance.

(2) An acceptance of an offer becomes effective at the moment the indication of assent reaches the offeror. An acceptance is not effective if the indication of assent does not reach the offeror within the time he has fixed or, if no time is fixed, within a reasonable time, due account being taken of the circumstances of the transaction, including the rapidity of the means of communication employed by the offeror. An oral offer must be accepted immediately unless the circumstances indicate otherwise.

(3) However, if, by virtue of the offer or as a result of practices which the parties have established between themselves or of usage, the offeree may indicate assent by performing an act, such as one relating to the dispatch of the goods or payment of the price, without notice to the offeror, the acceptance is effective at the moment the act is performed, provided that the act is performed within the period of time laid down in the preceding paragraph.

Article 29

(1) A contract may be modified or terminated by the mere agreement of the parties.

(2) A contract in writing which contains a provision requiring any modification or termination by agreement to be in writing may not be otherwise modified or terminated by agreement. However, a party may be precluded by his conduct from asserting such a provision to the extent that the other party has relied on that conduct.

Similar to UNIDROIT Principle 1.2, Art. 11 CISG states that there is no writing or any other form requirement and that a contract can be proved by any means, including witnesses. Under Art. 14 of the CISG an offer must be sufficiently definite and indicate an intention to be bound, similar to UNIDROIT Principle 2.1.2. Art. 14 goes further than the UNIDROIT Principles and clarifies that a sufficiently definite offer in an international sales context means that the offer contains price and quantity provisions. These terms are considered to be essential in the sales environment. Again, is quite reasonable that the CISG rules would be more detailed than the UNIDROIT Principles in many circumstances since the CISG has a specific application whereby the UNIDROIT Principles are general in scope.

Art. 18 of the CISG defines acceptance. Art. 18(1) is the same as Art. 2.1.6(1) of the UNIDROIT Principles. As in the UNIDROIT Principles, the CISG allows offers to be accepted expressly through words or impliedly through conduct, but silence or inactivity by itself cannot be acceptance. Art. 18(2) follows the same receipt theory approach as Art. 2.1.6(2) of the UNIDROIT Principles explaining that acceptance becomes effective once received by the offeror, and no earlier. Art. 18(2) then goes further and provides additional rules concerning acceptance, and similar to the UNIDROIT principles at Art. 2.1.7 states that the acceptance must be received in a reasonable time and that oral offers must be accepted immediately. In addition, like Art. 2.1.6(3) of the UNIDROIT Principles, Art. 18(3) also provides for acceptance by conduct without notification where there is a practice or usage between the parties.

EXAMPLE

Company A supplies a fixed amount of goods to Company B on a quarterly basis. For many years, A just sends B the goods, and B simply accepts the goods making payment within 30 days. A commercial practice has been established between A and B, and B is not required to notify A of its acceptance each quarter.

Finally, once a contract is concluded (e.g., after offer and acceptance), modification and termination of the contract is nonetheless possible based upon mere agreement of the parties according to CISG Art. 29. This is possible even if the contract is oral (similar to UNIDROIT Principle 3.1.2). The exception to this rule applies when the contract itself requires modification or termination to be in writing. Such contractual clauses requiring modifications or termination to be in writing are regularly found in international contracts.

Interestingly, the CISG does not have any rules relating to consideration or cause requirements for valid contract formation. Under the CISG, mere agreement is what is required, in other words, a common intention to form a sales contract. Additionally, as a practical matter the doctrines of "consideration" and "cause" would generally be satisfied in the sales context since in a typical sales transaction there is an exchange of goods for money or some other item of value.

Obligations of the Parties under the CISG

Having briefly examined contract formation under the CISG, it is pertinent to discuss the obligations of the parties under the CISG. What are the obligations of buyers and sellers in an international sales contract? These issues are directly addressed by the Convention, and here one will find that the CISG, as would be expected, becomes more detailed in addressing these topics. The UNIDROIT Principles do not go into such technical detail since they are of general application whereas the CISG is tailored to sales issues.

Selected Articles re: Seller's Obligations Under theCISG
Article 30
The seller must deliver the goods, hand over any documents relating to them and transfer the property in the goods, as required by the contract and this Convention.
Article 33
The seller must deliver the goods:
    (a) if a date is fixed by or determinable from the contract, on that date;
    (b) if a period of time is fixed by or determinable from the contract, at any time within that period unless circumstances indicate that the buyer is to choose a date; or
    (c) in any other case, within a reasonable time after the conclusion of the contract.
Article 35 (excerpt)
(1) The seller must deliver goods which are of the quantity, quality and description required by the contract and which are contained or packaged in the manner required by the contract.
(2) Except where the parties have agreed otherwise, the goods do not conform with the contract unless they:
    (a) are fit for the purposes for which goods of the same description would ordinarily be used;
    (b) are fit for any particular purpose expressly or impliedly made known to the seller at the time of the conclusion of the contract, except where the circumstances show that the buyer did not rely, or that it was unreasonable for him to rely, on the seller's skill and judgement;
    (c) possess the qualities of goods which the seller has held out to the buyer as a sample or model;
    (d) are contained or packaged in the manner usual for such goods or, where there is no such manner, in a manner adequate to preserve and protect the goods.

Quite simply, the basic obligation of a seller under the CISG is to deliver the goods to the buyer as required by the contract (Art. 30) by the date required by the contract, or at least within a reasonable time (Art. 33). In other words, the seller must deliver conforming goods by the delivery date. The term conforming goods means that the goods are of the quantity, quality, and description provided for by the contract. If the seller does not do this, it has breached the contract.

In determining whether goods conform, Art. 35 of the CISG provides additional rules. Normally, a sales contract will (and should) describe the goods and give the parties guidance as to what characteristics the goods should have. The contract may even provide certain warranties, which are expressly stated in the contract. However, even if the contract merely contains a basic description of the goods Art. 35 of the CISG will assist the parties in determining whether the goods are conforming since it contains what are often referred to as implied warranties. This means that these warranties are in place, even if the contract is silent on these issues. Art. 35(2)(a) contains a warranty of merchantability, or in other words, a guarantee that the goods will be fit for their ordinary use.

EXAMPLE

A seller sells "100 Personal Laptop Computers" to a buyer. The contract contains no additional description of the goods. The buyer receives the computers but they do not have the capability to access the internet. One of the ordinary uses of a personal laptop computer is for accessing the internet. Therefore, even though the contract was silent on the issue, the goods breach the implied warranty found in Art. 35(2)(a).

Similarly, Art. 35(2)(b) contains what is referred to as the implied warranty that the goods will be fit for a particular purpose. If the buyer makes its purpose known to the seller and reasonably relies on the seller's expertise in selecting the goods, the goods must conform to the particular purpose made known to the seller by the buyer. This applies even if the contract says nothing about this warranty.

EXAMPLE

A buyer approaches a seller to purchase an industrial printer for printing on food packaging, and in particular for all types of plastic wrappers for cheese products. The buyer tells the seller what it is looking for and what it needs and the seller says "I got just what you need, printer model XJT 3000." When the buyer receives the machine after running some tests it immediately realizes that the machine will not print on standard sized thick plastic cheese wrappers and only works on thin plastic wrappers. If it was reasonable for the buyer to have relied on the seller's skill and judgment in choosing the XJT 3000 and the buyer can show that it did in fact rely on the seller's expertise, then the implied particular purpose warranty was breached by the seller.

Art. 35(2)(c) contains similar warranties[9] for samples. Under this article of the CISG there is an implied warranty that goods will have the qualities of samples that a seller shows a buyer. Art. 35(2)(d) contains the final implied warranty concerning packaging, stating that goods will be packaged and contained in their usual fashion, or in the default an adequate manner. The warranties found in Art. 35 may be disclaimed by the parties in their contract including a clause stating that they do not wish for any implied warranties to apply to the contract. In other words, if the parties do not wish for any warranties, express or implied, to apply to their contractual relationship, they need to be clear about this in the contract.

Selected Articles re: Buyer's Obligations Under theCISG
Article 38 (excerpt)
(1) The buyer must examine the goods, or cause them to be examined, within as short a period as is practicable in the circumstances.
Article 39
(1) The buyer loses the right to rely on a lack of conformity of the goods if he does not give notice to the seller specifying the nature of the lack of conformity within a reasonable time after he has discovered it or ought to have discovered it.
(2) In any event, the buyer loses the right to rely on a lack of conformity of the goods if he does not give the seller notice thereof at the latest within a period of two years from the date on which the goods were actually handed over to the buyer, unless this time-limit is inconsistent with a contractual period of guarantee.
Article 53
The buyer must pay the price for the goods and take delivery of them as required by the contract and this Convention.
Article 60
The buyer's obligation to take delivery consists:
  (a) in doing all the acts which could reasonably be expected of him in order to enable the seller to make delivery; and
  (b) in taking over the goods.

In examining the buyer's obligations under CISG, assuming the goods are conforming, pursuant to Art. 53, the buyer must simply take delivery and pay the price for the goods. According to Art. 60 taking delivery means that the buyer might have to take some steps in order to allow the seller to make delivery in addition to actually taking physical possession of the goods. Depending on where the contract calls for de-

---

[9] The CISG does not use the word warranty, but contains equivalent obligations (Jones, 1989)

livery to take place, this could be as simple as informing the seller of the point of delivery, or designating the ship at the port of shipment under, e.g., an F.O.B. contract (*see infra*).

In addition to paying the price and taking delivery, under Art. 38 CISG the buyer must also inspect and examine the goods as soon as soon as practicable under the circumstances. If the goods are non-conforming, pursuant to Art. 39, the buyer must give notification to the seller of the non-conformity within a reasonable period, with an outer limit of two years (unless contractually agreed otherwise). The notice must be specific in identifying the non-conformity, a general statement that the goods are non-conforming will not suffice. The buyer must highlight what the problem is. If the buyer fails to inspect and notify pursuant to Arts. 38 and 39, they lose the ability to rely on the non-conformity of the goods. In other words, even if the goods are not what the buyer wanted, they cannot claim a breach and recover damages.

EXAMPLE

A large industrial firm in a CISG contracting state orders supplies from a small supplier in another CISG contracting state. The large industrial firm receives the supplies, which are received at and immediately stored in its warehouse. Before the supplies are put into storage where they may stay for an undetermined amount of time, it is important for the large firm to have procedures in place for inspecting the goods as soon as practicable after their arrival at the warehouse. It is also important for the large firm to have additional procedures in place for notifying suppliers of any alleged non-conformities in supplies received at the warehouse. The people on the ground need to effectively carry out inspections as well as notifications when non-conforming goods arrive so that rights to claim damages or other remedies related to non-conformity of goods are not lost under CISG Art. 38 and 39. Otherwise, if the non-conformity is not discovered until after a reasonable amount of time has passed, the large firm may be stuck with the non-conforming goods.

The result of the failure to inspect goods and/or notify the seller of non-conformities may seem harsh. The buyer's advocate would feel somewhat justified simply pointing the finger at the seller and arguing that since the contract called for one thing and the seller provided another, the seller should not escape liability. However, there is valid reasoning for this seemingly harsh rule. First, in many sales contracts the seller has until a fixed date to perform his obligations (e.g., to deliver conforming goods by December 1). If non-conforming goods were delivered prior to this pre-determined fixed date, the seller has a right to remedy the lack of conformity pursuant to CISG Art. 37 (e.g., to deliver replacement goods). The seller has an incentive to make early delivery if possible as they will then have the right to resolve any problems. Furthermore, even if the fixed date for the seller's performance has expired, the buyer may choose to give additional time for performance under CISG Art. 47, referred to as a *Nachfrist* period. (Kimbel, 1999) Even if the buyer does not want to give more time to the seller to perform, unless the breach of contract was fundamental (*see infra*), under CISG Art. 48 the seller can still remedy a breach at its own expense as long as it does not cause unreasonable delay or inconvenience.

In short, even though it was the seller who did not comply with the terms of the contract, the CISG still provides the seller with certain rights to remedy the breach. These rights cannot be exercised unless the seller knows about the non-conformity or other breach, hence the importance of the buyer's inspection and notification obligations. Notice obligations are found throughout the CISG, as well as the UNIDROIT Principles. The idea is to encourage the parties to communicate and prevent problems from happening with the end goal of concluding the contract successfully. There is also a practical element to these rules which protects sellers from unfair results, illustrated by the following example:

EXAMPLE

Paper, Ltd. sells "multi-colored A3 paper" to Office Supply, S.A. Office Supply, S.A., receives the shipment from Paper, Ltd. and immediately puts the shipment of paper in its warehouse without proper inspection. The paper remains in the warehouse for 8 months at which point Office Supply, S.A. realizes that the paper is not 'multi-colored A3 paper', but is instead "white A3 paper". They call Paper, Ltd. who apologizes, but also informs Office Supply, S.A. that they cannot fix the problem since they stopped producing "multi-colored A3 paper" 2 months prior and have sold out all of their stock. Had Office Supply, S.A. notified them shortly after receipt of the shipment, the problem could have been remedied quite easily and with little expense.

This hypothetical example illustrates a situation where it would in fact be a harsh result to allow the buyer to make claims against the seller for breach of contract based on non-conforming goods since the problem could have been easily resolved if the buyer had not sat on its rights. Many would argue that this result is equitable and just.

Non-Performance of Obligations under the CISG Sales Contract

Once a sales contract is validly formed and the parties' obligations are set pursuant to the contract and the CISG, hopefully each party will perform its obligations without any problems. In reality problems will arise on occasion. When a party fails to properly perform its contractual obligations under a contract governed by the CISG, it "breaches" the contract. It is imperative to understand that under the CISG, there are two separate types of breaches leading to different possible consequences; the fundamental and the non-fundamental breach.

This approach differs from that of many domestic legal systems where even a minor breach of contract can have severe consequences. For example, under Art. 2 of the Uniform Commercial Code applicable throughout the United States, the "perfect tender" rule allows a buyer to reject goods delivered by a seller if the tender of the goods is not perfect in any respect. (UCC, §2-601) Under this rule, minor imperfections in contractual performance, in other words, minor breaches such as the incorrect quantity, or barely late delivery, can lead to serious consequences such as a claim of damages for breach of the whole contract. Such a rule is untenable in an international context. Recall, one of the purposes of the CISG is to facilitate international trade, reduce barriers to trade based on technicalities found in domestic sales laws, and keep parties in their contractual bargains. This means that the CISG takes an approach whereby even imperfect tender or performance of obligations, as long as the imperfection is minor, can be sufficient to keep the parties in their contractual obligations. The party who does not perfectly perform may be subject to certain remedies, such as a price reduction if the quantity of goods delivered by the seller is less than what is required by the contract (CISG Art. 50), but the contract still exists despite the minor imperfection in performance. Where the imperfection in performance is greater, however, the non-breaching party may be permitted to escape its contractual obligations.

Therefore, when one party to a sales contract does not properly perform their obligations and breaches the contract, the CISG first requires a determination of whether the breach was fundamental or not. If the breach was fundamental, the non-breaching party may then pursue the remedy of avoidance, which means that they may terminate the contract and no longer have any obligations thereunder (*see* CISG Art. 81) by simply making a declaration of avoidance and providing it to the other party (*see* CISG Art. 26). This is frequently referred to as "unwinding" the contract and restoring the parties to the position they were originally in prior to conclusion of the contract. Again, this remedy is only available when the breach is a fundamental breach.

So what is a fundamental breach? The CISG remains vague as it does not define a non-fundamental breach, and while the concept of fundamental breach is explained, there is no black and white definition of this concept. Therefore, whether a breach is fundamental must be determined on a case by case basis. How is this done?

Selected Articles re: Fundamental Breach and Avoidance under the CISG

Article 25

A breach of contract committed by one of the parties is fundamental if it results in such detriment to the other party as substantially to deprive him of what he is entitled to expect under the contract, unless the party in breach did not foresee and a reasonable person of the same kind in the same circumstances would not have foreseen such a result.

Article 72

(1) If prior to the date for performance of the contract it is clear that one of the parties will commit a fundamental breach of contract, the other party may declare the contract avoided.

(2) If time allows, the party intending to declare the contract avoided must give reasonable notice to the other party in order to permit him to provide adequate assurance of his performance.

(3) The requirements of the preceding paragraph do not apply if the other party has declared that he will not perform his obligations.

Article 81

(1) Avoidance of the contract releases both parties from their obligations under it, subject to any damages which may be due. Avoidance does not affect any provision of the contract for the settlement of disputes or any other provision of the contract governing the rights and obligations of the parties consequent upon the avoidance of the contract.

(2) A party who has performed the contract either wholly or in part may claim restitution from the other party of whatever the first party has supplied or paid under the contract. If both parties are bound to make restitution, they must do so concurrently.

To determine whether a breach of contract constitutes a fundamental breach, one must turn to CISG Art. 25. A breach is fundamental when the non-breaching party is substantially deprived of what it was entitled to expect under the contract. Their expectations must be destroyed. The result also must be foreseeable to the breaching party.

> **EXAMPLE**
>
> Company A in one CISG country orders goods from Company B in another CISG country, and explicitly makes known that the goods must meet all regulatory requirements in the country of importation. If Company B then provides goods that do not meet such regulatory requirements Company A will be able to avoid the contract due to a fundamental breach. However, if Company B provides the goods, but the quantity is short by 5%, this would be a non-fundamental breach and Company A would not be able to avoid the contract, but would still be able to claim a price reduction and any associated damages.

For further reference, the CISG further provides specific rules for determining when buyers (Art. 49) and sellers (Art. 64) may exercise the right of avoidance as a result of a fundamental breach by the other party.

Finally, there may arise a situation where one party to a sales contract recognizes that the other party is unlikely to perform their obligations under the contract. CISG Art. 72 allows a party who anticipates that the other party will breach to avoid the contract as a defense mechanism. This is often referred to as anticipatory breach, and generally takes place prior to full performance of the contractual obligations.

> **EXAMPLE**
>
> A seller finds out that a buyer with whom it recently signed a contract has entered into bankruptcy proceedings. After learning of these proceedings the seller does not want to ship goods to the buyer since they are justifiably concerned about future payment. CISG Art. 72 would allow the seller in this situation to declare the contract avoided in order to terminate their obligations under the contracts.

Remedies and Damages under the CISG

As discussed above, where there is a breach of a contractual obligation under a contract governed by the CISG, the first relevant determination is whether the breach is fundamental or not. A fundamental breach provides the non-breaching party with the remedy of avoidance. Other remedies and damages are possible regardless of whether the breach is fundamental or not. Some of these other potential remedies and damages will be addressed herein.

> ## Selected Articles re: Remedies under the CISG
> ### Article 74
> Damages for breach of contract by one party consist of a sum equal to the loss, including loss of profit, suffered by the other party as a consequence of the breach. Such damages may not exceed the loss which the party in breach foresaw or ought to have foreseen at the time of the conclusion of the contract, in the light of the facts and matters of which he then knew or ought to have known, as a possible consequence of the breach of contract.
> ### Article 77
> A party who relies on a breach of contract must take such measures as are reasonable in the circumstances to mitigate the loss, including loss of profit, resulting from the breach. If he fails to take such measures, the party in breach may claim a reduction in the damages in the amount by which the loss should have been mitigated.
> ### Article 78
> If a party fails to pay the price or any other sum that is in arrears, the other party is entitled to interest on it, without prejudice to any claim for damages recoverable under article 74.

An aggrieved party under a breached sales contract governed by the CISG may prefer to force the breaching party to perform their obligations under the sales contract, also referred to as the remedy of specific performance. For example, a jilted seller may force the buyer to take delivery of the goods and make payment (*see* Art. 62), or a non-breaching buyer may ask the non-performing seller to deliver conforming goods if possible (*see* Art. 46). It should be noted that these rules may not be applied the same way in each country since Art. 28 of the CISG provides national courts some flexibility to take into account their domestic legal systems with regard to requiring a party to perform the contract. (Schlechtriem, 2008) Therefore these remedies, in theory, are not always available in domestic legal systems (e.g., common law systems typically require goods to be unique for specific performance to be available…), and domestic courts still have the authority to follow their own rules in granting performance. Requiring that the breaching party specifically perform its contractual obligations is also not possible where there are inconsistent remedies (e.g., avoiding the contract or demanding a price reduction).

Often times, whether a breach is fundamental or not, the non-breaching party may be most interested in claiming monetary damages. Under CISG Art. 74, monetary damages are calculated by determining the sum which is equal to the loss suffered by the non-breaching party. This includes all reasonably foreseeable consequential damages, including lost profits. The calculation of such damages is based upon what the parties knew at the time that they entered into the contract. See the discussion of calculating consequential damages under UNIDROIT 7.4.2, *supra*, for an example of how consequential damages may be calculated, since similar principles apply under the CISG. The CISG also permits non-breaching parties to make claims for interest on money owed to them by the breaching party.

Moreover, the non-breaching party who wishes to make a claim for damages must attempt to mitigate its losses. Pursuant to CISG Art. 77, if a non-breaching party fails to take steps to mitigate their damages, or in other words, decrease the harm suffered as a result of the breach, then such damages may be reduced in the amount that the damages would have been reduced through mitigation efforts. For example, a buyer who wishes to resell goods purchased from a seller who never delivers the goods cannot claim damages for lost profits unless it attempted to secure replacement or cover goods from an alternative source. If the buyer was unable to find such replacement goods and reduce the damages suffered, then they may claim the full amount of the loss. In short, even when a party did not do anything wrong, under the CISG they still need to take various steps in order to preserve their rights to claim a full amount of damages.

Finally, as is the case in many domestic sales laws, and as discussed in the context of the UNIDROIT Principles, at times a party may be excused from the non-performance of its contractual obligations. The commonly cited example of *force majeure* (*see supra* UNIDROIT Principles Art. 7.1.7) is a concept which can also be found in the CISG, although the term *force majeure*, which may have slightly different meanings from country to country is not found in the treaty. Instead, CISG Art. 79 discusses 'impediments beyond...control" of the parties:

Article 79 (excerpt)
(1) A party is not liable for a failure to perform any of his obligations if he proves that the failure was due to an impediment beyond his control and that he could not reasonably be expected to have taken the impediment into account at the time of the conclusion of the contract or to have avoided or overcome it or its consequences.

Parties are free to insert their own definition of *force majeure* into a sales contract which either expands or contracts upon the definition found in Art. 79.

The preceding analysis of the CISG is meant only as a brief introduction to selected topics. The intent of this work is not to provide exhaustive analysis, but rather to introduce readers to the CISG along with some of its fundamental concepts. For more detailed analysis, explanation, resources, and generally all things CISG the Pace Law School CISG Database is hard to beat, and can be found at http://www.cisg.law.pace.edu/.

As detailed as the CISG may seem, by itself, it does not contain all of the rules necessary to govern the sales relationship between two private parties. In addition to the law governing the sales contract, whether the CISG or otherwise, various additional considerations and related issues must be addressed. For example, transportation and payment obligations must be resolved. The next sections will briefly discuss certain private legal principles and rules available to help parties navigate these additional issues. These private legal principles have been deemed *lex mercatoria* by some, and are regularly used in the context of an international sales contract.

Additional Private Rules and Practical Considerations Concerning the Sale of Goods between Private Parties

When negotiating sales contracts, buyers and sellers naturally need to think about much more than just those issues related to the goods themselves (e.g., price, quantity and description). There are many other issues that must be resolved before the parties engage in shipping goods over long distances, many times from one continent to another. These issues include, but are not limited to where delivery takes place, who bears the risk of loss if the goods are damaged in transit, at what point the risk of loss shifts from one party to another, and how and when the goods will be paid for, whether cash, wire transfer, bill of exchange, letter of credit or some other method. The well drafted sales contract should address these issues, however, practices related to transport, payment and other issues may differ in the domestic context from one country to another. Therefore, over time various private rules have developed to assist parties who are dealing in an international context. This section of the book will address some of these private rules.

Incoterms®

As discussed in the preceding paragraph, when parties are negotiating the transportation and delivery elements of their sales contract, various issues need to be resolved. When and where will delivery take place? Will it be at the seller's place of business, the buyer's place of business, some other final destination point, or some place in between such as a shipping port? If something happens to the goods while they are in transit, who pays for the damage or loss? Whose responsibility is it to insure the transport of the goods, and up to what point? While standard practices resolving these issues may exist within a particular country, those practices are not necessarily shared by parties from other countries. Additionally, individually negotiating each and every one of these terms for each sales contract that a company enters into may be tedious, difficult, and lead to disagreements which ultimately may prevent deals from being concluded. Even so, sellers and buyers need to clearly define their responsibilities concerning these important matters when entering into a sales contract.

The solution is found in a widely accepted set of common rules which resolve these issues and are often used in practice for international commercial transactions. The Incoterms® rules, short for International Commercial Terms, are a highly useful and widely accepted set of private rules used in an international sales context to allocate transportation responsibilities between private parties. Incoterms® rules are not law *per se*. Law is developed by governments and intergovernmental organizations. These are private rules developed by the International Chamber of Commerce ("ICC"). The ICC is a private organization based in Paris which was founded in 1919. The ICC is a very important player in the development of both private rules to be used by parties in an international commercial context, as well as a provider of private dispute resolution services (*see infra*).

Incoterms® rules were first published in 1936 and have since been updated on a periodic basis in order to keep up with changes and new developments in world trade and shipping practices. The most recent version is Incoterms® 2010, published in 2011. Since there are previous versions of the rules, it is possible that some parties who have not changed their practices are still using an older version of the rules, such as Incoterms® 2000. This is a permissible, if not necessarily advisable practice. What is advisable for parties is to clearly designate which Incoterms® version (e.g., 2010) they intend to use in their contract. Incoterms® rules or any other private rules may be adopted by parties to private relationships as the rules governing their relationship (*see* Freedom of Contract, *supra* UNIDROIT Principles). Incoterms® 2010 **do not** apply by default, therefore if parties to an international sales contract wish to use one of the terms found Incoterms® 2010 they must explicitly designate the applicable term in the contract itself.

Incoterms® 2010 splits the 11 terms into 2 categories. The first are terms that may be used for any mode of transport and the second should be used for waterway transport only. Each term is an abbreviation that refers to a detailed specific set of rules. If the parties wish to use a particular term in their contract, they simply need to refer to that term in the contract. All of the specific rules associated with the chosen term will be incorporated into the contract by this reference, and the parties do not need to include written articles in the contract for each particular concept covered by the chosen term. The parties can simply refer to the ICC's official publication which provides detailed descriptions of both the seller's and the buyer's obligations under each term. This leads to uniform application of commercial terms in the international commercial context reducing the potential for confusion, misunderstandings, and blockages in negotiation. It also leads to efficiency in contract drafting since all that is required to use the Incoterms® rules is a simple reference. Again, the parties' choice to use an Incoterm means there is no need to write out specific provisions covering transport costs, risk of loss, insurance, etc. unless the parties wish to somehow deviate from the chosen term. (Incoterms® 2010) A non-exhaustive summary chart of Incoterms® 2010 is found below:

Incoterm®	Description
Rules for Any Mode of Transport	
EXW (Ex Works)	EXW makes things very simple for the seller. Delivery is made by the seller at the seller's premises (or at another named place) by making the goods available to the buyer. The seller has no other responsibilities. The buyer needs to load the goods, pay for transport, clear the goods for export, etc. The seller bears no transport risk (e.g., if goods are damaged in transit).
FCA (Free Carrier)	The seller has additional obligations under a contract incorporating FCA in comparison to EXW. Delivery can be made by the seller at the seller's premises or at another named place, but the seller "delivers" the goods to a carrier or other named person (typically a transport company) chosen by the buyer. The seller clears the goods for export. Transport risk passes to buyer once goods are delivered.

CPT (Carriage Paid To)	The seller goes further under a CPT contract in comparison to FCA. Delivery takes place and transport risk transfers at a place agreed to by the parties (which could be the seller's premises, an intermediary port, or elsewhere), but the seller also agrees to pay and contract for the transport costs until the point of destination, even though they do not bear the transport risk. Since the delivery point and the point of destination will generally be different, the buyer would be well advised to purchase shipment insurance to cover transport risk between the two points.
CIP (Carriage And Insurance Paid To)	The CIP contract contains the same obligations for the seller as a CPT contract with an important additional obligation. The seller is required to provide minimum insurance coverage for transport risk until the point of destination. If the buyer wishes to have more than the minimum insurance coverage they need to either negotiate with the seller and expressly include a provision concerning such coverage in the contract, or purchase additional insurance coverage on their own.
DAT (Delivered At Terminal)	DAT imposes different obligations on the seller as compared to CIP. Whereas under CIP the seller delivers by handing the goods over to a carrier, under DAT the seller delivers at a named terminal (e.g., a particularly designated place within a port) at the port or other place of destination once the goods are unloaded by the seller. The seller pays for all transport and bears all transport risks up to unloading at this named terminal at the port (or other place) of destination, but has no insurance obligations.
DAP (Delivered At Place)	DAP is similar to DAT, however the named destination need not be a named terminal and can be any place of destination, e.g., the buyer's place of business. The seller pays for all transport and bears all transport risks up to the point where the goods are ready for unloading at the named place of destination. The buyer must unload and bears any costs and risks incurred at that point and beyond.
DDP (Delivered Duty Paid)	DDP goes a step further than DAP and provides the highest level of obligations on the seller, and can perhaps be seen as the opposite of Ex Works. The seller under a DDP contract pays for all transport and bears all risk until the goods are ready for unloading by the buyer at the named destination (e.g., buyer's place of business). The seller must also carry out all customs formalities on both ends of the transaction so that they are technically both the exporter and importer. This means that the seller will be responsible for any customs duties levied on the goods in the country of importation.

Rules for Sea and Inland Waterway Transport	
FAS (Free Alongside Ship)	Under FAS the seller pays for transport costs and bears transport risk up until the point where the goods physically placed next to (alongside) the ship at the port of shipment in a manner customary to the port. The buyer must choose the ship. Once the goods are alongside the ship, all costs and risks are borne by the buyer.
FOB (Free On Board)	The seller under the FOB contract has an additional obligation in comparison to the FAS contract. Under FOB the seller pays for transport costs and bears transport risk up until the point where the goods physically placed on board the ship at the port of shipment. The buyer must choose the ship. Once the goods are on board the ship, all costs and risks are borne by the buyer.
CFR (Cost and Freight)	The seller under the CFR contract has additional obligations in comparison to the FOB contract. Delivery occurs when the goods are on board the ship (similar to the FOB contract), however the seller is nonetheless obligated to pay for transport costs up to the named port of destination. The buyer would be well advised to purchase shipment insurance to cover transport risk between the point of delivery (when the goods are on board) and the port of destination.
CIF (Cost, Insurance and Freight)	The CIF contract contains the same obligations for the seller as a CFR contract with an important additional obligation. The seller is required to provide minimum insurance coverage for transport risk until the point of destination. If the buyer wishes to have more than the minimum insurance coverage they need to either negotiate with the seller and expressly include a provision concerning such coverage in the contract, or purchase additional insurance coverage on their own. CIF is limited to shipping by waterway and delivery takes place on board the vessel. If other modes of transport are being used, CIP is more appropriate.
For source and more detailed analysis:	http://www.iccwbo.org/products-and-services/trade-facilitation/incoterms-2010/the-incoterms-rules/ ; http://store.iccwbo.org/incoterms-2010 ; Incoterms® 2010

The choice of Incoterm is a highly important element of the sales contract as it directly affects other components of the contract. For example, an FOB contract requires an additional obligation of the seller in comparison to an FAS contract, i.e., taking the goods from alongside the ship and putting them on board the ship. The seller generally does not engage in these additional obligations out of the goodness of its heart. In other words, a buyer can expect that the price of goods quoted under an FOB contract will be more expensive than under an FAS contract since the seller engages in an additional step in taking the goods from alongside the ship and putting them on board the ship. The seller also bears additional risk since during the process of taking the goods from alongside the ship and putting them on board the ship, something could go wrong and the goods could be damaged or lost. This example illustrates how the choice of Incoterm correlates to the price of the goods in addition to the obligations of a party. Naturally a buyer would expect an EXW price to be the lowest and the DDP price to be the highest.

It is also important that parties attempt to use the Incoterms® appropriately. There have been many cases where the parties have incorrectly used an Incoterm, which may cause contractual uncertainty and confusion (one of the very things that the Incoterms® are designed to prevent). For example, when a party uses FOB, they are generally required not only to designate FOB as the desired term, but also provide additional information alongside the chosen Incoterm, specifically the port of shipment. So if the goods are being shipped from China to France, the sales contract might state "FOB, Guangzhou"[10]. However, in the same situation if the parties for some reason stated "FOB, Marseille", which is the port of destination, this would cause confusion under the Incoterms® 2010 since they are not being used as designed. This would not cause the contract to be invalidated, but if there arose a problem between the parties as to who pays for what, or who bears the risk at what point, these questions would be difficult to resolve under this example. Additionally, different Incoterms are specifically designed for different shipping methods, e.g., pursuant to the official text of the Incoterms® 2010, FCA is appropriate for container shipping whereas FOB is not.[11] Nevertheless, many parties use FOB as their standard term, even for container shipping every day. The choice of an Incoterm is not a decision to be made haphazardly, and wise buyers and sellers will fully understand their options before making such a choice.

---

[10] Incoterms 2010® instructs parties to specify the place or port as precisely as possible

[11] "FOB may not be appropriate where goods are handed over to the carrier before they are on the vessel, for example goods in containers which are typically delivered at terminal. In such situations, the FCA rule should be used."

Bills of Lading

As a practical matter, when goods are shipped from one country to another, most of the time they are handed over to a third party carrier. In common practice the carrier will issue the shipping party an important document called a bill of lading. Recall that the shipping party may be either the seller or buyer, depending on the agreement between the parties as well as the Incoterm chosen to apply to their relationship.

The bill of lading has various functions. First, it acts as evidence of a contract of carriage between the shipping party and the carrier. This is important if the goods are lost or damaged in transit. The bill of lading will contain a description of the goods stating the quantity and condition thereof. This may be important for fulfilling the terms of a Letter of Credit (*see infra*) or other payment obligation. It also shows that the goods have been shipped as agreed between the shipping party and the carrier, and will note the state of the goods when taken into the possession of the carrier. If the goods are received in a different condition, the bill of lading can be used to raise a claim against the carrier. (UNCTAD, 2003)

The bill of lading also acts as a document of title. This means that the person holding the bill of lading has the right to take possession of the goods from the carrier when they arrive at their destination. Often times an important element of the international sale is the exchange of documents, and in order to be paid a shipping seller is not required to physically provide the buyer with the goods, but rather must provide the buyer with the bill of lading. This document then entitles the non-shipping buyer to take possession of the goods upon their arrival. This exchange of documents is extremely important.

Additionally, a bill of lading is generally "negotiable", meaning that it can be transferred to another party, even while the goods are in transit. For example, the shipping seller provides the bill of lading to the non-shipping buyer, and the buyer pays the seller. The buyer then wishes to resell the goods. It is not required to wait until the goods physically arrive and are in its possession if it has a negotiable bill of lading. The buyer can transfer the bill of lading to a third party who can then take possession of the goods upon their arrival at the point of destination. A bill of lading can also be made non-negotiable, either by agreement (e.g. seawaybill or straight bill of lading) or when the bill of lading notes a problem with the goods when they were loaded (a claused bill of lading). (UNCTAD, 2003)

Letter of Credit

Payment for goods in an international context can be problematic. Parties may have to deal with currency fluctuations, obtaining financing and other possible issues such as enforcing promises to pay or difficulties in having banking instruments from one country recognized in another. Another important issue is related to the timing and security of payment, which is the topic on which this work will focus. The seller does not wish to ship the goods a long distance before receiving some security in knowing that it will be paid if it complies with its obligations under the sales contract. If the seller ships the goods and is subsequently not paid, as a practical matter it may be quite difficult to retake possession of the goods in a foreign country and find an alternative buyer for disposing thereof. It may also be very difficult to collect on any judgment or award for non-payment against the non-performing buyer. On the other hand, from the buyer's perspective it does not wish to pay for goods unless they have some security knowing that the goods will be shipped and will be what the buyer expects. It is not feasible for the buyer and the seller to meet somewhere in between and make the exchange, so what should the parties do in this situation?

One commonly used solution to this problem is the letter of credit ("L/C"). The L/C will be examined in the context of the sale of goods here, but it is important to understand that it can be used in various other contexts (e.g., construction projects). The L/C resolves the previously addressed timing and security problems in the context of an international sale of goods. It is a commitment given to the seller by a recognized bank on behalf of a buyer that payment will be made if the seller complies with the obligations outlined in the L/C agreement. When the parties agree to use the L/C, they simply put a provision in their contract to that effect. It is then the buyer's responsibility to obtain the L/C. The buyer will request that a bank issue the L/C, and if the bank agrees to issue the L/C on behalf of the buyer, the buyer and the bank enter into the contract, to which the seller is a third party beneficiary.

In the context of the L/C the buyer is called the "account party" or "applicant" and the bank issuing the L/C is called the "issuing bank". The seller who will receive payment is called the "beneficiary". While this work endeavors to simplify, it is important to understand that intermediary banks may be used in order to effectuate payment to the seller. For example, an "advising bank" may work on behalf of the beneficiary to assist in effectuating the L/C transaction. (UNCTAD, 2003) The issuing bank issues the L/C on behalf of the account party for a fee. As part of the L/C transaction the account party will require that certain documents be provided to the issuing bank by the beneficiary before the issuing bank releases payment. Commonly these documents include, but are not limited to, the bill of lading (evidencing shipment of the goods by the seller), an inspection certificate, a commercial invoice identifying the shipment, and possibly an insurance policy (if the seller is required to purchase one pursuant to the chosen Incoterm, e.g., CIF).

When the issuing bank receives the documents designated by the L/C from the beneficiary, it will then inspect the documents. The issuing bank is obligated to examine the documents and to pay if the documents appear to contain no discrepancies. If there are no discrepancies, payment is made on the basis of the inspection of the documents alone. The issuing bank will not physically examine the goods, this is beyond the scope of its obligations. The issuing bank will simply examine the documents, and if the documents appear to be regular on their face the bank must make payment.

The most commonly used rules governing L/C relationships are private rules developed by the ICC called the Uniform Customs and Practice for Documentary Credits ("UCP"). Like Incoterms the UCP is not law as it is developed by the ICC, a non-governmental organization. The UCP is a set of private rules that is chosen by parties to the L/C, i.e., the account party (buyer) and the issuing bank. It provides parties with a code of practice related to L/Cs. The UCP was originally promulgated in 1933, and has been subsequently revised on 6 occasions, the most recent revision being in 2007. The most current version of the UCP is referred to as the UCP 600. Again, parties are free to choose these rules to govern their private relationship (or they could choose a previous version, such as the UCP 500 if they wish, again...freedom of contract applies), and virtually all L/C transactions in this context incorporate the UCP.

One of the fundamental principles found in the UCP 600 is the principle of autonomy of the letter of credit. The L/C is a separate and autonomous agreement from the sales agreement between the seller and the buyer. (UCP 600, 2007) Therefore, if the beneficiary presents the documents required by the L/C, and there are no discrepancies in those documents, the issuing bank is required to honor the L/C and make payment. Any dispute between the buyer and seller, e.g., related to the conformity of the goods, does not affect the issuing bank's obligation to honor the credit upon the presentation of conforming documents.

The issuing bank will also follow the rule of strict compliance in examining the documents presented by the beneficiary. As previously mentioned, if there is a discrepancy between the documents called for by the L/C and the documents presented by the beneficiary, the issuing bank will not make payment. Banks may refuse to pay based on what may seem like minor errors, such as misspelling. It is therefore extremely important that a seller obtains the documents required under the L/C, and if there are terms of the L/C which need to be interpreted, the seller can work with its advising bank to assist with compliance. (UCP 600, 2007)

By default under the UCP 600, the L/C is irrevocable. This simply means that once the terms of the L/C are set, they cannot be changed unless there is an agreement between the buyer and seller to do so. (UNCTAD, 2003) This is logical, and a seller would generally require this security in order to proceed with including a term in the sales contract calling for payment using a L/C. The seller will be required to engage in quite serious steps which cannot easily be reversed in order to comply with the L/C. For example, typically one of the documents required to be presented to the issuing bank by the seller/beneficiary under a L/C is the bill of lading. The bill of lading, as previously explained, is issued by the carrier of the goods to the shipping party. This means that the shipping seller will have shipped the goods before receiving the funds. If the buyer was able to simply change the terms of the L/C, this would provide little security for the seller, and a wise seller would be wary of such a transaction.

In some cases, in addition to being irrevocable, the L/C may be confirmed. This is where a second bank confirms, or adds an additional guarantee to the L/C issued by the issuing bank. A confirming bank adds additional security for the seller/beneficiary. There are various reasons for requiring a confirmed L/C, however the confirming bank will also levy fees in addition to the issuing bank, so it is a more expensive option. Nevertheless the expense may be justified. For example, if the seller is unfamiliar with the buyer, and the buyer obtains the L/C from an unknown local bank the seller may not be very comfortable. This is especially the case in countries with higher political and/or economic risks. (UNCTAD, 2003) The seller may wish to require the L/C to be confirmed by a recognized and reputable international bank in order to proceed with the sale of goods.

To conclude, there are various ways to finance international sales, but the L/C provides a certain amount of security which may be preferred by parties, especially parties who are unfamiliar with each other. Since there are fees associated with the L/C, parties who have established a good working relationship and trust each other may be more inclined to forego this mechanism. The method for payment, like other elements of the sales contract is ultimately at the discretion of the parties.

Bibliography

AMERICAN LAW INSTITUTE. 1971. *Restatement (Second) of Conflict of Laws.*

BERGAMI, Roberto. 2016. "The Ship's Rail Is Dead: Incoterms 2010." Accessed March 25. http://www.shippingsolutions.com/blog/the-ships-rail-is-dead-incoterms-2010.

BORN, Gary. 2001. *International Commercial Arbitration: Commentary and Materials.* 2nd ed. Ardsley, NY : The Hague, The Netherlands: Transnational Publishers ; Kluwer Law International.

CODE CIVIL - *Article 1108.* 2016. *Code Civil.* Vol. 1108. Accessed March 23.

DRAGO, Thomas J., and Alan F. ZOCCOLILLO. 2002. "Be Explicit: Drafting Choice of Law Clauses in International Sale of Goods Contracts," May. http://www.cisg.law.pace.edu/cisg/biblio/zoccolillo1.html.

EUROPEAN UNION. 2007. *Regulation (EC) No 864/2007 of the European Parliament and of the Council of 11 July 2007 on the Law Applicable to Non-Contractual Obligations (Rome II).* http://eur-lex.europa.eu/legal-content/EN/TXT/HTML/?uri=CELEX:32007R0864&from=en.

———. 2008. *Regulation (EC) No 593/2008 of the European Parliament and of the Council of 17 June 2008 on the Law Applicable to Contractual Obligations (Rome I).* http://eur-lex.europa.eu/legal-content/EN/TXT/HTML/?uri=CELEX:32008R0593&from=EN.

Huber, Peter, and Alastair MULLIS. 2007. *The CISG: A New Textbook for Students and Practitioners.* München: Sellier.

INTERNATIONAL CHAMBER OF COMMERCE, ed. 2006. *ICC Uniform Customs and Practice for Documentary Credits: 2007 Revision.* ICC Publication 600. Paris: International Chamber of Commerce.

———. 2010. *Incoterms® 2010: ICC Rules for the Use of Domestic and International Trade Terms.* Version bilingue anglais-français. Paris: ICC.

———. 2016. "Incoterms Rules | Short Descriptions." *www.iccwbo.org.* Accessed March 25. http://www.iccwbo.org/products-and-services/trade-facilitation/incoterms-2010/the-incoterms-rules/.

INTERNATIONAL INSTITUTE FOR THE UNIFICATION OF PRIVATE LAW, ed. 2010. *UNIDROIT Principles of International Commercial Contracts 2010*. 3. ed. Rome: UNIDROIT International Institute for the Unification of Private Law.

INTERNATIONAL TRADE CENTRE UNCTAD/GATT. 2010. *Model Contracts for Small Firms: Legal Guidance for Doing International Business*. Geneva: ITC.

JONES, Glower W. 1989. "Warranties in International Sales: UN Convention on Contracts for the International Sale of Goods Compared to the US Uniform Commercial Code on Sales." *International Business Lawyer* 17: 497–500. http://www.cisg.law.pace.edu/cisg/biblio/jones.html.

KIMBEL, Ericson P. 1999. "Nachfrist Notice and Avoidance under the CISG." *Journal of Law and Commerce* 18: 301–31. http://cisgw3.law.pace.edu/cisg/biblio/kimbel.html.

KOEHLER, Martin F. 2006. "Survey Regarding the Relevance of the United Nations Convention for the International Sale of Goods (CISG) in Legal Practice and the Exclusion of Its Application." http://cisgw3.law.pace.edu/cisg/biblio/koehler.html.

LOOKOFSKY, Joseph. 2000. "Article 3 Contract of Sale v. Contract for Services." In *International Encyclopaedia of Laws*. Accessed March 24. http://www.cisg.law.pace.edu/cisg/biblio/loo3.html.

LOOKOFSKY, Joseph M. 2008. *Understanding the CISG: A Compact Guide to the 1980 United Nations Convention on Contracts for the International Sale of Goods*. 3. (worldwide) ed. Alphen aan den Rijn: Kluwer Law Internat. [u.a.].

MAGNUS, Ulrich, ed. 2012. *CISG vs. Regional Sales Law Unification: With a Focus on the New Common European Sales Law*. Munich: Sellier European Law Publishers.

MOSES, Margaret L. 2012. *The Principles and Practice of International Commercial Arbitration*. 2nd ed. Cambridge ; New York: Cambridge University Press.

NATIONAL CONFERENCE OF COMMISSIONERS ON UNIFORM STATE LAWS AND THE AMERICAN LAW INSTITUTE. 2016. *U.C.C. § 2-601. Buyer's Rights on Improper Delivery*. Accessed March 24. https://www.law.cornell.edu/ucc/2/2-601.

NAYLER, Peter. 2006. *Business Law in the Global Marketplace: The Effects on International Business*. Oxford, Eng. ; Burlington, MA: Elsevier Butterworth-Heinemann.

NEW YORK STATE. n.d. *New York General Obligations Law*. Vol. § 5–1401.

PACE LAW SCHOOL INSTITUTE OF INTERNATIONAL COMMERCIAL LAW. 2016. *Annotated Text of CISG - Article 96*. Accessed March 24. http://www.cisg.law.pace.edu/cisg/text/e-text-96.html.

Redfern, Alan, Martin HUNTER, Nigel BLACKABY, and Constantine PARTASIDES, eds. 2004. *Law and Practice of International Commercial Arbitration*. 4. ed, [student version]. London: Sweet & Maxwell.

SCHLECHTRIEM, Peter, and Petra Butler. 2008. *UN Law on International Sales: The UN Convention on the International Sale of Goods*. New York: Springer.

SCHROETER, Ulrich G. 2013. *CISG Advisory Council Opinion No. 15*. http://www.cisg.law.pace.edu/cisg/CISG-AC-op15.html.

SCHWENZER, Ingeborg H., Pascal HACHEM, and Christopher KEE. 2012. *Global Sales and Contract Law*. Oxford ; New York, NY: Oxford University Press.

STEINER, Eva. 2010. *French Law: A Comparative Approach*. Oxford ; New York: Oxford University Press.

UNCITRAL SECRETARIAT. *Secretariat Commentary on Article 2 of the 1978 Draft*. Accessed March 24. http://www.cisg.law.pace.edu/cisg/text/secomm/secomm-02.html.

UNCTAD SECRETARIAT. 2003. "The Use of Transport Documents in International Trade." UNCTAD/SDTE/TLB/2003/3. http://unctad.org/en/Docs/sdtetlb20033_en.pdf.

UNCTAD AND FRIDA YOUSSEF. 2003. "Documentary Risk in Commodity Trade." UNCTAD/ITCD/COM/Misc. 31. http://unctad.org/en/Docs/itcdcommisc31_en.pdf.

UNITED NATIONS COMMISSION ON INTERNATIONAL TRADE LAW. 1980. *United Nations Convention on Contracts for the International Sale of Goods*. New York: United Nations.

————. 2016a. "Status - United Nations Convention on Contracts for the International Sale of Goods (Vienna, 1980)." *www.uncitral.org*. Accessed March 24. http://www.uncitral.org/uncitral/en/uncitral_texts/sale_goods/1980CISG_status.html.

————. 2016b. *UNCITRAL Model Law on International Commercial Arbitration 1985, With Amendments as Adopted in 2006.* Accessed March 22. https://www.uncitral.org/pdf/english/texts/arbitration/ml-arb/07-86998_Ebook.pdf.

WORLD TRADE ORGANIZATION. 2014. *World Trade Organization International Trade Statistics 2014.* https://www.wto.org/english/res_e/statis_e/its2014_e/its2014_e.pdf

Intellectual Property

Much of this work has focused on trade in goods. Nevertheless, often times a business' value is not necessarily derived from the goods it sells or the services it provides. There are a plethora of companies who capitalize on their ideas. Ideas and the expression of ideas can be the property of their creator, just as a house can be the property of a landowner (real property), or a car can be the property of a driver (personal property). Unlike land and cars, ideas and expression are intangible, so while they are a form of property a different set of laws is required to deal with the unique nature of this type of property. This field of law is referred to as intellectual property ("IP") law. IP law is a vast and complicated field; therefore the scope of this work is limited to introductory topics in the field, such as defining the different forms of IP which exist. Myriad resources exist for those who wish to go further, and a good starting point for such additional research can be found at the World Intellectual Property Organization's ("WIPO") website; www.wipo.int.

IP law is different in every country. Countries have the ability and autonomy to create their own systems of IP law. It is national law which creates IP rights and which sets the rules for transferring IP rights, via licensing or otherwise. That being established, great differences between national IP law regimes act as a barrier to trade for companies who wish to use their IP in other countries just as differences in domestic sales laws act as a barrier to trade for sellers of goods who wish to sell their goods in other countries. Unlike the sale of goods though, there is no widely accepted treaty, convention or other international law (like the CISG in a sales context) for private parties engaging in intellectual property transactions around the world. Since this work endeavors to cover international law, it will not examine the IP legal regime of any one country; rather it will briefly engage in a description of some of the basic standards emanating from the WTO TRIPS Agreement. For IP law specifics one must consult the detailed IP laws of the country at issue.

1. TRIPS

The WTO Agreements recognized the need for a base level of certainty in the context of IP law in the international realm, and created the Agreement on Trade Related Aspects of Intellectual Property Rights ("TRIPS", *see supra*). TRIPS obligates WTO Member States to implement certain basic minimum IP standards which must be incorporated into the domestic legal regimes of all WTO Member States. Therefore, while IP law is not identical between WTO Member States, it is harmonized to a certain extent. Prior to TRIPS multiple IP conventions were in place. The 1883 Paris Convention for the Protection of Industrial Property covers trademarks, patents, and industrial designs. The 1887 Berne Convention for the Protection of Literary and Artistic Works provides principles for the protection of copyrights. While these conventions were very important in the development of IP law and protection thereof in an international context, by the time the Uruguay Round negotiations for began in the 1980s, which included intellectual property negotiations, they were seen as being inadequate and did not cover various relevant issues. Nevertheless, these pre-existing IP law treaties were incorporated by reference and expanded upon in the TRIPS Agreement (an exception being found for the moral rights related to copyrights under the Berne Convention, which were not included in TRIPS). Among other things TRIPS provides updated basic IP principles, including uniform general rules and standards concerning the different forms of IP. It also provides basic standards and procedures to be followed in WTO Member States for the enforcement of IP rights, typically via the judicial system. (WTO, 1995)

2. Forms of IP

Different types of ideas require different types of protection. For example, the nature of an artistic creation such as a painting is different than the nature of a scientific creation such as an invention like a new type of catalytic converter for large trucks. Therefore IP law classifies different types of ideas into different categories. Each of these categories provides different protections to the creators (or owners of the ideas). The standards examined here will be based on those found in, or incorporated by reference in the TRIPS Agreement. Keep in mind that these are the basic minimum standards for protection found in WTO Member States. They are a floor, not a ceiling, meaning that countries which are WTO Member States can provide additional protections to IP if they wish, but not less.

Copyrights

Copyrights protect artistic creations. The Berne Convention (which was incorporated into TRIPS) refers to "literary and artistic works", and is broadly defined to include the literary, scientific, and artistic fields. A detailed list of works protected by copyrights can be found in the Berne Convention itself. It includes books, pamphlets, musical compositions, cinematographic works, photographic works, maps, drawings, paintings, translations, musical arrangements, and various other types of works. TRIPS also makes clear that computer programs, whether in source or object code, are also subject to copyright protection.

The minimum term of copyright protection to be applied in WTO Member States is the life of the author plus 50 years after the death of the author. Many countries go beyond this minimum term in practice. For example, in the US the term of a copyright is 70 years after the death of author. However in the US there is a special rule for when a corporation is deemed to be the author. In this context the rule is a bit different since a corporation, even though a legal person, will not "die" in the traditional sense. Therefore works of corporate authorship are protected for 95 years from publication or 120 years from creation, whichever expires first. (17 U.S.C. § 302) Each country has its particularities, and details must be confirmed in each country where a party wishes to seek copyright protection. Once a copyright expires, the work becomes part of the public domain, simply meaning that people other than the copyright holder are able to use the work as they wish.

In order to receive copyright protection, the work generally needs to be, to use terminology from the US, "fixed in a tangible medium of expression". (17 U.S.C. § 102) According to Art. 9 of TRIPS, copyright protection extends "to expressions and not to ideas, procedures, methods of operation or mathematical concepts as such." (WTO, 1995) And this makes sense. If an idea which may be subject to copyright never leaves the head of the author, then it cannot be protected. There are no formalities required to obtain the copyright. (Berne Convention) While authors generally can register copyrights, they are not required to do so. That being said, the more steps a party takes to protect their copyright, for example, stating the name, author, and date of publication, using the © symbol, and registering, the less likely there is to be a dispute concerning copyright ownership. Additionally, once a copyright is obtained in the country of origin, the work shall also be protected in other countries by the domestic rules of protection in each respective country.

Importantly, the copyright gives the holder pecuniary rights. This is the right to exploit a work for an economic gain. (August, 2004) Quite simply, this is the right to make money using the work. Only the copyright holder can reproduce the work and distribute copies thereof. The right to reproduce a copyrighted work always remains with the copyright holder during the duration of the copyright. However, a copyright holder's right to control distribution of each copy is exhausted for each copy after the first distribution. (WIPO) This allows for the resale of previously distributed copyrighted works that we all see on a daily basis, in used bookshops for example. To be clear though, the used bookshop would not be able to make and sell copies of books that it lawfully obtained. The copyright holder also has the right to authorize performance of its work.

Copyrights, like the other forms of intellectual property, are freely transferable. This means that they can be licensed, sold, or even given away. Transferred copyright terms are still determined by the life of the author (not the life of the owner), but in a strange twist an owner of a copyright can force the author of a copyright to pay royalties (use fees) for using the copyright. Take the example of Paul McCartney. When John Lennon and Paul McCartney were young and perhaps naive, through a saga that will not be addressed in detail here, they lost the rights to many of their famous songs during a dispute with their record company. Many years later these songs were auctioned off and purchased by Michael Jackson. The rights were then further partitioned after Jackson's purchase. Long story short, when Paul McCartney plays "Hey Jude" in concert, he is required to pay a royalty fee to be able to do so, although he is currently fighting to get these rights back. (Moyer, 2016) This illustrates the importance of understanding and protecting copyright interests.

Trademarks

Trademarks protect words, phrases, and logos which allow for identification of goods or services. TRIPS defines a trademark as: "Any sign, or any combination of signs, capable of distinguishing the goods or services of one undertaking from those of other undertakings." TRIPS further clarifies that trademark protection extends to "personal names, letters, numerals, figurative elements and combinations of colours as well as any combination of such signs." (WTO, 1995) Trademarks can be extremely valuable pieces of intellectual property, and some companies go to great lengths to protect against trademark infringement (unauthorized use of a trademark). Certain companies' trademarks allow them to charge a premium for their products or services. Think about Apple, Inc. In addition to selling products which are desirable to many people for their functionality, some people also want to be identified as having their products since the logo found on such products carries with it a certain cachet. This allows Apple to charge more than its competitors are able to charge for similar, and some would say superior, products.

The minimum term of trademark protection under Art. 18 of TRIPS is 7 years; however a trademark can be renewed indefinitely. Many countries provide more than 7 years for trademark protection, for example, France, the US, and other countries provide 10 years of protection. This short, but renewable term is sensible. If one company has a trademark, but then winds up its business and does not use the trademark for many years, it would not be equitable to prevent another company from using a similar trademark 20 years afterwards. Trademarks are generally obtained through registration. Some countries, like the US, also allow for trademarks to be acquired via use of the mark. Whether trademarks are available via use will depend on local IP law regimes. Trademarks are freely transferrable, and can be licensed, sold, or given away. Again, the specific rules for trademark transfer will vary from country to country. Companies seeking trademark protection in multiple countries can use the Madrid System to do so with one filing (*see infra*).

Patents

Patents protect inventions. According to Art. 27 of TRIPS, "patents shall be available for any inventions, whether products or processes, in all fields of technology, provided that they are new, involve an inventive step (non-obvious) and are capable of industrial application (useful)." In short, to use the U.S. terminology, a creation which is new, non-obvious, and useful is entitled to patent protection. (35 U.S.C Chapter 10) Patent protection, as is the recurring theme of this chapter, is national in scope. Generally, patents must be applied for in each country where the party seeking patent protection wishes to establish such protection. For parties seeking patent protection in multiple countries, the Patent Cooperation Treaty allows one filing to be made in multiple countries (*see infra*). Each WTO Member State retains autonomy in deciding whether to grant patents, therefore there are scenarios where one country decides to grant a patent application and another country denies the same application. A party seeking patent protection in Europe can also seek regional protection if they choose to file an application through the

European Patent Office. In short, obtaining patent protection worldwide can be a difficult and expensive endeavor.

To obtain a patent an idea must first and foremost be a new idea. No other inventor can have previously obtained a patent for the idea. Nor can it be an idea which is public knowledge. In addition to being new, it must be non-obvious, also referred to as having an inventive step. This means that the invention was not obvious in light of the prior art, which is any evidence that your invention is somehow previously known. In the context of the prior art, a patent office will examine the idea from the perspective of an expert in the field in which the patent application is filed, and attempt to determine whether it would be an obvious idea to such an expert. (35 U.S.C Chapter 10) If so, the idea will be obvious and not entitled to patent protection. For example, if the patent application simply involves changing the material of a pre-existing invention to make the invention more durable, this may be an obvious change not subject to patent protection. Finally, the invention must be useful, which means that it can be used in an industrial or commercial context.

Under Art. 33 of the WTO TRIPS Agreement, the basic term for patent protection is 20 years from the filing date. Once the patent expires, the invention becomes available to others. Therefore it is very important that a patent holder exploit their invention during the term of the patent. National IP law regimes typically stick to the 20 year term found in TRIPS, although many allow for term adjustments if, for example, there is a significant delay in granting the application. Patents are freely transferrable, and can be licensed, sold, or given away. Specific rules for patent transfer will vary from country to country.

Designs

Industrial designs, also known as design patents, protect the aesthetic and ornamental elements of an article. This includes patterns, lines, colors, and shapes. The design of a product is particularly important for a wide variety of products. An obvious example is in the world of fashion. For example, if a shoe company creates a style of shoes that becomes fashionable, they have an interest in protecting that style and industrial design protection allows them to do so. Pursuant to Art. 26 of TRIPS the duration of industrial design protection shall be no less than 10 years. Like the other forms of IP, countries have discretion in determining whether to grant industrial design protection, and countries are free to provide more than 10 years of protection. For parties seeking protection in multiple countries there is the Hague System that provides an international filing system for industrial designs (*see infra*).

Trade Secrets, Know-How, and other Proprietary Information

There also exists valuable information that does not necessarily fall within an established category of IP. For example, perhaps a company has highly effective marketing techniques which allow it to gain a competitive advantage in its field. This would not be subject to a grant of rights from a government under one of the previously addressed categories of IP; however, the company will still wish to take important steps to protect this information. Often this is referred to as know-how or trade secrets. Companies should take steps to protect their know-how, trade secrets, and other proprietary information. The basis for such protection is typically found in contract law. This could be as simple as taking steps to ensure that know-how remains confidential by only disclosing such information to those who need to know it, and only after signing a non-disclosure and confidentiality agreement. Additionally, some countries have trade secret laws which can provide protection for valuable know how under certain circumstances. In fact, Part II, section 7 of TRIPS requires WTO Member States to provide protections for "undisclosed information." In general, information is not considered to be a trade secret unless the party claiming trade secret protection took some tangible steps in an effort to keep such information confidential. If such steps were taken, and the information is nonetheless dispersed by someone with access, that person who disperses may be subject to penalties under a trade secrets law.

3. WIPO

The World Intellectual Property Organization ("WIPO") is a United Nations organization which plays an important role in the field of IP law. One element of WIPO's work is to assist states in modernizing IP law. WIPO supports international developments in IP law. It provides dispute resolution services for IP related disputes, including for domain name disputes. Importantly, it also maintains databases of IP applications and rights granted throughout the world. (WIPO, 2007) One thing WIPO **does not** do is grant IP rights to private parties. WIPO is not a central authority which has the power to grant intellectual property rights (e.g., patents, trademarks, etc.) which will then be valid all over the world. There is no such central international authority since IP rights are granted by national legal authorities. So if, for example, you want a patent in various countries, you need to apply for a patent in each of those countries where patent protection is sought. This can make international protection of IP rights quite difficult to obtain since the possibility exists that while one country may decide to grant an application for IP rights, another country may decide to deny the same application.

All the same, WIPO has an important role to play in making it easier to protect IP rights in an international context. Specifically, it administers various agreements which make it procedurally easier for a party seeking IP protection in various countries to achieve their goal. In other words, a party can file one application for a grant of IP rights with WIPO, who will then forward the application to national granting authorities who will have the final word. We will briefly examine the Madrid System for trademarks, the Patent Cooperation Treaty, and the Hague System for industrial designs.

Madrid System

The Madrid System permits international trademark applications to be made through WIPO. It is based on two legal instruments, the 1891 Madrid Agreement Concerning the International Registration of Marks, and the more recent Protocol Relating to the Madrid Agreement which came into force in 1996. The system is in place in 97 states covering 80% of world trade. (WIPO, 2016) Where a party desires trademark protection in multiple countries, the Madrid System allows for the use of one application. The applicant must first apply for the trademark in its country of origin, which must be a party to the Madrid System. The country of origin then forwards to WIPO. If WIPO approves the initial international application, it then forwards the application to the Madrid System countries that the applicant designated on its application. WIPO approval does not mean that the applicant has the trademark in the designated countries, since those countries each have the final say concerning whether the trademark will be granted in their territory. (WIPO, 2013) Nonetheless, the Madrid System reduces the administrative burden associated with seeking trademark protection in multiple countries.

Patent Cooperation Treaty

The Patent Cooperation Treaty ("PCT") has been accepted in 148 countries. The PCT dates to 1970 and has since been amended on various occasions. Similar to the Madrid System for trademarks, the PCT allows an inventor to seek patent protection in various countries via one international filing. An initial application is made in the country of origin (or in some cases, the region of origin, e.g., the European Patent Office). The international application is then forwarded to WIPO, who will publish the international application and forward the international application to the national patent authorities in the countries designated by the applicant. The national authorities retain the power to grant or deny the application. (WIPO, 2015) Therefore an inventor may end up with patent rights in some of its designated countries, but not necessarily others. Nevertheless, like the Madrid System for trademarks, the PCT can significantly reduce the administrative burden associated with seeking patent protection in multiple countries.

The Hague System

The Hague System is in place for parties seeking industrial design protection in multiple countries. It originally dates to the Hague Agreement of 1925, with the more recent 1960 and 1999 Acts currently being in force. Member States who have accepted at least one of the instruments of the Hague System are part of what is called the Hague Union, which is currently composed of 65 states. (WIPO, 2016) Under the Hague System an application for design protection can be filed via WIPO. If WIPO initially approves the application, similar to the Madrid System for trademarks, and the PCT for patents, the application will be forwarded to the national authorities in the countries designated by the applicant, who will have the final word on granting the industrial design protection. (WIPO, 2012)

4. Private International Relationships re: Intellectual Property

When a party obtains a grant of intellectual property rights, if the rights are valuable, they can be exploited directly by the party who owns the rights, or transferred to a third party who obtains the right to exploit the rights. The rights can be sold, given away, or commonly, licensed (a temporary grant of use in exchange for compensation) to a third party. IP rights are often transferred in an international commercial context, commonly via licensing arrangements, in an effort to decrease costs and increase profits.

> **HYPOTHETICAL**
>
> Bobo Deluxe, S.A., is a French manufacturer of luxury goods. One of their most popular items is a fancy designer handbag marketed towards women. For decades, Bobo Deluxe, S.A. has made the handbags in France and sold the bags principally in European markets. Each bag is made up of various forms of IP. Bobo Deluxe S.A.'s trademark appears on each bag, the design of the bag is protected as an industrial design, and the company uses a patented manufacturing process to efficiently manufacture the bags. In recent years, there has been an enormous increase in demand for luxury goods of all stripes in Asian markets, particularly in China. Bobo Deluxe, S.A. wishes to capitalize on this growth by entering into Asian markets via China.

One option for Bobo Deluxe, S.A. in the above hypothetical is to simply sell their goods to buyers or distributors in China. This would entail entering into a sales contracts and distribution contracts, manufacturing the goods in France where its operations are located, and shipping the goods to China. If Bobo Deluxe, S.A. decides to proceed in this fashion, there are several disadvantages. France has high costs of labor. There are costs and risks associated with shipping. Tariffs will be levied on the goods when they enter the Chinese market. There are nonetheless some advantages to this approach. It allows Bobo Deluxe, S.A. the possibility of entering into the Chinese market without making a significant investment in China. Additionally its IP faces less serious risk since Bobo Deluxe, S.A. will not be required to provide designs or the use of the patented processes to manufacturers located in China.

The company could also decide to set up its own operations in China, perhaps by directly setting up a manufacturing facility. This would allow Bobo Deluxe, S.A. to benefit from the lower Chinese labor costs, avoid tariffs on the goods manufactured and sold in China, and significantly decrease transport risk and cost. It would also allow the company to retain control over its operations, disclosing its IP only to those who it fully trusts, directly employs, and have a need to know. However, this foreign direct investment promises to be a very complicated and expensive endeavor. A serious amount of capital would be required to acquire or build the necessary facilities. Additionally, Bobo Deluxe, S.A., or more likely a subsidiary set up by the company would be subject to Chinese law and tax regulations, may need to have partial Chinese ownership, and will generally face the risks common to all similar businesses operating in China.

Finally, Bobo Deluxe, S.A. could decide to find a reputable Chinese manufacturer who is capable of producing the bags and allow the manufacturer to access its IP in exchange for compensation of some form. This licensing arrangement would allow Bobo Deluxe, S.A. to benefit from the lower labor costs in China, avoid tariffs, and significantly decrease transportation costs and risks without having to engage in a significant investment of capital or even setting up a company in China. This would allow the company to sell its goods at the same prices (or even a higher price) in China while significantly decreasing its costs.

Nonetheless, there are some very serious possible drawbacks to this licensing arrangement. First, there is a high risk of IP theft. Since Bobo Deluxe, S.A. is allowing a licensee to access its trademarks, patents, and designs in China, the company's intellectual property needs to be protected in China. Even if it is protected, there exists the real possibility that someone associated with the licensee steals the IP in order to sell it or use it on their own. Additionally, since Bobo Deluxe, S.A. is a luxury goods company, quality is important. If the Chinese manufacturer's work does not meet the quality expected by customers, there would be significant reputational damage. There would also need to be procedures in place for regular quality and quantity audits (to make sure that the goods are not overproduced), as well as a way to verify that accounting being provided by the licensee is accurate (to accurately calculate any royalty payments). Also, since Bobo Deluxe, S.A.'s goods are normally made in France, this may be an element that is desirable in the Chinese market, and licensing to a Chinese manufacturer may actually decrease the value of the goods in that market.

Ultimately, how a company decides to take advantage of its IP should be determined on a case by case basis only after examining the particularities and relevant laws of each case. Licensing can be an effective way to internationally exploit IP, but only after fully assessing the risks. If licensing is the way to go, then the IP holder will need to enter into a licensing agreement with the third party to whom they will license their rights.

Licensing Agreements

A license is first and foremost a contract. As discussed *supra*, each country has its own laws governing contracts. Many countries will have specific rules in place for IP licensing contracts, for example, a requirement that the agreements are registered with the public IP authority, etc. When using a licensing agreement, special attention will need to be given to the governing law. This work will not examine the particular law governing licenses in any particular state, but will briefly discuss some common contractual provisions found in IP licenses around the world.

A license is typically revocable. The licensor (the owner of the IP) prefers this since if the licensee (the party using the IP) is misusing the IP, then the licensor wants to be able to retake control thereof. A licensing agreement will state the permitted uses of the IP allowing for revocation if the IP is used otherwise. Theoretically the license could be made irrevocable, but this would be highly disadvantageous for the licensor. Additionally, the default license is non-exclusive, meaning that the licensor can enter into similar arrangements with various licensors. This can, and often is changed by licensees who only wish to engage in the licensing arrangement if they have some form of exclusivity (perhaps in a specific geographic region, etc).

Often a license will contain various specific restrictions on how the IP can be used. (Schaffer, 2012) For example, if the owner of a luxury goods trademark licenses the trademark to a foreign manufacturing entity to be put on luxury handbags, they may wish to limit the licensee's use of the trademark to the handbags. Otherwise the trademark may end up on t-shirts, coffee mugs, and anything else that the licensee thinks may be profitable, potentially having significant negative effects on the value of the trademark. Other restrictions might be geographic. The licensee might have the rights to manufacture and distribute handbags with the licensed trademarks in China, but not outside of China. The licensor may also wish to put restrictions on the amount of products that the licensee can produce to reduce the risk of overproduction and the market being flooded. Specific restrictions will be determined on a case by case basis.

While IP licensing agreements are common, a licensing agreement may make up just one part of a larger contract. For example, a technology transfer agreement may go further than a licensing agreement by obligating the IP holder to provide training and support to allow the licensee to effectively use the transferred technology. (Meiselles, 2013) Licenses are also generally included in franchise agreements, whereby the IP holder/franchisor allows the franchisee to use the IP, along with a plan of business operation. The franchisee must strictly follow the franchisor's plan, and the use of various forms of IP may be a significant part of that plan. Franchising is a complex area of the law which will not be further examined herein. For purposes of simplicity; it suffices to understand that an IP license is often an integral part of a franchising agreement.

Bibliography

17 U.S. Code § 102 - Subject Matter of Copyright: In General. 2016. Accessed March 25. https://www.law.cornell.edu/uscode/text/17/102.

17 U.S. Code § 302 - Duration of Copyright: Works Created on or after January 1, 1978. 2016. Accessed March 25. https://www.law.cornell.edu/uscode/text/17/302.

35 U.S. Code Chapter 10 - PATENTABILITY OF INVENTIONS. 2016. Accessed March 25. https://www.law.cornell.edu/uscode/text/35/part-II/chapter-10.

AUGUST, Ray. 2004. *International Business Law: Text, Cases, and Readings.* Upper Saddle River, N.J.: Prentice Hall.

BERNE CONVENTION FOR THE PROTECTION OF LITERARY AND ARTISTIC WORKS. 1979. http://www.wipo.int/treaties/en/text.jsp?file_id=283698.

MEISELLES, Michala. 2013. *International Commercial Agreements: An Edinburgh Law Guide.* Edinburgh: Edinburgh University Press.

MOYER, Justin Wm. 2016. "Paul McCartney Takes Battle for Beatles Songs to Copyright Office." *The Washington Post,* March 22. https://www.washingtonpost.com/news/morning-mix/wp/2016/03/22/paul-mccartney-takes-battle-for-beatles-songs-to-copyright-office/.

PARIS CONVENTION FOR THE PROTECTION OF INDUSTRIAL PROPERTY. 1979. http://www.wipo.int/wipolex/en/treaties/text.jsp?file_id=287556.

SCHAFFER, Richard, FILIBERTO AGUSTIT, Lucien J. DHOOGE, and Beverley EARLE. 2012. *International Business Law and Its Environment.* 8th ed. Mason, OH: South-Western Cengage Learning.

WORLD INTELLECTUAL PROPERTY ORGANIZATION. 2007. *World Intellectual Property Organization: An Overview.*

———. 2012. "The Hague Agreement COncerning the International Registration of Industrial Designs: Main Features and Advantages." http://www.wipo.int/edocs/pubdocs/en/designs/911/wipo_pub_911.pdf.

———. 2013. *Protecting Your Marks Abroad: The Madrid System.*

———. 2015. "PCT FAQs." April. http://www.wipo.int/pct/en/faqs/faqs.html#note1.

————. 2016a. "Hague Union Status on March 18, 2016." March 18. http://www.wipo.int/export/sites/www/treaties/en/documents/pdf/hague.pdf.

————. 2016b. "Madrid System Status on March 18, 2016." March 18. http://www.wipo.int/export/sites/www/treaties/en/documents/pdf/madrid_marks.pdf.

————. 2016a. "International Exhaustion and Parallel Importation." *Www.wipo.int.* Accessed March 25. http://www.wipo.int/sme/en/ip_business/export/international_exhaustion.htm.

————. 2016b. "The PCT Now Has 148 Contracting States." Accessed March 25. http://www.wipo.int/pct/en/pct_contracting_states.html.

WORLD TRADE ORGANIZATION. 1995. *Annex 1C - Agreement on Trade-Related Aspects of Intellectual Property Rights.* https://www.wto.org/english/docs_e/legal_e/27-trips.pdf.

Dispute Resolution

Despite the best efforts of commercial parties to negotiate and obtain a clear, well-drafted contract, even where the parties have the best of intentions, disputes inevitably arise from time to time. It is extremely important for commercial parties to have manageable dispute resolution policies in place **before** disputes arise to the extent possible. This is of course important in a domestic context, but becomes of paramount importance in an international context. Where there is a dispute in the domestic context, even when no choices of law or forum are made in the initial contract, the parties will know and understand that domestic law and legal procedures will prevail. They also share linguistic and cultural similarities that allow the dispute resolution process to proceed in a smoother fashion. Finally, and most importantly, the parties are certain that if the court grants a judgment in the case in favor of one of the parties, the judgment will be enforceable against the other party. This gives the dispute resolution proceedings significant weight.

In the international context, if the parties fail to make a valid choice of law and forum a multitude of questions become immediately apparent. All of these questions need to be resolved before the parties can even begin to resolve the underlying dispute. First, what law applies? Second, what court is the proper court? Third, will the judgment from the proper court be enforceable in other countries where the losing party has assets? These questions could have significant bearing on who wins and loses a particular case since the law in one country may be quite different than the law in another country. Additionally, procedures in courts vary greatly from country to country (*see supra* discussion about court procedures in Common Law and Civil Law countries). Finally, and most importantly, even if the disputing parties engage in a long, expensive dispute resolution proceeding in the courts of one country, there is no guarantee that the end result, the judgment, will be enforceable in other countries. If the losing party does not have assets in the country where the judgment was rendered, and does not wish to voluntarily comply with the judgment, the winning party may have to attempt to enforce the judgment in foreign countries. Those foreign countries, unless there is a treaty to the contrary, may decide to recognize and enforce the foreign court judgment, but will not be obligated to enforce the judgment. A court proceeding will be required to determine this in the country of enforcement. This means that the winning party may be in possession of nothing but a really expensive piece of paper!

As previously discussed, parties can attempt to manage these issues at the outset by making choices in their contracts. The doctrine of party autonomy allows parties in international commercial contracts to choose the law and procedures which apply to potential disputes by making these choices in their contracts. In exercising their choice parties should explicitly include the forum where they wish for their dispute to be heard and decided, whether a state court, or a private arbitration tribunal. This can be an extremely important choice since it will determine the procedures which will be used to resolve the dispute, which may have an effect on the ultimate outcome thereof.

1. Litigation

Litigation is the traditional and default method of dispute resolution. It simply refers to going to the courts of a particular jurisdiction. Hopefully when a dispute arises between commercial parties their first instinct is not to just immediately run to the courthouse. In most circumstances some form of negotiations will precede litigation, however, if negotiations fail, to the courthouse the parties will go. This could be the result of a choice to use a particular court which was made in a contract, or it could be by the default operation of law where there was no contractual choice. Oftentimes in contracts where one party has significant bargaining leverage over the other, the choice of the stronger party's preferred court will be imposed on the weaker party. If there is no choice, in general, private international law principles will lead to the jurisdiction of the courts of a state which is somehow connected with the dispute (*see supra*).

Some parties prefer litigation to any alternative forms of dispute resolution. They know the procedure in their country and are comfortable with it. That being said, many others prefer to avoid litigating their disputes where possible, preferring alternative means of dispute resolution. There are various disadvantages associated with litigating as opposed to using some alternative, private form of dispute resolution. First, in most circumstances litigation is in public since courts are public places. This means that a company's competitors, consumers, the media, or anyone else can learn the gritty details of a dispute that is in litigation. Second, litigation can take a very long time. Again, since litigation is in public courts you must get in line and wait your turn. In addition, the courts may take a long time to give a judgment, and even after the judgment there may be appellate procedures that last for years. This may lead to significant increases in costs. Additionally, the results of litigation can be unpredictable, especially in a country such as the US where a jury may have the final say! For these reasons, various alternative forms of dispute resolution ("ADR") have developed over time. This work will examine two very common forms of ADR, mediation and arbitration.

2. Mediation

Mediation is a popular form of alternative dispute resolution. It involves the intervention of a neutral third party, the mediator. The mediator works with the disputing parties in an attempt to assist them in resolving their dispute. It is a private form of dispute resolution, meaning that it takes place outside of the courts. Nor is the mediator like a judge. A judge has the power to make a final decision in a case and determine who wins and who loses. Mediation is a non-binding form of dispute resolution; therefore the mediator does not have this type of power. Instead the mediator aims to help the parties find a mutually agreeable solution in an effort to resolve their dispute. It is not a replacement for binding dispute resolution procedures (litigation or arbitration), rather it is a method for attempting to avoid binding dispute resolution procedures. A successful mediation generally ends with a settlement agreement. This is where the parties contractually agree to resolve their dispute in accordance with mutually agreed upon terms. An unsuccessful mediation means that the parties simply will continue to the next (binding) stage of dispute resolution, generally either litigation or arbitration.

Normally, mediation is agreed to by the parties to the dispute. This agreement may be found in the initial contract between the parties, which may have been drafted long before the dispute arose, or it may be something that they agree to do after a dispute arises in an effort to efficiently resolve the dispute. In some jurisdictions courts have the power to refer cases to mediation before proceeding to a final trial in the court. (*see, e.g.* C.R.S. 13-22-311) These schemes have been put in place to reduce the caseload on overburdened courts, but such schemes are far from universal. (*see, e.g.* Smith, 2015) Typically though, mediation is consensual, meaning that both parties agree to use the procedure. Mediations are also usually confidential, which is seen as being an advantage in many circumstances.

Since the mediator has no hard power to make a decision and force the parties to do anything against their will, mediation is only successful if all parties to the dispute are willing to compromise and find a mutually agreeable solution to their dispute. The procedure is informal, and each mediator may have his or her own style and handle mediations differently. A mediator can be any person who is jointly acceptable to the parties, and often times are lawyers, ex-judges, psychiatrists, therapists, or people with required technical knowledge for a particular dispute (e.g., an engineer for a construction dispute). The key is that the mediator is somebody who is trusted by all parties to the dispute.

Typically mediation will begin with a discussion between all of the parties and the mediator. The mediator will attempt to identify points of agreement. When the mediator notes significant points of disagreement, it is often times at this point where the mediator decides to split the parties up into different rooms, and have separate (a.k.a. caucus) sessions with the parties. In these separate sessions the mediator will speak more freely about the strength and weaknesses of the claims in the case, in an effort to give the parties a neutral view of the case. Additionally, parties may speak with more candor and be more willing to compromise when they are not face to face with their adversary. The successful mediation ends with a settlement agreement, which is an agreement which resolves the dispute and alleviates the need to go to court or any other dispute resolution proceeding such as arbitration.

3. Arbitration

Arbitration can act as a replacement to litigation, and therefore is a popular alternative thereto. Whereas the end result of litigation is a court judgment, the end result of arbitration is an arbitral award. Despite the different terminology, they have the same result, which simply put is that the parties are obliged to comply with the final decision.

Like mediation the parties must choose to use arbitration. Arbitration is a "creature of contract". The choice to use arbitration is most often found in the initial contract between the parties, or from time to time the parties might agree to use arbitration in lieu of litigation after a dispute arises. Like mediation, the parties choose the neutral third party, who is referred to in this context as the arbitrator. Similar to mediation, the parties have great flexibility (depending on the arbitral rules chosen) as to who will be the arbitrator. Arbitrators are generally professionals, legal or otherwise, who are highly reputable. The major difference between arbitration and mediation lies in the power of the neutral third party. As discussed above, mediation is non-binding the mediator has no power to force the parties to do anything, whereas the arbitrator has the power to make binding decisions to which the disputing parties must comply. It is a binding form of dispute resolution, and replaces litigation.

Arbitration is more formalized than mediation, but offers more flexibility than litigation. It is like a private court where the parties retain a certain amount of control over the procedure. In addition to being a private proceeding, it can also be made confidential by the agreement of the parties. In litigation, the parties follow the rules of procedure in the jurisdiction where the dispute is being heard, and they do not have the ability to modify or tailor these procedures to meet their needs. In arbitration, the parties have great flexibility and can choose pre-existing rules of procedure developed by arbitral institutions that meet their needs, or even create their own custom procedure (although this may not be very practical). For example, parties can choose an arbitration procedure that calls for one sole arbitrator to be mutually selected by the parties, or they can choose to use a panel of three arbitrators where each party chooses their own arbitrator and the two party appointed arbitrators choose the third. This latter approach is suitable for larger scale arbitrations as it can be expensive.

Also, arbitration procedures are typically, although not always, decided faster than cases in litigation. This is in part because the procedure is in a private court, where the parties are paying for the time of the arbitrator(s). It is also due to the fact that in arbitration there is normally no appeal. Appeal of an arbitration award is possible only under very limited circumstances, and generally those circumstances are related to defects in the arbitration procedure itself, and not the substance of the arbitration award. For example, you cannot appeal an arbitration award because you think that the arbitrator misapplied the law, but you could possibly appeal the arbitration award because the arbitrator did not allow both parties equal time to present their cases.

In short, arbitration is many times an attractive alternative to litigation. It can be faster, and more efficient. It is more flexible allowing parties to choose the procedure that best fits their needs. There are disadvantages to arbitration. It can be expensive since the parties are not only paying their lawyers, but are also paying the costs of the arbitral proceeding, including the fees of the arbitrators, which can be significant. Additionally, the loss of appeal rights may be a risk that a company feels that it cannot take, especially for very high stakes disputes. Despite certain drawbacks arbitration remains a popular avenue in many countries for avoiding the courts in disputes between domestic companies. In addition to domestic use arbitration is highly popular around the world for international commercial disputes for various reasons which will be examined herein.

International Commercial Arbitration

As previously touched upon in this work, parties from different countries want to avoid each other's courts. They wish to avoid unfamiliar court procedures, for which they will be obliged to retain local representation. There are cultural and linguistic differences in addition to legal differences between different countries. Importantly, there is the potential for bias in favor of the domestic company, and in some countries corruption may be a serious concern. These are some of the reasons that parties in an international commercial context search for a neutral playing field to resolve their disputes. Arbitration is often times able to provide them with this playing field.

Again, parties are free to choose the arbitral procedures they wish to use in resolving their disputes. Commonly, international commercial contracts will call for arbitration using a well-known, reputable arbitral institution. These institutions are service providers who administer arbitration proceedings, usually by giving procedural support to the disputing parties. Among other things this procedural support can take the form of procedural rules to be followed by the parties, assistance in finding the arbitrators (often from pre-approved lists), and providing a means for communication between the parties and the arbitrators.

Some of the commonly used international arbitration institutions are the aforementioned International Chamber of Commerce ("ICC"), London Court of International Arbitration ("LCIA"), International Center for Dispute Resolution ("ICDR"), The Stockholm Chamber of Commerce ("SCC"), or the Singapore International Arbitration Center ("SICA"). There are many more such institutions and each have their unique characteristics and different procedures. These organizations tend to be headquartered in major cities, but are willing to provide their services wherever the parties desire. There are also many specialized arbitration institutions that specialize in resolving disputes related to specific industries. For example, the coffee trade has its own specialized arbitration tribunals set up for international coffee trading disputes.

One of the key goals of each of these organizations is making sure that their arbitrators are issuing awards which are enforceable. As discussed above, one of the problems in the context of international dispute resolution is that in general the judgment of a court in one country is not automatically enforceable in another country. If the losing party has no assets in the jurisdiction from where the judgment emanates, then they will have to attempt to enforce the judgment in the place(s) where the losing party has assets. This can become a Herculean effort since in the absence of specific treaties for the enforcement of judgments, each country retains autonomy in determining whether and how their courts will enforce judgments from foreign countries.

The lack of enforcement mechanisms in the context of international dispute resolution can act as a significant barrier to trade. The international community long ago recognized this problem, and created a system whereby arbitration awards (as opposed to court judgments) in one country can be recognized and enforced in other countries via the widely accepted New York Convention on the Recognition and Enforcement of Foreign Arbitral Awards.

New York Convention on the Recognition and Enforcement of Foreign Arbitral Awards

The New York Convention on the Recognition and Enforcement of Foreign Arbitral Awards ("NY Convention") was negotiated in 1958, became effective in 1959, and is currently in force in 156 countries. (UNCITRAL, 2016) It is fair to say that this is one of the most important and successful treaties in the field of international commercial law. The treaty stands for the relatively simple proposition that countries who sign the treaty agree to recognize the validity of arbitration awards made in other countries[12], and provide for the enforcement of such awards through their courts.

There exist limited grounds allowing for courts to refuse recognition and enforcement of foreign arbitration awards, such as situations where there were procedural defects in the arbitration or lack of consent to arbitrate from one of the parties. (NY Convention, 1958) If none of these grounds can be invoked, then the foreign arbitration award will be recognized by the domestic courts and become enforceable in the state. This means that the winning party can use the arbitration award to seize the assets of the losing party in states where the NY Convention has been ratified. This is perhaps the biggest advantage to arbitration in the international context.

---

[12] Many countries which ratified the NY Convention made a declaration that it would only apply in situations where the award emanates from another NY Convention country. This is referred to as reciprocity.

Form	Where	Costs	Third Party	Result
Litigation	Public Courts	Covered by taxpayers	Judge	Binding Judgment.
Mediation	Anywhere private, generally at an office somewhere	Covered by the parties to the mediation	Mediator, can be anyone who the parties choose	Successful mediations end in settlement agreements, which are binding contracts. Unsuccessful mediations proceed to the binding stage of dispute resolution.
Arbitration	Private Arbitration Tribunals. Can be anywhere private, generally at an office somewhere.	Covered by the parties to the arbitration.	Arbitrator, can be anyone who the parties choose.	Binding Arbitration Award.

In conclusion, various forms of dispute resolution exist, and it is important that parties entering into commercial contracts are award of the various forms available to them. This knowledge can and should be used to craft a viable dispute resolution strategy so that when a dispute arises, there is an element of predictability in terms of how and where the dispute will be resolved. In commercial contracts the dispute resolution clause is an important provision, and is not to be overlooked.

Bibliography

COLORADO REVISED STATUTES. 2015. *Dispute Resolution Act.* C.R.S. 13–22–311. http://www.lexisnexis.com/hottopics/Colorado/.

"The Arbitration Institute of the Stockholm Chamber of Commerce." 2016. Accessed March 25. http://www.sccinstitute.com/.

"ICC International Court of Arbitration." 2016. Accessed March 25. http://iccwbo.org/about-icc/organization/dispute-resolution-services/icc-international-court-of-arbitration/.

"Singapore International Arbitration Centre." 2016. Accessed March 25. http://www.siac.org.sg/.

SMITH, Chloe. 13 May 2015. "Neuberger Backs Compulsory Mediation for More Civil Cases." *Law Society Gazette*. Accessed March 25. http://www.lawgazette.co.uk/law/neuberger-backs-compulsory-mediation-for-more-civil-cases/5048784.fullarticle.

"The International Centre for Dispute Resolution." 2016. Accessed March 25. https://www.icdr.org/

"The London Court of International Arbitration (LCIA)." 2016. Accessed March 25. http://www.lcia.org/.

UNCITRAL. 1958. *Convention on the Recognition and Enforcement of Foreign Arbitral Awards (New York)*. http://www.uncitral.org/pdf/english/texts/arbitration/NY-conv/New-York-Convention-E.pdf.

———. 2016. "New York Convention Status." http://www.uncitral.org/uncitral/en/uncitral_texts/arbitration/NYConvention_status.html.

Achevé d'imprimer par Corlet Numérique - 14110 Condé-sur-Noireau
N° d'Imprimeur : 138571 - Dépôt légal : septembre 2016 - *Imprimé en France*

Information Processing in
The Nervous System

Information Processing in The Nervous System

Proceedings of a Symposium held at the
State University of New York at Buffalo
21st–24th October, 1968

Edited by

K. N. LEIBOVIC

SPRINGER-VERLAG
BERLIN · HEIDELBERG · NEW YORK
1969

Preface

In recent years, several symposia have been held on subjects relating to the general theme of information processing in the nervous system. It is now widely recognized that this whole field is rapidly developing and changing in a manner beyond our imaginings of a few years ago. When confronted with conceptual revolutions of this kind, it is justifiable to have a continued on-going discourse and disputation so that there is maximum opportunity for interaction between the leaders of thought in all the related disciplines. The conference organized by K. N. Leibovic, and held at the State University of New York at Buffalo from October 21st to 24th, 1968, made a notable contribution to this interaction. It is fortunate that there is here being published, not only the papers contributed to the symposium, but also much of the stimulating discussion.

The term "neuronal machinery" can be validly used because there is now good understanding of the operational mechanisms of at least some of the neuronal centers in the brain, and our knowledge of these mechanisms is progressing in a most encouraging manner. The stated objective by Prof. Leibovic, the organizer of the symposium, was that it was designed to correlate neuronal machinery with psychophysiological phenomena. He calls attention to the urgency of achieving a common conceptual basis for neuroanatomy, neurophysiology, and psychology. The latter discipline has been interpreted very broadly in this symposium because it merges into all considerations of the theorists in linguistics and automata theory; and of course hovering, as it were, over all of these considerations were the theoreticians with models largely of mathematical design. These models are becoming of increasing value to us neurobiologists because the model builders are now understanding much more about the actual scientific problems that confront us. It is very encouraging for us to find that more and more they are reading the neurobiological literature with greater understanding.

I think one of the most interesting features of the conference was the parallel that Dr. Longuet-Higgins drew between memory and holography. There is now good evidence, particularly that provided by Dr. Karl Pribam, that memory can be thought of in the terms of holography, and Dr. Longuet-Higgins even showed how it would be possible to construct an automaton which would be analogous to the holograph, but in the temporal domain, and which he felicitously called a holophone. There are many possible parallels which could be drawn between the holophone and brain operation. We neurobiologists must be tuned in to perceive the imaginative insights deriving from such a concept. In fact, I believe that we are ready for tremendous intellectual adventures in this new field. The mathematicians and model builders are certainly facing up in a most exciting way to the conceptual challenges offered by the brain, as may be seen in the contributions to this section by Arbib and Rosen.

Another field that was dealt with in the symposium is psychophysiology. There is a progressively expanding future for experimental investigations on problems of neuronal activity, on the one hand, and of perceptual experience, on the other. And again, models become important in developing our concepts in all these new directions.

Though we often do not know it, we neurobiologists continuously use models in designing and interpreting experiments. It is important to gain insight into the thinking of those who may be called professionals in the art of constructing models. Though we may disagree with the specific models that are presented for our instruction and inspiration, we must agree that there should be continuous efforts by theoreticians to create formal models that more and more closely simulate experimental reality. We must insist, of course, that models be continuously redesigned in the light of experiments so that they will be of use in the design of future experiments. This requires the model builders—the mathematician, the cyberneticist, and the communication theorist—to have in their respective fields, a full understanding of the existing interrelationships between models and the hypotheses developed by neurobiologists in their attempts to explain their experimental observations. Conferences such as the one published here are justified in so far as they facilitate the dialogues between experimentalists and theoreticians. We each have much to learn from the other.

JOHN C. ECCLES

Introduction

This volume contains the proceedings of the symposium "Information Processing in the Nervous System" held at the State University of New York at Buffalo from the 21st to the 24th, October, 1968.

A theme of this symposium, as Professor Eccles has pointed out in the Preface, was "neuronal machinery in relation to psychophysiology," a subject which has not received the attention it deserves. Too often anatomy, physiology, and psychology are treated in isolation. But the biological unity to which they refer needs a counterpart in our theoretical formulations. This unity must become ever more evident as our understanding is advanced by theory and experiment. In his Nobel lecture in 1967, Granit said of his early work some 30 or 40 years ago: "It seemed to me likely that psychophysical data might, with some profit to the field, be translatable into neurological equivalents." Since then, much experimental evidence has been accumulated on such problems as the neural correlates of brightness discrimination, flicker fusion, visual masking, and movement control, and now there is a newly emerging interest in the physiological basis of language. It seems that the time may be ripe for the reverse process described by Granit, namely, the translation of neurological data into psychophysiological equivalents. This is more than looking for neural analogs of behavior—it is concerned with the quantitative description of behavior in terms of neural processes.

Many recent advances were influenced directly or indirectly by theoretical developments. A dominant viewpoint has been that of automata theory, which was pioneered by McCulloch some 25 years ago. But he was by no means the last to point to its restricted framework. He called his threshold elements "impoverished neurons." New viewpoints and theories are needed. The formal basis of automata theory is mathematical logic, joined to computing theory and modern algebra. If only as a creation of our brain, we may expect mathematical logic to have something to say about the way our brains work. Language is another creation of our brain, and some would maintain that no well formed thoughts can exist without being formulated linguistically. If this be so, then what is the relationship between the mental processes which reflect mathematical logic on the one hand and those which reflect the comparative vagueness, redundancy and apparently illogical aspects of language on the other hand? Moreover, well formed thoughts do not account for all brain processes—in fact, they probably constitute a small fraction of total brain activity. We must study not only the manifestations of the brain in thought and behavior—we must study it as a physiological organ.

Little as we know of the physiology of memory, we cannot for long remain unaware of its importance. To take the example of language again: in speech we communicate by means of temporal sound sequences, in which nearest word neighbors are not necessarily logically closest, but are placed according to rules of grammar which may appear arbitrary. Clearly, there must be a short term memory store, where groups of words can be processed as a whole. But, this is not peculiar to language. It occurs in sensory perception, for example in vision, and in various central nervous system operations. A short term visual memory has been shown to exist experimentally, and some of its characteristics can be studied by means of masking experiments which reveal peripheral and central effects.

In order to understand such phenomena and relate them to the activities of nerve cells, it is necessary to pool knowledge from many specialized fields. This need was reflected in the program of the symposium and in the contributions which are reproduced in this volume.

The first part deals with automata theory. In this Arbib, reviews some of the developments in relation to brain models and discusses the status of present work on stimulus-response theory, pattern recognition and complexity of computation. Rosen considers the problem of hierarchical theories which describe events at molecular and macroscopic levels or at the single cell and organ levels. He is concerned with the basic premises of automata theory and its applicability to models of the nervous system. Longuet-Higgins represents the view that automata theory need not be confined to the mathematical techniques described earlier, but is legitimately concerned with the theory of "intelligent" automata. He considers an ingenious device, the "holophone" which has some intriguing analogies to biological memory.

The second part deals with linguistics, a field which has been influenced significantly by mathematical logic. Peters considers the structure of language and its automata theoretic formulation, as developed, e.g., by Chomsky. He points out some constraints on brain models imposed by the theory. Wickelgren addresses himself to the problem of context in speech perception, while Liberman deals with some deep problems of the physiological basis of speech and language by analyzing the detailed relationships between phonological and acoustic elements.

The third part is on psychophysiology. Haber describes some experiments dealing with short term memory. He shows that even without visual persistence, successive visual stimuli are somehow integrated so that their recognition is improved. He distinguishes between clarity of presentation at a peripheral level and recognition, the latter involving central processes. Haber uses visual noise as a mask, and masking is the subject of Schiller's contribution which relates psychophysics directly to neural responses. Masking is a powerful technique which is likely to reveal many more interesting results in the future, since it allows one to study in a controlled manner the interference of successive stimuli. An example is Boynton's little paper dealing with Bloch's law, in which he shows that there must be a stage in the visual system where stimuli are weighted depending on their intensity or duration, and that this stage is followed by another during which summation takes place.

The fourth part is concerned primarily with physiology. Barlow adduces evidence for the proposition that increasingly fewer impulses are transmitted, but in more numerous fibers, as information is relayed in the visual pathway. He considers this in relation to the increasing response specificity of single neurons. Brooks recounts his and his colleagues' important and fascinating findings on the organization of the functional columns, in the motorsensory cortex (MS 1). Eccles is concerned with cerebellar function, to the understanding of which he has contributed so much; and he describes the dynamic loops between this organ, the cerebrum, the midbrain, and the spinal centers. The cerebellum functions moment to moment in close conjunction with the ongoing movement, with the latter being itself an active part of the control loop.

The fifth part contains papers on models and theory. Leibovic and Sabah consider the transformations of signals at synapses and in nerve membranes with a view to a better understanding of the neuronal basis of psychophysiology. McCulloch and Kilmer describe their present work on a computer model of the reticular formation. Reiss addresses himself to the problem of finding significant observables among a system of 10^{10} units and a super-astronomical number of possible states. Schmitt appeals for a theory of "interpenetrating domains" to reflect biological coupling. This might unify, for example, the treatment of the various processes occurring in axoplasm, nerve membranes, and interstitial fluid of a nerve net.

The sixth part contains the concluding discussions on some general topics: information theory, neural coding, interdisciplinary communication, and education.

Thus, the subject matter of the symposium covers the spectrum from the activity of the single cell to that of the organ and the responses of the whole man in psychophysical experiments. The specialized developments remain within the context of a broader perspective.

Theory and experiment are both strongly represented. Some theory can necessarily be only suggestive of possible meaning, rather than explanatory or predictive. Some experimental data may be only observational. But we need to look before we can understand, and yet, we see little more than we understand. This is why it is so important to have good communication between theoreticians and experimentalists, and this was achieved, in large measure, at this symposium.

The size of the symposium was small enough for the participants to interact freely, and yet it was large enough for each specialized group to make a significant contribution.

At the opening of the meeting the participants were welcomed on behalf of University President Meyerson by Dr. F. M. Snell, then Dean of the Graduate School, and past Chairman of the Department of Biophysical Sciences.

There was a special occasion due to the near coincidence of the date of the symposium with Warren McCulloch's 70th birthday, and he was duly honored, especially in the sessions on automata theory and on theory and models at which he presented his paper on digital oscillators.

At a time of financial stringency it was gratifying to have the support of University funds channeled through the Graduate School of the State University of New York at Buffalo, the departments of Biophysical Sciences, Computer Science and Mathematics of the University, and the Clynes Biocybernetic Foundation. The sponsors of the symposium included the J. C. Eccles Laboratory of Neurobiology, the above named University departments, the Center for Theoretical Biology at SUNY/B and last, but not least, the Center for Visual Science of the University of Rochester. The symposium owed its success to all these, to the lively contributions of the participants, and to numerous helpers in organizing it, among whom Mrs. Margaret Smith deserves special mention.

Finally, it is appropriate to acknowledge the help and expertise of the publishers in producing this volume.

THE EDITOR

Sadly, Warren McCulloch died after this volume went to press. His memory will live with the many he has inspired.

ED.

Symposium Participants

ABEL, S. M., Department of Psychology, McMasters University, Hamilton, Ontario, Canada

ANNINOS, P., Department of Physics, Syracuse University, Syracuse, New York

ARBIB, M. A., Stanford Electronics Laboratories, Stanford University, Stanford, California

AXELROD, S., Department of Psychiatry, State University of New York at Buffalo, Buffalo, New York

BALSLEV, E., Department of Mathematics, State University of New York at Buffalo, 4246 Ridge Lea Road, Amherst, New York

BARLOW, H. B., Department of Physiology-Anatomy, University of California at Berkeley, 2570 Life Sciences Building, Berkeley, California

BELLINO, F., Center for Theoretical Biology, and Department of Biophysical Sciences, State University of New York at Buffalo, 4234 Ridge Lea Road, Amherst, New York

BIANCHI, L. M., Center for Theoretical Biology, State University of New York at Buffalo, 4248 Ridge Lea Road, Amherst, New York

BLUM, H., National Institutes of Health, Department of Health, Education & Welfare, Division Computer Research Technology, Building 12A, Bethesda, Maryland

BOYNTON, R. M., Director of the Center for Visual Science, University of Rochester, River Campus Station, Rochester, New York

BRIGHT, P. B., Center for Theoretical Biology, State University of New York at Buffalo, 4248 Ridge Lea Road, Amherst, New York

BROOKS, V. B., Department of Physiology, New York Medical College, Flower & Fifth Avenue Hospitals, Fifth Avenue at 106th Street, New York City, New York

CAMPBELL, D., Department of Psychology, State University of New York at Bulaffo, Buffalo, New York

CLYNES, M., Chief Research Scientist & Director, Rockland State Hospital, Biocybernetics Laboratories, Orangeburg, New York

CORWIN, T., Center for Visual Science, University of Rochester, Rochester, New York

CROCKER, J. R., Loyola University of Chicago, 6525 North Sheridan Road, Chicago, Illinois

CSERMELY, T., State University of New York, Upstate Medical Center, Department of Physiology, 766 Irving Avenue, Syracuse, New York

DAINOFF, M., Center for Visual Science, University of Rochester, Rochester, New York

DANIELLI, J. F., Director, Center for Theoretical Biology, State University of New York at Buffalo, 4248 Ridge Lea Road, Amherst, New York

DIX, D., Department of Biochemistry, State University of New York at Buffalo, Buffalo, New York

DYER, R. S., Department of Psychology, State University of New York at Buffalo, Buffalo, New York

ECCLES, SIR JOHN C., Laboratory of Neurobiology, State University of New York at Buffalo, 4234 Ridge Lea Road, Amherst, New York

FINDLER, N. V., Department of Computer Sciences, State University of New York at Buffalo, 4250 Ridge Lea Road, Amherst, New York

HABER, R. N., Chairman, Department of Psychology, College of Arts & Sciences, University of Rochester, River Campus Station, Rochester, New York

HAMANN, J. R., Center for Theoretical Biology, State University of New York at Buffalo, 4248 Ridge Lea Road, Amherst, New York

HARTH, E. M., Syracuse University, Department of Physics, Syracuse, New York

HAYS, D. G., Director, Program in Linguistics, State University of New York at Buffalo, 301 Foster Hall, Buffalo, New York

HILGARTNER, C., Center for Theoretical Biology, State University of New York at Buffalo, 4248 Ridge Lea Road, Amherst, New York

HULL, E. M., Department of Psychology, State University of New York at Buffalo, 107 Vivarium, Buffalo, New York

IRELAND, L., Department of Psychology, State University of New York at Buffalo, 107 Vivarium, Buffalo, New York

KILMER, W. J., Department of Electrical Engineering, Engineering Building, Michigan State University, East Lansing, Michigan

KINTZ, R. T., Center for Visual Science, University of Rochester, Rochester, New York

LEBOVITZ, R. M., Department of Biophysical Sciences, State University of New York at Buffalo, 4248 Ridge Lea Road, Amherst, New York

LEIBOVIC, K. N., Department of Biophysical Sciences, State University of New York at Buffalo, 4234 Ridge Lea Road, Amherst, New York

LEITNER, M., School of Medicine, State University of New York at Buffalo, Buffalo, New York

LIBERMAN, A. M., Department of Psychology, The University of Connecticut, The College of Liberal Arts & Sciences, Storrs, Connecticut

LINDSAY, R. D., Department of Physics, Syracuse University, Syracuse, New York

LONGUET-HIGGINS, H. C., University of Edinburgh, Department of Machine Intelligence & Perception, 2 Buccleuch Place, Edinburgh, Scotland

LORINSTEIN, I. B., University of Rochester, Department of Psychology, Rochester, New York

LOWN, B., Department of Psychology, State University of New York at Buffalo, Buffalo, New York

MATHIESON, T., Department of Biophysical Sciences, State University of New York at Buffalo, 4234 Ridge Lea Road, Amherst, New York

McCULLOCH, W. S., Research Laboratory of Electronics, Massachusetts Institute of Technology, Cambridge, Massachusetts

NOELL, W. K., Department of Physiology, State University of New York at Buffalo, 2211 Main Street, Buffalo, New York

PERTILE, G., Department of Physics, Syracuse University, Syracuse, New York

PETERS, P. S., Department of Linguistics, University of Texas, College of Arts & Sciences, Austin, Texas

REISS, R. F., Oakridge, Red Copse Lane, Boars Hill, Oxford, England

ROSEN, R., Center for Theoretical Biology, State University of New York at Buffalo, 4248 Ridge Lea Road, Amherst, New York

RUSHTON, W. A. H., Florida State University, Institute of Molecular Biophysics, Tallahassee, Florida

SABAH, N. H., Department of Biophysical Sciences, State University of New York at Buffalo, 4234 Ridge Lea Road, Amherst, New York

SCHILLER, P. H., Department of Psychology, Massachusetts Institute of Technology, Cambridge, Massachusetts

SCHMITT, O. H., Department of Electrical Engineering, University of Minnesota, Minneapolis, Minnesota

SELKOW, S., National Institutes of Health, Room 2051, Building 12A, 9000 Rockville Pike, Bethesda, Maryland

SINGER, A. M., Graphic Controls Corp., 189 Van Rensselaer Street, Buffalo, New York

SMITH, B. H., Department of Neurology, Meyer Memorial Hospital, Buffalo, New York

SMITH, C. E., Department of Biology, State University of New York at Buffalo, Buffalo, New York

SMITH, G. K., Department of Psychology, McMaster University, Hamilton, Ontario, Canada

SREBRO, R., Neurosensory Laboratory, State University of New York at Buffalo, 2211 Main Street, Buffalo, New York

STANDING, L., Department of Psychology, University of Rochester, Rochester, New York

TRABKA, E., Kodak Research Laboratories, Building 81, Kodak Park, Rochester, New York

TURKEL, J., Department of Psychology, McMaster University, Hamilton, Ontario, Canada

WALLEN, D., Center for Visual Science, University of Rochester, Rochester, New York

WEISSTEIN, N., Department of Psychology, Loyola University, 6525 North Sheridan Road, Chicago, Illinois

WHALEY, D., Department of Biophysical Sciences, State University of New York at Buffalo, 4234 Ridge Lea Road, Amherst, New York

WICKELGREN, W. A., Department of Psychology, Massachusetts Institute of Technology, Cambridge, Massachusetts

WISSLER, F. C., Department of Biophysics Research, Roswell Park Memorial Institute, Buffalo, New York

YOUNG, F. C., 202 Harvard Place, Syracuse, New York

ZUCKERMAN, R., Center for Visual Sciences, University of Rochester, Rochester, New York

Contents

Part I

AUTOMATA THEORY

MICHAEL A. ARBIB
Stanford University
Stanford, California

1 · *Automata Theory as an Abstract Boundary Condition for the Study of Information Processing in the Nervous System*

I. Introductory Remarks

This conference convenes 25 years after Warren McCulloch and Walter Pitts (1943) initiated the automaton-theoretic approach to information processing in the nervous system with their paper "A Logical Calculus of the Ideas Immanent in Nervous Activity," and a few weeks before Warren McCulloch celebrates his 70th birthday. I should thus like to dedicate this paper to Warren McCulloch, in honor of his continuing stimulation to many who would understand "What's in the Brain that Ink may Character?" [McCulloch, 1965].

McCulloch and Pitts noted the following properties of real neurons: that they had many inputs and one output which could branch toward other neurons, that some of the inputs were excitatory (had positive weights) and some were inhibitory (had negative weights), and that the neuron would only fire if the excitation on its inputs exceeded the inhibition by a certain critical threshold. They simplified the model by assuming that the neuron acted in a synchronous fashion, so that on some absolute time scale we could speak about the inputs at time t to any neuron determining the output at time $t + 1$. In view of the critical importance of variable frequencies, interaction of afferents, spontaneous activity, burst coding, and so on, in actual nervous systems, we see that this is a gross oversimplification (see, e.g., sec. 2.2 of Arbib, in press). Nonetheless, it plays a

3

crucial role in our understanding of the possibilities of nervous activity. If we consider networks of such formal neurons, we may observe that there is a set of inputs, namely the possible binary vectors describing firing patterns of those neural input lines which are not connected to other neurons of the net—a set of internal states, namely the binary vector describing the firing pattern of the output lines of all neurons in the net—and an output set, namely the collection of binary patterns on those output lines of neurons which actually emerge from the network rather than being fed back to other neurons within the net.

Recalling the critical time-scale assumption on the neurons, we may see that the state and input of the whole net at any one time determine the state of the whole net at the next time—for, to determine the firing of a neuron we must know the previous firing pattern of its inputs, and this is determined partly by the overall input to the network and, for those lines which come from other neurons, by the state of the network. Thus specifying the function of each neuron and the connectivity of the neural network determines a next-state function, which lets us update the state at each time once we know the input. Further, since the output at any time is just the firing pattern on a subset of those lines which determine the state at any time, we see clearly that there is a function which determines the present output solely in terms of the present state.

The crucial point to observe here is that the current output of the automaton need in no sense be a response to the current input regarded as a stimulus. Rather, the firing of those neurons which feed the output can be influenced by activity within the network reflecting quite ancient history of the system. In any case, we recognize from the above discussion that any McCulloch-Pitts network is an example of what is called a finite automaton or sequential machine (Arbib, 1969, chap. 1). Formally: a finite automaton is a quintuple (X,Y,Q,δ,β) where X is a finite set (the set of inputs), Y is a finite set (the set of outputs), Q is a finite set (the set of states), and $\delta:Q \times X \to Q$ is the next state function and $\beta:Q \to Y$ is the output function. Thus if the system is in state q and receives input x at time t, then its output pattern will be $\beta(q)$ at time t, and it will change to state $\delta(q,x)$ at time $t + 1$. Conversely, we may note that for every finite automaton there is a McCulloch-Pitts network with corresponding behavior (for a proof see Arbib, 1969, chap. 3; or Arbib, 1964, chap. 1).

The study of finite automata is one of the essential problems of automata theory, but it must be admitted that nowadays most automata theorists treat this as a formal system and explore its mathematical properties rather than being interested in relating it to the neural model of McCulloch and Pitts.

We have seen that one root of current automata theory is the notion of finite automaton, an outgrowth of the McCulloch-Pitts network. The

other main root of automata theory is the notion of what is now called a
Turing machine, which was first set forth by Turing (1936) and Post
(1936) as one possible formalization of the notion of an algorithm or
effective procedure. Here we may contrast the availability of an algorithm
for finding the highest common factor of two numbers with the way in
which we find a proof for a given theorem. We use hunches, intuition, and
experience on related problems. Even if we could make explicit all the
steps whereby we had generated a proof for a given statement, we would
not—except in extremely restricted domains of mathematics—feel able
to guarantee that this description could be turned into a recipe which would
work in producing a proof for any given theorem. The metamathematicians
of the 1930's sought to know whether this was a result of current limitations
of our understanding of the mental processes of the mathematician, or
whether in fact there was no possible way of finding a recipe which could
work for all possible theorems. But, of course, one could not prove theorems about *this* problem, unless one had a formalized notion of effective
procedure. Many different definitions were generated, but they all turned
out to be equivalent to or weaker than the notion of "computable by a
Turing machine."

We may view a Turing machine as consisting of a finite tape divided
into squares, each of which may bear a single symbol from some fixed
set, together with a control box, containing a finite program, which can
move back and forth along the tape scanning a single square at a time.
The finite program is such that each instruction, except for the halt instruction, consists of a process of testing the square under scan, and on
the basis of the symbol observed printing another, possibly the same,
symbol on the square, moving the control box one square to left or right
along the tape, and finally jumping to a new instruction of the program.
We start a computation by placing the control box executing its first instruction on the left-hand square of the tape bearing the initial data. If the
control box comes to either end of the tape, we add new blank squares
as desired. Further, we note that for a given input the machine may halt
eventually, or may go into various endless loops. Thus we may associate
with each Turing machine a function from strings of symbols to strings of
symbols, which is partial in that for some of the input values no result
may be defined.

We should note that many changes can be made in Turing's original
model. For instance, we may consider Turing machines in which the control box controls many heads on many different tapes, perhaps some of
the tapes even being multidimensional. However, it can be proved (see,
e.g., Arbib, 1969, chap. 4) that the functions computable by these machines are all computable by the conventional one-head, one-tape, one-
dimensional machine. What we do gain by using more complicated machines is speed and efficiency. For instance, Barzdin (1965) has proved

that no machine with one head can tell whether or not a word is sym-metric, i.e., is a palindrome, in less than a time that increases propor-tionately with the square of the length of the word; whereas it is easy to see if we have two heads we may move the heads to the opposite end of the tape and have them move in to the middle, reporting back to the con-trol, so that when they meet, in a time that only goes up with the length of the tape, they will have been able to tell whether or not the string is a palindrome. Here is an extremely important question for automata theory: given a problem, what is the computing structure best suited to it? For instance, I presume that one could rigorously prove that adding extra heads to the two-head machine could not make its recognition of palin-dromes any more efficient, and so the two-head structure is the one most suited for a device for recognizing palindromes. We may note, too, that authors such as Wang (1957) and Minsky (1967) have shown that even simpler instruction sets than that of the Turing machine suffice to give us all effective procedures—the price one pays is even less efficiency than that of the Turing machine. We thus see the need to understand better the tradeoff between complexity of the "genetic" structures, and the complexity of the computations which take place within those structures.

Turing (1936) was able to give, in terms of his machines, an elegant proof of a result which had been discovered somewhat earlier by Church—namely that there was no effective procedure whereby one could tell of a given statement whether or not it was a theorem in the theory of numbers. If we cannot tell of a statement whether or not it is a theorem, we are certainly in no position to provide a proof for every statement when it is a theorem. Thus, we are assured that our inability to think of an effective procedure for going from theorems to their proofs is not a result of the present limitations of our knowledge, but is an inescapable consequence of the finitely based nature of effective procedures. Of course, there is nothing in this theorem to deny the well-established fact that for many important subclasses of possible types of mathematical statements, effec-tive procedures do exist to tell whether or not they are theorems, and to provide proofs when they do exist.

We may now see the connection between the work of Turing, and the work of McCulloch and Pitts. For it is clear that the control box of a Turing machine may be regarded as a finite automaton, and so, if we regard a brain as being a neural network, then we may view the work of McCulloch and Pitts as telling us that every Turing machine has a formal "brain." However, whereas the memory of the finite automaton is purely limited by its internal state, the memory of the Turing machine resides not only in the current state of execution of its program, but also in the array of symbols on its expandable tape, so that there is no fixed bound on the amount of memory such a device may possess. In a sense, we may regard the work of Turing as the first application of automata theory to psychology, and the work of McCulloch and Pitts as the first application of automata theory to neurophysiology—and we have the satisfying result that there is an underlying neurophysiological mechanism for each psychological activity—at least in this restricted world of synchronized processes and effective procedures using discrete alphabets. The finite automaton is by no means the best model for information processing in the nervous system. We have already mentioned that it comes from a very schematic view of the possibilities of neuronal processing. But we should also note that in the theory of finite automata we are only modeling the passive behavior of the neural network, seeing how an externally selected sequence of inputs is processed by the network to produce a sequence of outputs. By contrast, in the theory of Turing machines, we may regard, in some sense, the tape as being the world's simplest model of an environment, and so we see that the organism can change its environment and can move back and forth within the environment so that the actual sequence of inputs presented to the network or control box is no longer determined completely externally, but is also determined in large part by the organism itself. Thus behavior gains new complexities when we allow a dynamic interaction between the organism and the environment, since it can be proved that finite automaton computations lie very low indeed on the hierarchy of all effective symbol-manipulations (Ritchie, 1963).

Another limitation of the ordinary finite automaton model is that we consider the next-state function fixed. In fact, we must also study how the next-state function changes in time. This is one of the places in which the hierarchical approach (Rosen, this volume) pays off—at one level and on one time scale we study the immediate activity of the animal, whereas at another level of the hierarchy and on a longer time scale we see how the underlying processes of that activity change with time. One model for this process is presented by Longuet-Higgins in his paper (Longuet-Higgins, this volume). One could introduce a huge, but still finite, state-space to encompass not only the state of activity, but also the state of learning. However, this multiplicity of states obscures the essence of the computational process revealed by considering a smaller state-space, activity in which changes the dynamics over time.

Automata theory began to gain momentum from 1951 on, and gained a larger audience with the publication of "Automata Studies," a collection edited by Claude Shannon and John McCarthy (1956). In this collection, we still see that a preoccupation of many of the workers is with questions in psychology and neurophysiology. In the twelve years since then, however, automata theory has expanded greatly and so now there are many well formalized mathematical problems in the area—and it is probably true that well over 95% of all current automata theorists act as what might be called pure applied mathematicians exploring the implications of various formalized properties of automata, without any professional interest in their bearing upon questions of information processing in the nervous system. Nonetheless, amongst this plethora of mathematical research, there do exist a number of results and trends of research which are relevant to our current problem, and it is my task in the rest of this paper to introduce you to some of these problems, and to indicate why, in spite of the great gap between this type of theory and current experimental problems in brain research, I believe, nonetheless, that automata theory does have great contributions to make to the neurosciences.

II. The Relationship of Automata Theory to Stimulus-Response Theories

My first task is to emphasize the new power which automata theories give us over conventional stimulus-response theories of the organism. Any real theory of behavior must take account of the fact that the current action of the animal need not be at all tied to the current sensory bombardment. The animal is active in its perception, seeking to find information from the environment, and as often as not we may gain insight by regarding the action of the animal as a stimulus to the environment, and the sensory information—which may or may not be ignored by the animal—as the response of the environment. In their book *Plans and the Structure of Behavior,* Miller, Galanter and Pribram (1959) (see also Minsky, 1961 and Arbib, 1970) have pointed out that stimulus response theory, besides these perceptual shortcomings, cannot take account of plan and intention. The authors propose, instead, a model which they call a TOTE hierarchy— which is, in fact, a certain type of finite automaton—as a model of behavior which can take these into account. Interestingly enough, Suppes (1968) in a recent article entitled "Stimulus Response Theory of Finite Automata," has claimed, in fact, that he can show the existence of a stimulus-response reinforcement schedule which will make an organism act asymptotically like any given finite automaton; and thus he claims to have shown—contra Miller, Galanter and Pribram—that stimulus response theory does indeed subsume plan and intention. However, Suppes' proof that, given any finite automaton, there is a reinforcement schedule that can get asymptotic performance prescribed by that automaton, involves some hidden assumptions (Arbib, in press *a*) which vitiate the claim that the models of plan and intention provided by Miller, Galanter and Pribram are thus subsumed into stimulus-response theory. Briefly, the assumptions are these: firstly, that the states of the automaton must correspond to distinct responses of the organism; secondly, that the stimulus to the organism at any trial must consist of two components, one of which is an externally applied stimulus, and the other of which is a complete indicator of the animal's response at the previous trial; and thirdly, that the distinct inputs of the automaton correspond to distinct externally applied stimuli. The

third assumption is that of the automata theory approach, and so we take
no exception to it. However, the first two assumptions ask that we throw
away all the state information contributed by the neurons within the network, and only keep that state information provided by the neurons which
feed the output lines of the network. Of course, if we accept the input to
all neurons of the network as constituting the total stimulus, no matter
how deeply buried the neurons are within the net, then any automata
theorist is a stimulus-response theorist, and the whole argument is vacuous.
However, if we actually demand that the output which encodes the state
is purely external, then we are forcing the animal to make an incredible
number of distinctions. I have argued elsewhere (Arbib, in press a) that
655,360 state-input pairs is a reasonably small number for a TOTE hierarchy, but an extremely high number for a set of discriminable stimuli in
a classical reinforcement schedule. If we allow one minute for the learning
of each stimulus-response pair, and work a ten-hour day, it will still take
the organism three years to master such a TOTE hierarchy, which would
be but one of thousands for any complex organism. Our conclusion, then,
is that whereas certain simple forms of memory can in fact be obtained with
stimulus-response schemes, nonetheless, for truly complex planned and
motivated behavior, we need large numbers of states which can only be
encoded internally, rather than in terms of overt responses. We learn to
behave in ways conditioned by complex hierarchies simply because they
are hierarchical; thus, by learning a few simple schemes and ways to
interrelate them, we can in a reasonable time master that which a reinforcement schedule would insist that we learn item by item over a period
of years.

Another problem with stimulus-response theory is that it assumes, usually, that the animal knows what we consider to be the stimulus and the
response. Thus, we may present many different patterns of visual stimulation, knowing that one set of these patterns corresponds to a letter A
and another set corresponds to a letter B. It is usually a distinct problem
from that considered by the stimulus-response theorist to provide a mechanism for the stimulus generalization whereby the animal can accept patterns in the two different classes as corresponding to simply two different stimuli. The whole area of pattern recognition theory addresses itself to
this problem. Similarly, we may note that a response of an animal may be
expressed in a staggering variety of different patterns of muscular coordination. For instance, once a rat has learned to run a maze, he may do this
in the normal fashion, in a flooded maze by swimming, or with his legs
tied by rolling over in the appropriate directions. Thus, many different
actual patterns of activation can yield the same "response." Again, it is
an extremely important study for us, transcending the work of the stimulus-
response theorist, to understand what manner of neutral network can fashion
such activity.

Automata theory provides algorithms for going from the function which describes how each sequence of stimuli presented to a finite automaton in an initial state yields the response at the end of the sequence, to an internal state description of the machine (Moore, 1956, Arbib and Zeiger, 1969). Thus, if we are to allow the infinitely many superstimuli consisting of arbitrary, finite sequences of ordinary stimuli, then building up a complete stimulus-response table does indeed build up a complete automaton behavior. However, this does not seem to be the issue. The stimulus–response theorist would seem to associate the stimulus with the present moment, and to explicitly deny that we must take account of a complicated history of stimulation to understand the effect of the present stimulus in producing a response. Presently, more sophisticated stimulus-response models do seem to allow states of need and states of conditioning, but these are only minor modifications to a theory which looks at the present response in terms of immediate stimulation. On the contrary, I would argue that a much better—though still grossly simplified—approximation would view the animal as executing a program, so that the present input may be either ignored or changed by the organism, or incorporated into its current activity, depending on where it is in the execution of its program. Further, it is misleading to view the present action as being a response even to a whole history of input stimulation, so the great virtue of automata theory is to stress that a relatively small number of states may serve to code the salient features of many different input histories. For instance, it is much less efficient for an animal to remember every place that it has ever found food, than it is for the animal to have some trace like "food is abundant, so go anywhere to find it" or "food is scarce, and the best strategy is to go down to the river bank and prowl back and forth there." We see the problem of encoding long stimulus-response histories into a form which will allow the animal to retrieve relevant information quickly to guide his future actions.

Although automata and systems theory can give us the complete answer to the identification problem of how to go from the external behavior of a system to a description of its internal behavior in that it can provide the minimal realization of any input-output behavior, there is no guarantee that this minimal realization is in fact the actual one. However, such a realization may prove most useful in guiding our experimental investigation of the contributions of different subsystems to the overall structure. Again, however, we must emphasize that the algorithms are only efficient if the number of states of the system is small (and since there are well over ten billion neurons in the brain and well over two states per neuron, we have well over $2^{10^{10}}$ states, a number with respect to which any algorithm proves pale indeed) or if the system is linear and the dimension of the state space is small (Arbib and Zeiger, 1969). Since the brain is not a particularly linear device, we have a great deal of theory ahead of us in finding gross states of the organism to which such a theory can be applied and approximation methods which will help us see how to handle nonlinear systems without involving ourselves in the full cardinality of the state set. The experimenter, on the other hand, has the task of finding significant subsystems to which existing theory can be meaningfully, if not completely rigorously, applied.

Another question about which automata theory can give rigorous general answers (Arbib, 1968—see especially the chapters by Krohn, Rhodes, and Tilson; Hartmanis and Stearns, 1966), but ones which unfortunately are not amenable to simple computation even for systems far less complex than the brain, is the problem of decomposition: given an overall behavior of a system, how can we find simpler systems which can be connected in some simple way to yield the same overall behavior? Even though we cannot expect these subsystems to necessarily be *the* subsystems present in the real brain, again we may expect that knowledge that such subsystems can be important may well lead us to crucial experiments on brain structure.

This discussion emphasizes that to understand complex behavior it will not even be satisfactory to use the classical description of finite automata which specifies the next state for every state-input pair. Rather, we must see how various small automata are built up, one upon the other, in a hierarchical fashion. It may be that the simplest building blocks of behavior do take years to fashion in a manner upon which Suppes' theorem throws some light, but to really understand the way in which humans learn to behave, we must see how learning can be accumulative, with the learning of one time period forming the building blocks for the higher order learning of the next (Arbib, in press, chap. 3).

III. Complexity of Computation in Relation to Neural Processing

Evolutionary advantage may accrue to an organism in changes in the metabolic range of the organism, with new enzymes allowing the organism to utilize new materials as foodstuffs; to study their advantages for the organism, it would seem that the biochemist is far better suited than the automata theorist. Another type of important genetic change may lead to what we might call gross structural changes, such as, limbs better adapted for motion in a certain type of environment which, for example, may allow an animal to live in the hills rather than the plains, or teeth better adapted for combat and eating of certain types of prey. Here it would seem that the structural engineer or the physicist of classical mechanics can tell more than the automata theorist.

It is at a third level of change that the automata theorist would seem to be able to make the most significant contribution; namely, that of information processing in the nervous system. Here we try to analyze how, for an animal with a given metabolic machinery and a given gross structure, changes in its receptor organization and its ability to combine present information with past experience can best contribute to its improved handling of its environment. An animal can survive better in an environment if it has receptors which can detect an enemy far away; but these receptors are only useful if the animal can compute on that information to find appropriate avoiding action before the enemy is upon it. Even more useful is the development of language in man, which enables us to learn how to avoid an enemy without having had to go through such a close scrape as nearly being captured in the past.

A task of automata theory then is to try to learn how much computation can be done in a given time, and further, for a given task to study how complex a computation or network is required. Of course, a time will come when this approach must be integrated with the biochemical and the structural approach, for it is no good detecting a certain type of foodstuff if one cannot metabolize it, and it is no good detecting an enemy if one has neither the ability to fight it nor to run away from it. We may note here that much of man's development has come from the discovery of things like cooking and tools which allow him to change his metabolic and structural interface with the environment around him.

Evolution proceeds on the basis of cooperation as well as on the basis of competition—man eats better because he increases the number of edible plants and domestic animals. An animal that was too efficient at capturing its prey might extinguish its food supply, whereas an animal that was too clever at eluding its enemy might in turn lead to the extinction of the enemy. There seem to be some interesting higher-level questions involved with what is the optimum imperfection in a computational system involving many species of animals so that the ecological balance will be maintained in an optimal fashion.

With this in mind, we can see that a crucial question for automata theory must be the study of complexity of computation—for instance, to understand how long a network of given components must take to compute a certain function, or what is the range of functions that can be computed by networks of a given structure. We shall give some examples of such theory, but we should stress how far removed such theory remains from the full complexity of the biological situation. For instance, we might want theorems which would enable us to tell whether the ganglion cells in the retina of a frog are optimum for an animal which essentially lives in ponds and feeds on flies. It seems that they are fairly well suited since the brain of the animal receives direct information about the presence of food and enemies within the visual field (Lettvin, *et al.,* 1959)—but the price the animal pays is that it is limited in flexibility of response because its information is so directly coded. A cat (Hubel and Wiesel, 1962), on the other hand, has to process a greater amount of information to be able to find its prey—but has the advantage, presumably, that mice are more nutritious than flies. The animal cannot compute its appropriate action as quickly, perhaps, as the frog can—but it makes up for this in that it has extra computational machinery which enables it to predict and to make use of previous experience in developing a strategy in governing its action. We should note that even here we see the interrelationship between the automata theory level of computation and the nutritional and structural levels. Again we have some appreciation of the complexity involved, because we see that to adequately model the behavior of the animal we must make an adequate model of its environment, and it is highly dubious that we can adequately set limits to this model at this time. We should note, too, that our model is not simply computational but must take into account structural features of the animal. It is not enough to work out an optimum network whereby a frog can locate a fly, but we must also compute whether it is optimal to couple that network to the frog's tongue, or have the frog bat the fly out of the air with its forelimb, or to have the frog jump up to catch the fly in its mouth. Clearly, the evolution of receptors, effectors and central computing machinery will be completely interwoven—and it is only for simplicity of analysis that we shall find it expedient for much of the time to concentrate on the computational aspects, holding much of the environmental and effector parameters fixed.

One problem of the theory of pattern recognition is to compute the most effective features to be used in characterizing a certain object in the environment. For instance, to characterize a mouse one could go into many details which might even include the placement of hairs upon its back, but for a cat it is perhaps enough to recognize a mobile object within a certain size range, of a gray or brown color, with pointed ears. It should be clear that this problem must depend again, upon the environment. If there exists a creature which meets the above prescription for a mouse but happens to be poisonous, then it will clearly be necessary for a successful species of cat to have a perceptual system which can detect features which will enable the cat to discriminate the poisonous creatures from the genuine edible mice.

With these strictures in mind, let us turn to mathematical theory, realizing that at present it cannot be "plugged in" to solve biological problems, but may help us refine the questions we ask of the experimenter and may suggest important new ways of interpreting his results.

Let us consider the question of what the quickest way is that a function can be computed by a network in which we place some limitations upon the complexity of components. Winograd (1967) and, later, Spira and Arbib (1967) and Spira (1968) studied networks whose components were limited in that there was a fixed bound on the number of input lines to any component. Otherwise, the elements were like McCulloch-Pitts neurons, though there was no limitation upon what Boolean function they could compute of their inputs. Clearly, if we have components with only two input lines, then there is no way of combining information distributed over four input lines to yield information on one output line that takes less than two time delays. In fact, if the input-output function is at all complicated, then considerably more time may in fact be required. The contribution of the researchers on this topic was to show that for a certain class of mathematical functions one could prove that no possible scheme of wiring "neurons" could compute the function in less than a certain time delay intimately related to the structure of the function. In particular it was shown how to go from the structure of a finite group to a minimal time for a network which computed the group multiplication. Further, Spira was able to provide for any group a network which was time-optimal, in that it produced its output within one time unit of the time specified by the previously mentioned theorem. We thus have here an extremely important result for any theory of neural networks, namely we can show for a certain type of restricted component how to build a network which is actually optimal with respect to the time required for computing. However, to appreciate the full complexity that lies ahead of the automata theorist who would contribute to the study of information processing in the nervous system, we must make several observations. Firstly, to achieve time optimality in his network, Spira had to use an extremely redundant encoding for the input and output to ensure that "the right information would be in the right place at the right time." (The reader may wish to compare this with Barlow's observation, in the present volume, that as we move up into the visual cortex, what we reduce is not the number of channels but rather the activity of the channels, as each will respond only to more and more specific stimuli.) The result is a network with many, many neurons in parallel, even though the network is rather shallow in terms of computation time. It might well be that we could save many neurons at the price of increased computation time, both by narrowing the net but increasing its depth, and also by using feedback to allow recirculation of information for quite a long time before the correct result emerges. We see here the need for a critical investigation of the interplay between space and time in the design of networks. Secondly, we should note that the really first-class results here have only gone through for groups, where we can make use of the mathematical theory elaborated over the past hundred years. It will be much harder to prove equally valuable theorems about functions which are not related to classical mathematical structures. Thirdly, we have made a very simple restriction upon the components. If we are to move towards more realistic neurons, with much greater complexity, or if we are to replace the simple limitation on number of inputs assumption by an assumption limiting the actual types of functions that the neurons can compute, then we shall have to expect a great increase in the complexity of the theory. Some would conclude from this analysis that automata theory is irrelevant to our study of the nervous system, but I would argue that it simply shows how determined our study of automata theory must be before we can hope to really understand the function of the nervous system.

To complement the work of Winograd and Spira, let us briefly recall the work of Minsky and Papert (1967) on pattern recognition. They consider a "retina" divided up into squares from each of which proceeds the input line for a network which consists of a single layer of "neurons" whose outputs feed into a threshold logic unit. We want to analyze what classifications of input patterns can be realized by the firing or nonfiring of the output of such an array. Clearly, if we allow "neurons" of the first level to receive inputs from all the squares of the "retina," then, allowing arbitrary Boolean functions at that level, any pattern classification is possible. The question only becomes interesting, then, if we ask how the complexity of pattern recognition increases with the number of input lines to the neurons of the first layer. Minsky and Papert have been able to show that to tell whether the number of squares that are "on" is even requires "neurons" which are actually connected to all of the squares of the network; whereas to tell whether the number of "on" squares exceeds a certain threshold only requires two input "neurons" in the first layer. To tell whether or not the pattern of activated squares is connected requires a number that increases at least as fast as the square root of the number of cells in the retina. Their work thus complements that of Winograd and Spira by showing how the complexity of the components in the first layer of a two-layer network must increase with the complexity of the pattern recognition problem required. Again, you will note that their results are most interesting and point the way toward further insight into the functioning of the nervous system but are still restricted to highly mathematical functions, rather than the complex perceptual problems involved in the everyday life of an organism. We might note, too, that any full model of perception must not have the purely passive character of this model, but must involve an active component in which contention and hypothesis formation is shaped by the inner activity of the organism, and is related to its past and present responses.

Besides theorems associated with finite computing networks, there are theorems associated with Turing machines which may indirectly help our thinking about the problems of cybernetics. The metamathematicians of the 1930's showed that for interesting mathematical theories, such as the theory of numbers, no axiomatization using effective procedures for the rules of inference could have as theorems all true statements about the theory of numbers (see, e.g., Gödel, 1931); and, further, that given such an axiomatization, no machine which provided proofs of theorems within that theory could actually provide proofs of all of them, unless it also provided false proofs of nontheorems. It became well known that given any axiomatization one could add new axioms in a consistent way to provide a theory in which many new theorems were provable—in particular, of course, the independent statement that we had added as a new axiom. Less well known is the fact, which we may call the Gödel (1936) speed-up theorem, that if we add a new axiom in this way, not only are there truths which become theorems for the first time, but, also, that theorems which were already provable in the old system may have shorter proofs in the new system. In fact, given any criterion of what you mean by speeding up a proof, there will exist at least one, and in fact infinitely many, theorems whose proofs are sped up by this criterion. This accords well with the intuition of those who have studied measure theory, and who know how much easier proofs are when we make use of the axiom of choice, rather than trying to give a constructive proof which can be formalized within a system which does not include the axiom of choice. If we make the highly artificial assumption that the contents of the memory of an organism correspond to the axioms, and theorems so far, of a formal system—with the ability to add new axioms given by induction—then this theorem reminds us that the virtue of adding new data to memory is not simply that that particular piece of information now becomes available to the organism, but also that the organism may compute other information much faster than it could otherwise, even though that information was not denied to the organism before. It suggests to me that an appropriate measure of information content for a statement is to be found in a measure of the reduction it effects in the average computation required by the system when operating in a certain limited environment. In any case, we see that in looking at the design of memory structures, we must consider not only speed of storing and retrieval of particular items, but we must also study ways in which we can choose what is to be stored in such a way as to most speed up the necessary computations of the system. In line with this, we shall want a precise understanding of the cumulative effects of small initial changes— one change favors certain other changes by making them relatively easy, and the next change in turn shifts the balance of probable computational structure, until a huge spectrum of styles prove to be consistent with an initial "genetic" structure, and selections are made by virtually insignificant changes.

A crucial point here is that, unlike those of the mathematician, most of the computations of the organism are in real time—in other words, he cannot persevere until he has a definite answer, but must instead produce an answer in time to make some appropriate action within a dynamic environment. This means that much of our activity cannot be optimal, because our computational network does not have the capacity to find an optimal solution within the time allowed by events continuing outside. Thus we cannot judge our actions as being most appropriate, but can only judge them as being the most appropriate computable in a given time.

This is an appropriate point to comment that much foolish thinking has been done with the nervous system by comparing it too closely with the systems of logic. This is because logical systems are only studied if they are consistent, whereas the computational system of any real organism is of necessity inconsistent. The "axioms" that we use are based upon a limited experience, and thus share, with all statements based on induction, a non-zero probability of error. Thus, we cannot, as many have done, make pronouncements about the brain by comparing its activity to theorem-proving within a perfectly consistent system. Rather, I feel that much insight will come from trying to understand what we should mean by proof in an inconsistent logic. Here, the credibility of a statement is the higher, the sooner we can prove it in such a logic, without generating statements which are seen to contradict currently acceptable statements accessible to the organism. I think that the prime example of an inconsistent logic is judicial logic; in this logic, any statement can be proved, but the more implausible the statement, the more expensive the lawyer who can prove it! Thus, although the Gödel speed-up theorem is far removed from a realistic study of the brain, it indicates once again how a clear formal understanding of an area within automata theory can spur us towards asking much more incisive questions about the fundamental nature of information processing in the nervous system than might otherwise be possible.

IV. Concluding Remarks

We see that there are two different ways in which automata theory may prove useful here. One is that in which one makes a model in which the basic constructs are closely tied to actual elements of the brain, and then seeks to see to what extent one's deductions yield results consistent with the experimental reality. The other approach is simply to look at abstract processes which have some vague metaphorical connection with brain processes and, then, to use the results one finds in such a theory to enliven and inform one's discussion of the brain, without expecting the sort of correspondence that can be subjected to experimental test. Of course, the latter type of approach can be very dangerous, and one must take exquisite care at every stage to avoid confusing the discussion of reality and the discussion of theory. Such topics as complexity of computation in finite networks, the identification problem, and the study of decomposition would seem to be necessary topics for us to really understand the nervous system; whereas it would seem to be a matter of taste as to whether one finds discussions of Gödel's theorem more misleading or more helpful than otherwise.

I would suggest that the proper posture for the automata theorist interested in information processing in the nervous system is a somewhat schizophrenic one; he must study purely formal questions within automata theory, biasing his choice of topics and his new definitions in terms of his interest in the brain, and he must study the neurophysiological and psychological literature, perhaps even involving himself in some experimental work, trying to impose some order and formalization upon a rather chaotic array of experimental data. For theorists who cannot stand so disparate an approach, and I believe that few can, such topics as applying statistical analysis to experimental results on spike trains or on electroencephalograms, or applying standard control theory to such problems as muscular coordination, may be more palatable. But even here we can see that divergence is possible—one man may find himself getting more and more immersed in the details of the experiments, trying to gain a greater feel for the intricacies of the actual data, whereas another man may discover that the data involves adaptive characteristics which cannot be handled by conventional control theory, and so will find more and more of his time being devoted to the search for a better theory of adaptive control systems. And so it goes. We can only conclude that for the health of the study of the nervous system, both active theory and active experimentation are necessary, with all manner of blends of the two in the heads of different people.

REFERENCES

Arbib, M. A. (1964). Brains, machines and mathematics. New York: McGraw-Hill.

Arbib, M. A. (ed.) (1968). Algebraic theory of machines, languages and semigroups. New York: Academic Press.

Arbib, M. A. (1969). Theories of abstract automata. Englewood Cliffs: Prentice-Hall.

Arbib, M. A. (in press a). Memory limitations of stimulus-response models. Psych. Rev.

Arbib, M. A. (in press). The metaphorical brain. Englewood Cliffs: Prentice-Hall.

Arbib, M. A. and Zeiger, H. P. (1969). On the relevance of abstract algebra to control theory. Automatica.

Barzdin, Y. M. (1965). Complexity of recognition of symmetry in Turing machines. Problemy Kibernetiki, 15.

Davis, M., (ed.) (1965). The undecidable. Hewlett: Raven Press.

Gödel, K. (1931). Über formal unentscheidbare Sätze der Principia Mathematica und verwandter Systeme I. Monatshefte fur Mathematik und Physik, 38: 173–198. [Translation in Davis (1965)]

Gödel, K. (1936). Über die Länge der Beweise. Ergeb. eines math. Kolloquiums, 7:23–24. [Translation in Davis (1965)]

Hartmanis, J. and Stearns, R. E. (1966). Algebraic theory of sequential machines. Englewood Cliffs: Prentice-Hall.

Hubel, D. H. and Wiesel, T. N. (1962). Receptive fields, binocular interaction, and functional architecture in the cat's visual cortex. J. Physiol., *160:* 106–154.

Lettvin, J., Maturana, H., McCulloch, W. S. and Pitts, W. (1959). What the frog's eye tells the frog's brain. Proc. IRE, *47:* 1940–1951.

McCulloch, W. S. (1965). What's in the brain that ink may character? In W. S. McCulloch, Embodiments of mind. Cambridge: MIT Press.

McCulloch, W. S. and Pitts, W. (1943). A logical calculus of the ideas immanent in nervous activity. Bull. Math. Biophys., *5:* 115–133.

Miller, G. A., Galanter, E. and Pribram, K. H. (1960). Plans and the structure of behavior. New York: Holt, Rinehart and Winston, Inc.

Minsky, M. L. (1961). Steps toward artificial intelligence. Proc. IRE, *49* (1): 8–30.

Minsky, M. L. (1967). Computation: finite and infinite machines. Englewood Cliffs: Prentice-Hall.

Minsky, M. L. and Papert, S. (1967). Linearly unrecognizable patterns, in Mathematical aspects of computer science, Vol. XIX of Proceedings of Symposia in Applied Mathematics. Providence: Amer. Math. Soc. 176–217.

Moore, E. F. (1956). Gedanken-experiments on sequential machines. In C. E. Shannon and J. McCarthy, (eds.), Automata studies. Princeton: Princeton University Press. 129–153.

Post, E. L. (1936). Finite combinatory processes—formulation I. J. Symbolic Logic, *1:* 103–105.

Ritchie, R. W. (1963). Classes of predictably computable functions. Trans. Am. Math. Soc., *106:* 139–173.

Shannon, C. E. and McCarthy, J., eds. (1956). Automata studies. Princeton: Princeton University Press.

Spira, P. M. (1968). On the computational complexity of finite functions. Unpublished Ph.D. Thesis, Dept. of Electrical Engineering, Stanford University.

Spira, P. M. and Arbib, M. A. (1967). Computation times for finite groups, semigroups and automata. Proc. IEEE 8th Ann. Symp. Switching and Automata Theory, 291–295.

Suppes, P. (1968). Stimulus-response theory of finite automata. Technical Report No. 133, Psychology Series, Institute for Math. Studies in the Social Sciences, Stanford University.

Turing, A. M. (1936). On computable numbers with an application to the Entscheidungs-problem. Proc. London Math. Soc., *Ser. 2–42:* 230–265; with a correction, Ibid., *43* (1936–7): 544–546.

Wang, H. (1957). A variant to Turing's theory of computing machines. J. Assoc. Comp. Math., *4:* 63–92.

Winograd, S. (1967). On the time required to perform multiplication. J. ACM, *14:* 793–802.

ROBERT ROSEN

Center for Theoretical Biology
State University of New York at Buffalo
Buffalo, New York

2 · *Hierarchical Organization in Automata Theoretic Models of the Central Nervous System*

I. Introduction

Perhaps the most striking feature of biological organization is its hierarchical character. Conversely, hierarchical organization in biological systems has characteristics quite different from those we customarily observe in the physical world and in the world of mechanical artifacts with which we are increasingly surrounding ourselves. For this reason our scientific intuition, which has been largely built on physics and engineering, has always been somewhat at a loss in dealing with hierarchical organizations of all kinds, biological and sociological.

Much of the thinking about hierarchical systems has been concerned with finding some kind of anchor in the hierarchy; some specific distinguished level which is somehow more important than the others and around which we can bring to bear the intuitions we have developed through the study of non-hierarchical organizations. For many years in biology, the cell theory served to identify such a level; the cell was the distinguished basic unit of biological structure and function, from which we could ascend upward in the biological hierarchy through tissues and organs to physiology and even ecology if we wished, and also descend to subcellular levels—organelles, macromolecular complexes and biochemistry. This line of thought is still current in the study of the central nervous system, which is often regarded as if it were an independent organism; the cell level is still the distinguished one, except that the cell here is called

21

a neuron; it is from the cell level that we wish to move up and down in the CNS hierarchy. This viewpoint of the cellular level as biologically distinguished has been challenged in the past 15 years by that of the molecular biologist; that it is the biochemical (or even purely physical) level which is distinguished, and that the only direction to move in the hierarchy is up. More of this later.

An analog of the cell theory in central nervous system studies is the theory of automata, particularly as developed in terms of modular networks. Just as in its use in general biology, part of the motivation for using automata theory here lies in its serving as a possible basis for a hierarchical description. Yet, as far as I know, no one has systematically approached the problem of whether or not the theory of automata is in fact a suitable vehicle to serve as the basis for hierarchical structure. Yet, this is obviously a key question; if, as we all agree, the central nervous system displays a pervading hierarchical organization, then any theory of the central nervous system which does not permit of a similar hierarchical description must be seriously incomplete. The present paper is addressed to this question, whether and how the theory of automata can serve as the basis for a hierarchically organized system, i.e., whether automata theory, alone or properly supplemented, can tell us anything about hierarchies in the central nervous system. Naturally, a qualitative discussion of this kind can only scratch the surface, but it is hoped that the most important relevant ideas have been identified, and some initial conclusions will be drawn.

II. Hierarchies in Systems

We shall begin somewhat impudently by proposing a working operational definition of hierarchical activity in an organized system, and then proceed to illustrate this definition in a special case, indeed, the only special case in which the problem of hierarchical description has been at all successfully treated. This will necessitate an apparent detour from our main subject, but I hope it will become clear in due course that the detour is only apparent.

At the outset, I would like to claim that a hierarchical system is simply one which is (a) engaged simultaneously in a variety of distinguishable activities, and (b) such that different kinds of system specification or description are appropriate to the study of these several activities. In my view, it is property (b) which is decisive for a hierarchical description; a system may be doing many things simultaneously, but if the same kind of system description is appropriate for all of these activities, the idea of hierarchical description simply does not arise.

The essential problem in studying a system which is hierarchical, in the sense defined above, is then to specify the relationships which exist between the several system descriptions appropriate to the various levels in the hierarchy. Most particularly: to what extent does a knowledge of the system at the lowest level of the hierarchy specify or determine its properties at the higher levels (lower and higher for the present remaining formally undefined, but presumably not without intuitive content for this audience)? This last problem is the essential problem of reductionism, as it is seen, for example, in molecular biology; here the lowest level description is a purely physico-chemical, quantum-theoretic one, and the problem is to determine whether, and to what extent, the purely physico-chemical description of a biological system determines all of its other properties. Indeed, it is hoped that the formulation I have just given allows a glimpse of the close analogy between hierarchical properties of the central nervous system and problems of reductionism in cell biology; this is an analogy which I shall return to later, and which I feel can be exploited to the great advantage of both subjects.

Before we wander off too far in the direction of formal analogies, I believe it will be helpful to pass to the example I mentioned earlier; a very simple case of a true hierarchical description (according to my definition) in which the essential problem of passing between the appropriate system descriptions has been to some extent successfully solved. This example will serve both to illustrate the problems in concrete terms, and to provide the basis for an analysis of what must be done to solve problems of hierarchical description in general.

The example I wish to consider is that of a thermodynamic system—more particularly the kind of system which we call a gas. We all know that we can regard a gas in two quite different ways. On the one hand, we can regard a gas as a system consisting of a large number of individual (Newtonian) particles, while on the other hand, a gas may be considered simply as a continuous fluid, without any substructure. Each of these viewpoints requires a different kind of system description. If we consider the gas as a system of particles, then we know from the theory of Newtonian dynamics that the state variables appropriate to describe the system are the co-ordinates and momenta of the individual particles of the system; this corresponds to what we usually call the micro-description of the system. If we view the gas simply as a fluid, then the state variables appropriate to this view are quite different—they are the thermodynamic variables, pressure, volume, temperature, etc. These correspond to the macro-description of the system. Which description we use depends entirely on which aspects of the behavior of the system we are interested in, i.e., on the way in which we are interacting with the system. We have before us, then, a true example of a hierarchical system, in which two apparently independent system descriptions are appropriate to different activities being simultaneously manifested by the same system.

We have said that the basic problem of hierarchical descriptions is to determine the extent to which the lowest-level description determines the properties of the system at the higher levels. In the present example there are only two levels, the lower described by the micro-description, the higher by the macro-description. The solution of the basic problem thus requires a tool which will enable us to relate these two descriptions, and, as we are well aware, such a tool exists—it is called statistical mechanics.

Let us briefly illustrate what this tool looks like and how it works; this will be important to our later developments. We want to begin with the micro-description, and work upward to the macro-description. What is the micro-description? We know that here the fundamental state variables are the displacements and momenta of the individual particles which make up our system. According to Newtonian dynamics, the kinetic properties of the system are given by the equations of motion of the system, which express the momenta as functions of the state variables. As we know, this leads to a system of first-order simultaneous differential equations which, when integrated, determine all possible motions of the system; any individual motion of the system is specified when the initial values of the state variables at a particular instant are given.

The really important thing to notice about the equations of motion, and the machinery for setting them up, is that they are supposed to contain all the information which can ever be obtained about the system. This is one of the basic postulates of Newtonian dynamics; knowing the state variables at one instant and the equations of motion, we are supposed to be able to answer any meaningful question that can be asked about the system at any level (or at least, at any higher level). Of course, this answer may be wrong, to the extent that Newtonian dynamics provides an incorrect description of the system at the micro-level; this does not concern us here. What is important is that, whatever the underlying micro-dynamics, it must be postulated at the outset to have a universal character with respect to all higher levels.

This initial postulation of universality seems to solve the problem of hierarchies by tautology, but it really does not, for we must supplement this postulate by giving a specific recipe for answering higher-level questions in terms of the micro-description, and Newtonian mechanics does this. The relevant data here are contained in appropriate state functions, or observables, of the system. Answers to questions about individual states of the micro-system are obtained by evaluating the appropriate observables on those states; answers to questions about families of states are obtained by some kind of operation on the values assumed on the states of the family by the appropriate observables. And in classical mechanics, once the state is known, any observable can be evaluated.

In particular, the universality postulate implies that thermodynamic questions can be answered in terms of the underlying micro-description. How? The state variables appropriate to the system at the gas level must be expressed in terms of the observables of the underlying mechanical system;

i.e., as functions of the state variables of the micro-system. It is then a question of finding the appropriate observables, and the operations which must be performed on them. This is what statistical mechanics does. It identifies a thermodyamic state (macro-state) with a class of underlying micro-states, and then expresses the thermodynamic state variables as averages of appropriately chosen micro-observables over the corresponding class of micro-states. The equations of motion of the underlying micro-system are then inherited by the thermodynamic state variables, allowing us to express in principle (though in practice only as yet in very special situations) the kinetic behavior of the system at the macro-level.

To sum up, what we needed in order to solve the problem of hierarchical description in this simple case were:

1. The universality of the underlying micro-dynamics, which assured us that we could express any aspect of system behavior in terms of the micro-description in principle.

2. A determination of how the state variables of the macro-description could actually be described in terms of the micro-dynamics; i.e., in terms of the observables of the micro-system. This determination is highly non-trivial, and without it, the universality assumption is operationally vacuous.

3. The implementation of (2) to actually derive the kinetic properties of the macro-system from those of the micro-system. (2) and (3) are what statistical mechanics does in this case.

There is yet a third aspect to the problem of hierarchies in thermo-dynamic systems, which must be explicitly recognized, and which can be illustrated in the following way. The unique role of statistical mechanics in physics (i.e., that of effectively relating two levels in a hierarchical system) has tempted a number of authors, working in a variety of biological areas, to try to mimic the statistical mechanical formalism in an attempt to get some insight into particular hierarchical structures in biology, including the central nervous system. These attempts have not been very successful, and it is of importance to inquire why this is so. The fault does not lie in the formalism itself, which does not depend on the underlying dynamics, and should in principle work regardless of whether the dynamical equations are those of Lotka-Volterra populations, biochemical control systems, or model neurons. The difficulty becomes clear when we consider the historical order of ideas in the development of statistical mechanics in physics. The development was as follows: first came the gas laws; i.e., the phenomenological specification of macro-system behavior, and the determination of the state variables appropriate to this specification; secondly came the specification of the micro-system dynamics, and lastly came the statistical mechanical formalism connecting the two. This order is crucial; I feel secure in asserting that if the gas laws had not been known first, they would never have been discovered through statistical mechanics alone. This is because the formalism will indeed enable you to form any averages you want, but it will not tell you what these averages mean, and which of these are useful and important in specifying and describing macro-system behavior.

In all attempts to apply the statistical mechanical formalism to biology, however, this historical order has been permuted. First has come the formalism, imported from physics. Secondly comes the micro-system description, and lastly comes the attempt to apply the formalism to the micro-system description to generate information about the macro-system. It is obvious now why this information is not readily forthcoming. The fault lies in our initial ignorance of system descriptions at the upper levels of the hierarchy, and the basic fact that statistical mechanics alone cannot decide the relevance of any particular average to the macro-system description.

Let us sum up the thrust of what we have said so far. According to the very definition I have proposed for hierarchical description, the first essential point is that no one type of system description can possibly display by itself a definite type of hierarchical structure, for the simple reason that we recognize such structure only by the necessity for different kinds of system description at the various levels in the hierarchy. But, as we have seen in the case of Newtonian mechanics, certain kinds of system description (universal ones) contain, in principle, information which can be identified with system descriptions at higher levels. This property is clearly the first requisite which must be demanded of a theory which purports to deal with a hierarchical system. There are, as we have seen, two other requisites, independent both of the first requisite and of each other, namely: a supplementary procedure for isolating this information in a convenient form (a role played by statistical mechanics in our example), and a decision procedure for identifying the relevant information with system properties at the upper levels (a role not played either by the lowest level description or by statistical mechanics, and seeming on the basis of our experience so far to require a previously formulated independent description of the upper levels).

In what follows, we shall view automata theory as a candidate for a lowest level system description. Our discussion has thus enabled us to narrow our goals; we concern ourselves here, therefore, only with the first requisite mentioned above, namely, does automata theory, as a system description, contain information which pertains in principle to higher levels in a hierarchy? Is automata theory universal?

III. Automata Theory

It is now time to turn our attention to the second major component of our discussion; namely, automata theory and its role in the description of central nervous system activity. I view automata theory here as the general theory of finite-state, discrete-time systems. This theory, at least insofar as it relates to biological applications, has developed from two rather different points of view, which it will be useful to describe in some detail.

One large component of automata theory has derived from the study of specfic systems, especially from neural networks and switching systems. This may be called the theory of modular networks. It deals with the properties of systems of similar units or modules (which may be called neurons, relays, switches, etc.) interconnected with a specific topology. The concept of such networks has a major root in biology. In the years 1934–1938, Rashevsky and his co-workers constructed a class of "neuroelements" which generalized the excitatory and inhibitory characteristics of their theory of peripheral nerve excitation. These "neuroelements" had a mixture of digital and continuous characteristics; they were described by ordinary differential equations, but their output was a step function. It was recognized that these "neuroelements" could be considered as modules and strung into networks with logical and computational capabilities, and that some of these networks possessed functional properties that were at least reminiscent of behavioral properties of organisms—they could "learn" and "discriminate."

Such modular networks were completely digitalized by McCulloch & Pitts (1943), who replaced Rashevsky's "neuroelements" with purely digital "formal neurons." These shared with real neurons the properties of excitation, inhibition, temporal summation, threshold, etc. They could show that one could build networks of these neurons which would realize any logical behavior one could write down, including presumably any the brain would be capable of. It is difficult to overestimate the impact that these neural networks have had on the study of the central nervous system. Doubters have pointed out that there is not one single aspect of CNS activity which has been unequivocally explained in terms of neural networks; this may be so, but the persuasiveness of the formalism is so great that it has permeated our present theoretical ideas on the activity of the central nervous system. As noted previously, I believe that the basis for this persuasiveness lies equally in its being a restatement of the cell theory for the CNS, thus providing a distinguished level, an anchor in the CNS hierarchy.

The other large component of automata theory comes from mathematics, particularly from the theory of recursive functions and its offshoots. At about the same time Rashevsky was stringing "neuroelements" into networks, Turing invented a formal "Gedankenmaschine" which could implement any arithmetic algorithm in essentially the same manner that a human arithmetician would. He was interested in these machines mainly as they applied to certain decision problems in logic and algebra, but their relation to intelligent and purposive behavior was not lost, either on their inventor or on others. Today we have a general formal theory of such machines, which together with their memoryless brothers (finite automata) we may call the theory of sequential systems.

The theory of sequential systems is generally formulated in axiomatic terms, as a set of data and the relationships between them. Most of these take the form of the familiar machine, which it will be helpful to review:

1. A finite set of states Q, a finite set of input symbols X, a finite set of output symbols Y.

2. A next-state map $\delta : QxX \to Q$.

3. An out-put map $\lambda : QxX \to Y$.

The data defining the sequential machine are purely abstract entities. We can realize these data in a variety of ways. In particular, we can associate the abstract set of states Q with the states of a particular modular network, and thus obtain a realization of an abstract sequential machine in terms of modular net. Indeed, given any abstract sequential machine, there is a modular network (built, say, out of McCulloch-Pitts neurons) which will realize it. There is no reason why such a realization should be unique, and indeed, in general each abstract sequential machine will determine a class of modular networks, each of which will be a realization of the abstract machine. These realizations will differ in their specific structure, but will all be functionally indistinguishable; to use another word, they will be analogs of one another. Thus, we can study a sequential system either entirely in the abstract, or in terms of any one of the analogous networks which realize the abstract machine.

The above considerations point up the fact that there is a fundamental ambiguity in automata theory which, depending on one's point of view, is either a basic strength or a basic weakness of the theory in describing the activity of the central nervous system. I believe it is fair to say that most workers in neural networks are seeking to establish isomorphisms between model networks and their biological counterparts; correspondences which will proceed to identify each formal neuron in the network with its counterpart biological neuron; each formal synapse with a biological synapse, and conversely. But "the real" network we seek is, if it exists, but one of a class of functionally identical networks; if we work, as we always do, from functional properties of networks, how can we extract "the one" which we seek? On the other hand, the theory also tells us that, if we want to deal with functional properties of a network, we can learn a great deal by working with any convenient analog which exhibits these properties, and even entirely in the abstract with a sequential machine. We shall return later to the question of whether it is of interest to seek such structural isomorphisms, and if so, how to go about it.

We now turn to the question of how the theory of automata is in fact used to describe the activities of the central nervous system. Since we have seen that a particular modular net can always be replaced by a sequential machine, and if we assume that the central nervous system is a modular net, we may as well work with the more general and convenient sequential machine terminology.

It looks at first sight as if the sequential machine formalism is quite different in principle from other kinds of system description; for instance, from the kind of description envisaged in the Newtonian description of a mechanical system. But closer scrutiny reveals that this is not the case, and in fact, that the sequential machine formalism is really a close paraphrase of Newtonian dynamics in a discrete setting. The set of (discrete) states Q plays exactly the same role as does the phase space of Newtonian dynamics; the set of inputs X plays exactly the same role as do the forces applied to a mechanical system; and the next-state map δ plays exactly the same role as do the dynamical equations of motion. In each case, knowing the initial state and the forces acting on the system (i.e., the input sequence to the sequential machine) we can predict the entire temporal course of the system.

What I am saying, then, is that the description of a modular network as a sequential machine is really the same kind of animal as the description of a mechanical system in conventional dynamical terms; the differences between them are purely technical and do not involve matters of principle. This is a key observation, for it is now tempting to suppose that, matters of technique aside, we can do anything with a sequential machine description that we can do with a purely dynamical description. In particular, the question will now be: can we use an automata-theoretic description of a modular net as a micro-description, from which we can effectively generate hierarchical descriptions of models of the central nervous system?

IV. Automata Theory and Hierarchies

As we have seen, an automata-theoretic description of a modular network is, in principle, very similar to a conventional dynamical description. We have already exhibited a situation in which a dynamical description could be made to yield information concerning higher levels in a hierarchy. It thus remains to see whether the automata-theoretic description can likewise be made to yield such information. Indeed, if automata theory is to provide more than a very partial picture of activity of the central nervous system, this must be the case.

We have seen that the first essential for a hierarchical theory is that the system description lying at the lowest level in the hierarchy be universal, in the sense that it contain all the information which can be obtained about the system at any higher level. In order that this postulate be not vacuous, we also need explicit recipes for extracting this information and ascertaining its relevance, i.e. for expressing higher-level system descriptions in terms of what is happening at the lowest level.

What is the vehicle for this information in the dynamical description? The vehicle consists in the enormous set of observables of the system which is at our disposal, i.e., all real-valued functions on the state space of the system, together with all the operations that can be performed on them (e.g., averaging over classes of states). This is, in fact, the specific machinery in which resides the effective universality of Newtonian mechanics.

Let us look now at the parallel we have drawn between dynamical and automata-theoretic descriptions. These parallels have involved the respective state spaces and the equations of motion. The observables of the dynamical description are, as we have seen, numerical functions on the state space, all explicitly visible in the dynamical description. But when we turn to the automata-theoretic description, what do we find? We find but a single observable, namely, the output function of the machine. To get another observable, we need another machine. In other words, the theory of automata has paraphrased everything about dynamical descriptions except the explicit machinery required in order for the dynamical description to have a universal character.

Exactly the same shortcoming arises if we retreat to the modular network level, except that in this case we have a few more potential observables coming along as a consequence of the specific structure of the network. In this case, by the usual identifications, the output function of a modular net is obtained by a specific choice of neurons to be called output neurons. If we choose these differently, we automatically get a new output and a new output function, which is, of course, an observable of the network. Thus, a particular modular network can give us a certain finite number of observables, instead of the single one we obtain when we advance to the sequential machine formalism. But it is clear that without any external criteria to guide us, universality requires the full richness of the set of observables of the system; no sample (certainly no finite sample) will do.

From these considerations, it appears very much as if there can be no question of hierarchical descriptions being based on automata-theoretic descriptions, even in principle, since the mechanism to generate higher-level descriptions has been explicitly abstracted out of the description right at the outset. In other words, though we may increase complexity in a modular net by adding more and more units interconnected in richer and richer ways, this increase in complexity cannot, by itself, elevate us into upper hierarchical levels. The machinery by which we might have hoped to do this is missing.

If we have come this far, we have probably come far enough to observe that all is not yet lost. By attempting to re-introduce the absent machinery, we may yet retrieve a possibility of accounting for hierarchical descriptions by automata theory. We know what is missing—more observables. An observable is a function on the state space; it is a computation. But automata and modular nets can do nothing if not compute; therefore, we can retrieve any particular observable we may want by allowing an appropriate computing automaton access to the state set of our original system. In this fashion we may hope to regenerate, at least formally, the groundwork for a universal micro-description, the first prerequisite for a hierarchical description.

In fact, this is exactly what is done in network models which do exhibit some kind of hierarchical activities; i.e., explicit behavioral properties at a higher level. For instance, we have the cell assemblies of Hebb; the various pattern-recognizing devices, like the "Perceptron," which appear to make abstractions; and the heuristic problem solvers. But these are not simply modular networks; they are modular nets to which further structure has been appended. And this further structure serves precisely to generate new observables in terms of which the higher-level activities may be (at least partially) characterized. For instance: most of the above-mentioned models involve a totally new idea; facilitation, the manipulation of threshold or connection strength. Facilitation is an idea utterly foreign, by itself, to automata theory; it is a new construction principle, which can be reduced to conventional automata-theoretic terms only by the appending of new observables. A net with facilitation can be replaced by a (much bigger) net without facilitation; the difference in size between the two networks is due to the incorporation of new computing apparatus to generate new observables and use them as the basis for describing the higher level activities.

All this is in accord with what should happen in automata theoretic descriptions, in terms of the parallels we have drawn between these descriptions and conventional dynamics. We also see something else happening, again expected in terms of our parallel, which has a bearing on our interpretation of modular network theory in terms of the central nervous system. It is perhaps most easily stated initially in dynamical terms, and it is this: when we have succeeded in building the state variables of a higher-level description in terms of appropriate observables of a lower-level description, we may use these new state variables, and the equations of motion they inherit, as the micro-description for the next level up in the hierarchy. The forms of these successive micro-descriptions will remain very much the same; only the interpretations vary. In the study of biochemical control systems, we start phenomenologically with a dynamical description in which the state variables are concentrations, and where the equations of motion contain certain "rate constants." These "rate constants" can themselves be derived, from statistical mechanical arguments of the kind we have sketched, from a set of similar-looking equations, but where the state variables now describe the specific structure of the molecules involved. Likewise, in the automata-theoretic description, a net with facilitation behaves very much again like a modular net, except that we must now interpret the modules as being assemblies (in Hebb's terminology, Hebb, 1949) of the original modules at the lowest level. In other words, we may use the automata-theoretic description independently for each of the several levels of the hierarchies of our system, just as we do in the dynamical case. The interpretations (i.e., the state descriptions) change, but the descriptive machinery is preserved.

All of this reduces simply to the conclusion that, if we want a hierarchical description on the basis of an automata-theoretic description at the cell (i.e., the neural) level, a desire implicit in neural network theory, then we must abandon our attempt to find a structural isomorphism between network models and the central nervous system itself. We must do this because, while the real neurons have all of their observables built into them as dynamical systems and, hence, do allow the generation of hierarchies, the automata-theoretic description only allows us one, or at best a few, observables at a time. This, I think, is the deeper significance of McCulloch's assertion that his formal neurons are impoverished. It is true, as we have seen, that we can build back into the network any particular observable we want, using any particular kind of module (e.g., a McCulloch-Pitts neuron or other kind of neuromime) but this requires extra modules which have no structural counterpart in the real network. There is, of course, a functional counterpart to the supernumerary modules, but this functional counterpart is buried inextricably in the incredibly rich dynamics of the real neuron. It is precisely here that the possibilities for the generation and representation of hierarchical descriptions resides, and it is precisely this aspect which has been, as a matter of principle, systematically neglected in automata-theoretic descriptions of central nervous system activity.

The above analysis, as I said before, is only a beginning investigation, dealing only with the very first requisite for the building of a theory of hierarchies in automata-theoretic terms. It does not tell us what kind of observables we should want to build into modular networks to allow for particular kinds of hierarchical behavior. It does not tell us what operations to perform on these observables in order to put them into a useful form for higher-level studies (that is, it does not provide an automata-theoretic analog to statistical mechanics). It does not tell us which of this higher-level information is relevant as a system description at the higher levels. All this it does not do, and yet I believe that this analysis may serve to recast the problem in a more manageable form, one in which conceptual difficulties are replaced by technical ones. And as one deeply interested in hierarchical organizations in biological systems, I hope that this analysis, or something like it, will represent a forward rather than a backward step in our struggle to understand these systems.

V. Some Further Considerations

I should like to conclude this talk with a few speculations which may bear upon the unanswered questions raised by the above analysis (and I might remark that I do not consider this analysis to have any speculative aspects at all). These speculations are based on what understanding I have of another hierarchically organized biological system, namely the cell itself. They have to do with the exploitation of the analogies between cellular organization and that of the central nervous system, which I have already touched on by formulating the problem of reductionism in cell biology in the same terms as the problem of hierarchies which we have considered at such length.

Many may be aware that there is developing a modular theory of cellular control mechanisms, a theory which seeks to describe how a single cell modulates the kind and amount of material which it synthesizes. The mechanism may be formulated neatly in terms of the Jacob-Monod operons, which interact with each other through excitatory and inhibitory signals, and the flow of these signals imposes a particular topology of interconnections among an array of operons; i.e., turns them into a network. It was first implicitly recognized by Sugita (1961) that such a network could be completely digitalized; i.e., described entirely in automata-theoretic terms. It is interesting to note that the modules here do not correspond to a structural entity within the cell to which we can point, but rather to a functional entity, which inter-relates various structural entities in a complicated way. Thus, we are at the outset not tempted in this theory to seek any kind of structural isomorphism, as we may be in neural networks, when we seek to identify each real structural neuron with its formal counterpart in a modular net. But as we have just seen at length, this is a temptation which must be resisted; the modules are functional units, and they must be combined to yield functional units at the higher levels as well. All this is quite clear in the cellular system.

The problem of control in these cellular networks is just the same as in the nervous system: to determine which modules shall be firing and which shall not be firing in a particular set of environmental circumstances. Furthermore, in the cellular system, we know that the control of cellular processes proceeds at the level of the activity itself; this same idea has recently been suggested by Dr. Eccles to be applicable to the central nervous system on the basis of his studies of cerebellar function. In general, we may pass from the theory of cellular control networks to neural network models of the central nervous system by just replacing a few nouns by other nouns. When this happens, it means precisely that the systems represented by the two theories are analogous. This in turn means that the formal statements of the theory can be realized in quite different ways, just as the differential equation describing an oscillatory system can be realized by a mechanical, electrical, or biochemical oscillator. Such analogies can be meaningfully exploited, just as they are in analog computation: the dynamical characteristics of any pair of analogs, in this sense, are the same. The exploitation of such analogies between the central nervous system and cellular control systems seems valuable to me for a variety of reasons, among them:

1. The conceptually unifying effect that may follow from the discovery

of principles governing the behavior of such important but structurally dissimilar systems. This is a unification which seems, to me at least, far more fruitful and satisfying than any which can be derived from a simple reductionism. Such a unification is already visible in physics, in the organization of physics around variational principles, as opposed to the reductionist attempt to derive all of physics from the theory of elementary particles.

2. The interplay of intuitions developed on two analogous but physically highly dissimilar systems cannot help but be valuable to both. For the moment, most of the flow seems to be from the direction of the highly developed theory of modular nets in the central nervous system toward the theory of biochemical control (especially in connection with differentiation because of the constructive aspect of the theory, the actual building of networks with specific logical capacities). But the flow is bound to go the other way as well, particularly in connection with hierarchical activities which are perhaps more clearly visible and quantifiable in cellular systems than in the central nervous system.

3. The technological applications of experience we can gain in the study of alternate realizations of a common functional organization. The analogy we have indicated points up the fact that we can construct modular networks, with hierarchical properties, out of biochemical components in at least two essentially different ways (namely, one in which the modules are operons, and one in which the modules are neurons). There may be other ways as well, perhaps involving artificial engineering components. The synthesis of such systems is one of the goals of both the area of bionics and of biologists themselves. It seems to me that it is more fruitful to approach this as a problem of alternate realizations of functional properties than through the study of purely physical characteristics which, as we have seen, need not be simply related to functional behavior, particularly at the higher levels.

REFERENCES

Hebb, D. O. (1949). The organization of behavior. New York: Wiley & Sons.
McCulloch, W. and Pitts, W. (1943). On the ideas immanent in neural activity. Bull. Math. Biophys., 5: 115–133.
Rashevsky, N. (1938). Mathematical biophysics. Chicago: University of Chicago Press.
Sugita, M. (1961). Functional analysis of chemical systems *in vivo* using a logical circuit equivalent. J. Theoret. Biol., 1: 415–430.

DISCUSSION

ARBIB: I should like to ask why you need different automata to realize different observables. In any network you can use all possible measurements of the activity of every unit in the net. You need not confine yourself to any one unit and consider that as the only output from the net.

ROSEN: I was talking of modular networks of formal neurons and attempts to model biological neurons by individual formal neurons. There are many more observables in the former than are represented in the latter. Unlike thermodynamics, we do not have a suitable macro-description of central nervous systems, which would make it possible to devise a decision procedure for passing from the micro-description to the macro-description. Hence, we cannot, a priori, reject any of the observables at the cell level since we do not know which of these, if any, are irrelevant to the hierarchical description.

H. C. LONGUET-HIGGINS

Edinburgh University
Edinburgh, Scotland

3 · *The Non-local Storage and Associative Retrieval of Spatio-Temporal Patterns*

I. Introduction

It is an undeserved honor for someone who is a newcomer both to brain science and to automata theory to be asked to speak to a gathering such as this, so perhaps I had better begin with a brief apologia. I think all of us would agree that in order to understand the brain we have got to study the brain itself, and that the study of computers, for example, is no substitute. But equally, it is no good just poking around in the brain without some idea of what one is looking for. That would be like trying to find a needle in a haystack without having any idea what needles look like. The theorist, it seems to me, is the man who might reasonably be asked for an opinion about the appearance of needles. Or, to abandon the metaphor, he is a man whose job it is to construct or to elaborate models for experimental test. Having, almost by accident, joined the ranks of the neural modellers, I am well aware of the irritation with which our offerings are sometimes received by experimentalists; but constructing good theories is hard, as is quite clear from the limited success we have achieved so far.

One of the troubles, it seems to me, with neural modelling, is its name, that is, the word "neural." This word induces in the modeller a certain psychological "set": he feels, perhaps unconsciously, that any model which he propounds must commit him to some view or other about real neurons or synapses, or even about their molecular constituents such as the nucleic acids. This I regard as a mistaken attitude, at least for the present time. It

37

is as though the people who invented FORTRAN had felt obliged to concern themselves with solid-state switching devices—with electronic hardware rather than with logic. At the present juncture in brain science we must make sure that our models are formulated in sufficiently abstract terms, and leave the question of their detailed implementation to be settled by future experiment. But being abstract, they must, nevertheless, be definite enough to offer non-trivial predictions which are open to experimental test at either the psychological or the physiological level. This is the major problem.

For a moment let us imagine that someone had succeeded in constructing a model—an abstract automaton—and had shown that its predicted behavior agreed with what was known about, say, the verbal memory. What guarantee would one have that its design principles bore any relation at all to those of the brain? My answer to this question is twofold. First, there can never be any guarantee of the correctness of any scientific theory; theories exist to be unused and discarded, not to be believed. Secondly, and more important, tomorrow's theory of the brain is likely to be at least as complex and sophisticated as, say, quantum mechanics. If the physicists had rejected quantum mechanics merely because there was nothing to guarantee its superiority to other possible theories, as yet unformulated, physics would have come to a complete standstill forty years ago. The difficulty in brain science, it seems to me, is going to be not so much the choice between equally plausible theories as the construction of even one theory which remotely does justice to the rich and extensive experimental data.

II. Non-local Information Storage

With these general thoughts in mind, let me now embark on my main topic—the long-term memory. One of our most remarkable faculties is our ability to commit to memory a vast number of sensory impressions and experiences, and to recall or recognize them when presented with appropriate cues. What kind of question can we usefully ask about the long-term memory in our present state of ignorance about anatomical detail? Two questions immediately come to mind. First, about the addressing system. There are two ways in which an information store may be organized, known respectively as location-addressing and content-addressing. If I am a bad correspondent and allow incoming letters to pile up in the in-tray in order of receipt, regardless of content, I am using location-addressing. But if I deal with them systematically and let my secretary put them in the appropriate files, that is content-addressing: she can find a letter if I tell her who wrote it and what it was about. So our first question, about the nature of the addressing system, virtually answers itself: our memories must certainly be content-addressable, at least in large measure, as has been stressed by George Miller and many others. The second question which comes to mind concerns the degree of distribution of the individual items in our memories. (The concept of an "item" is not, of course, a rigorous concept, but I hope that a little goodwill may suffice to make it acceptable: a particular word might be allowed to count as a single item in the verbal memory, for example.) Let me now say something about this matter of distribution.

Broadly speaking, one may distinguish between two possibilities—local storage and non-local storage. The distinction is well illustrated by the difference between photography and holography. In photography we have a typical example of local information storage; there is a one-to-one correspondence between points on the object and grains on the plate, and every scene has to be recorded on a separate print. There are, however, three objections against supposing that our memories are stored like the pictures in a photograph album. First, if every item of my recorded experience were stored in a separate piece of neural tissue, either I should run out of store abruptly at an early age, or much of my cortex would remain unused for most of my life. In fact the whole cortex appears to be in a state of continuous activity when one is awake—though, of course, one cannot be sure what this means.

Secondly, there is the addressing problem, which I have already mentioned. If I want to look out a particular photograph—say the one which my niece was making a face at the camera—I must either hunt through the whole album to find it or consult an enormous ready-made index, in which case I am not relying solely on the album itself.

The third difficulty with the idea that our memories are stored locally is their relative sturdiness against anatomical damage. If each item were recorded in a separate small region, then the removal of cortical tissue should result in the irretrievable loss of specific memories. In fact this does not seem to happen, although again it is difficult to be sure.

With holography the situation is different. I need not, perhaps, go into detail about the technique except to say that a hologram is an optical record in which every grain in the emulsion has been influenced by light from every point on the object, and therefore records something about the object as a whole (Collier, 1966). This many-to-many relation between the points on the object and the grains on the plate has two interesting consequences. The first has to do with the conditions under which the recorded image can be made to reappear. To the naked eye the hologram is a meaningless jumble of grey markings, but if it is illuminated with part of the wavefront which produced it, the rest of the same wavefront will automatically emerge from it. This is essentially why holography calls for laser illumination and highly stable optics; only a coherent light source can yield an accurately reproducible wavefront. The second consequence of distributing the optical information evenly over the plate is that holograms are remarkably insensitive to damage; quite a passable image of the original object can be conjured up even when part of the hologram has been removed, though of course the quality of reproduction falls off with the degree of ablation.

These facts are well known. What is not so widely known is that one can use the same hologram for recording a number of different scenes. What one does is to expose the plate, before development, to the wavefront from each scene. Then if the light from part of one scene is allowed to fall on the hologram, the rest of that particular scene makes its appearance. The apparition is rather blurred, to an extent which depends on the amount of regularity in each recorded scene and on the degree of resemblance between the various scenes. But within this limitation a multiply exposed hologram behaves as an associative, or content-addressable, memory.

As an analogue to the long-term memory, then, holography is free from the three objections which apply to photography—a fact which has not escaped attention in the literature (I think Beurle, 1956, was the first to draw the analogy, but it has since been reiterated by Julesz & Pennington, 1965, and others). There is no sharp limit to the number of scenes which can be recorded on one hologram, though an attempt to record too many will result in a severe deterioration in clarity of recall. The problem of content-addressing is solved automatically: a scene can be recalled in outline by supplying any part of it and—which is a positive advantage—in no other way. And, as already remarked, an ablated hologram can be used for re-creating images which, although fuzzier than those obtainable from the complete hologram, are correct in their main features.

It would be naive to accept holography as a literal model of, say, the visual memory, and I would be embarrassed to be associated with such a simple-minded view. But there does seem to be a strong case for supposing that our memories rely on non-local information storage, to at least a considerable extent, so perhaps it is worth while making one or two additional points about holographic recording, since they apply to non-local storage in general. First, about the famous or infamous "engram." If one tried to find on a hologram an "engram" sufficient for the reconstruction of a recorded scene, one would look in vain. This is because the pattern on a hologram is basically ambiguous, like the Patterson function of a crystal. What the hologram records is essentially the power spectrum of the wave from the object, regarded as a superposition of spatial Fourier components. Each grain carries a record of the intensity of a particular component—a feature of the wave as a whole—but the phase relations between the different components are not recorded. They can be reconstructed, but only by supplying information from outside—by putting in enough of the object wave itself to determine them. The recorded features are themselves non-local, that is to say, each of them defines some internal relationship between the parts of the object. Only when some "absolute" information is made available can the "relative" information embodied in the hologram be used to re-create the original object. A reassuring thought for anyone who fears that his innermost thoughts and memories might be accessible to a surgeon with enough skill and patience to make a complete anatomical map of his cortex!

III. Non-local Storage in the Time Dimension

In trying to make theories of the memory one cannot afford to ignore the time dimension. Certainly not if one is considering an input stream from the outside world, such as audible speech; nor, surely, if one is thinking about the signals which pass up to the cortex for recording or recognition. Any such signal must be thought of as a pattern of cerebral events which are extended not only in space but in time, and the significance of any signal must depend not only on its neural path or paths but on the temporal relations between the pulses travelling along these paths. It is therefore natural to ask whether the principle of non-local information storage, realized in space by the holograph, could also be realized in the dimension of time. A temporal hologram, or "holophone," would be a physical system which could record one or more time-varying signals in such a way that the input of a cue from any one of them would immediately evoke the continuation of that particular signal. The answer is that there is no difficulty in principle about doing this, and a little later I shall describe how one could construct such an automaton (Longuet-Higgins, 1968). But first, perhaps, I should explain exactly what the holophone is designed to do, viewing it simply as a black box with one input channel and one output channel. For our purposes three properties are of particular interest:

First, the holophone can be used for recording any input signal which lies in a certain frequency range and does not exceed a certain length. If part of the recorded signal is then fed into the holophone, the continuation of the signal emerges immediately, in real time. The amount of noise in the playback depends on the details of the signal and cue.

Secondly, several signals can be recorded on the same holophone. If the signals are uncorrelated, an input cue from one of the signals will evoke the continuation of that same signal. The accompanying noise increases, not unnaturally, with the number of recorded signals.

Thirdly, the holophone can be used, like an optical filtering system, for detecting the occurrence of a given segment in the course of a long signal. What one does is to record on the holophone the segment of interest followed immediately by a strong pulse. The long signal is then played into the holophone; immediately after an occurrence of the recorded segment a pulse will emerge from the holophone.

In thinking how to construct such a black box it is easiest to argue by analogy with the holograph. In holography one records the power spectrum of a spatial pattern, regarded as the superposition of its Fourier components. So, the holophone should have elements which can record the power spectrum of a time-varying signal. In holography the incident wavefront is mediated by a set of darkened grains in a photographic emulsion. By analogy, the signal passing into a holophone should be mediated by a bank of narrow-pass filters, and the output of each filter must be weighted by an amount depending on the loudness of that frequency in the recorded signal. In viewing a hologram, our eyes resynthesize the signals transmitted by the individual grains on the plate. The weighted outputs of the filters must therefore be combined in parallel to give the final output signal.

Let us imagine, then, a bank of narrow-pass filters, each of which can be regarded as an oscillator with a certain resonant frequency and damping constant. Taken together they will behave rather like the strings of a grand piano, which can be set into oscillation by singing into the piano with the sustaining pedal held down. What one hears afterwards is the combined effect of the individual oscillations, which continue, of course, long after the acoustic stimulus has ended. The holophone is a similar system, but with the additional feature that the output of each oscillator is fed into an amplifier of variable gain, and the memory of the system resides in the gains of all the amplifiers. In recording a signal one keeps a tally of the amount of work done by the signal on each oscillator, and then turns up the gain of its amplifier by a proportional amount.

The layout of the holophone is shown in Fig. 1.

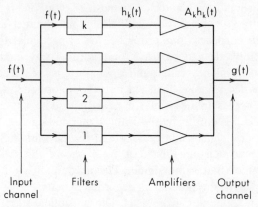

FIGURE 1. Layout of holophone. (Reprinted from D. Michie (ed.). Machine intelligence 4. Edinburgh: Edinburgh University Press, in press.)

On the left is the input channel, connected in parallel to the filters, represented as rectangles. Then come the amplifiers, indicated by triangles; their outputs are combined in parallel to give the overall output of the device. Not shown in Fig. 1 are a set of integrators, one for each filter, which are called into operation when an input signal is to be recorded. To see how the holophone works we must now run over the essential parts of the mathematical theory; we shall then be in a better position to assess its possible relevance to cerebral function.

Let $f(t)$ be an input signal and let $h_k(t)$ be the output of the kth filter. Each filter responds linearly

$$h_k(t) = \int_0^\infty R_k(\tau)f(t - \tau)\, d\tau,$$

and its response function has to be of the form

$$R_k(\tau) = (\mu/\pi)e^{-\mu\tau} \cos k\mu\tau.$$

The quantity μ in this expression determines both the bandwidth of every filter and the spacing between the resonant frequencies of neighboring filters, so that the frequency range is fully covered. For a particular set of amplifier gains the output signal $g\,(t)$ is given by

$$g(t) = \sum A_k h_k(t),$$

where A_k is the gain of the kth amplifier.

Suppose now that we wish to record a signal $f(t)$ which has come to an end before $t = 0$. We arrange for the integrators to measure the quantities

$$W_k = \int_{-\infty}^0 f(t)h_k(t)\, dt,$$

which may be thought of as the amounts of work done by $f\,(t)$ upon the various filters, with greater weight attaching to the more recent past. (It can be shown that the W_k are necessarily positive quantities.) Subsequently, at leisure, we increase the gains of all amplifiers in proportion to the W_k:

$$\Delta A_k = \frac{2\pi\lambda}{\mu} W_k.$$

This has the effect of altering the response function $M(\tau)$ of the holophone, defined by the relation between its input and its output:

$$g(t) = \int_0^\infty M(\tau)f(t - \tau)\, d\tau.$$

Detailed analysis shows that when μ is small the change in $M(\tau)$ due to the recording of $f(t)$ is

$$\Delta M(\tau) = \lambda e^{-2\mu\tau} \int_{-\infty}^0 f(t)f(t - \tau)\, dt.$$

This is a weighted autocorrelation integral of the recorded signal. If the duration of $f(t)$ is short compared to μ^{-1}, the exponential term in the integrand may be neglected; if it is much longer, the early part of the signal will be forgotten. The quantity μ^{-1} thus sets an effective upper limit on the length of signal that can be recorded.

What the holophone essentially records, then, are *correlations* between the amplitude of the signals at one time and the amplitude at a later time —later by an interval τ. It does this by storing separately each rhythm in the signal. There are two senses in which the storage is non-local. First, the information about the recorded signal $f(t)$ is stored in a number of different places—as the gains of the various amplifiers—and damage to a few of these will affect only the general quality of the playback, not result in the total loss of particular sections. Conversely, the recorded items of information all relate to the signal as a whole, not to particular sections of it. In both these respects the holophone parallels the holograph precisely.

To understand how the holophone works in storing, recognizing, and reconstructing temporal sequences it is necessary to pursue the mathematics a little further. Suppose that initially all the amplifiers have zero gain, so that no signal gets through and $M(\tau)$ is identically zero. A signal $f(t)$ is now recorded. After the recording the response function $M(\tau)$ will be given by our earlier expression for $\Delta M(\tau)$ and a new input signal $f^1(t)$ will evoke the output

$$g(t) = \int_0^\infty \Delta M(\tau) f^1(t - \tau) \, d\tau.$$

It might be supposed that the output $g(t)$ is merely an indistinct "echo" of the new input signal $f^1(t)$, and in general this will be true. But a different conclusion must be drawn if f^1 happens to be an excerpt from the recorded signal f. To see why, we transform the expression for $g(t)$ into the alternative form

$$g(t) = \lambda e^{-2\mu t} \int_0^\infty C(\tau) f(t - \tau) \, d\tau,$$

where

$$C(\tau) = \int_{-\infty}^\infty f^1(s) e^{2\mu s} f(s - \tau) \, ds,$$

an expression which applies if t denotes a time after the end of the cue f^1. In this form $g(t)$ is seen to be an echo of the recorded signal f, carrying on from the moment at which the quotation f^1 came to an end. The echo will be more or less indistinct, according to the statistical properties of the signal f and the excerpt f^1, but under favorable conditions may be almost noise-free.

One cause of virtually noise-free recall is that in which the signal $f(t)$

was a strong pulse followed by a weaker extended signal, and the cue f^1 is simply a pulse. On receipt of the cue the holophone will immediately emit the rest of the recorded signal, in real time and virtually free of noise. The pulse excites all the oscillators simultaneously. While they oscillate they can deliver a signal to the output channel, and if the amplifier gains were properly adjusted in the recording process the output from the holophone will be a resynthesis of the remainder of the recorded signal. The detailed theory corresponds almost exactly to that of the holographic experiment in which a collimated laser beam is employed both in the recording of an image and in its later reconstruction.

I have already mentioned the use of the holophone for recognizing the occurrence of a particular segment in the course of a long signal. Here again the problems of noise are relatively unimportant, but the strength of the pulse that signals an occurrence of the recorded segment will obviously depend on the length of the segment and the loudness of its occurrence in the message which is being processed.

IV. Problems in Relation to the Brain

As a model of the memory the holophone must not be taken too literally, for various reasons. First, its design specification is very demanding. The filters or oscillators of a holophone must be very accurately tuned if long signals are to be recorded, and must stay in tune for as long as the record is to be kept. This exacting requirement is probably satisfied by the cochlea, but there is no evidence for other systems of this kind in our heads. Secondly, there is the problem of the noise which inevitably accompanies the playback from a holophone which is presented with an extended cue. This noise would have to be got rid of somehow before the playback could be put to good use, and it is difficult to imagine how this could be done without introducing some non-linear feedback into the system. Thirdly, the holophone as I have described it will not recognize cues played at the wrong tempo. Whether this matters or not will depend on the role—if any—in which one proposes to cast the device. But obviously it could not, in its present primitive form, be regarded as a model of speech recognition, since the elements of speech can suffer considerable distortions of tempo without serious loss of intelligibility.

It would be a mistake, I am sure, to belittle these difficulties which weigh heavily against the holophone as a literal model of the long-term memory. But I would like to suggest that the general principles underlying its operation should be given very serious consideration in connection with the brain. If, as seems likely, non-local information storage is important in the dimensions of anatomical space, it is probably no less important in the dimension of time. One issue at least is raised by the holophone, and by models in the same line: do neurons respond only when they are stimulated—do they speak only when spoken to—or do they chatter away for a long time afterwards? Are there any natural neural oscillations which can be excited by brief stimuli, and which, by constructive interference, can later resynthesize some previously encountered signal? The theory I have been presenting, in terms of a particular automaton, is really no more than an attempt to highlight such questions.

REFERENCES

Beurle, R. L. (1956). Phil. Trans. Roy. Soc. B, 240, 55.
Collier, R. J. (1966). IEEE Spectrum, July 1966, 67–74.
Julesz, B., and Pennington, K. (1965). J. Opt. Soc. Am., 55, 604.
Longuet-Higgins, H. C. (1968). Nature, 217, 104. Longuet-Higgins, H. C.
    Proc. Roy. Soc. B, 171, 327.

DISCUSSION

LONGUET-HIGGINS: (in reply to a question): The signal to noise ratio depends almost entirely upon the statistics of the signal itself. That is to say, the reason you get noise out is not because you do not have an infinite range of filters covering the entire range: it is because the signal, in general, will match itself to a certain extent, not only in the right position, but also in the wrong position. White noise, in a way, is ideal for the purpose, because white noise is the one thing of which you can say it does not match itself at all well except when it is in the right position. The only essential is that you should cover with your filters the frequency range in question and you cannot record a signal unless its length T is significantly less than $2\frac{\pi}{\mu}$ where μ is the frequency spacing.

BLUM: Is it possible to elicit a given response by a signal which is not the original signal, but which has the same auto-correlation function?

LONGUET-HIGGINS: No. The auto-correlation function which you record does not determine the signal. In order to recover the original signal you have to feed in part of that signal so as to get the phase relationships right. Say, you feed in the first half of the signal; then you will practically have locked in the phase relationships and, since the amplitudes are fixed by what has been recorded, the rest of the signal will come out properly. So the system records, if you like, relative information. In order to get out absolute information you have to put in some absolute information, combine it with the relative information which is recorded, and produce the rest of the absolute information.

BLUM: How do you prevent different patterns from being mapped onto the same holographic sheet and interfering with each other?

LONGUET-HIGGINS: There are various things one could say about that. For instance, one can use the same filter bank together with several sets of amplifiers for different signal sources, which one can switch in according to what signal one has in hand at the moment. If you try to record too many signals on the same set of amplifiers you build up noise rather quickly. This little bit of theory I have given has all been concerned with a single input channel and a single output channel. But it is possible to have one input channel and several output channels or a whole multitude of input channels working in parallel and, correspondingly, whole alternative sets of output channels also working in parallel. Then, there is no reason why one should not handle the multiplicity of input channels in a holographic manner so that one could combine holographic and holophonic principles in the same system. The holographic part would deal with the spatial aspects and the holophonic part with the temporal aspects of a pattern.

Part II

LINGUISTICS

P. STANLEY PETERS, JR.

University of Texas at Austin
Austin, Texas

4 · On the Complexity of Language Processing by the Brain

I. Introduction

Language is man's most powerful system for processing information internally and his most general system both for this purpose and for that of transmitting and receiving it externally; and language itself is subject to processing by the human nervous system, so that when we process information with the aid of language, our nervous systems process that information only indirectly. Language, then, implicates information processing in at least two ways and is, accordingly, quite a fitting topic at this Symposium.

The question which presents itself is: what does linguistic theory have to contribute to our efforts to understand the neural processing of language? That it has anything to offer may not be obvious, since linguists have dealt with the system of language itself, concentrating on describing it as a sociological or psychological phenomenon and touching on its neurophysiological aspects only to a small extent. This seeming dilemma is fortunately only apparent; the utility of linguistic theory for neurophysiologists is a consequence of the fact that linguists have obtained a characterization of language in terms which are entirely independent of neurophysiology. If one wishes to study the neural correlates of some particular psychophysiological phenomenon, then one must, of necessity, have some way of identifying that phenomenon other than by neural activity. For, even if we are given an arbitrary amount of single cell recordings from, say, the motor cortex, we can learn nothing from such records alone about the connection between neural events and motor activity. It is only because we are able to describe

51

motor activity in terms of such physical properties as direction and amplitude of the forces exerted, that we can correlate aspects of this activity
with neural events.

The lack of progress in discovering the mechanisms underlying higher
phenomena such as thinking, is due in part to the absence of independent
characterizations of these phenomena. Obviously, other factors play a role,
for example, the problems of doing single cell recordings on humans. Yet
even if these impediments were suddenly removed, no progress could be
made toward discovering the brain mechanisms underlying, say, the mental
activity of solving a crossword puzzle unless an independent characterization of this activity were available. In addition, the use of language involves many features of intrinsic interest to physiology. Thus, the process
of understanding a sentence has an obvious temporal aspect; it involves
extensive use of short term memory and reference to long term memory.

It will be convenient, at this point, to introduce a distinction which will
facilitate future discussion. If one were writing a computer program to
process language, a useful stratagem would be to divide the program into
two subparts. One subpart would control transactions with the external
environment by detecting incoming linguistic messages and converting from
their representation in the external medium to a convenient, equivalent,
internal representation and, in addition, by converting internal representations of outgoing messages to their external representations. The other
subpart of our program would then be free to process linguistic messages
purely in terms of an internal representation which can be chosen to maxi-
mize efficiency in the performance of this function, and to minimize constraints imposed by the structure of whatever system is used for external
representation of messages and by the transmitting and receiving equipment. The latter subpart would, of course, perform the essential functions
in language processing; the former would merely handle the task of transmitting and receiving incoming and outgoing messages much as a telegra-
pher or teletype operator would. We will divide the neural task of processing language into two subtasks analogous to the subparts of such a computer
program. The input/output subtask is accomplished by a combination of
central and peripheral neural structures with the aid of the inner ear for
input and the lungs, larynx, mouth, and nose for output. The other subtask,
which constitutes the principal work of language processing, is apparently
accomplished by the central nervous system alone.

To distinguish between these two subtasks is not to imply that they are
ultimately effected by distinct anatomical structures. The distinction is,
instead, one of function and is supported by clinical data. For example, some
types of aphasia are due to deficits in the input/output subtask with no
apparent impairment of the primary processing subtask. Lenneberg (1967,
pp. 191–192) reports that certain patients affected by receptive aphasia
can still process language internally, as evidenced by their continuing

ability to read. Other patients, unable to speak because of a faulty "output mechanism," are still capable of understanding (Benton, 1964, p. 42; Lenneberg, 1962).

Making use of this distinction, one can characterize the work which has been done on the investigation of the physiological aspects of language. This has been concerned with input and output, including an enormous amount of work on the articulation of speech sounds. Furthermore, the connection between these articulations and the acoustic nature of the sounds is fairly well understood in terms of physical laws. Some work has also been done on the innervation of muscles in speech production. But the subtask of primary processing has been dealt with by linguists only as a psychological or sociological entity, not as a neurophysiological process. Yet, primary processing is what accounts for the generality and power of language as an information processing system. Therefore, we will concentrate here on this part of the neural processing of language and, in this context, it is correct to say that linguists have not investigated to any great extent the neurophysiological basis of language (see, however, Liberman, 1969, this volume).

Before proceeding with our discussion of linguistic investigations, we ought first to review the results of research on language by neurophysiologists, research which has chiefly been concerned with the localization of a speech center in the brain. This will be the topic of Section Two.

Following this, we will proceed in Section Three with an outline of the theory which linguists have formulated to explain their findings, briefly justifying some of its features. Section Four then surveys some results of automata theory which will be useful in Section Five, where we investigate in detail some implications of linguistic theory regarding the complexity of the neuronal mechanisms which underlie human linguistic behavior. In Section Six, we will consider some possibilities which these results suggest for neurophysiological research.

II. Neurophysiological Investigations

Two types of investigation into the neurophysiological aspects of speech are described in the literature: clinical studies of speech deficits associated with brain damage (e.g., Head, 1926; Russell and Espir, 1961) and experimental studies using electrical stimulation of the brain (Penfield and Roberts, 1959). Both types of study are directed to questions about localization in the nervous system of neural structures controlling speech. Extensive—and conflicting—evidence on this matter has issued from these investigations but very little has been said about the detailed organization or operation of the mechanisms underlying speech.

The literature on aphasia is large and contains many descriptions of more or less gross language deficits associated with more or less major lesions of the brain. Unfortunately, it has been impossible to associate any details of symptoms with specific aspects of the lesions. Thus this work provides little support for theories of any specificity which attempt to relate neuro-anatomy and language use. As Lenneberg (1967, pp. 56–61) has pointed out, traumatic lesions provide a different map of even gross deficits from that which surgical excision determines. Thus, these data are equivocal even on the question of localization.

For different reasons, electrical stimulation of the brain has not yielded much insight into the neural operation of language. Such stimulation is, of course, very unusual excitation for the neurons it directly affects. Further-more, apparently only aphasic symptoms, and never actual speech, are elicited by such stimulation (cf. Penfield and Roberts, 1959). Thus the chief value of this tool is in mapping the neural structure implicated in language.

With the exception of some speculation on neural associations (Gesch-wind, 1965), neurophysiological studies of language have yielded results concerning the localization of speech only. As I remarked in my intro-duction, we would expect just such a situation at present. Thus, it appears that, if we are to unravel the mystery of what neuronal mechanisms underlie language, we will have to learn more about the nature of language itself and then we may be able to look more intelligently for the mechanisms.

III. Linguistic Theory

In order to deduce from known psychological properties of human linguistic capacity some properties of the underlying physical mechanisms, we will concentrate on two such capacities about which most is known from the linguistic and psychological points of view. These are speech perception and speech production. Of these, the former is by far the best studied and so we will devote most of our consideration to it.

Speech perception, like all perceptual problems, can be formulated as a problem of determining the contents of a "black box" which takes the perceived sensory stimuli as inputs and gives the corresponding percepts as outputs. In the case of speech perception, the input is a continuous time varying signal which is represented internally as a sequence of discrete speech sounds. For the purposes of the present discussion we will suppose that this conversion is effected through the input/output language process-ing subtask (see, however, Chomsky and Halle, 1968; Halle and Stevens, 1962; Stevens and Halle, 1967). The output of the black box is a percept of the utterance embodied in the input sequence of speech sounds. We are able to specify the input to our perceptual device quite precisely—and, thanks to psycholinguistic research, even rather narrowly as to what proper-ties of the acoustic signal are relevant to speech (see Liberman, et al., 1967) —and this leaves us with the problem of specifying the nature of the output.

In studies of other types of perception an impasse is reached at this point since little or nothing is known about the nature of the percept. By contrast, in speech perception we know a good deal about the percept. We will presently see what its properties are.

The problem of speech production can also be formulated as a black box problem. In this case, the output is a sequence of speech sounds, but it is not clear what the input is. The latter should include a specification of the meaning of the sentence to be uttered, but more information than just this is needed to determine a unique output. Although the exact content of this other information is not clear, the process of speech production subsumes at least a process for converting a representation of the meaning of a sentence into the sequence of speech sounds which determines its pronunciation.

There is a similarity between devices for speech perception and speech production. What we mean by perception of speech is not simply hearing acoustic disturbances which carry that speech through the air but rather understanding what has been spoken. So, for example, a cat is not capable of speech perception even though it may hear and attend to speech; more importantly, a person who does not know a given language is not capable of perceiving speech in that language. We would expect, therefore, to find a similarity between a perceptual device and a production device resulting from the necessity each has of incorporating the knowledge of some specific language. I will return to this point shortly. First, however, let me note that when a linguist sets out to describe a language, he tries to come up, not with a description of the mental processes by which a speaker-hearer of that language speaks and understands, but rather with a description of the knowledge that such a speaker-hearer has which enables him to speak and understand the language—the knowledge put to use in those processes. Thus, a linguistic description of a language omits something crucial to speech perception and speech production; namely, specification of the strategies employed in using knowledge of the language.

Linguists describe a language in terms of the regularities inherent in it; that is, they formulate the linguistically significant generalizations that can be made about the language. These grammars have traditionally been stated as rules for "making up" sentences, but the rules can be used for "breaking down" sentences, too. The more explicit grammars—called "generative grammars"—written by linguists today, also take the shape of rules for composing sentences. Linguists do not claim that humans literally use these rules to make up or break down sentences but instead that the rules capture the regularities of a language. Correspondingly, it is not at all obvious that human "perceptual devices" or "production devices" incorporate in any direct way the set of rules that a linguist writes for a language. In fact, since linguists pay no attention to formulating their rules in such a way as to be "convenient" for the purposes of speech perception or speech production, there is no reason to expect that a strategy for either process can be formulated which makes easy use of a linguist's rules. If these devices need not directly incorporate linguists' grammars, then what is the relation between such grammars and the mechanisms which perceive and produce speech? The answer is that these mechanisms must contain representations of the knowledge of a language which are equivalent to grammars of that language. They cannot process each sentence on an *ad hoc* basis and, therefore, they must incorporate a description of the regularities of a language, which may not be identical to a linguist's description but must at least be equivalent to it in a very strong sense. The description of regularities which is intrinsic in the perceptual device (or production device) must make the same statements, must present the same information, as a linguist's description does about each sentence of the language. These descriptions specify a particular association of sequences of speech sounds with a representation of speech percepts, and a perceptual device or production device must determine precisely the same association. In this sense we hope to be able to learn something about perception and production from linguistic research.

Now, a grammar is an account of a speaker-hearer's knowledge of his language, of the regularities characteristic of a language. But what shape do these regularities take? Can they be of an arbitrary sort or are they constrained? For example, could some language allow the generalization that if $w_1 w_2 \ldots w_{n-1} w_n$ is a sequence of words forming a sentence in the language, then $w_n w_{n-1} \ldots w_2 w_1$ is also a sentence—say, the negation of the former? The answer, as everyone will immediately guess, is certainly not. It appears that all the regularities in any language must be statable in terms of grammatical descriptions of a very restricted type, called transformational grammars. These grammars provide several representations of each sentence of a language, indicating its structure at varying degrees of abstraction from the speech signal itself. One such representation will indicate the meaning of the sentence, another its division into words and their grouping into phrases, and still another the words' phonetic manifestations as sequences of speech sounds. Linking these are a large number of intermediate representations which, unlike these, have no significance outside the grammar, and all this is arrayed in a hierarchy from the most abstract (semantic representation) to the least abstract (phonetic representation). The reason why a transformational grammar provides a variety of such codings for a sentence rather than a single one (which, for example, would state the segmentation of the sentence into speech sounds and the meaning associated with that sequence) is because (*a*) meaning is connected with sound only extremely indirectly and (*b*) most of the linguistically significant generalizations about a language are not about sequences of speech sounds (the superficial shape of sentences) but rather about abstractions which represent sentences in terms of properties not even possessed by sequences of speech sounds.

The former point is illustrated by such English sentences as

(1) (i)   The boy is certain to win a medal.
     (ii) The boy is anxious to win a medal.
     (iii) The fish is too small to eat.
     (iv) Everyone believes that Nixon won the election.
     (v)   Nixon is believed by everyone to have won the election.

Sentences (1,i) and (1,ii) show that similarities in phonetic composition do not necessarily signal likeness of meaning. These sentences are understood quite differently despite their phonetic resemblances; in (1,i) certainty is predicated of the proposition "The boy will win a medal" although (1,ii) does not predicate anxiety of this statement. On the other hand, (1,ii) asserts that the relation "is anxious for" holds between the boy and the content of the sentence "The boy will win a medal" while (1,i) does not maintain that these two stand in the relation "is certain of." In the limiting case of this phenomenon we have ambiguous sentences such as (1,iii), which can be thought of as having two exactly identical phonetic realizations associated with two different meanings. The meaning of individual words is the same on both semantic interpretations of sentence (1,iii), only their grammatical relations are different. One interpretation is parallel to "The fish is too small to swim"; "fish" is understood as subject of eat (and the object of "eat" is unspecified). The other is like "The fish is too small to keep"; "eat" is understood as having an unspecified subject and "fish" as object. This difference is obviously not manifested in the phonetic composition of sentence (1,iii) since the pronunciation is the same on either interpretation. The opposite phenomenon is illustrated in sentences (1,iv) and (1,v), which have very similar, perhaps identical, meanings but quite different phonetic representations. Precisely the same semantic relations hold in the two sentences; for example, in both cases "everyone" is the subject of "believe" and this verb has the sentence "Nixon won the election" as its object. This sentential object is not recognizable in (1,v), however, since its parts are not even contiguous. Thus very gross discrepancies in pronunciation of two sentences need not indicate any semantic difference at all.

The fact that most regularities of a language must be stated in terms of abstract representations of sentences will become apparent as we explain in more detail the nature of transformational grammars. This will be done by discussing as an example the analysis of reflexive pronouns in English. Before proceeding to our example, however, I will illustrate the type of structure which provides the more abstract representations of se-

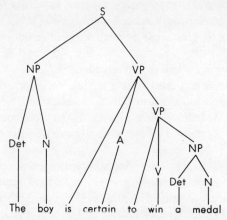

(2). On this phrase structure and on all subsequent ones, the labels on non-terminal nodes of the tree have the following interpretation:
S = Sentence, NP = noun phrase, VP = verb phrase, AUX = auxiliary verb, A = adjective, V = verb, Det = determiner, N = noun, PP = prepositional phrase and P = preposition.

quences of speech sounds which are needed in grammatical description.

Transformational grammars provide syntactic descriptions of sentences which indicate the grouping of speech sounds into words and of those words into phrases. For example, the sentences (1,i) and (1,ii) would receive syntactic structures such as (2) and (3) respectively.

Diagrams of this type, called phrase structures, are more adequate versions of the structures used to parse sentences in high school and are read as follows: any subsequence of a sentence which is traceable back to a node with a particular label (say, A) and is the longest subsequence traceable back to that node, is a phrase of type A in the sentence. So "the boy"

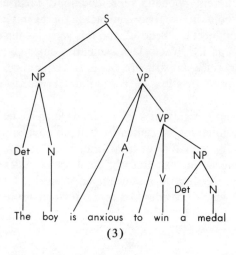

(3)

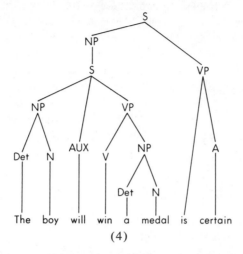

(4)

and "a medal" are both noun phrases (*NP*) in sentences (1,i) and (1,ii). This information exemplifies the fact that such structures represent features not present in the sequence of speech sounds constituting the pronunciation of a sentence. While the trees (2) and (3) represent a higher degree of abstractness in representation than phonetic transcriptions of sentences (1,i) and (1,ii), they are still too concrete to provide a basis for determining the vastly different semantic relations which hold in the two sentences. Transformational grammars provide syntactic structures which are abstract enough to permit this determination, structures which in the cases of sentences (1,i) and (1,ii) would look approximately like (4) and (5), respectively.

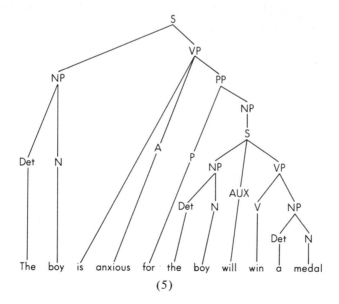

(5)

The grammar of English assigns these particular structures rather than any other because it is these which permit the statement of linguistically significant generalizations. Having exemplified what is meant by abstractness here, we can now proceed to investigate in somewhat greater detail, the regularities exhibited by reflexive pronouns in English.

When two noun phrases intended to refer to the same entity are in the same clause of a sentence, the second of them must be realized as a reflexive pronoun. Thus, we have such data as the following (a prefixed asterisk means that the associated sentence is ungrammatical):

(6) (i) He saw himself in the mirror.
     (ii) They pinched themselves.
     (iii) I can hardly hear myself over the loudspeaker.

(7) (i) * He saw themselves in the mirror.
     (ii) * They pinched myself.
     (iii) * I can hardly hear himself over the loudspeaker.

This illustrates the fact that reflexive pronouns occur only when they refer to the same entity as an earlier noun phrase in their clause. If we examine some other complex sentences involving two clauses, we will see that this statement is borne out, since reflexive pronouns are not possible—even when there is another, coreferential noun phrase in the sentence—unless it is in the same immediate clause.

(8) (i) I said that he saw himself in the mirror.
     (ii) * I said that he saw myself in the mirror.
     (iii) * I said that myself saw him in the mirror.

At one level of abstraction we can represent the structure of sentence (8,i) roughly as (9). The phrase structure (9) is to be read as we speci-

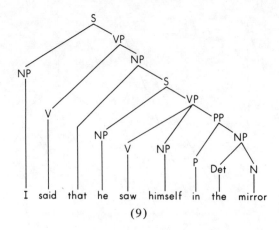

(9)

fied earlier: for example, "that he saw himself in the mirror" is a noun phrase, in fact the object of "said." Notice that in terms of phrase structures, clauses of a sentence are segments traceable back to a node labeled "S" (for sentence). We can summarize the generalization governing reflexive pronouns in English in terms of these abstract representations as follows: a reflexive pronoun may occur if, and only if, (*a*) it is coreferential with a noun phrase to its left and (*b*) each node labeled *S* dominates that noun phrase (i.e., is higher than it and is connected to it by branches of the tree) if, and only if, it dominates the reflexive pronoun. (While there are other uses of reflexive pronouns—e.g., the emphatic use in "He himself told me"—we will confine our attention to their major, coreferential use.)

We can next examine some more interesting cases. There is a reflexive pronoun in the sentence:

(10) He saw himself swing the bat.

This sentence is composed of two clauses just as is

(11) He saw that he swung the bat.

In terms of our generalization that reflexive pronouns occur only in the same immediate clause as their antecedent noun phrase, this means that the sentence (10) must have a structure such as (12) at some level of ab-

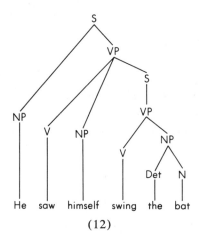

(12)

straction. But the necessity of assigning sentence (10) a structure such as (12) at some level, does not obviate the need to assign it a different structure at a deeper level of abstraction (as one might expect from its relation to [11]). For, notice that the similar sentence (13) also contains reflexives.

(13) I saw him pinch himself.

Thus, while the sentence (13) must have a structure parallel to (12) at
one degree of abstraction, it must have a structure such as (14) at a
deeper level. Observe also that we do not have grammatical sentences in
English with reflexive pronouns such as (15).

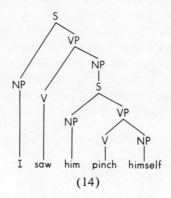

(14)

(15) * I saw him pinch myself.

This corroborates our assignment of structures such as (12) at a superficial level of abstraction, and (14) at a deeper level. Given our generalization about reflexive pronouns, we would not expect sentences such as (15)
to be grammatical unless there were a level at which a single clause immediately contains the first and last noun phrases of the sentence. But
we have no evidence in favor of the existence of such a degree of abstractness and, in fact, (15) constitutes counter evidence. The important
point that we have been illustrating is that there is a generalization concerning the occurrence of reflexive pronouns in English sentences which
we can capture if sentences have structural representations of several degrees of abstractness; furthermore, once we have stated that generalization
in a natural fashion, it forces us to recognize more than one degree of abstractness in representation.

Now let us ask how to state in a precise rule the regularity we have been
discussing. Observing that reflexive pronouns occur in the environments
we have specified—and for the purpose of this discussion only in those
environments—it is apparent that a natural way to capture this generalization is to assume that reflexive pronouns are not present in the most abstract structural representation of any sentence. We can then postulate a
rule which will convert representations at one level of abstractness to those
at the next lower level and which introduces reflexive pronouns in just
those environments which we have been discussing. Such a rule must apply
to phrase structures and convert them into other phrase structures. Rules of
this type are called grammatical transformations. We can state the reflexive
rule as a transformation written informally as (16).

(16) $X - NP - Y - NP - Z$
 1 2 3 4 5 $\Rightarrow 1 - 2 - 3 - 4 + \text{SELF} - 5$

Condition: 2 is coreferential with 4 and a node labeled S dominates 2 if and
only if it dominates 4.

The rule is to be applied as follows. A phrase structure is affected by rule
(16) only if it meets the structure index (the statement to the left of the
arrow, including the condition) of the rule; otherwise, it is left unchanged
by the rule. If a phrase structure can be divided into five successive parts
which do not overlap and do exhaust the structure, where the second and
fourth of these parts must be trees headed by a node labeled NP (for noun
phrase) and further must be marked as referring to the same entity, and
must be in the same immediate clause, then application of the rule is completed by attaching the marker SELF to the right end of the fourth part of
the phrase structure.

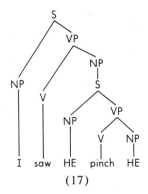

(17)

Then the sentence (13) will have the structure (17) as a fairly abstract
representation which will be converted by (16) into (18), a more nearly
correct version of (14). The structure (18) is not the most superficial

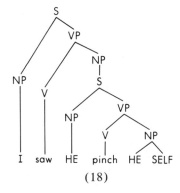

(18)

phrase structure that the sentence (13) has, however. As we shall see, (18) will be operated on by rule (19) to yield (20), a still less abstract structure of (13), analogous to structure (12) of sentence (10). The structure index

$$NP - \left\{ \begin{matrix} saw \\ heard \\ \bullet \\ \bullet \\ \bullet \end{matrix} \right\} - \left[NP - VP \right]_S$$

$$1 \qquad\qquad 2 \qquad\qquad 3 \qquad 4 \Rightarrow 1 - 2 + 3 - \emptyset - \emptyset - 4$$

(19)

of this transformation specifies that the rule will apply to a phrase structure if it can be divided into four parts: the first and third are headed by nodes labeled *NP,* the second is any of the verbs listed between braces, and the fourth is headed by a node labeled *VP* for verb phrase, where a node labeled *S* exhaustively dominates the third and fourth parts. Application of the rule to such a phrase structure results in attachment of the third part and of the fourth part (with its dominating node labeled *S*) under immediate domination of the node which immediately dominates the second part.

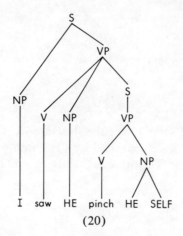

(20)

The effect of applying rule (19) to structure (18) is to raise the noun phrase "he" from the subordinate clause to the main clause and to remove the rest of the subordinate clause from domination by the object noun phrase node of the main clause. Rule (19) is not motivated by sentences such as (13) but rather by sentence (10), as we will see. But note that it creates a structure for (13) in which the noun phrase that started off as subject of "pinch" has become object of "saw." Thus, the rule governing case of pronouns in English will convert this noun phrase to "him." If rule (19) had not applied to (18), then we would have incorrectly predicted that instead of (13) we would have in English a sentence such as (21,i).

(21) (i) * I saw he pinch himself.
     (ii) I saw that he pinched himself.

If, on the other hand, rule (19) is blocked from applying, for example, by the prior application of an optional transformation inserting "that" as in (21,ii) or (11), then the pronoun remains "he." Thus rule (19) correctly applies to (18) even though it is not strongly motivated on the basis of sentence (13).

The sentences like (10) do, however, strongly motivate (19). For sentence (10) the structure that corresponds to (17) in degree of abstractness is (22). This structure is left unchanged by rule (16) since its structure

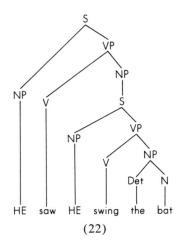

(22)

index is not satisfied by any division of (22) into five parts. But we must somehow introduce the marker SELF into (10). Rule (19) does apply to (22) converting it into (23). Now rule (16) applies and yields (24), which is a more nearly correct version of (12). Thus, introducing rule (19) into the grammar of English allows us to preserve the generalization stated in rule (16) and still describes sentences such as (10) correctly since it converts a highly abstract representation of that sentence (structure [22]) which does not fall under the generalization governing reflexive pronouns (rule [16]) into a less abstract representation (structure [23]) which does fall under that generalization (to which rule [16] does apply). Rule (19), furthermore, is motivated by other facts about English. Thus, it supports the correctness of rule (16) rather than suggesting that the latter should be modified to apply to structure (22). Many other generalizations about

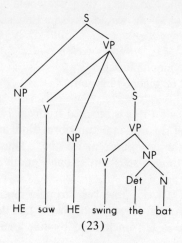

(23)

English will also be stated as transformational rules like (16) and (19). The order of application of these rules and the positions at which they apply in a phrase structure are determined by the interaction of general principles such as the transformational cycle (Chomsky, 1965) and ordering specifications contained in the grammar. In particular, the grammar of English contains the two transformations illustrated in the order: rule (19) first, then rule (16). The principle that rules are applied, first to the most deeply embedded clause of a phrase structure, then to the next most deeply embedded clause, etc., plus this ordering, requires that the rules be applied as we did in our discussion.

The above examples illustrate the basic features of grammatical transformations. They apply in sequence rather than all at once, progressively converting the most abstract representation of a sentence into its least abstract syntactic representation through many intermediate stages. These

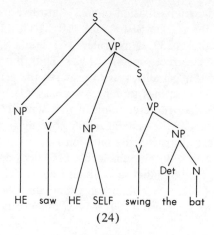

(24)

stages are not superfluous but are necessary in order to capture the linguistically significant generalizations about a language (for example, sentence [13] falls under the reflexive generalization by virtue of structure [17], but it falls under the generalization about case of pronouns only by virtue of structure [20]). After all grammatical transformations have been applied, further rules apply which do not change the phrase structure of a sentence but rather change the shape of the formatives—the elements at the bottom of phrase structure trees. These phonological rules, which ultimately determine the way a sentence is pronounced, would, among other things, convert "he SELF" in (20) and (24) into "himself." The phonological rules also apply sequentially, progressively converting very abstract representations of formatives into contextually determined phonetic shapes. The ability of these rules to capture linguistically significant generalizations depends on their having available the most superficial syntactic representation, called a surface structure, and on the existence of intermediate degrees of abstraction in phonological representation of formatives. The major split between syntactic rules, which alter phrase structure, and phonological rules, which do not, is also dictated by the goal of capturing regularities. Thus, transformational grammars are composed of a syntactic component, a semantic component, and a phonological component. The syntactic component generates a set of surface structures. These constitute the input to the phonological component, which has as output a set of sequences of speech sounds. The set of surface structures must be constrained by some device, and so, in addition to an ordered set of transformations, the syntactic component must contain a base component which makes available a limited set of phrase markers for the transformational component to operate on. This set must not include (25), for example, since this structure would be converted by the transformational and phonological rules into (15), which is not a grammatical sentence of English.

The base rules are started by making available a partially formed tree consisting of a single node labeled *S*. They then enlarge partially formed

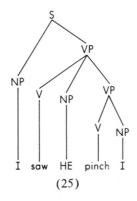

(25)

trees in stages. One base rule of English might say that a partially formed tree can be enlarged by adding under any of its bottom nodes labeled *S*, two nodes labeled *NP* and *VP*, respectively. Other base rules will permit further enlargement until a complete tree is formed. All such trees which can be converted by the transformational rules into surface structures are called deep structures. The nature of base, transformational and phonological rules has been studied extensively. For a discussion of the constraints on syntactic rules (see Chomsky, 1961, 1963, 1965, in press; Katz and Postal, 1964; Perlmutter, 1968; Peters and Ritchie, in preparation; and Ross, 1967). Constraints on phonological rules are discussed in Chomsky and Halle (1968) and Halle (1959, 1962).

As syntactic research goes deeper into the details of various languages, more and more abstract representations are seen to be needed in the syntactic component—that is, they are needed for transformational rules to operate on. These structures exhibit nearly the degree of abstractness required for semantic representations. It is an interesting open question whether there is a sharp division between the syntactic and semantic components. If there is, as in (26), then there must be semantic rules converting

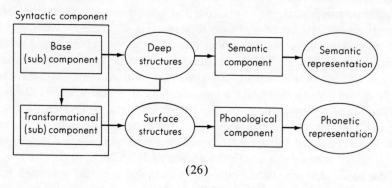

(26)

deep structures into semantic representations. If deep structures are semantic representations, then there is no sharp division and we would have the situation shown in (27).

Let us return for a moment to the syntactic component. This component

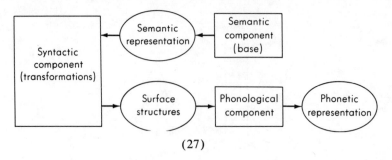

(27)

interrelates the two principal syntactic representations of a sentence: namely, its deep structure—which determines its meaning either directly or by interpretation in a semantic component—and its surface structure— which determines its phonetic realization by means of the phonological rules. We will take a structural description of a sentence to be a pair consisting of its deep structure and its surface structure. In addition to these two, every sentence has many intermediate structures which are real in that the linguistically significant generalizations about the language are generalizations about these structures. But these structures do not have the same sort of prominence as have deep and surface structures because the latter completely determine the former.

A grammar connects with the input to a perceptual device and the output of a production device by providing phonetic representations. How does it connect with the output of a perceptual device and the input of a production device (semantic representation plus other unknown information)? We have just seen how it provides a semantic representation of a sentence. But what constitutes a speech percept? A structural description of a sentence is clearly an important part of a percept because it specifies (a) the manner of combination of speech sounds into formatives and the manner of combination of these into phrases (surface structure) and (b) the grammatical relations between these elements at the greater degree of abstraction relevant to semantic interpretation (deep structure). This information is certainly a part of a speech percept; the meaning of a sentence is also a part, possibly not distinct from its deep structure. Thus, we can specify that the output of the perceptual device in which we are interested is a structural description of the sentence embodied in the input sequence of speech sounds (plus its semantic representation, if that turns out to be different from its deep structure). In the event of a sentence having more than one structural description, that is, in case it is ambiguous, a perceptual device should give all structural descriptions of the sentence as output.

We have arrived at this concept of a speech percept by following an essentially psychological line of reasoning. It is worth noting, however, that there is independent, experimental evidence supporting the psychological reality of structural descriptions as speech percepts. The literature is full of reports of experiments confirming that hearers perceive language in terms of both deep and surface structures. Fodor and Bever (1965), Garrett, et al. (1966), and Johnson (1966) have shown the relevance of surface structure for perception of sentences. Miller (1962), Blumenthal (1967), Savin and Perchonock (1965), Mehler (1964), Gough (1965), Slobin (1966), and Coleman (1964) have demonstrated that deep structures are significant in the perception of sentences. Furthermore, Maclay and Osgood (1959) and others have demonstrated that structural descriptions are relevant to speech production as well.

We now know what the inputs and outputs of a speech perceiver are, and we also know what the outputs are as well as a great deal about the inputs of a speech producer. Furthermore, we have seen how a grammar— a linguist's description of a language—mediates between these inputs and outputs. Such a grammar is a statement of the knowledge that humans put to use in speaking and understanding. We do not, however, know how this knowledge is used. Although linguists have not investigated the operations that go into the performance of these processes, as I mentioned earlier, some psychologists have both speculated and experimented on their nature.

In the earliest psycholinguistic studies dealing with sentence perception in terms of the types of grammars we have been surveying, it was assumed that a perceptual device contained just such a grammar plus a set of strategies for using it. We can diagram this conception as in (28). According to

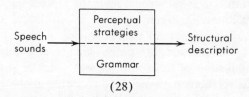

$$(28)$$

this view, speech perception consists in finding a way to apply just the right sequence of rules in a transformational grammar to derive the phonetic sequence which was fed into the perceptual device. The original experiment within this framework was performed by Miller, *et al.* (1962). Miller and McKean (1964), Mehler (1963), McMahon (1963), and Savin and Perchonock (1965) supported the above conception of speech perception with further experiments. Although this theory seemed promising, later experiments have cast doubt on its correctness. Slobin (1963) found that the theory failed to explain his experimental results. Subsequent experiments have amassed a body of data which conflict with at least the simplest version of such a theory (Fodor, *et al.,* 1965; Bever and Mehler, 1966; and Bever, *et al.,* 1966). Thus, this theory, not a particularly plausible one, anyway, is not well confirmed. In response to these difficulties, Fodor and Garrett (1967) and Fodor, *et al.* (1968) have suggested that psycholinguists attempt to formulate a theory which would not employ a transformational grammar directly but which would use, instead, a set of heuristic devices deduced from the rules of such a grammar to arrive at structural descriptions of sentences, given their phonetic representations as input. This suggestion remains rather nonspecific at present.

Thus, psycholinguistic investigations into speech perception are in a state of uncertainty, and the only safe summary we can give of their results is that no one really knows how knowledge of a language is put to use in understanding sentences. Hence, if we are to discover anything about the nature of the human "perceptual device," it will have to be from a point of view so abstract that the specific strategy of this device is irrelevant. Needless to say, the situation is even more fluid in the study of production of speech, and, hence, anything we are to learn about the human "production device" will have to be extremely abstract. Nevertheless, as we will see in Section Five, it is still possible to learn something about the constraints on the neuronal mechanisms of both of these devices. For this purpose we next turn to a brief summary of some results in automata theory.

IV. Mathematical Linguistics and Automata Theory

If nothing is known about the strategies of speech perception or speech production from a psychological perspective, how can we hope to discover neurological constraints based on psychological facts? The answer is that we do know a great deal about the nature of grammars and therefore about the nature of the association which perception and production induce between speech signals and structural descriptions. We can, therefore, investigate general properties which must be possessed by any device capable of mapping sequences of speech sounds into their structural descriptions or, conversely, of mapping semantic representations into speech which expresses the particular meaning represented. Since humans as perceptual devices and production devices have these capabilities, we will then hope to learn something about how speaking and understanding proceed in humans. In this very abstract manner we will apply some results from the field of automata theory. Our immediate question, then, can be formulated as follows. Viewing a perceptual device simply as performing a mapping of input sequences of speech sounds into output sets of structural descriptions, we ask what the complexity of this mapping is. Similarly, thinking of a production device as mapping semantic representations into the set of all sequences of speech sounds which can receive that semantic interpretation, we ask how complex this production mapping is.

To attack these questions we may use a notion of computational complexity which has been developed in automata theory. This notion scales functions for complexity in accordance with the amount of memory required to compute them. We could investigate the question of complexity in many ways; for example, we might have chosen to introduce a scale of complexity based on the amount of time required by automata of a certain type to compute particular mappings, and then we could place the perceptual and production mappings on this scale. However, the use of memory in perception and production has been much more thoroughly studied by psychologists and so there is a better chance of our results being related to experimental findings than would otherwise be the case. Since most automata use one or more linear tapes as memory, a natural index of the amount of memory required for a particular computation is the number of tape squares used in that computation. This choice of measure for memory is very convenient for our purposes, since it is equivalent to a measure of the amount of information contained in the memory at any instant during a computation. More precisely, suppose an automaton has one tape (with an alphabet of k symbols), a control unit with n internal states and a read-write head in contact with the tape. Suppose that for a given computation we limit the automaton to using a finite piece of tape which is l squares long. Then the number of distinct configurations of tape contents and control unit states that the automaton can enter during the computation is at most $l \cdot n \cdot k^l$: the head is scanning one of l squares, the control unit is in one of n states and the tape contains one of k^l possible sequences of length l over the k symbol alphabet. A more convenient upper bound is $k_0{}^l$ for a new constant, say $k_0 = k \cdot n$. Now, specifying that the automaton is in a particular configuration at some instant provides approximately $\log_2 k_0{}^l$ bits of information and this is equal to $k_1 \cdot l$ where $k_1 = \log_2 k_0$. This number gives the amount of memory used by a deterministic automaton. Since these considerations generalize from the case of one tape to others, except for a constant factor determined by each particular automaton, the number of tape squares used in a computation is an upper bound on the number of bits of memory required to perform that computtation. We now introduce a scale of computational complexity of mappings which ranks them according to the memory required by the automaton to perform the mapping, as compared to the memory required to store the input.

The most general automata in terms of computing power, the Turing machines, can use an arbitrarily large amount of memory in any computation. At the other extreme of the spectrum of interesting automata, the finite automata use only a fixed, finite amount. In between, there are many classes of automata which use a bounded amount of tape depending on the input. Thus, above the finite automata with a fixed memory, we can place the pushdown-storage automata, which need no more tape for a particular computation than required to store the input they are processing and use this tape in a very restricted fashion. Next are the linear bounded automata, which are allowed an amount of tape bounded by a constant multiple of the length of their input. Then we have a variety of classes of automata which use no more tape squares than K^l, K^{K^l}, etc., in a computation on an input of length l, where K is a constant depending on the automaton. The functions computed by all of the automata which we have mentioned so far, are elementary in the sense of Csillag-Kalmar (1947), and the mappings are relatively easy to compute from a mathematician's point of view. Above these automata in the hierarchy would be those which compute primitive recursive functions, total recursive functions, and partial recursive functions, the latter being computed by general Turing machines.

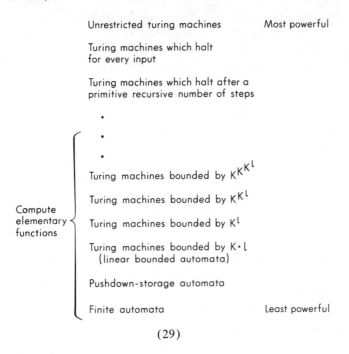

Unrestricted turing machines   Most powerful

Turing machines which halt
for every input

Turing machines which halt after a
primitive recursive number of steps

.

.

.

Turing machines bounded by $K^{K^{K^l}}$

Turing machines bounded by K^{K^l}

Compute
elementary   Turing machines bounded by K^l
functions

Turing machines bounded by $K \cdot l$
(linear bounded automata)

Pushdown-storage automata

Finite automata   Least powerful

(29)

The diagram (29) portrays this hierarchy in a graphic fashion. We will be most interested in the more restricted automata, which compute elementary functions, since, as we will see, they can perform the perceptual and production mappings between sequences of speech sounds and their structural descriptions. The hierarchy of automata diagrammed in (29) gives us a convenient scale of complexity, since we can define the degree of complexity of a mapping to be the lowest class in the hierarchy which contains an automaton capable of computing the mapping.

V. Properties of the Perceptual Device and of the Production Device

Consider, now, a black box which performs the process of speech perception. All we know about the box is that its behavior in mapping inputs into outputs is described by a transformational grammar which relates phonetic representations and structural descriptions in just the same way as the perceptual device. In addition, we have similar information about the contents of a black box which produces sentences.

Let us investigate a possible lower bound on memory for the perceptual device. To simplify our reasoning, let us make use of the fact that this device will not only be capable of understanding grammatical sentences of the language which it knows, but will also be able to recognize an ungrammatical sentence when one is presented as input. This suggests that for the sake of simplicity of argument we might place a lower bound on the memory of the device by considering only its ability to tell grammatical from ungrammatical sentences. We can rule out the possibility that only a fixed amount of memory is required, i.e., that the perceptual device is a finite automaton. This was originally demonstrated in 1956 by Chomsky, using the argument outlined below.

English shares the defining properties of certain artificial "languages" such as the one containing all strings that begin with an arbitrary sequence of the letters *a* and *b* and are completed by the reversal of the same sequence. This language, call it L_1, contains such sequences as *abbbba*, *abbaabba* and *ababbabbababa*. The essential defining characteristic of L_1 is that there are nested dependencies of unbounded depth. That is, the first letter must be the same as the last, no matter how many letters intervene, the second letter must be the same as the next to last, and so on. English has many constructions which give it these same properties. Thus, there are sentences of English of the types (30), where S_1 and S_2 are also English sentences.

(30) (i) If S_1, then S_2.
       (ii) Either S_1 or S_2.

These are just two of the many constructions which are relevant here. The point is that there is a dependency between "If" and "then," and another between "Either" and "or," and since S_1 in (30,i) and (30,ii) may be taken to be a wide range of English sentences, including such sentences as (30,i) and (30,ii), these dependencies can be nested to an unbounded depth. Thus (31), for example, is a sentence of English:

(31) If either someone realizes that if the Earth is a sphere, then it necessarily rotates or he is stupid, then many people are stupid.

Although not very elegant, (31) exhibits the regularities which characterize English sentences. With a little effort it can be interpreted by any English speaker and its truth or falsity could be determined. Naturally, the inelegance of sentence (31) does not disqualify it as a grammatical sentence of English; some sentences will be more elegant, others, less, but all will be sentences nonetheless. By the same token the complexity of sentence (31), which makes it somewhat difficult to understand, does not affect its status as an English sentence. Some grammatical sentences are more difficult to understand than others, and the difficulty is determined by such properties as length, degree of self-embedding, etc. Sentence (31) has a structure which embeds clauses inside clauses several times. We can schematically represent this as in (32)

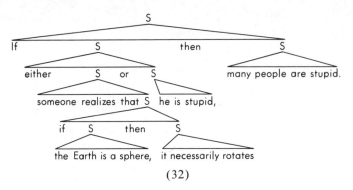

(32)

The degree of self-embedding of this structure is three, since there is a clause embedded internally in a clause which is itself embedded internally in a clause that is internally embedded in the main clause. As degree of self-embedding increases above this, sentences become even more difficult to understand. They continue to be grammatical sentences of English, however, since they exhibit all the regularities of English sentences as specified by English speakers' grammatical knowledge, despite the difficulty speakers have in ascertaining this fact. Therefore, English possesses the defining properties of L_1. But L_1 is an example of a language which cannot be recognized by a finite automaton (for a proof of this, see Chomsky, 1956, or Rabin and Scott, 1959). Hence, English cannot be recognized by such an automaton, either.

The next class of automata which we have introduced is the class of pushdown-storage automata. These, too, can be ruled as too restricted, at least as regards the fashion in which they use their memory, if not because of the amount which they have. As before, we restrict our attention to the task of distinguishing grammatical from ungrammatical sentences. This time let us consider an artificial "language" containing all strings which begin with any sequence of the letters a and b and are completed by a repetition of the identical sequence. This language, call it L_2, contains such sequences as *abab*, *abaaba*, and *abbaababbaab*. In L_2 there are constraints (as in L_1); however, these constraints are not nested but rather overlap. That is, in a sequence in L_2 the first letter must be the same as the first one after the midpoint, the second letter the same as the second one after the midpoint and so on. Interestingly enough, Postal (1964) discovered that Mohawk, an American Indian language, has a construction with the same defining property as L_2. Without getting into technicalities, there is a certain class of verbs in Mohawk which permit incorporation of an object noun phrase into the verb as a prefix, no matter how long the noun phrase is. Thus, alongside a Mohawk sentence which we might roughly represent in English as (33,i), there is another sentence (33,ii), the same in meaning except for emphasis on the object noun phrase.

(33) (i) The-girls see the-house.

  (ii) The-girls house-see the-house.

In Mohawk sentences, if there is a noun phrase incorporated into the verb and the verb has an object, then the incorporated noun phrase and the object noun phrase must be identical. Since the incorporated noun phrase can be indefinitely long, this construction in Mohawk shares the defining properties of overlapping constraints with L_2. It happens that this property is one which cannot, in general, be detected by a pushdown-storage automaton. Chomsky (1963) and Postal (1964) argue that such an automaton cannot recognize the grammatical sentences of Mohawk, either, due to the similarity between Mohawk and L_2. There is a mathematical error in Postal's paper, but it is easily repairable. Hence, no perceptual device for Mohawk can have its memory organized in the same way as a pushdown-storage automaton.

In our framework, the class of linear bounded automata is the smallest one not known to fail in computing the perceptual mapping for some natural language. This is the highest lower bound that I have for the amount of memory required by a perceptual device. Although it is conceivable that performing the perceptual mapping for some natural language may be beyond the power of a linear bounded automaton, or even some more powerful type of automaton, I know of no evidence to that effect.

In arguing for an upper bound, we will make crucial use of the transformational grammar which is supposed to pair phonetic representations and structural descriptions in the same way as the perceptual device and production device. In showing that these devices could not be so impoverished that their memory is that of a finite or pushdown-storage automaton, it was sufficient to exhibit even a single language which could not be properly processed by such an automaton. To show that a certain amount of memory is sufficient, however, it is necessary to give an argument that it will suffice for all languages.

Recent research on transformational grammars, with an eye to understanding their mathematical properties, has resulted in the discovery that in describing natural languages it has been necessary to use only a small part of the resources of transformational description. Although there are transformational grammars which can describe any language recognizable by a Turing machine—the most general kind of language which is recognizable by a strictly mechanical device—in describing actual languages, only grammars belonging to a highly restricted subset of the transformational grammars have been used. In fact, for any grammar in the subset out of which linguists have drawn their grammars, the perceptual and

production mappings can be performed with at most $K^{K^{K^l}}$ bits of memory for an input requiring l bits of memory to store (an input l phonetic symbols in length)—where K is here a constant depending on the grammar. The reason for this has to do with the particular way in which these grammars assign deep structures.

From Section Three it will be recalled that each sentence has a deep structure that consists of one or more clauses arranged in a hierarchical fashion. The number of clauses in the deep structure of a sentence need not be the same as the number in its surface structure. For example, the sentence

(34) USC is likely to win the game.

has only one clause in its surface structure but at least two—roughly corresponding to (35,i) and (35,ii)—in its deep structure.

(35)   (i) It is likely.
       (ii) USC will win the game.

Grammars will vary in the number of clauses of the deep structures they assign to particular sentences. The particular subclass of transformational grammars from which linguists have drawn in describing actual languages, is characterized by the fact that its members assign to each sentence a deep structure without very many clauses. For each transformational grammar of an actual language that linguists have written, there is a constant K such that, every sentence l speech sounds in length, has a deep structure with, at most, K^l clauses in it. But then it can be shown (see Peters and Ritchie, in preparation) that, at most, $K^{K^{K^l}}$ bits of memory are required to perform the perceptual or production mapping. Note that we have no way of proving that our black boxes housing the perceptual device and production device do not use more memory than our bound. We have, however, proved that they do not need any more than $K^{K^{K^l}}$ bits of memory to process an input which requires l bits to be stored. Thus we have placed the perceptual and production mappings within a fairly narrow range on our scale of complexity. Furthermore, since it is reasonable to assume that the human "perceptual device" and "production device" use no more memory than is necessary in performing their tasks, we may place an upper bound on the amount of memory the human brain uses in processing particular sentences. Far from needing to act like an arbitrary Turing machine in order to speak and understand, the brain can behave like a much more restricted type of automaton and still perform these functions perfectly.

VI. Neurological Corollaries

Let us now ask how our deductions fit what we know about the brain from other sources. In this connection, the first thing that is likely to come to mind is that the brain apparently has only a finite amount of memory available. We will return shortly to the apparent contradiction with the fact that a perceptual device for speech cannot be a finite automaton.

It is rather natural to use the amount of memory required to understand a sentence as a measure of the difficulty of that sentence. Notice that if this is the correct measure of difficulty, our result of Section Five does not imply that all sentences of a given length are equally difficult to understand. The reason is, of course, that the expression we arrived at for a bound on memory is an upper bound on the memory required for any sentence of a given length. It may very well happen, however, that not all sentences of that length will require the maximum amount of memory. If memory required is the measure of difficulty, then not all sentences of a given length need be equally difficult to understand. Our memory bounds do make a prediction about difficulty of understanding, but it is somewhat more complex. On the assumption that difficulty of comprehension is linearly determined by amount of memory required in the perceptual process, our bounds predict that if we look only at sentences which are hardest to understand of all sentences of their particular length, then we will find that as the length of these sentences increases the difficulty of understanding them will increase at a rate which is at least linear—at least $K \cdot l$ bits of memory are required to process the hardest sentences of length l—and is no greater than $K^{K^{K^l}}$. Coupled with the fact that the brain has only a finite amount of memory capacity, we would then predict that there is a certain length L such that one cannot understand the hardest sentences of any length greater than L. Furthermore, we would predict that as the length of sentences increases, the structure of those we can understand will have to become relatively simpler. So when we are dealing with sentences only a few words in length, we can understand sentences which are rather deeply embedded; whereas, if we examine very long sentences, any appreciable depth of embedding renders them impossible to understand. Additionally, we predict that if even the easiest sentences of a given length get harder to understand as their length increases—not a necessary consequence of anything we have discussed so far—then there should be a length beyond which we cannot understand any sentences at all, due to the finiteness of our brains; thus there would be only a finite number of understandable sentences. These are predictions which psychologists could look into. But what about neurophysiological consequences?

Clearly the neurological organization of language must be such that memory available for use in processing an input sentence increases in accordance with a law that lies somewhere between $K \cdot l$ and $K^{K^{K^l}}$. It makes sense to ask what sort of organization of memory would have such a consequence. This is an example of the way in which even very abstract considerations of the sort we have been discussing may be relevant to neuronal organization.

Let us now pose a question which is implicit in what we have said about perceptual devices and production devices and which demands an interesting answer. At several points, we have distinguished between grammatical sentences in a language and understandable sentences in that language. We observed that many sentences obey the regularities observed in the easily understood sentences of a language and, yet, are somewhat more difficult to understand because of greater length or some other structural property. In fact there is a gradation of sentences in every language, all exhibiting the regularities equally, but differing in their ease of comprehension. Obviously what is going on in such a case is that the sentences are all grammatical, but the difficulty a speaker-hearer of that language has in determining that fact differs from one sentence to another. There will be some sentences which exhibit all the regularities of the language but are incomprehensible to any of its speaker-hearers, and it makes no more sense to say that they are ungrammatical than it did for sentences which exhibited all the regularities of the language but were understandable with great difficulty. Instead we will say that sentences which exhibit all the regularities of a language, but are impossible to understand, are fully grammatical sentences which are so complex that no human can understand them. Thus, we distinguish between a speaker-hearer's linguistic competence—his knowledge of his language—which forms the basis for his ability to speak and understand his language and his performance—what he actually does in speaking and understanding. A sentence is grammatical if it is specified, as such, by a speaker-hearer's competence; it is acceptable or understandable if his perceptual strategies are adequate to allow him to determine that it is grammatical (and, of course, what it means). In discussing perceptual devices and production devices abstractly in Sections Three through Five, we assumed that we were dealing with perfect devices which were adequate to understand or speak any grammatical sentence of their language, and we asked how much memory they required for this task. Since they require more memory for longer sentences, it now develops that one reason why real, imperfect, human "perceptual devices" and "production devices" are incapable of coping with all the grammatical sentences of their language, is that the brain is apparently finite in its memory capacity. Rephrasing this, the brain's language processor behaves like an automaton with expandable memory up to the point where it runs out of memory (short-term memory, in this case). If the human brain actually had an infinitely expandable memory, it could perform up to its competence. Since there is a finite limit on the amount of memory which the brain has available, it is inevitably going to fail to understand some sentences that are fully grammatical. This raises a puzzling question. If finiteness of memory is as securely built-in a constraint on humans as it seems to be, then why has language not evolved so that finite memory capacity is sufficient to understand every grammatical sentence? And if we can answer this question satisfactorily, for example, by showing that for language to serve its purpose it must possess certain properties that put it outside the capacities of finite automata, then we are still left with a puzzle. If we confine ourselves to a particular subset of some language, a subset which is to be processed by a finite automaton, we can build an automaton which will use the same amount of memory to process every sentence. Why, then, do we apparently use more memory for processing some of the sentences that we are able to understand than for others? These are questions which deserve deep answers.

REFERENCES

Benton, A. L. (1964). Developmental aphasia and brain damage. Cortex, *1:* 40–52.

Bever, T., Fodor, J., Garrett, M. and Mehler, J. (1967). Transformational operations and stimulus complexity. Unpublished manuscript, Massachusetts Institute of Technology.

Bever, T. and Mehler, J. (1966). The coding hypothesis and short term memory. Unpublished manuscript, Massachusetts Institute of Technology.

Blumenthal, A. (1967). Prompted recall of sentences. J. Verb. Learn. Verb. Behav., *6:* 203–206.

Chomsky, N. (1956). Three models for the description of language. IRE Trans. Inform. Theory, IT*2:* 113–124.

Chomsky, N. (1961). On the notion "rule of grammar." In Roman Jakobson (ed.), Structure of language and its mathematical aspects. Am. Math. Soc. Providence, Rhode Island.

Chomsky, N. (1963). Formal properties of grammars. In D. Luce, R. Bush and E. Galanter (eds.), Handbook of mathematical psychology. New York: Wiley and Sons.

Chomsky, N. (1965). Aspects of the theory of syntax. Cambridge: MIT Press.

Chomsky, N. (in press). Remarks on nominalizations. In R. Jacobs and P. Rosenbaum (eds.), Readings in English transformational grammar. New York: Blaisdell.

Chomsky, N. and Halle, M. (1968). The sound pattern of English. New York: Harper and Row.

Coleman, E. (1964). The comprehensibility of several grammatical transformations. J. Applied Psychol., *48:* 186–190.

Csillag, P. (1947). Eine Bemerkung zur Auflösung der eingeschachtelten Rekursion. Acta Scientarum Mathematicarum Szeged, *11:* 169–173.

Fodor, J. and Bever, T. (1965). The psychological reality of linguistic segments. J. Verb. Learn. Verb. Behav., *4:* 414–420.

Fodor, J. and Garrett, M. (1967). Some syntactic determinants of sentential complexity. Percept. and Psychophys., *2:* 289–290.

Fodor, J., Garrett, M. and Bever, T. (1968). Some syntactic determinants of sentential complexity, II: verb structure. Percept. and Psychophys., *3:* 453–461.

Fodor, J., Jenkins, J. and Saporta, S. (1965). Some tests on implications from transformational grammar. Unpublished manuscript, Center for Advanced Studies in the Behavioral Sciences.

Garrett, M., Bever, T. and Fodor, J. (1966). The active use of grammar in speech perception. Percept. and Psychophys., *1:* 30–32.

Geschwind, N. (1965). Disconnection syndromes in man and animal. Brain, *88:* 237–294, 585–644.

Gough, P. (1965). Grammatical transformations and speed of understanding. J. Verb. Learn. Verb. Behav., *4:* 107–111.

Halle, M. (1959). The sound pattern of Russian. The Hague: Mouton.

Halle, M. (1962). Phonology in generative grammar. Word, *18:* 54–72.

Halle, M. and Stevens, K. (1962). Speech recognition: a model and a program for research. IRE Trans. Inform. Theory, IT*8:* 155–159.

Head, H. (1926). Aphasia and kindred disorders of speech. London: Cambridge University Press.

Johnson, N. (1966). The psychological reality of phrase-structure rules. J. Verb. Learn. Verb. Behav., *4:* 469–475.

Katz, J. and Postal, P. (1964). An integrated theory of linguistic description. Cambridge: MIT Press.

Lenneberg, E. (1962). Understanding language without ability to speak: a case report. J. Abnorm. Soc. Psychol., *65:* 419–425.

Lenneberg, E. (1967). Biological foundations of language. New York: Wiley and Sons.

Liberman, A., Cooper, F., Shankweiler, D. and Studdert-Kennedy, M. (1967). Perception of the speech code. Psych. Rev., *74:* 431–461.

Maclay, H. and Osgood, C. (1959). Hesitation phenomena in spontaneous English speech. Word, *1:* 19–44.

McMahon, E. (1963). Grammatical analysis as part of understanding. Unpublished Ph.D. dissertation, Harvard University.

Mehler, J. (1963). Some effects of grammatical transformations on the recall of English sentences. J. Verb. Learn. Verb. Behav., *2:* 346–351.

Mehler, J. (1964). How some sentences are remembered. Unpublished **Ph.D.** dissertation, Harvard University.

Miller, G. (1962). Some psychological studies of grammar. Amer. Psychol., *17:* 748–762.

Miller, G. and McKean, K. (1964). A chronometric study of some relations between sentences. Quart. J. Exper. Psychol., *16:* 297–308.

Miller, G., McKean, K. and Slobin, D. (1962). The exploration of transformations by sentence matching. Amer. Psychol., *17:* 748–762.

Penfield, W. and Roberts, L. (1959). Speech and brain-mechanisms. Princeton: Princeton University Press.

Perlmutter, D. (1968). Deep and surface structure constraints in syntax. Unpublished Ph.D. dissertation, Massachusetts Institute of Technology.

Peters, S. and Ritchie, R. (in preparation). On the generative power of transformational grammars.

Postal, P. (1964). Limitations of phrase structure grammars. In J. Fodor and J. Katz (eds.), The structure of language: readings in the philosophy of language. Englewood Cliffs: Prentice-Hall.

Rabin, M. and Scott, D. (1959). Finite automata and their decision problems. IBM J. Res. and Devel., 3: 115–125.

Ross, J. (1967). Constraints on variables in syntax. Unpublished Ph.D. dissertation, Massachusetts Institute of Technology.

Russell, W. and Espir, M. (1961). Traumatic aphasia: a study of aphasia in war wounds of the brain. London: Oxford University Press.

Savin, H. and Perchonock, E. (1965). Grammatical structure and the immediate recall of English sentences. J. Verb. Learn. Verb. Behav., 4: 348–353.

Slobin, D. (1963). Grammatical transformations in childhood and adulthood. Unpublished Ph.D. dissertation, Harvard University.

Slobin, D. (1966). Grammatical transformations and sentence comprehension in childhood and adulthood. J. Verb. Learn. Verb. Behav., 5: 219–227.

Stevens, K. and Halle, M. (1967). Remarks on analysis by synthesis and distinctive features. In W. Wathen-Dunn (ed.), Models for the perception of speech and visual form. Cambridge: MIT Press.

DISCUSSION

FINDLER: Would you care to amplify your comments on the capabilities of the brain in relation to the size of an equivalent automaton memory?

PETERS: The performance of the brain falls short of its competence in the following sense. I know an algorithm which works infallibly in multiplying any two integers—this is one facet of my competence—yet, in fact, I cannot multiply these integers in my head when they get too large—this is a facet of my performance. To account for the competence of the brain we need an infinite automaton, but the brain is necessarily finite.

FINDLER: I think what you are saying is that besides the information structure, the brain must also contain procedures for subroutines and program segments. I see no contradiction there.

LONGUET-HIGGINS: Does not this argument indicate that Chomsky's proof that the brain must be bigger than a finite automaton is not really germane to the question how the brain works?

PETERS: I would contend quite differently, since the restriction of a finite automaton imposes limits on performance and yet permits numerous alternatives. For example, as a finite automaton, the brain could be designed to understand all those sentences it can understand with a fixed amount of effort or equally well. In fact, this is not the case: the brain is more complex than this.

BLUM: I am perturbed about the thought that insufficient attention seems to be given to natural language and so much to existing mathematical formalism. Perhaps more effort should go into understanding what natural language is about, rather than transforming it, so as to approximate computer language.

PETERS: I must contradict you here. In fact, linguists have investigated numerous languages, many of which are not written: Linguistic theories are not, as you seem to suggest, an outgrowth of computer programming theory. But it so happens that the mathematical logicians had just the tools available to describe syntactic processes. This may have given the false impression that the description of language is an outgrowth of mathematical logic.

WAYNE A. WICKELGREN

Massachusetts Institute of Technology*
Cambridge, Massachusetts

5 · *Context-Sensitive Coding in Speech Recognition, Articulation and Development* †

This paper describes a theory of the coding of speech at the phonetic level and applies that theory to the problems of speech recognition, articulation, and development. The theory specifies the elementary structural components of words and has nothing to say about the higher-level syntactic and semantic aspects of language. The theory is not contradicted by any of the facts that I know, and it provides a very simple explanation of many facts concerning speech recognition and articulation. However, the theory is extremely speculative, and no one should be misled concerning the amount of direct evidence for the theory. My enthusiasm for the theory is based largely on the clarity and simplicity with which it handles many of the basic problems of speech recognition and articulation, rather than on the definitiveness of its empirical support.

I. Context-Free and Context-Sensitive Coding of Ordered Sets

I define a context-free code for words to consist of an ordered set of symbols for every word, where some symbols in some words give insufficient information concerning the adjacent symbols to determine them uniquely out of the unordered set for the word. That is to say, the same

* Present address: The University of Oregon, Eugene, Oregon.
† This work was supported by grant, MH 08890–05, from the National Institute of Mental Health, U. S. Public Health Service.

symbol can be used in a variety of contexts of left and right adjacent symbols, and the ordering of the symbols in a word carries information not found in the conjunction of the unordered set of symbols with the sequential dependency rules.

I define a context-sensitive code for words to consist of an unordered set of symbols for every word, where each symbol restricts the choice of its left and right neighbors sufficiently to determine them uniquely out of the unordered set for any given word. In this case, the unordered set, in conjunction with the dependency rules, contains all the information necessary to reconstruct a unique ordering of the symbols for each word. Thus, context-sensitive coding provides a way to represent in a one-to-one mapping certain ordered sets by unordered sets in conjunction with some dependency rules.

This general formulation of the relationship between certain ordered and unordered sets seems to be of some value by itself. However, the general formulation was designed primarily to apply to a particularly simple example of a context-sensitive coding defined on a context-free coding for the vocabulary of a real language like English, and it is this particular example which is of primary interest here.

Let x y z be adjacent context-free symbols in a word. In the context-free coding of the vocabulary, words always begin and end with the symbol $\#$. The symbols x y z could be adjacent letters in a written word or adjacent phonemes in a spoken word. For certain vocabularies, a context-sensitive coding for the word is obtained by mapping each context-free symbol y ($y \neq \#$) into a context-sensitive symbol $_xy_z$, where x and y are the left and right neighbors of y in that word and x and z may be $\#$.

Note that a single-valued spelling of words with *context-sensitive symbols* does not imply that one has a *context-sensitive code*. The latter requires one to show that the mapping from the *context-sensitive spelling* back to the *context-free spelling* is also single-valued. If the vocabulary of the language was defined with ordered sets using n context-free symbols and if every possible triple of context-free symbols occurred in at least one word, then n^3 context-sensitive symbols would be required to define all the words in the vocabulary with unordered sets.

In general, reconstruction of the ordered set from the unordered set is easily accomplished by starting with the only $_\#u_v$ symbol in the word, then selecting the $_uv_w$ symbol in the word, assuming there is only one $_uv_w$ symbol in the word, and so on until all the symbols in the unordered set have been used and $_yz_\#$ has been written down as the last symbol. Whenever, by left-to-right generation, there is more than one choice for the next symbol in a word, the decision must be made by looking ahead to determine which choice leads to use of all of the symbols in the unordered set. It is possible to invent words with a context-free spelling for which the specified spelling with context-sensitive symbols is consistent with more than one ordering of the symbols (i.e., spelling with context-sensitive symbols does not yield a context-sensitive code). However, this is an extremely rare event even if words are spelled randomly in the context-free code, and is easily avoided with non-random spelling.

These formulations of context-free and context-sensitive coding can be applied to both written and spoken English in the following manner. The spelling of written English words using letters (graphemes) is a context-free code. Similarly, the phonemic spelling of spoken English words is a context-free code. In both cases, the previously specified mapping from context-free symbols to context-sensitive symbols appears to produce a context-sensitive code. That is to say, the unordered sets of context-sensitive symbols for each word can be mapped back into one and only one ordering of the context-free symbols. Thus, the English word *stop* can be coded by the unordered set of context-sensitive symbols $/_{\#}s_t, {}_st_o, {}_to_p, {}_op_{\#}/$, which is consistent with one and only one ordering of the associated context-free symbols $/s, t, o, p/$.

I do not know of any words in either written or spoken English where the proposed context-sensitive spelling would be consistent with more than one context-free (graphemic or phonemic) spelling. In any event, the cases are so rare that, if any are found, they could probably be handled by special means, for example, slight modification of the defined set of phonemes or graphemes. In fact, in my original paper on context-sensitive coding (Wickelgren, 1969a), I proposed (for other reasons) that vowels with different stress be considered as different phonemes. As pointed out in that paper, there are actually very few cases in spoken English where one encounters any choice in the straight left-to-right generation of the order of the context-sensitive (and associated context-free) symbols. Out of the 3,800 words beginning with *b, d, f,* and *l* and occurring at least once in 10^6 words according to the Thorndike-Lorge (1944) count, there are only 12 words in spoken English where simple left-to-right generation would not be sufficient: *barnyard, brethren, fair-haired, farmyard, foreshorten, forlorn, fourscore, lampblack, Lapland, lifelike, limelight,* and *lullaby.* These are words which have two identical pairs of phonemes followed by a different phoneme. The choices in all of these cases can be resolved by "looking ahead" to see which choice uses all of the context-sensitive symbols. Alternatively, they can be resolved by a simple left-to-right associative process having no look-ahead capability of this type, provided one assumes that stress is a feature that distinguishes between vowel phonemes.

Granted that one can represent English words with unordered sets of context-sensitive symbols, does this accomplish anything? Is there any reason to think that human beings use a context-sensitive code for spoken or written words? The rest of this paper is devoted to making as strong a case as possible for the use of context-sensitive coding in the recognition and production of spoken language. The case is nowhere near so strong for written language and will not be discussed in the present paper.

II. Speech Recognition

A. Acoustic Input

It hardly needs to be said that speech recognition in human beings has proven to be a very difficult problem to explain and to achieve artificially. Two of the principal problems discussed in the past have been: (*a*) the difficulty in subdividing the acoustic waveform for a word into segments corresponding to phonemes and (*b*) the lack of invariance in the acoustic cues for a phoneme across different left and right contexts of adjacent phonemes (Liberman, *et al.*, 1967). These are problems essentially because of the assumption that speech uses context-free (phonemic) coding. The second problem is completely eliminated by the assumption of context-sensitive (allophonic) coding, and the first problem is also eliminated for a device like the brain with parallel processing capability.

The fact that the cues for adjacent symbols in a word are often intermixed in time creates a problem if word recognition depends on recognizing the component symbols (phonemes) in a single correct temporal order. However, since context-sensitive coding permits recovery of the correct order from an unordered set, it is no longer very critical in what order the context-sensitive allophones are recognized. I will assume that the brain has an internal representative (one or more neurons) for each context-sensitive allophone. This internal representative is activated by some conjunction of acoustic features occurring over some maximum period of time (on the order of tens or hundreds of msec). The features are those characteristic of the context-sensitive allophone. For the brain, it is reasonable to assume that all the allophone representatives are "examining" the acoustic input in parallel, and when the word is finished some subset of the allophone representatives will have been activated above some variable threshold and the rest will not have been. Assuming no semantic context effects, the word representative which is maximally associated with this unordered set of context-sensitive allophone representatives will be selected. Nowhere in this process has it been necessary to subdivide the acoustic waveform for the word into segments, though, of course, it is still necessary in continuous speech to have marked the word boundaries.

For artificial speech recognition with serial devices, segmentation is highly desirable in order to reduce recognition time, even with context-sensitive coding. There are numerous ways to approach this problem from the standpoint of context-sensitive coding, but artificial recognition is beyond the scope of the present paper.

The success of context-sensitive coding obviously depends upon how invariant the acoustic cues are for a context-sensitive allophone. Frankly,

I do not know how invariant these cues are across different remote (non-adjacent) phonemic contexts, different syntactic and semantic contexts, different rates of talking, different speakers and different, recognizable dialects. However, the type of context-conditioned variation in the acoustic features of phonemes that has been most frequently discussed in the past (see Liberman, *et al.,* 1967), namely, dependence on adjacent phonemes, has been directly incorporated into the theory of context-sensitive coding and is no longer a problem. It remains to be seen how well the theory of context-sensitive coding will handle speech recognition, when extensive data become available on the effects of remote phonetic contexts, syntactic and semantic contexts (with their associated effects on suprasegmental stress), rates of talking, different speakers (particularly, men *vs.* women *vs.* children), and different, recognizable dialects. Nevertheless, we can say a little bit concerning how certain effects of these variables could be handled by a theory that assumed context-sensitive coding of speech.

Some remote phonetic context effects on acoustic features could be handled by expanding the number of phonemes (allophone classes) to include consonant clusters and distinguish between vowels with different segmental stress, for example.

If syntactic and semantic context greatly change the acoustic cues that are characteristic of particular context-sensitive allophones, then some basic modification would have to be made in the theory. To the extent that syntactic and semantic context affect cues that are not essential to recognition of each allophone, there is no problem. Thus, suprasegmental stress need not be a problem, if the cues for suprasegmental stress do not strongly interact with the cues for context-sensitive allophones.

The effects of rate of talking might be handled by variation in the time interval over which a context-sensitive allophone representative examines the acoustic input for its defining features. Faster rates of talking should be associated with shorter time-windows for each allophone representative. This hypothesis assumes that acoustic features for context-sensitive allophones can be defined which are invariant over rate of talking, except for the time interval over which they are found. If this hypothesis is false, then the theory of context-sensitive coding will require an important modification, at the very least.

Conceivably, the features of context-sensitive allophones can be defined so as to be invariant across different individual speakers and different dialects. However, such features would have to consist of relations (e.g., differences, ratios, rates of change) between formants at the same and different times, with a rather wide range of acceptable absolute formant values. Some of the capacity to recognize words in different dialects or spoken by different individuals might be handled by associations from different sets of context-sensitive allophone representatives to the same word. However, if neither of these two approaches is completely successful in accounting for human speech recognition capacity in the face of individual and dialect differences, then it might be necessary to assume that the input to each context-sensitive allophone representative is a disjunction of conjunctions of acoustic features. In a recent paper (Wickelgren, 1969b), I discussed some reasons for thinking that many single cortical neurons might have the powerful logical capability of computing disjunctions of conjunctions. But it certainly would be simpler if it were not necessary to assume that context-sensitive allophone representatives had this capability.

B. Contextual Input

Another major problem that has frequently been discussed in connection with speech recognition is the rather large contribution of the context, in addition to the specific features of the acoustic input, in determining what word representative or component (allophone or phoneme) representative will be activated. Note that I am not now referring to the context effects on speech recognition which are mediated by their effects on the specific acoustic features of each word or word-component (allophones or phonemes). These were discussed in the previous section. I am now concerned with the context effects which raise or lower the probability of recognizing certain words or word-components, without having any effect on the specific acoustic features of the word or word-component being recognized.

It seems useful to distinguish between phonetic context on the one hand and syntactic and semantic context on the other hand. Phonetic context refers to the known or previously recognized allophones or allophone-classes (phonemes) in a word which could assist in the recognition of other allophones or phonemes in the word because of the previously learned non-random probabilities of different allophones or phonemes when preceded or followed by other allophones or phonemes. These effects would most likely be due to a subset of fully recognized word components being sufficient to activate the correct word representative, which, in turn, is associated to all of its allophone representatives, rather than being due to associations directly from one allophone or phoneme representative to another.

Certain syntactic and semantic context effects on word recognition can be handled by assuming that the context sets *thresholds* (biases) for different word classes, which, in turn, set thresholds for different words, which, in turn, might or might not set thresholds for different context-sensitive allophone representatives. It hardly needs to be said that this is a sketchily presented, unoriginal idea for the solution of a very difficult problem. The same idea has been described in more detail by Morton and Broadbent (1967), though not in relation to context-sensitive coding.

The principal contribution of context-sensitive coding to the problem of explaining context effects is the somewhat greater ease of incorporating backward phonetic, semantic, or syntactic context effects because of the lack of any necessity to preserve the temporal order of the recognized and unrecognized allophones in a word.

III. Speech Articulation

A. Words

Context-sensitive coding in conjunction with an associative memory also provides a very simple theory of speech production, exclusive of the syntactic and semantic factors involved in the selection of word representatives. The application of context-sensitive coding to speech production has been discussed in more detail in a previous paper (Wickelgren, 1969a). This paper presents a briefer, slightly modified version of that application.

Once a word representative has been selected, for whatever reason, the ordered articulation of its components (allophones) is explained as follows: First, the word representative "primes" (partially activates) all of the context-sensitive allophone representatives either as an unordered set or with a slight temporal ordering favoring the earlier allophone representatives. The selection of the correct unordered set of around 7 allophone representatives from a total set in the tens of thousands is obviously an extremely important step, but one which is easily achieved by an associative memory.

The slight temporal ordering could come about because the long-term associations between the word representative and its allophone representatives are ordered in strength by degree of remoteness from the beginning of the word. There are reasons for thinking that this slight ordering of strength could not, by itself, account for the ordered generation of allophone representatives, though it could play a small role in helping to discriminate the order of non-adjacent allophone representatives. The basic mechanism by which a word's unordered set of context-sensitive allophone representatives is converted into an ordered set is by starting with the initial allophone representative $_\#u_v$, which activates $_uv_w$, and so on to the terminal allophone representative $_yz_\#$.

As mentioned earlier in the paper, there are rare instances in English where this simple left-to-right associative generation of an ordered set of allophones from the unordered set of allophones will be very slightly ambiguous, if one defines context-sensitive allophones on the usually accepted set of context-free phonemes. These rare cases can be handled in a variety of ways: (a) by expanding the number of phonemes to include vowel stress and perhaps also consonant clusters, (b) by assuming some "look-ahead" capability in the associative generation scheme, of the type previously described, or (c) by using any slight gradient of strength of association from the word representative to the allophone representatives as a function of remoteness from the beginning of the word.

In addition to explaining how a word representative could lead to the ordered activation of its component vocal gestures, the theory of context-sensitive coding provides a mechanism for achieving roughly the same vocal gesture from different starting positions of the articulators. At the same time, the theory explains why there are coarticulation effects both in the vocal tract and in the patterns of firing of speech motor neurons (Harris, 1963; Fromkin, 1966; Harris, *et al.* 1966; Liberman, *et al.* 1967; MacNeilage and DeClerk, 1967). With a different central articulatory representative for each context-sensitive allophone, there obviously can be differences in the pattern of speech motor neuron activity for each allophone. However, it can be (and is) the case that the allophones of the same phoneme are generally quite similar in speech motor neuron activity (MacNeilage, 1963; Harris, *et al.* 1965; Fromkin, 1966; Liberman, *et al.,* 1967).

Certain aspects of articulation, namely, the control of timing and supra-segmental features, are not handled by the present theory, but it is important to note that this in no way contradicts the theory.

Although one can regard the order of vocal gestures as a part of the general question of the timing of vocal gestures, it is also possible to regard the control of speech rate as being quite separate from the control of the order of speech. It is the latter assumption which is made by the present theory. I assume that timing is accomplished by some kind of neural clock that regulates the rate of switching from one allophone representative to the next in the series.

The present theory assumes that suprasegmental representatives do not interact with segmental representatives at some level of the articulatory system. That is to say, the theory assumes that a suprasegmental stress representative is associated to the word representative in the input to the articulatory system. The word representative selects the segmental allophone representatives in the manner described and the suprasegmental stress representatives are simply activated along with the allophone representatives. Speech motor activity depends on both segmental and suprasegmental representatives which are activated at the same time. This hypothesis needs to be made more specific to be tested, but the general outline is clear: At some level of the articulatory system, segmental and suprasegmental representatives are additive, though this does not necessarily imply additivity in the acoustic waveform, vocal trace configuration, or pattern of motor neuron activity.

B. Phrases

Context-sensitive coding, in conjunction with some assumptions about priming and short-term and long-term associative memory, also allows a human being to select an ordered set of word representatives for a novel phrase and then articulate the entire phrase as an automatic process. During the articulation process, the higher cognitive level that selected the word representatives for the phrase can be selecting the words for the next phrase, without the necessity of continued direction of the articulation process for the last phrase. This is achieved as follows:

The ordered activation of word representatives produces an ordered priming (partial activation) of the unordered sets of allophone representatives for each word in the phrase. The priming process selects the correct unordered sets of allophone representatives for the phrase (about 10^2) out of the vastly larger totality (about 10^4) of all allophone representatives. It also establishes short-term associations (due to relative contiguity of activation) among the allophone representatives. These short-term associations are strongest among the allophone representatives of each word and next strongest from the set of allophone representatives of one word to the set of allophone representatives of the next word in the phrase. Also, the unpronounced representative of the concept "begin" is primed before the priming of the first set of allophone representatives, so "begin" has its strongest short-term association to the allophones of the first word.

When the priming process is completed, "begin" is activated. This leads to the activation of the set of allophone representatives for the first word, with the ordering of full activation for the allophone representatives within a single word being determined by long-term associations in the manner described in the previous section. Then, the first word's allophone representatives will activate most strongly the set of allophone representatives for the second word, because they have stronger short-term associations to the set of allophone representatives for the second word than to the set of allophone representatives for any other word. The same process continues to the end of the phrase, when a new priming process can occur.

IV. Speech Development

No attempt will be made here to describe even an approach to a theory of the development of speech in children. However, it is worthwhile to point out that context-sensitive coding does somewhat simplify the problem facing the child in coming to understand and articulate words and word components. Throughout the following discussion, I will assume, for the sake of parsimony, that there is only one set of context-sensitive allophone representatives; not two sets, one for sensory functions and another for motor functions. I do not see how to distinguish these alternative hypotheses.

After development, there must be connections to the allophone representatives from lower-level auditory feature-representatives and connections from the allophone representatives to lower-level articulatory feature-representatives. We must be able to inhibit the motor output from these allophone representatives because we can perceive or think of words without repeating them aloud. These connections might be formed innately at some stage of maturation or be established by learning—both alternatives seem plausible.

Assume that the input and output connections of the allophone representatives are specified independently of experience. In this case, there is little more to be said from a psychological point of view, except that the complexity of the mapping is simpler on both ends with allophonic coding than with phonemic coding.

If we assume that the input and output connections of allophone representatives are specified by learning, then there is a great deal more which must be said than I am prepared to say at the present time. However, it is again the case that the input and output connections for context-sensitive allophone representatives will be simpler than for context-free phonemic representatives.

The sensory specification of the allophone representatives might come about in the following way. First, we must assume that there are a large number of free neurons in the cortex whose inputs are not specified innately. Neurons standing for features of the acoustic signal send their axons into this region of free neurons and tend to grow toward a common point (their "center of gravity") when activated at the same time. If the same (or a highly similar) acoustic pattern is repeated sufficiently, then these axons will come very close together. When they are very close, there will be some nearest free neuron. The axons will all zoom down onto this free neuron, synapse with it and specify it to stand for that pattern of acoustic input. In such a manner, the sensory input of allophone representatives might be specified. An even grander version of this wild idea is discussed in an earlier paper (Wickelgren, 1969b).

Learned specification of the motor output of these allophone representatives would seem to be more complex, which fits with the fact that speech recognition precedes speech production by several months in child development. Sets of speech motor feature representatives must be activated in a variety of at least semi-random patterns. Those patterns of articulatory feature representatives which lead to sounds sufficiently similar to an allophone representative to activate it to some degree, acquire connections from the allophone representative. This is simply the old motor-sensory feedback loop for speech postulated by many to account for the development of sensory-motor connections in the development of speech. The idea is just somewhat more plausible with allophonic coding than with phonemic coding because the pattern of connections is simpler. However, it seems clear that this learning is not a one-step process. The series of successive approximations that the child makes to adult speech makes it clear that the motor output connections of allophone representatives must be assumed to be undergoing a series of changes.

V. Conclusion

It is quite obvious that context-sensitive coding does not solve all the problems of speech recognition, articulation, and development at even the phonetic level. However, it does solve some problems, and this makes it worthy of consideration as a theory of one basic phonetic unit.

REFERENCES

Fromkin, V. A. (1966). Neuro-muscular specification of linguistic units. Language and Speech, 9: 170–199.

Harris, K. S. (1963). Behavior of the tongue in the production of some alveolar consonants. J. acoust. Soc. Am., 35: 784 (abstract).

Harris, K. S., Lysaught, G. and Schvey, M. M. (1965). Some aspects of the production of oral and nasal labial stops. Language and Speech, 8: 135–147.

Harris, K. S., Huntington, D. A. and Scholes, G. N. (1966). Coarticulation of some disyllabic utterances measured by electromyographic techniques. J. acoust. Soc. Am., 39: 1219 (abstract).

Liberman, A. M., Cooper, F. S., Shankweiler, D. P. and Studdert-Kennedy, M. (1967). Perception of the speech code. Psychol. Rev., 74: 431–461.

MacNeilage, P. F. (1963). Electromyographic and acoustic study of the production of certain final clusters. J. acoust. Soc. Am., 35: 461–463.

MacNeilage, P. F. and DeClerk, J. L. (1967). On the motor control of co-articulation in CVC monosyllables. Unpublished paper presented at the 1967 Conference on Speech Communication and Processing, Massachusetts Institute of Technology.

Morton, J. and Broadbent, D. E. (1967). Passive versus active recognition models or is your homunculus really necessary? in W. Wathen-Dunn (ed.), Models for the perception of speech and visual form. Cambridge: MIT Press, 103–110.

Thorndike, E. L. and Lorge, I. (1944). The teacher's word book of 30,000 words. New York: Columbia University Bureau of Publications.

Wickelgren, W. A. (1969a). Context-sensitive coding, associative memory, and serial order in (speech) behavior. Psychol. Rev., 76: 1–15.

Wickelgren, W. A. (1969b). Learned specification of concept neurons. Bull. math. Biophys., 31: 123–142.

DISCUSSION

BOYNTON: What happens if you record a set of allophones and then put them together in a different order to correspond to new words?

WICKELGREN: This sort of thing has been tried and it was found that it could not be done. If you cut, say, one section from one phoneme and put it together with another section from another phoneme, you do not get the sound you might expect. This is in line with my model, in which I would have to cut sound segments three phonemes wide and match them appropriately. Maybe Al Liberman will have some more to say about this problem. If one takes a large set of allophones, instead of some 40 or 50 basic phonemes, speech can be synthesized somewhat more successfully.

LIBERMAN: This was done with halves of syllables and still does not work very well.

WICKELGREN: Yes.

ARBIB: I do not see any difficulty conceptually in the serial ordering of behavior any more than in serial ordering in computers, where one is concerned with transfers of control from one instruction to another. I do think it is a mistake, however, to consider phonemes as primitive. It is only at quite a sophisticated stage that a child, for example, begins to break down its babblings into phonemes. I think that more appropriately sequential actions in a temporal sequence are primitive.

IGNATIUS G. MATTINGLY
Haskins Laboratories and University of Connecticut

ALVIN M. LIBERMAN
Haskins Laboratories, University of Connecticut, Yale University

6 · *The Speech Code and the Physiology of Language**

I. Introduction

To the physiologist who would study language in terms of the interests represented at this symposium, the most obvious linguistic processes—the selection of words to convey meaning and the arrangement of words in sentences—must seem far removed from familiar concepts and methods. Surely, he would prefer to study processes that are physiologically more accessible, but are yet linguistic. We believe that the production and perception of speech, in the narrow sense, is one such process; we suggest, therefore, that the physiologist might do well to start there. The questions we would have him ask can be put very simply: How does a speaker convert the phonetic units—the consonants and vowels—to a stream of sound? On hearing that stream, how does a listener recover the phonetic units?

For the purposes of this paper, we can do as well with one of those questions as with both; in principle, either one will do. We have chosen to deal primarily with the second—the one about speech perception— because we find more data there that speak to the points we want to make.

In the received view, speech perception in our narrow sense is thought to be neither very linguistic nor very interesting. Language is commonly supposed to be structured in levels (syntactic, phonological, phonetic) that represent successive recodings of the information. Each of these levels

* The preparation of this paper, and much of the research on which it is based, has been supported by grants and contracts from the National Institute of Child Health and Human Development, the Office of Naval Research, and the Veterans Administration. Earlier phases of our work were aided by grants from the Carnegie Corporation of New York and the National Science Foundation.

consists of simple units (words, phones) of some kind, organized into successively larger and more complex units (phrases, sentences; syllables, breath groups). It has been the business of the linguist to describe the rules by which the units are organized at each level, and to discover the code by which they are converted from one level to the next.

But the recoding is usually assumed to end with the phones, the empty units that lie at the lowest level of the whole linguistic structure; it is not supposed to include the process we want to talk about here: the conversion from phone to sound and from sound to phone.[1] The traditional view of this conversion is that it is by means of a simple alphabet, each phone being represented by a unit sound. On that view the relation between phone and sound is trivial and outside language proper; the linguist is interested in the sound alphabet only as a concrete base in which he can, when necessary, anchor his abstract assumptions.

An alternative view, which seems to us not very different in its consequences, is that the relationship between phone and sound, while indeed part of language, has a character too irregular to invite systematic description. This would appear to be the position of Chomsky and Miller (1963, p. 318) and Chomsky and Halle (1968, pp. 293–295). Though these investigators assume that a universal phonetics underlies speech production, they believe that speech perception depends not only on the acoustic properties of the signal but also on "the hearer's knowledge of the language as well as on a host of extra-grammatical factors," so that the perception and the sound cannot be rigorously related. They regard speech perception as a "heuristic" process in which a hypothesis about the speaker's utterance is suggested by a sampling of cues in the speech signal. That hypothesis is then tested and corrected by reference to all levels of the grammar—a task that can be carried out by successive iterations of an analysis-by-synthesis procedure—until a plausible reconstruction of the string of phones has been arrived at. But if it is sufficient to have recourse to higher grammatical levels in order to carry out a process that is now viewed as unruly rather than simple, then the process of speech perception must still be considered uninteresting. For an explanation of speech perception, the linguist is, in effect, diverted from serious consideration of speech and directed back to the higher linguistic levels.

Neither do these easy assumptions about speech pose problems of any

[1] The term "phone" is customarily used to mean the way a phonological segment is realized in a particular context. If one assumes that the perceptual, articulatory, and acoustic domains of speech are in one-to-one correspondence, then the phonological realization can be described equivalently as an acoustic event (or class), an articulatory event (or class), or a perceptual unit. But, as will be seen, we believe that these domains of speech are *not* in one-to-one correspondence. We will therefore use the term "phone" to mean the abstract unit which is the output of the phonology. This unit is, in effect, the elementary perceptual unit of speech. Our primary concern, in this paper, is to explore the relationship between the phone, so defined, and its acoustic representation.

special interest for the psycholinguist. If speech is, indeed, a simple alphabet, then the only requirement on its sounds is that they be spaced at comfortable distances apart, both in time and in some perceptual space, so as to be readily discriminated by the listener. If, on the other hand, speech perception is unruly, then the psycholinguist will do better to study the more orderly areas of language—syntax and phonology.

If all these assumptions about speech were true, the physiology of speech perception would be no different from the physiology of auditory perception in general. A physiologist who might be looking for new challenges would have no reason to study speech perception. And if he were, for some reason, already committed to the physiology of language, he would want to start his investigation at a higher level.

We will try to show, however, that the simple assumptions about speech are wrong. Phone and sound are linked by a recoding not different in principle from the more familiar recodings at higher linguistic levels. As a consequence, speech is, like the rest of language, well matched to man and part of his linguistic physiology.

II. Speech and Language as Codes

Linguistic communication requires that a string of phones be transmitted from one person to another. This cannot be done efficiently in any straightforward way. If, to take the simplest case, the phones were represented by an alphabet of discrete sounds, the temporal resolving power of the ear would set a low ceiling on the rate at which we could communicate. Morse "code," which is really an artificial sound alphabet, cannot be understood at rates much higher than five or six characters a second (Cooper, 1950). Many other sound alphabets have been developed, chiefly in the course of research on reading machines for the blind: the highest perceptual rates achieved, after long practice with highly motivated subjects, have been of the order of two characters a second (Freiburger and Murphy, 1961; Coffey, 1963; Studdert-Kennedy and Liberman, 1963; Nye, 1965, 1968; Studdert-Kennedy and Cooper, 1966). At rates of 20 or 30 characters a second, the subject can hardly separate the sounds, let alone identify them. Yet, we know that perception of natural speech at rates as high as 20 or even 30 phones per second is possible (Orr *et al.,* 1965).

To understand the remarkable speeds that can be achieved with speech, we must see that it provides a kind of parallel transmission: cues for two or more successive phones are carried simultaneously, and by the same acoustic event. Thus, the second-formant transition[2] typically carries essen-

---

[2] A formant is a resonance of the vocal tract represented by a relatively intense band of energy in the speech spectrum. Formants are numbered in order of their position on the frequency scale, the first being the lowest, the second the next higher, and so on. The first two or three carry the important linguistic information.

A formant transition is a rapid change in the frequency of a formant, reflecting articulatory movement.

tial cues about both consonant and adjacent vowel. (For a fuller account of the characteristics of speech perception referred to in this paper, see Liberman, *et al.*, 1967.) This parallel delivery of cues occurs in greater or less degree for most of the phones. As a consequence, the cues for what we hear as a series of discrete phones are typically organized as a syllabic unit in the sound stream. Indeed, this organization is the basis for the perceptual existence of the syllable.

We should note here that the syllable is by no means the largest acoustic structure. Syllables themselves are differentiated with respect to certain acoustic dimensions—duration, fundamental frequency, and intensity— and a series of syllables forms a longer pattern that is a cue for stress. A series of these stress patterns, in turn, forms a still longer acoustic pattern that cues the breath-group, the phonetic counterpart of a clause (Lieberman, 1967; Mattingly, 1968).

The organization of phones into syllables has a very important consequence for efficiency: the limit on rate is set now by the number of syllables per second, not by the number of phones. But the efficiency of speech is achieved at the expense of simplicity, since the parallel delivery of information that produces the syllable is possible only at the cost of a complex relation between the acoustic signal and the phonetic message. Speech is not a simple alphabet, then, but a difficult and demanding code. If a listener can nevertheless perceive speech, it is presumably because he possesses a special device powerful enough to decode the signal and recover the phones.[3]

The speech decoder must deal with several more or less closely correlated complications in the relation between sound and phone. One is that there are not, and, by the nature of the code, there cannot be, commutable acoustic segments that correspond to the phonetic segments. That is, there is no acoustic criterion by which one can delimit segments in the signal that correspond in number or structure to the segments in the message.

Not only are the cues for different phones carried simultaneously by the same acoustic event, but also the cues for the same phone are carried by different acoustic events at different times. A brief period of silence, or of weak low-frequency energy, signals a stop consonant, but which of the stops [b, d, g, p, t, k] is intended is cued by the character of the transition that begins the following vowel (Liberman, *et al.*, 1954; Delattre, *et al.*, 1955). When two vowels are separated by a medial consonant, the character

[3] Not all phones are encoded in the speech signal. Vowels produced in isolation, or in context at slow rates of speech, are represented alphabetically: there is an isolable acoustic segment that corresponds to the vowel phone, and there is no context-conditioned variation. Such phones might presumably be perceived without recourse to the speech decoder, and there are, indeed, striking differences in perception between these phones and those that are, like the stops, always encoded. This is true, in particular, of the characteristics of the speech mode—categorical perception and cerebral lateralization—to be discussed later. For an account of these differences the reader should see Liberman, *et al.*, 1967. Our concern in this paper will be primarily with the phones that are highly encoded and therefore truly linguistic.

of the transition from the first vowel to the consonant is determined not just by the consonant, but by the second vowel (Ohman, 1966); we would expect this transition to have some cue value for the second vowel. Similarly, in a sequence such as [stru] the acoustic quality of the [s] friction, which is a cue for the first phone, is also likely to be affected by a feature belonging to the fourth phone [u]; in that case we might expect to find the perception of the [u] cued to some extent by the characteristics of the [s] friction (Kozhevnikov and Chistovich, 1965, p. 124 ff.).

Parallel delivery of the cues produces yet another and equally serious complication in the relation between sound and phone: the same phone is signaled in different phonetic environments by acoustic cues that are vastly different. In the case of [d], for example, the essential acoustic cue is a formant transition. Before the vowel [i], that formant rises from 2200 to 2600 cps., but before [u], the formant falls from 1200 to 700 cps. (For a fuller account, see Liberman, *et al.*, 1967.) We should expect that the first of these would sound like a rising glissando on high pitches, the second like a falling glissando on low pitches. And when we take these formant transitions out of a speech context, that is, indeed, what we hear. But when the transitions are the only cues for [d] in the syllables [di] and [du], we hear the same initial segment [d]. The kind of context-conditioned variation exemplified here is found, usually in more extreme form, for almost all the consonants.

Within a given context, however, the perceptual boundaries between one phone and another are very well defined, despite the apparent variability of the acoustic signal. Consider, for example, the voiced stops [b, d, g], which are distinguished from each other by the direction and extent of the second-formant transition. If a listener is presented with a series of synthetic voiced stops for which the starting point of this transition is varied along the frequency scale, he will classify these stimuli consistently as [b], [d] or [g], but will be unable to distinguish one member of a class from another. This result is obtained quite generally with speech-like stimuli that differ only along an acoustic continuum that carries an essential encoded cue: a listener typically classifies such stimuli neatly as phones; if he is then asked to discriminate stimuli that lie close together on the continuum, he does very well in those parts of the continuum where his classifying responses indicated a boundary between phones, but very poorly elsewhere. This phenomenon, in which discrimination is no better than identification, has been called categorical perception. (Liberman, *et al.,* 1957; Liberman, *et al.*, 1961; Stevens, *et al.*, in press.)

Thus the phonetic decoding device appears to be capable of recovering the phones from the acoustic signal by (*a*) reassembling the essential cues, which are thoroughly intermixed in the sound stream, (*b*) correcting for an immense amount of contextual variation in the cues, and (*c*) sorting the cues categorically in a mode of perception that is very sensitive to differences between phones and quite insensitive to differences among tokens of the same phone. We have called this device a decoder because the relation between phonetic message and acoustic signal is highly complex and apparently arbitrary. Yet, we began by noting that to most users of the code—even to students of language—the relationship is seemingly transparent and trivial. Evidently, the speakers of the language have readily available to them a key to the code, a set of rules for the perception of speech, though they are quite unaware of its existence.

We can gain some insight into the nature of the key if we look at the utterances [di] and [du] in articulatory terms. For [di] the tongue moves toward the alveolar ridge and remains there for an instant, closing the vocal tract. Then the tongue moves slightly downward, releasing the closure; meanwhile the lips are spreading. For [du] the tongue gesture is similar, except that the final movement of the tongue is backward as well as downward; meanwhile the lips are becoming rounded. In both utterances the vocal cords begin to vibrate at or slightly before the release, and it is only then that the acoustic signal begins. If we compare this articulatory account of the production of [di] and [du] with the acoustic account given above, we note that two similar gestures of an articulator can have very different acoustic consequences; that by no means all the movement of an articulator is reflected in the acoustic signal; that the acoustic signal is the complex resultant of the independent but concurrent action of several articulators; and that the parallel transmission of information is achieved both by this concurrent articulation and by the transitional movement of an articulator from one position to the next (Cooper, 1966).

It appears, then, that we can describe speech more simply in articulatory than in acoustic terms. This suggests that the speech code is organized according to articulatory gestures or, more likely, the commands to the muscles that make these gestures (Liberman, et al., 1967). In effect, the key that the listener has available to him is an articulatory model that relates the phonetic message to the signal. The listener's model need represent only those features of articulation that are crucial to speech perception, but must represent those features in a way nonspecific enough to allow for a wide range of speaker variation. Moreover, since every language rings its own variations on the universal phonetic code, the model must be able to adapt to the version used in the listener's native language. Evidently, the model must be a very general and versatile one.

Let us briefly recapitulate the basic characteristics of the speech code. A message, consisting of a string of phones, is linked with a stream of cues embedded in an acoustic signal. These cues do not correspond straightforwardly to the phones; they are an encoding of the message. The arbitrary appearance of the code can be rationalized by reference to an articulatory model. Such a model, therefore, must be available to the listener, though he is quite unaware of the code or of the model that rationalizes it.

Two or more cues can be transmitted simultaneously; by such parallel transmission, the limitations set by the temporal resolving power of the ear are circumvented. Yet, simultaneous cues do not necessarily represent one phone, nor, conversely, are the cues for one phone simultaneous; hence no simple pairing can be made between successive phones and successive segments of the acoustic signal. The acoustic shape of a cue varies extensively with the context; yet there are sharp restrictions on this variation. Acoustically similar events carrying cues for different phones are categorically perceived. Finally, cues are organized into larger units: syllables, stress patterns, breath-group patterns.

If language and speech are controlled by the same neurophysiological apparatus, we should expect to find resemblances between the speech code and the linguistic code, i.e., the grammar of language. We do, indeed, find such resemblances. In fact, we find them two or three times over, because grammar consists of a series of structural levels, each linked to the next by a recoding process. Each of these recodings invites comparison with the speech code. The resemblances are partly obscured by more striking differences, but the differences are natural consequences of the different functions of the various grammatical recodings; the resemblances, we suggest, stem from the basic nature of the apparatus.

We can make the comparison clearer if we make use of a specific theory of grammar. Though the comparison would hold good in most of its details for almost any serious grammatical theory, let us, for argument's sake, use the generative grammar proposed by Chomsky and his colleagues (Chomsky, 1957, 1965; Chomsky and Miller, 1963).[4] According to this theory there is a linguistic level, "deep" structure, at which a string of grammatical and lexical morphemes, the latter represented by classificatory distinctive-feature matrices, is developed from more complex units, the structure taking the form of a labeled tree. One or more of these strings is processed by the rules of the transformational component, which nest, rearrange, and delete the morphemes of deep structure to produce a new string of morphemes at the level of "surface" structure. A tree structure is assigned to this string also. The surface structure is processed, in turn, by the phonological component of the grammar, which applies morphophonemic rules and converts the columns of the classificatory feature matrices—the phonemes—into columns of phonetic features—the phones. Because of the cyclic character of the phonological rules, the phones are organized into more complex units corresponding to gradations of stress and other prosodic features.

In generative grammar, then, there are two conversions, one syntactic,

[4] Lamb (1966) argues that the successive recodings of his "stratificational grammar" can be regarded as a neuro-physiological model. His examples are quite consistent with the points we make here about linguistic recoding. But for him the relationship between "phonon" and sound is of interest only to the physiologist of the vocal tract, not to the linguist or to the neurophysiologist concerned with language.

one phonological, relating three streams of information. In neither conversion is the relationship between the two related streams trivial or straightforward; each can reasonably be called a code. For each code, on the other hand, a model of some kind can be suggested which rationalizes what would otherwise appear arbitrary and eccentric. Generative grammarians have occupied themselves in devising such grammatical models: sets of syntactic or phonological rules that try to account in some elegant and economical way for the correspondence between the two streams of information linked by the code. The rules of the transformational component, together with the branching rules which organize deep structure, are a syntactic model: they explain the relationship between deep structure and surface structure. The rules of the phonological component, similarly, explain the relationship between the surface structure and the phonetic level.

Whatever the virtues and defects of particular models, we presume that models of some kind are available to the speaker-hearer in terms of which he "knows" the grammatical rules that relate the higher levels of linguistic information, just as we concluded that an articulatory model rationalizes for him the interconversion of phone and sound. Yet, the linguistically naive speaker is no more consciously aware of his competence in generative grammar than he is of his competence in phonetics.

In both of these grammatical codes we observe parallel transmission of information. The values in any one column of the phonetic feature matrices that are the output of the phonology may depend on the values in more than one column of the input classificatory matrices that represent the lexical morphemes; this is done by the application of allophone rules like the one that de-aspirates voiceless stops after initial /s/.[5] Grammatical morphemes are often combined in the phonetic representation, notably in the inflectional languages. Thus in Latin the values of the number and case categories (singular, plural; nominative, genitive, dative . . . . .), which are distinct grammatical morphemes in the input to the phonology, are represented together at the phonetic level by a set of unanalyzable suffixes—the declensional endings—each having both a case value and a number value. Similarly, in English, a tense and root combine in certain irregular verbs, e.g., "sing, sang, sung."

In the syntax, also, parallel processing is the norm; indeed, it is reasonable to suppose that one of the main purposes of the transformational component is to speed up communication by transmitting several deep-structure strings at the same time. Suppose there were no transformational component. Discourse would consist of a series of simple deep structure sentences like:

---

[5] A symbol set off by slashes / / represents a phoneme, or column of classificatory distinctive feature values, at the input to the phonology: a symbol in brackets [ ] represents a phone, or column of phonetic feature values, at the output of the phonology. Thus, the phoneme /t/ is recoded at the phonetic level as aspirated [tʰ] in many contexts (such as *top*), but after /s/ by unaspirated [t] (as in *stop*).

The man sings.
The boy is tall.
The dog chased the cat.
The girl is blond.

If the deep structure were assumed to have rules for sentence nesting, a more complex string could be generated in cases where referential identity occurs. Thus the series

The man sings.
The man is tall.
The man married the girl.
The girl is blond.

(where the three occurrences of *man* refer to the same person; likewise the two occurrences of *girl*) would yield:

The man (the man (the man is tall) sings)
married the girl (the girl is blond).

But this complex string would surely take at least as long to process as the first series, since there are still four sentences to be dealt with. By means of deletion and substitution rules that exploit the referential identities, the transformational component condenses the nest of four sentences to:

The tall man who sings married the blond girl.

While this string is still four sentences at the deep structure level, it is only one sentence at the acoustic, phonetic, and surface structure levels, and so can be produced and perceived much faster. For the first series no such condensation is possible, but it is the second series, not the first, that is typical of the deep structure strings underlying ordinary discourse. There is usually a great deal of referential identity, which permits an enormous amount of transformational condensation and hence the transmission of a number of underlying strings at once. In this way, the limitation on the rate at which sentences can be processed by the brain is circumvented, much as the limitation on the temporal resolving power of the ear is circumvented by parallel transmission of different cues.

Just as in the case of the speech code, the price of parallel processing in syntax and phonology is a lack of simple correspondence between higher- and lower-level elements. As Chomsky (1957, pp. 38–40) has shown, we can only account for the various forms of the English verb by a transformational rule—the "auxiliary" transformation—that transposes the order of certain elements of the string to which it applies. Thus, the perfect and progressive are represented in deep structure by 'have + past participle' and 'be + present participle', respectively. By the auxiliary transformation

have + pp. + be + pres. p. + sing

becomes

have + be + pp. + sing + pres. p.

i.e., 'have been singing'.

In the phonological component, similarly, voicing of a syllable-final stop in the input results, at the phonetic level, in the lengthening of the preceding vowel. By this allophone rule, /bæd/ becomes [bæ:d]. Moreover, a phonologically voiceless stop is phonetically voiced post-vocalically before a low-stressed vowel. When both these allophone rules apply, the essential information distinguishing what are phonologically a voiced stop and a voiceless stop is displaced at the phonetic level to the preceding vowel. Thus /lædɝ/, 'ladder', becomes [læ:dɝ] and /lætɝ/, 'latter', becomes [lædɝ].

The two grammatical codes share with the speech code the property that, depending on context, an item of information in one stream may have various representations in the other stream that the speaker-hearer does not distinguish. The deep structure terminal string 'John is a fool' may develop into 'Is John a fool?', 'What is John?', 'Foolish John . . . ', or into part of 'John and Tom are fools' or of 'I consider John a fool', and so on. The morpheme which signifies plural, "s", may become [s], [z], or [iz], or any of several irregular forms. One of the distinctive features in the matrix representing /t/ is '-voiced', and normally /t/ is phonetically as well as phonologically voiceless. By a rule we have already given, however, /t/ may become phonetically [d] in a certain context.

The speaker-hearer copes equally well with all developments of 'John is a fool', responding only to the difference in grammatical context. He fails to notice the variation in the regular plural at all, and accepts the irregular forms as exactly equivalent. He takes the two allophones of /t/ (and several others as well) in stride; in the context specified by the rule, he will never notice the occurrence of the [d] variant. But he will notice the "normal" [t] allophone of /t/ if it should occur in this context, and wonder about the speaker's dialect.

The grammatical rules sharply restrict the range of variation, however, and in each case the restriction is categorical. If the categorical character of speech perception, which we described earlier, is not yet widely appreciated, the categorical nature of language has long been accepted as one of its most obvious properties. Sentences are active or passive, not something in between; noun phrases are singular or plural. Changing a phonetic feature, except in accordance with an allophone rule, changes a distinctive feature to its opposite and yields an entirely different morpheme, or no morpheme at all, not a similar morpheme. Presented with a set of varied syntactic or phonological items, the speaker-hearer unerringly deals with them categorically, just as he immediately perceives the phones [b, d, g], in categorical fashion. Categoricalness is thus found to be an important design feature of linguistic perception, from the level of the acoustic signal to the level of deep structure. This is the more interesting, because categorical behavior of this kind is not commonly found in human beings apart from their use of language.

Finally, we note that just as the basic coding units of the acoustic signal are organized into larger and more complex units, the three grammatical levels are also highly structured. A string at the level of deep structure can be represented as a labeled tree with lexical and grammatical morphemes at the ends of the branches and N, NP, VP, and S at the nodes, from which develop nouns, noun phrases, verb phrases, and sentences, respectively. The surface structure is represented by another branching tree. And since certain phonological rules, notably those relating to stress, are applied cyclically to longer and longer phonemic strings, the phonetic level also has, in effect, a tree structure.

From the formal point of view, then, there is good reason to regard the acoustic signal as another linguistic level, and the conversion from the phonetic message to the acoustic signal as a process comparable, in an important sense, to the conversions at higher linguistic levels. If this is so, then it is likely that speech and the various levels of grammar are processed by similar physiological apparatus.

III. Speech and Linguistic Physiology

To this point we have tried to establish speech as part of language by exposing certain formal similarities between the two. But the case does not depend entirely on such resemblances. There are data that point to more direct and concrete links; these suggest that the physiology of speech perception is not merely auditory, but also linguistic.

Consider, first, the tendency to categorical perception we described earlier. As will be recalled, this is a kind of perception in which discrimination is no better than absolute identification. To perceive the consonants categorically means that the listener identifies the several phones—for example, [b, d, g]—but cannot hear differences among the physically different tokens of the same phonetic type. The most easily measurable consequence of this kind of perception is that discrimination of equal physical differences will be better at phone boundaries (between [b] and [d], for example) than within a phone. When we measure discrimination of continuous changes in the essential acoustic cue, we do, indeed, find high peaks in the function at each phone boundary.

There are at least two broadly different interpretations of categorical perception. One is, that what is perceived categorically is the acoustic cue, not speech. In that case we should expect that the listener would perceive the second-formant transitions categorically, whether, in a speech context, they cue [b, d, g] or whether, outside that context, they do not. If that were so, we should conclude that categorical perception is a consequence of the way our auditory physiology processes certain kinds of acoustic stimuli. The opposite possibility is that what is perceived categorically is speech, not the acoustic cue. We should expect in that case that perception of the acoustic variable would be categorical only when it cues a phonetic distinction, and we should conclude then that the mechanism underlying categorical perception is not auditory but linguistic.

A recent experiment by Mattingly, *et al.* (in press), provides data that help us decide between those alternatives. These investigators compared the discrimination of various second-formant transitions in speech and non-speech contexts. In the speech case, the various second-formant transitions were part of simple, two-formant patterns, and served as the only acoustic cues on the basis of which these synthetic patterns could be heard as [bæ], [dæ], or [gæ]. In the nonspeech case, the second-formant transitions were presented alone and were heard as glissandi or else as chirp-like sounds. In both cases, the second-formant transitions were the only acoustic differences among the stimuli.

The results were quite clear. In the case of the speech patterns there were, as usual, high peaks of discriminability at the phone boundaries. Discrimination of the nonspeech controls, on the other hand, was very different. There were, in general, no peaks at locations corresponding to the phone boundaries. Such peaks as did occur were in positions different from those obtained with the speech patterns, and they were, in general, a good deal lower. Discrimination of the nonspeech stimuli was also, in contrast with the speech, quite variable in level, both between and within subjects.

Since the second-formant transitions are perceived categorically only when they are heard as speech, we should conclude that such perception is not merely auditory, but is also an aspect of our capacity for language. The incoming speech signal must, of course, first undergo some processing by the auditory system. What the experiment on categorical perception suggests is simply that a significant part of phonetic perception is carried out in the linguistic mode, and that speech is part of language in that very physiological sense.

That speech is part of the physiology of language is also suggested by the results of other recent experiments which show that phonetic perception, like language in general, tends to be located more on one side of the brain than the other. The first step was the finding, by Kimura and others, that when competing spoken digits are presented to the two ears, most listeners hear better the signal in the right ear (Kimura, 1961; Bryden, 1963; Broadbent and Gregory, 1964). When the stimuli are simple melodies or sonar signals, the opposite result is obtained—that is, the stimulus to the left ear is heard better (Kimura, 1964; Chaney and Webster, 1965). These results are thought to be relevant to cerebral lateralization because the representation of the ears in the cerebral hemispheres is presumably stronger contra-laterally than ipsilaterally. The finding has then been taken to mean that the spoken digits are more easily processed in the left cerebral hemisphere where, as has long been known, linguistic functions tend to be located.

Music and sonar signals (and, presumably, many other complex nonspeech sounds) are processed by most people in the right hemisphere.

The experiments with the spoken digits were not conclusive, from our point of view, because these signals are meaningful and therefore require something more than simple phonetic perception. The next step was taken by Shankweiler and Studdert-Kennedy (1967a, 1967b). Using dichotically presented nonsense syllables that differed only in the initial stop consonant (for example, [ba] to one ear and [da] to the other), they found a significant right-ear (hence, left hemisphere) effect. We know, then, that phonetic perception, even when separated from syntax and meaning, is cerebrally lateralized; it is, moreover, on the same side of the brain as language, while music, and presumably many other complex nonspeech sounds, are on the other side.

The fact that phonetic and nonphonetic perception take place on opposite sides of the brain reinforces the view that they are carried out by different processes. That phonetic perception is on the same side with the rest of language suggests, further, that the difference between the phonetic and nonphonetic processes is related to the difference between language and nonlanguage. We shall have illuminated this matter still more when we know the outcome of an experiment on the ear effect that is similar to the experiment on categorical perception we described earlier. In the case of categorical perception, it will be recalled, we asked what it is that is perceived categorically: is it the auditory event corresponding to the acoustic cue, or is it speech? With respect to the ear effect, we should ask, similarly, whether the left hemisphere deals on a purely auditory basis with the particular kinds of cues that underlie phonetic perception, or whether it processes such cues only when they are part of speech. To answer that question, we should compare the lateralization of synthetic stop consonants, for example, that are cued only by differences in the second-formant transition, with the lateralization of those same second-formant transitions when they are presented in isolation and do not sound at all like speech. The experiment is now being carried out (Shankweiler, et al., in progress).

If speech, in our narrow sense, is as much a part of language as we think, then it ought, like language, to be found only in man. We should assert that if it is reasonable to suppose that animals do not talk because they have nothing to say, it is at least as reasonable to suppose that they have nothing to say because they do not talk. In a recent study of several species of primates, Lieberman concluded that these animals do not produce a repertoire of speech-like sounds (Lieberman, 1968; Lieberman, et al., in press). Vocalizations consist of a single [ə] vowel, characteristic of the vocal tract in neutral position, i.e., when its shape approximates that of a uniform tube. The vowel formants move, but they do so in exact proportion, indicating that the length of the vocal-tract tube changes because of lip rounding or shifts in the position of the larynx, but that the shape remains uniform because the tongue is inert. Unlike the prelinguistic child, the monkey does not babble. Moreover, laryngeal excitation is quite irregular; there is little sign of the precise timing of phonation and aspiration so characteristic of human speech and so important for distinctions of phonemic significance (Lisker and Abramson, 1964; Abramson and Lisker, in press). The monkey's apparent incapacity to produce many speech sounds is due not just to his having a vocal apparatus that is less flexible in certain respects than that of a human being, but also to an inability to program in speech-like fashion the gestures of the vocal apparatus available to him. Apparently, the monkey's lack of the neural apparatus for language renders him incapable of speech as well.

Unfortunately, we know as yet almost nothing about the way animals perceive speech. We are reasonably sure that they do not understand speech in the usual sense, but one might suppose that this is only because they lack the machinery that comprises the semantic and grammatical components. If our view is correct, however, we should expect that animals would not perceive speech as we do, even at the phonetic level. Lacking a speech-sound processor, they are presumably unable to discover the segments of the message, or to hear as the same segment a consonant that appears in different vowel contexts and has, as a consequence, very different acoustic shapes. To the extent that the animal's auditory system is like ours, it should hear speech much as we hear the essential acoustic cues when they are sounded outside a speech-pattern context. On being presented with the syllables [di] and [du] cued only by the second-formant transition, the animal should perceive, not the unanalyzable linguistic event we human beings call [d], but instead the glissandi or chirps we hear when we listen to isolated second-formant transitions. If the animal's auditory physiology is significantly different from ours, then it should hear not glissandi or chirps, but something else, or, perhaps, nothing at all. But if it lacks the speech processor, as we suspect all nonhuman animals do, then, no matter what its auditory physiology, it should not hear [di] and [du] as utterances that begin with the same first segment.

It is possible, at least in principle, to determine experimentally how animals hear various kinds of speech sounds. This has not been done yet, at least not in such a way as to indicate whether they decode the sounds of speech as we do. If experiment should prove that they do not, then we shall have found that the conversion from sound to phone is, in a very deep biological sense, one with the rest of language.

IV. The Primacy of Speech

To support the assertion that speech is an integral part of language, we have used arguments based on data provided by experiments. But we should note, if only briefly, that there is relevant evidence of a non-experimental kind. Speech is the only universal vehicle of language; in contrast, reading and writing are recent, rare, and comparatively difficult for most human beings. Furthermore, language is acquired by the congenitally blind, but not by the congenitally deaf. We know well enough why a deaf child should have trouble learning to speak, but why, if speech is merely a way of transmitting language, should he find it so very difficult to learn to read and write? As a sensory channel, the eye is at least as good as the ear; why, then, are the optical shapes of an alphabet not easily substituted for the acoustical shapes of speech?

It is both tempting and easy to attribute such facts about the primacy of speech to conditions that have nothing to do with language. One thinks, for example, of the possibility that speech is better responded to than print because the child has no earlids to shut out the sound, or because he can hear speech no matter how his head is turned. But we believe that such peripheral considerations have little importance. In our view speech is the primary vehicle for language because both speech and language belong to the same special system.

V. Summary

We have tried to show that the interconversion of phone and sound is an integral part of language and of its underlying physiology. For that purpose we have considered three kinds of evidence.

The relation between phone and sound is that of a complex and efficient code bearing formal resemblances to the codes we know as syntax and phonology. Each of these codes is characterized by parallel transmission of information and by a consequent lack of direct correspondence between the elements of the linguistic levels that are linked by the code. Because we human beings have ready access to models that rationalize these codes, we are normally unaware that they might appear arbitrary or eccentric, or indeed, that they even exist.

Data from several experiments indicate that phonetic perception is not carried out entirely on an auditory basis, but rather requires the participation of mechanisms that are part of the linguistic system. Certain acoustic variables that are perceived categorically when they cue a phonetic distinction are not perceived categorically outside a speech context. Experiments with dichotically presented signals have shown that phonetic perception tends to be lateralized, like the rest of language, on the left side of the brain, while complex nonspeech sounds are processed primarily on the right.

It is a matter of common observation that speech has a privileged relation to language. Centuries of experience with reading and with the problems of deaf children make it clear that no other vehicle for language is so natural or easy as the sounds of speech.

We conclude, then, that a knowledge of the mechanisms underlying the encoded relation between phone and sound would throw light on more general linguistic processes. Because such mechanisms are more accessible than those that govern the higher levels of grammar, they should be of special interest to the physiologist who cares about language.

REFERENCES

Abramson, A. and Lisker, L. (in press). Discrimination along the voicing continuum: cross-language tests. Proc. 6th Int. Cong. Phonetic Sci., Prague, 1967.

Broadbent, D. E. and Gregory, M. (1964). Accuracy of recognition for speech presented to the right and left ears. Quart. J. Exp. Psychol., 16: 359–360.

Bryden, M. P. (1963). Ear preference in auditory perception. J. Exp. Psychol., 65: 103–105.

Chaney, R. B. and Webster, J. C. (1965). Information in certain multi-dimensional acoustic signals. Report #1339, U.S. Navy Electronics Laboratory Reports, San Diego.

Chomsky, N. (1957). Syntactic structures. The Hague: Mouton.

Chomsky, N. (1965). Aspects of the theory of syntax. Cambridge, MIT Press.

Chomsky, N. and Halle, M. (1968). The sound pattern of English. New York-Evanston-London: Harper and Row.

Chomsky, N. and Miller, G. A. (1963). Introduction to the formal analysis of natural languages. In R. D. Luce, R. R. Bush and E. Galanter (eds.), Handbook of mathematical psychology. New York: John Wiley, 2: 269–321.

Coffey, J. L. (1963). The development and evaluation of the Batelle aural reading device. Proc. Int. Cong. Tech. and Blindness I. New York: American Foundation for the Blind, 343–360.

Cooper, F. S. (1950). Research on reading machines for the blind. In P. A. Zahl (ed.), Blindness: modern approaches to the unseen environment. Princeton: Princeton University Press, pp. 512–543.

Cooper, F. S. (1966). Describing the speech process in motor command terms (abstract). J. Acoust. Soc. Amer., 39: 1221 (Text: Status Report on Speech Research SR-5/6, Haskins Laboratories, New York, 1966).

Delattre, P. C., Liberman, A. M. and Cooper, F. S. (1955). Acoustic loci and transitional cues for consonants. J. Acoust. Soc. Amer., 27: 769–773.

Freiberger, J. and Murphy, E. F. (1961). Reading machines for the blind. IRE Professional Group on Human Factors in Electronics, HFE-2: 8–19.

Kimura, D. (1961). Cerebral dominance and perception of verbal stimuli. Canad. J. Psychol., 15: 166–171.

Kimura, D. (1964). Left-right differences in the perception of melodies. Quart. J. Exper. Psychol., 16: 355–358.

Kozhevnikov, V. A. and Chistovich, L. A. (1965). Rech' Artikuliatsia i vospriiatie. Moscow-Leningrad. (Trans. as Speech: articulation and perception. Washington: Joint Publications Research Service, 1965).

Lamb, S. (1966). Linguistic structure and the production and decoding of discourse. In E. C. Carterette (ed.), Brain function III speech, language and communication. Berkeley-Los Angeles: U.C.L.A. Press, 173–199.

Liberman, A. M., Cooper, F. S., Shankweiler, D. P. and Studdert-Kennedy, M. (1967). Perception of the speech code. Psychol. Rev., 74: 431–461.

Liberman, A. M., Delattre, P. C., Cooper, F. S. and Gerstman, L. J. (1954). The role of consonant-vowel transitions in the perception of the stop and nasal consonants. Psychol. Monogr., 68 (8, Whole, No. 379).

Liberman, A. M., Harris, K. S., Hoffman, H. S. and Griffith, B. C. (1957). The discrimination of speech sounds within and across phoneme boundaries. J. Exp. Psychol., 54: 358–368.

Liberman, A. M., Harris, K. S., Kinney, J. S. and Lane, H. (1961). The discrimination of relative onset time of the components of certain speech and nonspeech patterns. J. Exp. Psychol., 61: 379–388.

Lieberman, P. (1967). Intonation, perception, and language. Cambridge: MIT Press.

Lieberman, P. (1968). Primate vocalizations and human linguistic ability. J. Acoust. Soc. Amer., 44: 1574–1584.

Lieberman, P., Klatt, D. L. and Wilson, W. A. (in press). Vocal-tract limitations of the vowel repertoires of rhesus monkeys and other non-human primates. Status Report on Speech Research SR-15, Haskins Laboratories, New York.

Lisker, L. and Abramson, A. (1964). A cross-language study of voicing in initial stops: acoustical measurements. Word, 20: 384–422.

Mattingly, I. G. (1968). Synthesis by rule of general American English. Supplement to Status Report on Speech Research, Haskins Laboratories, New York.

Mattingly, I. G., Liberman, A. M., Syrdal, A. K. and Halwes, T. (in press). Discrimination of F2 transitions in speech context and in isolation (abstract). J. Acoust. Soc. Amer.

Nye, P. W. (1965). An investigation of audio outputs for a reading machine. Autonomics Division, National Physical Laboratory, Teddington, England.

Nye, P. W. (1968). Research on reading aids for the blind—a dilemma. Med. Biol. Engineering, 6: 43–51.

Ohman, S. E. G. (1966). Coarticulation in VCV utterances: spectrographic measurements. J. Acoust. Soc. Amer., 39: 151–168.

Orr, D. B., Friedman, H. L. and Williams, J. C. C. (1965). Trainability of listening comprehension of speeded discourse. J. Educ. Psychol., 56: 148–156.

Shankweiler, D. and Studdert-Kennedy, M. (1967a). An analysis of perceptual confusions in identification of dichotically presented CVC syllables (abstract). J. Acoust. Soc. Amer., 41: 1581 (Text: Status Report on Speech Research SR-10, Haskins Laboratories, New York, 1967).

Shankweiler, D. and Studdert-Kennedy, M. (1967b). Identification of consonants and vowels presented to left and right ears. Quart. J. Exp. Psychol., 19: 59–63.

Shankweiler, D., Syrdal, A. Halwes, T. and Liberman, A. M. (in progress). Left-right ear effects in the perception of second-formant transitions in and out of speech context.

Stevens, K. N., Liberman, A. M., Ohman, S. E. G. and Studdert-Kennedy, M.

(in press). Cross-language study of vowel discrimination. Language and Speech.

Studdert-Kennedy, M. and Cooper, F. S. (1966). High-performance reading machines for the blind: psychological problems, technological problems and status. Proc. St. Dunstan's Int. Conf. on Sensory Devices for the Blind (London), 317–342.

Studdert-Kennedy, M. and Liberman, A. M. (1963). Psychological considerations in the design of auditory displays for reading machines. Proc. Int. Cong. Techn. and Blindness I. New York: American Foundation for the Blind, 289–304.

DISCUSSION

HABER: Presumably the neural inputs to the speech center in the left hemisphere have undergone some decision processing since their input to the ear. What puzzles me is that a subject cannot tell many differences between auditory sounds in a forced choice discrimination and yet, somewhere else in the nervous system he can tell a great deal about speech sounds.

LIBERMAN: There are two different decisions involved here and I think they are orthogonal. One decision is whether it is speech or not speech. There are numerous cues on the basis of which we can make that decision though it is not known which of these cues are most effective. We do know, however, that the perception of these cues must be independent of the cues by which we distinguish one speech sound from another. Somewhere we make a decision whether the signal is speech or not and then begin processing it differently depending on the decision. Of course, if there is something wrong with the auditory system, one will not perceive speech; but being able to hear does not mean one will perceive speech.

SCHMITT: I have three questions. Firstly, would you comment on communication by whispering; secondly, can cues be separated and discriminated ear to ear?—and thirdly, I am surprised that there is no intensity parameter in the coding.

LIBERMAN: Let us take these points in reverse order: Intensity, for all practical purposes, has very little cue value. There is only one place I know where it is of very great importance, that is in the voicing distinction of fricatives, for example, [sa-za], where the intensity of the noise relative to the vocal portion is a significant cue. With stress, e.g., súbject or subjéct, you may think it is intensity, but it turns out it is really duration or pitch that is the important cue.

LONGUET-HIGGINS: Is it duration or is it larynx frequency?

LIBERMAN: For stress it is larynx frequency or duration or both, but not intensity. You can change intensity and the worst that happens is that you change your approximation to realism.

Now, with regard to the second question, we know that a listener will put dichotically presented cues together when they are separated in the frequency domain. For example, the first formant of a vowel put into one ear and the second formant into the other will fuse to give the vowel. If we split the cues in the time domain, the result is a good deal more complicated.

Finally, with regard to whisper, you produce the same formant pattern, whether you whisper or vocalize normally. Let me illustrate this with a steady state vowel. If I had my vocal tract shaped to produce the vowel sound *a* there would be formants—that is, bands of relatively intense energy—at about 700 cycles and 1,200 cycles. These are the first two formants of the vowel, and they are quite sufficient to give you *a*. Now, if I substitute whisper, I keep the same vocal-tract configuration, hence the same formants, but I have a different sound source. Now there is noise rather than discrete harmonics. As a consequence, the formants are filled with noise rather than harmonics.

SCHMITT: This does not apply when you substitute hydrogen breathing.

LIBERMAN: No, because that changes the velocity and hence the resonances. For example, speech in a helium atmosphere sounds like Mickey Mouse. The atmosphere does not change the fundamental, but it does change the resonances of the vocal-tract cavities and hence the frequencies of the formants.

CLYNES: The customary use of Fourier analysis to look at sound and hearing is inappropriate with respect to what really happens in the nervous system and what one hears. I will mention two aspects. As Dr. Liberman has also pointed out in terms of speech, the sensitivities of the ear to frequency and amplitude are quite different. In certain of our experiments we found that a barely noticeable change in amplitude was about 15 per cent, whereas, it was only 0.2 per cent in frequency. We found that the rate of change of frequency was very important. When we measured the evoked responses we found that at the vertex of the head a large, "unspecific" response failed to appear after small amplitude steps were replaced by large glissandos or siren-like sounds. It turned out that even a small (sustained) frequency slide inhibited the vertex response to subsequent large changes in pitch in either direction. The effective inhibiting threshold of the slide parallels the threshold for perceiving it as an unsteady or sliding pitch. This reaction of the brain, which we have called R-M function (Rest-Motion) occurs once with each word, and lasts about 0.3 seconds with a peak latency of O.2 seconds. The response occurs when a steady tone (or silence) is changed into a sliding tone, but not when a sliding tone is changed into a steady tone.

The second point I would like to make concerns the mixture of qualities one hears with simple physical stimuli. If one takes two single electrical pulses of, say, 0.5 msec. width separated by 3 msec., say, one can get a properly damped speaker system to reproduce reasonably accurately two such acoustic pulses. One can now vary the time between these two pulses, say between 2 msec. and 5 msec. What one then hears are two sensations: a "knock" that stays the same, and a pitch sensation which changes as the time between pulses is varied. If one increases the number of pulses, the knock sensation is relatively reduced and the pitch sensation increased. The knock sensation is apparently inhibited if there are enough pulses. This, too, illustrates the highly non-linear behavior in which several modalities of hearing interact. The idea that "timbre" is "overtones" of Fourier analysis is clearly false. But what is perhaps even more surprising is that there should be a pitch sensation at all for only two pulses: this appears difficult, if not impossible, to reconcile with Békésy's theory of hearing.

BOYNTON: How long can you delay two sound segments relative to each other either in one ear or dichotically, before it becomes non-speech?

LIBERMAN: I do not remember the figure, but, not too long. Timing is important.

LONGUET-HIGGINS: Do children who have been dumb from birth have any great difficulty in acquiring a speech recognition ability?

LIBERMAN: There is a claim by Eric Lenneberg in his book *The Biological Foundation of Language* that there are such children. He cites one case of a boy who presumably does not speak and presumably understands speech. Since this boy has normal hearing, I suspect that, like most infants, he used to babble. I do not recall whether there was any evidence about that.

AXELROD: Is it possible to put the consonants in one ear and the vocalic components in the other and get dichotic integration?

LIBERMAN: We have not done that, but we did something similar some time ago when we were not yet able, as we are now, to control the timing very carefully. We took a synthetic version of a fricative-vowel syllable like *sag*, cut it, and put the noise portion corresponding to the *s* noise in one ear and the remaining segment in the other ear. There was no question that we heard *stag,* not *sag.* However, if you play the second segment by itself you get *dag* and if you just separate the two segments by, say, 50 msec. you also get *stag* even though you put both segments into the same ear. Though I cannot be too sure, in view of possible timing errors in our experiment, I believe that we do not fuse across the ears with respect to time, only with respect to frequency.

Part III

PSYCHOPHYSIOLOGY

RALPH NORMAN HABER

University of Rochester
Rochester, New York

7 · *Repetition, Visual Persistence, Visual Noise and Information Processing**

I. Introduction

I plan to discuss two somewhat different lines of research. The first concerns my work (largely with Maurice Hershenson) over the past five years with the effects of repeated, brief exposures on the growth of a percept, primarily of words and letters. We have shown that even in the absence of an increase in energy or stimulus adequacy (duration, luminance, contrast, visual angle, or print discriminability), well-spaced, repeated presentations not only enabled the subject (*S*) to guess the word correctly but, much more critically, each letter of the word becomes progressively clearer and more distinct. In most of this work we have not been especially concerned with the interflash interval—the time between repetitions of the same stimulus—except that all of these times are several orders of magnitude larger than the critical durations usually associated with temporal integration processes. It is obvious that successive flashes heighten the receptability of some cortical process (cell assembly or receptive field?) concerned with the registration and representation of the stimulus in such a way as to produce a percept the perceiver can be aware of, encode, store, and retrieve.

* The research reported here has been supported in part by grants from the United States Public Health Service, MH 03244 and MH 10753, and from the National Science Foundation, GB 4547 and GB 5910. Part of this paper was presented at a symposium on Temporal Integration in Vision and Audition at the American Psychological Association Convention, San Francisco, 1968.

121

Recently, Lionel Standing and I pursued this one step further. We had already shown that if a brief suprathreshold flash is repeated rapidly (interflash intervals less than 250 msec.), S can report that it never completely fades away before the next flash. We have tried this with subliminal stimuli (rare and frequent words) and have shown that for a word the S cannot recognize or see on a single flash, if it is repeated with delays up to 900 msec. between flashes, the letters become clear so that S can easily recognize the word. Thus, the effects of one flash of a stimulus clearly persevere for a long time thereafter, even beyond the time S says it persists visually.

The second area of research covers the effects of visual noise on information processing of brief visual stimuli. I have argued that rather than reducing the clarity of the registration or the short-term visual storage of the stimulus, visual noise following a stimulus reduces the amount of time S has to process the information of the stimulus into memory. Thus, until the visual noise occurs, the adequacy of the stimulus representation is unimpaired.

Several lines of evidence have already been developed (primarily with Lionel Standing) to support this argument, although the issue is far from closed. In one study we have shown that the amount of information processed from a sequential presentation of letters is determined, not by the duration that each item is presented, but by the combined time it is *on* plus the *off* time before the next item appears—hence, the time to process each item. If the *on* time is reduced, performance can be held constant by a comparable increase in *off* time. Other studies in progress are examining the number of items that can be recognized as compared to the clarity of items under masked and degraded presentations. A similar study is concerned with how many items can be counted under degraded and masked presentations.

If this argument continues to gain support, then the effects of visual noise are not the result of some combination it forms with the stimulus, as a concept of temporal integration would suggest, but rather of the restriction on the time available to process the information in the stimulus. This implies a mechanism quite different from temporal integration. Let me elaborate on the first of these areas of work briefly and then talk in more detail about the second.

II. Persistence and Growth of Percepts

Nine experiments have been published jointly or individually by Hershenson and myself on the repetition effect (see Haber, 1967, and Haber and Hershenson, 1969, for reviews). Since our interest has been with the report of percepts rather than with guessing or recognition responses, we trained each of our Ss in every experiment to report the letters he actually sees rather than to guess the word he thinks must have been shown to him. Our attention to reports of percepts rather than to guessing is a critical concern throughout these studies, and often assumes greater importance than the repetition effect itself.

The first experiment (Haber and Hershenson, 1965) used 504 frequent English words, presented at five different durations in 1 to 25 trials each. The durations were determined for each of the 10 Ss separately by finding the highest duration at which he rarely saw more than one or two letters on the first presentation. This was very near 15 msec. for each S. The other durations were then set 5 msec. less and 5, 10, and 15 msec. above this value. A marked effect of trials was found on the probability of seeing all seven letters of each word for the three middle durations (see Fig. 1). The highest was too high and the lowest showed no increase in clarity, even after 25 flashes.

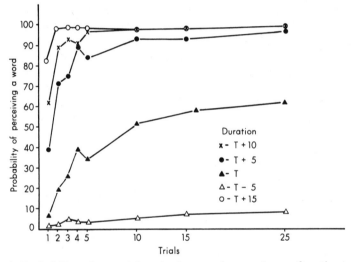

FIGURE 1. Probability of perceiving the letters of a word as a function of 1 to 25 repetitions for 5 durations. Data taken from Haber and Hershenson (1965).

The phenomenal reports of each S indicated that early flashes generally were blank (if the duration was low), but with further flashes, first the beginnings of letters would appear, then whole letters, and often the entire word. The percept of the word that developed with repetition was not fuzzy or unclear, nor was it the result of a guess or hunch. It assumed a clear status, so that S was never uncertain about his reports, even though he had been unable to see anything a few exposures earlier.

Several internal checks were available to determine if Ss were actually reporting their percepts or were guessing. Having once reported seeing a letter of a particular word, it was not uncommon for that letter to be invisible on the next exposure. During the process of development of a percept over trials, frequent fading and reappearing of letters occurred, although usually once all seven letters were seen the percept became stronger and increasingly clear. Further, Ss were usually able to guess what the word was after they had seen three or four letters. However, subsequent flashes resulted in the same rate of adding letters to the percept, as compared to flashes before S had correctly guessed the word. Therefore, guessing the word did not seem to affect the development of the percept of the word. Finally, there was no reason to doubt S's reports—they said they were reporting what they saw, not what they guessed.

This first experiment demonstrated that repetition alone increased the probability of seeing words, independent of any changes in the energy or duration of the stimulation. Thus, the "ascending method of limits" confounds duration with repetition, since both of these manipulations alone will produce an increase in perceptibility. Further, it showed that the phenomenal percept of the letters increased steadily with repetition, thus suggesting a developmental process of the appearance of the percept. This effect was independent of duration of exposure.

A second study showed the effect with seven letter Turkish words (Hershenson and Haber, 1965). Additional training was given Ss to report letters, rather than guess, with practice trials using English words with a letter missing. Only 2.4% of the reports on the practice words produced a "false alarm." The repetition effect held for both types of words equally, though the letters of English words were clearer. Therefore, growth in clarity with repetition is not at all dependent upon familiarity of the words, though the absolute level of clarity may be.

The issue of the S's criterion has been a critical one, especially whether the repetition effect could not be simply the result of S changing his confidence in what he sees without actually seeing any more. We tested this (Haber and Meiselman, 1969) by showing four letter nonsense words in 1 to 10 flashes, in which some of the letters were either missing or mutilated in specific ways. The normal letters in all words increased in clarity with repetition. More importantly, there were relatively few errors of calling a blank a letter or of misnaming one of the mutilated letters. In fact, these kinds of error declined over repetitions. This would seem to imply that the increase in clarity with repetition, which had been consistently found in previous work, cannot be due to the subject easing up on his criterion for reporting that he saw a letter. Rather, because the number of this "false alarm" type of error is constant or declines, it suggests that repetition provides a subject with more stimulus information and hence an increase in clarity.

Two experiments have been concerned with the prior experience S has with the stimuli and whether this has any direct effect on the clarity of percepts. In the first (Haber, 1965), seven letter rare and frequent English words were used. However, for half of them, immediately preceding their first flash, the word was exposed for 5 seconds and S spelled the word out aloud. Then the regular trials commenced. Giving prior knowledge immediately before the exposures increased the probability of seeing the letters. Without prior knowledge, a difference between rare and frequent words was found, favoring frequent words, but when S had prior knowledge of the word, this difference was eliminated. Most important, there was no difference in the rate of development of the letters with repetition, regardless of the experimental conditions, suggesting that this rate of development was independent of word frequency and prior knowledge.

Hershenson (1969) used seven letter nonsense words of varying approximation to English. In one condition, Ss were shown the words prior to presentation and asked to spell them, as in Haber (1965). In a second condition, they first had to memorize all of the words. Unlike the previous study, however, merely having prior exposure of these words was not sufficient to eliminate differences due to redundancy—stimuli structurally more similar to English were seen more clearly. However, after memorization, all differences in clarity among the different types of words disappeared. In both conditions, a substantial repetition effect was still found. This suggests that the frequency effect found in the preceding study, and the structure effect found here in the first condition, are not part of the percept, but are due to S's ability to remember the stimulus while he is reporting it. Thus, when S is able to give a true perceptual report of what he sees (Natsoulas, 1967), frequent words do not produce clearer percepts than rare words. Any differential in response accuracy is due to effects occurring after the initial registration of the percept. While this conclusion is not specifically challenged in any of the other experiments in this series, many of them do find differences at what appears to be the percept level due to frequency, meaning, emotionality, and the like. Thus, this problem is not yet completely answered.

I will skip over the other studies more briefly. We have shown the repetition effect with small single English letters, so it cannot be due to multiple fixations or shifting attention (Haber and Hillman, 1966; Dainoff and Haber, 1967). We were curious about the growth of clarity of taboo words, so we compared such words to neutral ones of very high or very low frequency (Sales and Haber, 1968). Apparently, even on the first trial the clarity of the taboo words is poorer and they never catch up to either rare or frequent words. Finally, in this series, three studies (Haber and Hershenson, 1965; Dainoff and Haber, 1967; Standing, et al., 1968) were concerned with the possible reciprocity of repetition and energy—could extra repetitions make up for reduced luminance or duration? The answer in each case was no, although for luminance the effect was closer to reciprocity. Thus, while the repetition effect was always significant and large, it apparently was not as large as those produced by corresponding changes in energy.

Briefly summarizing this series of studies, it is clear that repetition can affect clarity directly, and that in the traditional word recognition experiment, repetition is confounded with changes in energy. Here clarity will increase without any energy change, but just from repetition alone.

The principal argument that can be raised against this interpretation assumes that the S is guessing rather than naming the letters that he sees and that he is using cues provided by these stimulus variables to aid in guessing more accurately. Five arguments can be raised against this objection, drawn from the data of these various experiments. (1) If predictable cues were used to make letters more easily guessed, then these cues should increase the *rate* of improvement in guessing as well as the absolute level. However, this is not true. The rate of increase in clarity with repetition is invariant over all of these experimental conditions. It seems very likely that if the S was gaining greater access to information to enable him to guess, then this rate should increase even faster with many cues than with few. However, what happens is that the absolute level changes but not the rate. (2) Prior knowledge should wipe out all variation due to predictability cues, since there is no reason for the S to guess; he is absolutely certain. While the prior knowledge condition does eliminate the difference between rare and frequent stimuli and the structure difference, the rate of increase over repetitions does not interact with the prior knowledge manipulation. So, here again, increase in clarity with repetition seems to occur even though the S knows what the letters are to be. (3) The false alarm rate of making incorrect responses does not increase, but either remains level or decreases. Hence, there is clear evidence that the Ss are not guessing more on later trials to account for their improved accuracy. (4) Examining the Ss' responses, it is evident that very often they have clearly seen a letter after one flash and then did not see it on the next. This would not be a good strategy if they were attempting to guess. Finally (5), the Ss themselves are convinced that we are manipulating stimulus intensity or duration. "The letters become clearer," they report. They do not feel they are guessing, but rather, on early flashes they see relatively little and by later flashes the letters are perfectly clear, as if we had turned up the intensity.

For these reasons then, it is unlikely that the Ss are in fact guessing. Or, if they are, the contribution made by guessing would account for a relatively small amount of the variance. Haber and Hershenson (1969) explore the evidence to support this conclusion in some detail.

While there are a number of obvious avenues along which further research is needed, can these effects be explained on the basis of data already gathered? Since the interflash intervals are never less than two seconds, and are usually five to ten seconds, temporal integration over this span of time cannot be the mechanism. Yet it is obvious that some residual effect of the flash remains, to increase the receptivity of neural units to the next flash. At a symposium in 1964 (Haber, 1967), I suggested that a Hebbian cell assembly notion might serve as an appropriate model. More explicitly, each flash makes contact with an appropriate cortical assembly or phase sequence representing that word and all similar words. That assembly is heightened in its reactivity, though if the flash was not sufficiently adequate, the reactivity does not result in a complete percept. Each successive flash increases this activity until the entire assembly is fully aroused and the S can see all of the letters. Thus, repetition of inadequate stimuli can make them adequate.

Repetition is not the only variable that can affect reactivity. Stimulus adequacy itself is obviously a critical one. The brighter, larger, longer, etc. the stimulus, the more likely it will be to arouse an assembly. Equally important, any pre-arousal that can come from prior instructions, set, or attentional mechanisms will undoubtedly differ in initial strength of organization as a result of experience and frequency of prior exposure.

Each of these variables have been shown empirically to affect the clarity of percepts, as this descriptive model predicts (and as it should, since some of the predictions are *post hoc,* although most are strictly common sense). This model also makes it clear that reactivity is cortical and not retinal. One new testable prediction derived from this model is that the repetition effect should not depend on exact fixations for each flash, nor even that the type face of the letters need remain constant for each flash. We already know that fixation stability cannot be too critical since it has never been maintained precisely in any of the experiments. We are currently testing these predictions more explicitly.

Another prediction concerns the interflash interval between repetitions. If receptivity grows with well-spaced repetitions, would it grow even more with flashes coming closer together? Or stated differently, could a repetition effect be shown for sub-threshold flashes, if they were repeated more rapidly than every five seconds?

These would seem to be reasonable expectations. For a repetition effect to occur, as these experiments have shown, something must persist after each flash so that the effect of the next flash will be greater. The model presented above assumes the persistence is in some persisting activity of a neural representation of the stimulus. Presumably that persistence decays with time. Therefore, the interval between each flash should be a determinant of the repetition effect. Following this reasoning, Lionel Standing and I have begun several lines of work to test this expectation more directly.

The first of these (Standing, *et al.,* 1968) manipulated repetition rate directly. Rare and frequent English words were used. For each S, some words of each type were shown with well spaced repetitions (10 seconds interflash interval). The duration of the flashes was adjusted to locate a threshold, defined as the duration for which *S* might see an occasional letter on an occasional one of the 10 flashes. If he saw more, the duration was lowered; if he saw less, it was raised. For the contrast, size and luminance used, this threshold was about 100 msec. for the frequent words and 130 msec. for the rare words. Once this value was located reliably for an *S*, then, with new words, the duration was set at some fraction of this threshold and a train of 10 flashes was shown at decreasing interflash intervals until *S* could see all of the letters. Fig. 2 presents the results for different du-

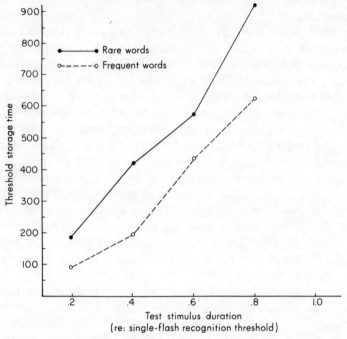

FIGURE 2. Minimum repetition rate needed to see the letters of rare and frequent words as a function of exposure duration of the flashes. Data taken from Standing, Haber, Cataldo and Sales (1968).

rations. Thus, for a train of flashes of rare words at 0.8 of threshold (about 100 msec. for most *S*s), all of the letters became clear if the inter-flash interval is between 900 and 1000 msec. If the duration is 0.6 of threshold, the word must be repeated every one-half second for the letters to become clear.

The longer interflash intervals possible for rare words are undoubtedly an artifact of the longer threshold duration for these words initially.

These results support the expectations very closely. The more adequate the stimulus (closer to threshold) the more time can elapse between flashes while still bringing the percept to full clarity. Note that a subliminal flash, which cannot be seen or recognized after a single flash, or even 10 well spaced flashes, becomes very clear and perceptible if the flashes are presented closer together in time. We tested the Ss in the same experiment on the judgment of whether the words faded away between flashes. At the interflash intervals at which accumulation occurs, the Ss always said the letters faded away. Thus, this accumulation is not due to a persistence of the percept.

But to what is it due? This is where our work stands today—there are many questions and only some hunches and a very general model. The second half of this presentation concerns a different set of questions and a rather different methodology. The two parts are not unrelated, however, as I hope I can show.

III. An Information Processing Interpretation of Visual Noise

For someone like myself who has been interested in information processing analyses of visual perception (e.g., see Haber, 1969b), especially encoding of information from a rapidly fading short term visual storage (STVS) into short-term memory (Haber, 1969c), the use of visual noise to interrupt these processing stages has seemed like an ideal experimental strategy. Sperling used visual noise in several studies (e.g., Sperling, 1963) to show that the noise terminated or erased the STVS from which the S was extracting information. I want to describe a series of studies designed to explore such processing. First, however, I need to make a slight digression to discuss visual storage itself and some recent work Lionel Standing and I have undertaken.

We have been interested in the general problem of visual persistence and its relation both to a repetition effect and more generally to the concept of short term visual storage (STVS) that George Sperling brought to such prominence with his Ph.D. dissertation ten years ago (Sperling, 1960). However, his procedures were very indirect: his estimate of the duration of the STVS was based upon a post-stimulus indicator being used to retrieve from memory part of the information in the stimulus. For light-adapted Ss, his estimate of the duration of the STVS was about 250 msec. While Sperling never specifically described the STVS as a persistence, the analogy seems reasonable and testable.

Standing and I argued that if a visual representation actually persisted for 250 msec. or so after the termination of the flash, it should be possible to have S estimate this persistence directly. It is not possible, however, to ask an S to provide a judgment of absolute duration, since with suitable adjustment in intensity, flashes from one nanosecond to 10 milliseconds all seem equivalent in duration—mere point sources of time. Since this indiscriminance covers a range of 7 log units of time, it seems unreasonable to expect *S* to be able to make very sharp absolute judgments of temporal extent.

We have tried two other procedures, both considerably more direct than Sperling's estimates based on information processing and retrieval from memory. If a brief flash creates some visual persistence lasting perhaps 250 msec. longer than the flash, then each flash in a train of flashes should trail this persistence. Fig. 3 illustrates schematically what this might be like.

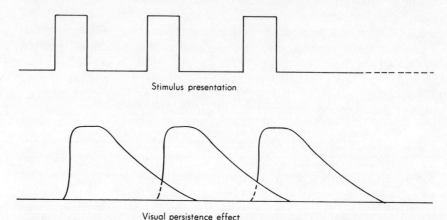

Stimulus presentation

Visual persistence effect

FIGURE 3. Schematic drawing of a hypothetical central persistence resulting from repeated stimulus presentations. Taken from Haber and Standing (1969a).

If the interflash interval is set at or slightly shorter than the persistence of each flash, then *S* should be able to report that no flash completely faded away before the next one came on. The train would be clearly flickering, but no dark intervals should occur.

We did this (Haber and Standing, 1969) by recycling a briefly presented form (a circle) while asking *S* to tell us whether the form completely fades away each time before it is re-presented. We found that if it is *off* for no more than about 250 msec., all *S*s reports that it never completely faded away. This is true regardless of how long the circle itself is displayed (from 4 to 200 msec.). Persistence can be increased to over 400 msec. if the adaptation field is turned off. Further, we had no trouble demonstrating this effect dichoptically, using a procedure in which alternate flashes of the circle were delivered to alternate eyes. Judgments of persistence were not changed in the least, clearly suggesting that while some neural persistence may be at the retinal level, the phenomenal effect must be central.

While this technique is simple, the results seem clearcut and striking. While we attempted no manipulation or control over the *S*'s response criterion, we still found estimates strikingly close to Sperling's and Averbach and Coriell's (1961). Further, the changes produced by luminance shifts, while small, are of the same relative magnitude and duration as in the literature. The same is true for the much longer changes due to adaptation state. Finally, we found support for another of Sperling's important suggestions—that visual storage ought to be independent of the duration of the stimulus itself. I will return to the implications of this finding again.

This study shows that at least one of the meanings of visual persistence can be measured directly. Sperling (1967) suggested a second way, though he did not carry out the full experiment to demonstrate it. We are in the process of doing that now, though the main purpose of this experiment will not be apparent until later.

Sperling (1967) reported that he trained one S to listen to a pair of clicks while he looked at a light flash. He was told to adjust the temporal asynchrony of the clicks so that one coincided with the onset of the light flash, and the other coincided with its offset. He always followed the light immediately by a visual noise flash designed to destroy any visual information storage or visual persistence. Had he not used a noise flash, this technique would have provided a measure of the apparent duration of the stimulus plus any persistence, given by the magnitude of the interclick interval set by the S. With the noise field, Sperling reported that S set the interclick interval very close to the physical duration of the stimulus, showing only a slight overestimate.

We have extended this procedure (Haber and Standing, 1969b), though the research is still in progress. Relevant to this discussion, however, is the clear finding that when S is light adapted and no masking flash follows the target, S will set the interclick interval about 200 msec. longer than the stimulus duration, regardless of its actual duration from 10 to 200 msec. The interclick interval is even longer—over 300 msec. more than the stimulus—when S is dark adapted. These results essentially replicate those from the previous technique.

These results would seem to provide a much firmer foundation for the concept of a short term visual storage than that given by just relying on the indirect assessment of Sperling and others. Let me now return the discussion to information processing and the role that an STVS might play in the sequence of events.

If a perceiver has a visual persistence (STVS) of a brief stimulus, from which he extracts information, then one research strategy to study this would be to terminate or interfere with the STVS and observe how that affects the amount and kind of information processed. Sperling (1963) did this by presenting an array of letters briefly followed after a variable delay by visual noise designed to erase the STVS. He found that for each 10 msec. of delay of the visual noise, S could report one additional letter. From this he argued that the S requires 10 msec. to process (read out from STVS) each letter up to a limit of four or five letters.

The assumption on the basis of which Sperling interpreted his results can be stated more generally (see Liss, 1968; Haber, 1969c). It is assumed that the processing of the information in the stimulus begins from its representation as soon as that representation develops. If a mask follows the stimulus after some delay, processing is assumed to have occurred during that delay, but is terminated or interfered with by the mask, probably in part because the neural representation is at that time altered. Thus, the mask has no "backward" effect, but rather only serves to interrupt the processing that began with the initial registration of the stimulus. Sperling's result goes one step further to show that processing proceeds sequentially and probably serially at a rate of one letter every 10 msec.

This information processing interpretation of the effects of visual noise on perception is not the one most generally accepted. The alternative view pays little attention to any information processing aspects of visual noise presentations but rather stresses the effect it has on the sensory character of the visual representation itself. This position has been presented by Neisser (1967), by Kahneman (1968), and by Weisstein (1968) and has been implicit in most of the recent work of Eriksen (e.g., 1966). Each has argued that a visual noise mask following a stimulus within about 100 msec. of its offset combines in some way with the stimulus so that its acuity, brightness, contrast, or clarity never reaches the level it would have achieved in the absence of the mask. The most detailed work on this has been Eriksen's on contrast reduction caused by luminance summation between two temporally adjacent stimuli.

The critical issue is what happens during the interval between the onset of the stimulus and the onset of the visual noise. The information processing interpretation stresses an active extraction of information from a representation of the stimulus. The processing may be stopped if that representation is subsequently destroyed or altered, but in the absence of great energy differentials, subsequent events do not act backward. The sensory interpretation apparently assumes either that no processing begins until the end of a summation or integration interval (about 100 msec.), or that visual noise can act backward in time up to 100 msec. to degrade the stimulus representation. In either event, this interpretation holds that a subsequently masked stimulus is never represented more clearly than that representation available after the mask has had its effects.

I see these distinctions between the two interpretations to be critical ones for current perceptual theory, especially for those aspects concerned with information processing approaches. Many empirical situations lead to very similar predictions from the two hypotheses, although I will discuss in some detail several that do not. However, it is not at the empirical level that the distinction is important. If the information processing interpretation is correct, not only does visual noise provide a powerful tool with which to study processing of information from visual displays, but the very extraction process becomes more amenable to investigation.

My first excursion into this controversy was two years ago (Haber and

Nathanson, 1969) with a study using sequential presentation of letters. We made the assumption that the arrival of the second letter (in the same retinal location as the first) acts to stop processing of the first letter, and so forth for each subsequent letter. Processing time can then be computed as the time from the onset of a letter until the onset of the next letter and is the sum of the letter duration plus the time from the offset of one to the onset of the next letter. Thus, it is possible to vary processing time and stimulus duration independently by appropriate variation of the *off* time between letters.

Four Ss were tested. Each saw 1250 frequent English words, subdivided into five lengths (four, five, six, seven, or eight letters), five *on* times (10, 25, 50, 100 and 150 msec.), and five similar *off* times.

The letters were presented using a 15 segment alpha-numeric display on an electro-luminescent panel controlled by a PDP-8 computer. The S pressed a button which initiated the sequence and then he reported the letters that he was sure he saw (not guessed) as soon as the last letter ended.

We found, for every *on-off* combination summing to the same processing time, that the ratio of *on* time to *off* time could be varied as much as 15:1 without changing the performance. The only predictator of the number of letters correctly reported was the duration of processing time. This is true for each S and for each word length. This finding supports the notion that it is the time available to process the stimulus and not merely its duration alone that is the proper independent variable. If the subsequent letters (masks) were simply reducing the contrast of the prior letters, then we never would have found that report accuracy was constant for any sum of *on* and *off* time under such wide variation of the *on* and *off* times. For example, the sensory interpretation should predict that for any given sum of the two times, long *off* and short *on* times would be better than long *on* and short *off* (as long as the *on* time was above threshold, which it was for even the shortest one used). A long *off* time delays a subsequent letter the most from the end of the previous letter and hence can affect the representation of the prior letter least. However, we found that either time could be lengthened or shortened without affecting the report of letters as long as their sum was held constant. The only variable that affected reports was this sum of *on* and *off* time, defined here as the time available to process each item.

While this experiment had not been designed with this interpretation in mind, it provides some important support. First, it shows the independence of stimulus duration and information extraction when time immediately following the stimulus is also available for processing. Second, it shows the total time for processing is controlled not by the stimulus duration but by a subsequent event, in this case the next letter which acts to stop processing. Finally, as in other examples not described here, it is clear that it is far more difficult for the perceiver to process letters in a sequential presentation task than in one in which all letters are presented at once.

To be sure that these conclusions would generalize to the more typical presentation case, the next experiment was undertaken (Haber, 1969a) and is still in progress. Two Ss have shown one, two, three or four randomly chosen letters for an *on* time from 1 to 400 msec. followed by an *off* time of 1 to 400 msec. before a 500 msec. visual noise field appears. The letters are about 30 minutes of arc in size. Luminance of all fields for the first 12 sessions is 2 ml, with 12 sessions then at 0.2 ml, finally 12 sessions at 20 ml. The number of letters shown is held constant for an entire session, but the *on* times and *off* times are randomized within each session. A three-field tachistoscope is used in this study, in which S first adapts to a background and then, when ready, he presses a switch which displays the letter (s) for the *on* time, followed by the background again for the *off* time, followed by the visual noise for 500 msec. Then the background returns until the next trial commences.

For the 2 ml condition for both Ss, the results showed that as long as the letters were *on* for 15 msec. or more, the *on-off* ratios were irrelevant for all processing times. Thus, 15 msec. *on* and 100 msec. *off* is equivalent to 100 *on* and 15 *off* for all letter lengths. Similarly, 15-50 was equivalent to 50-15, and so forth. This suggests, first of all, that for the stimulus energy used, 15 msec. is needed to establish an STVS and that a stimulus duration any longer makes no further difference, holding processing time constant. This STVS read-in time of 15 msec. is independent of letter length since the same value is found for one, two, three or four letters.

While only one S has been run at the 0.2 ml, the data are quite consistent. The read-in time increases to about 25 msec., but as long as the *on* time is 25 msec. or greater, the *on-off* ratio is still irrelevant. Further, the 25 msec. lower bound is found for each of the four word lengths. Thus, read-in time seems to be a function of stimulus energy but not of word length.

While many other analyses are being done, and are even relevant to this discussion, I want to stress only the one reported. Once *on* time exceeds 15 msec., accuracy of reporting letters is unaffected by any further variation of *on* to *off* time. Further, once the sum of *on* and *off* time reaches about 20 msec. per letter, even the sum ceases to be a variable. Hence, it seems impossible that the visual noise can be degrading the representation of the letters since the delay before the arrival of the visual noise is not a critical variable at all, if the amount of information to be extracted is small and has been completed before the noise occurs.

I already mentioned the experiment in which S has to adjust a click to coincide with the onset and offset of a light flash (Haber and Standing, 1969a). That study was undertaken to demonstrate more than just that visual persistence could be measured more directly. Sperling (1967) followed the flash with visual noise immediately and found an interclick interval only very slightly longer than the flash, which varied from 10 to 200 msec. From that he concluded that the noise eliminated the STVS or persistence and all S saw was the stimulus duration itself.

We have extended this, though with only two Ss so far. First, Sperling's finding with an immediately subsequent mask is replicated. When no mask is used, a very brief flash (10 to 100 msec.) leads to an inter-click interval of about 200 msec. longer than the flash. For much longer flashes (200 to 300 msec.), the inter-click interval is set very close to that of the flash—as if either no STVS persists after a long flash or the S can discriminate between the stimulus and the STVS with a long flash. When a mask is used but delayed, as the delay is shortened, so is the inter-click interval until, with the visual noise immediately following the offset of the stimulus, the inter-click interval becomes equivalent to the stimulus duration.

This task does not ask S to extract information but only to estimate how long he would have to do so if asked. The results provide fairly direct support for a process-stopping effect of visual noise. These results would also seem to make a sensory interpretation a bit farfetched. The S is being asked to estimate the duration of the stimulus, not its adequacy. Hence, even if the mask is irretrievably interfering with the representation of the stimulus, why should it also be affecting its apparent duration in this way unless the mask was also determining how long S has to process (in this case perceive) the representation of the stimulus.

Another experiment (Haber and Standing, 1968) presented an opportunity for a more direct test between the two interpretations of the effects of visual noise. Four randomly chosen letters were presented in two conditions. In one, they were followed after some delay by visual noise; in the other their duration was varied but no visual noise followed them. On one-half of the trials, S had to rate the clarity of the letters without regard to how many he could recognize. On the other half, he had to attempt to recognize all of the letters.

Both theories would predict that clarity and recognition should improve together as the stimulus is lengthened in duration. The sensory interpretation would make the same prediction as the visual noise is delayed. However, the information processing interpretation predicts that clarity should increase faster than recognition as visual noise is delayed, because clarity would be associated with the initial state of the representation and should develop to some high level even if it is subsequently masked.

The results support this latter interpretation (see Fig. 4).
Clarity exceeds recognition for the masked presentation as compared to those in which duration is varied. The difference is found for the range in which the mask is delayed at least by 20 msec. (shorter delays show no difference presumably because insufficient clarity has yet to be created) but no more than 100 msec. (beyond which neither clarity nor recognition is affected much by the mask). The Ss described the condition in which the

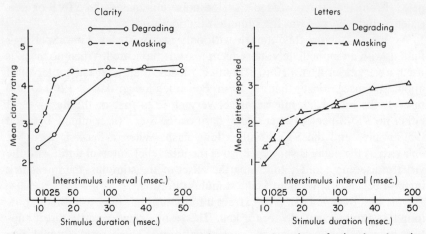

FIGURE 4. Clarity and recognition of letters as a function of stimulus duration (degrading) and delay of mask. Data taken from Haber and Standing (1968).

mask was delayed by, say, 50 msec. as one in which they saw the letters perfectly well but did not have enough time to recognize them. Liss (1968) also reported results from a similar study very much like these. This, therefore, suggests that the factors responsible for the development of a representation of a stimulus are at least in part independent of the factors determining the extraction of information from it (recognition). This is a critical implication of the information processing interpretation.

The final experiment to be described (Lorinstein, *et al.,* 1969), still in progress, varies the task but contrasts the same predictions. Here, rather than recognizing or rating the clarity of letters, *S* is presented with patterns of dots which he has to count (not estimate). Some trials vary the duration of the display while others hold the duration constant but vary the delay with which a mask follows. Both interpretations would predict that accuracy of counting would improve linearly with increasing durations because from a more adequate stimulus presentation, more dots would be visible. They differ, however, in the prediction regarding the effects of visual noise. The sensory interpretation predicts that accuracy will increase linearly with increasing delay of the mask, the same prediction it makes for the increasing duration condition. The information processing interpretation, however, says that it should take *S* a finite amount of time to count each dot.

This is an explicit serial interpretation of counting and denies the Hunter and Sigler (1940) assumption that six or less dots are counted in a glance and only beyond that is counting serial. The latter effect is more likely if *S* is asked to estimate rather than count, but many have carried their interpretation over to counting as well (e.g., Miller, 1956). I am saying it should take a specific number of msec. to count one dot, twice that long to count two, and so forth. There might be some additional search time added if the display is large or if the potential locations of dots are unpredictable, but I expect these times to be small compared to counting time.

Therefore, my expectation is that if the mask is delayed for longer than the time needed to count all of the dots present, performance will be perfect. If the mask comes before all dots have been counted, S will be able to count only the number he has time for, regardless of how many are presented; thus, performance as a function of number of dots presented will increase perfectly until some number and then level out.

Data collected on four Ss support this latter interpretation very closely. When the stimulus adequacy is reduced by lowering the duration of the display (but without any mask), S misses a greater proportion of dots presented as the duration is lowered. These functions are linear and are predicted by both models nicely. However, when the duration is high and unvaried, and a visual noise field is used, an entirely different pattern of results is found, contrary to the sensory interpretation. For a given delay, performance is perfect up to some number of dots presented, and then S is unable to count any more, regardless of how many were presented. While more data is needed on each S before a precise estimate can be made of the time needed to count each dot, it appears to be between 10 and 20 msec. Even now, however, it is clear that this is just as true for one to five dots as it is for larger numbers.

Much of the research just described is still in progress or being written up. One of the advantages of a symposium presentation, though, is a chance to talk about more current work than is in the literature. This privilege has permitted me to describe a small group of new studies designed to advance knowledge about the processes by which information is represented briefly in some visual storage and then extracted or processed into a slightly more permanent form, at least sufficient for retrieval. I have not reviewed others' work, though there are a number of additional experiments which support the model of information processing offered here. Nor have I examined all of the implications of even the few studies reported. My purpose is narrower—to present a model and show some of the research that follows from it. Many people are working on this problem and within another two years far more data will be available to refine the answers.

In summary, I have presented two areas of research, one concerned with repetition effects and the other with visual storage and information processing. A few threads hold the two sections together, though in actuality the research has been moderately independent. One thread is a positive one— both areas of work require assumptions of brief representation of stimulation after the stimulus itself has terminated. Another thread is negative— neither area of work can be explained by traditional models of sensory interaction, especially ones resting on temporal integration effects. Stimulus events can persist over times far longer than temporal integration would predict and a succeeding interfering stimulus can affect extraction of information from an earlier one without doing so through integration with it. More work will hopefully provide more positive answers.

REFERENCES

Averbach, M. and Coriell, A. S. (1961). Short-term memory in vision. Bell Syst. Tech. J., *40:* 309–328.

Dainoff, M. and Haber, R. N. (1967). How much help does repetition give to recognition processes? Percept. Psychophys., *2:* 131–136.

Eriksen, C. W. (1966). Temporal luminance summation effects in backward and forward masking. Percept. Psychophys., *1:* 87–92.

Haber, R. N. (1965). The effect of prior knowledge of the stimulus on word recognition processes. J. exp. Psychol., *69:* 282–286.

Haber, R. N. (1967). Repetition as a determinant of perceptual recognition processes. In W. Wathen-Dunn (ed.), Symposium on models for the perception of speech and visual form. Cambridge: MIT Press, 202–212.

Haber, R. N. (1969a). An information processing analysis of the perception of letters. (in preparation).

Haber, R. N. (Ed.) (1969b). Information processing approaches to visual perception. New York: Holt, Rinehart and Winston. 412.

Haber, R. N. (1969c). Information processing analysis of visual perception: an introduction. In R. N. Haber (ed.), Information processing approaches to visual perception. New York: Holt, Rinehart and Winston. 1–15.

Haber, R. N. and Hershenson, M. (1965). The effects of repeated brief exposure on the growth of a percept. J. exp. Psychol., *69:* 40–46.

Haber, R. N. and Hershenson, M. (unpublished). Perception and recognition.

Haber, R. N. and Hillman, E. R. (1966). Changes in single letter clarity with repetition. Percept. Psychophys., *1:* 347–350.

Haber, R. N. and Meiselman, C. H. (1969). Estimates of false alarm rates for perceptual reports of letters. (in preparation).

Haber, R. N. and Nathanson, L. S. (1969). Processing of sequentially presented letters. Percept. Psychophys., *5:* 359–361.

Haber, R. N. and Standing, L. G. (1968). Clarity and recognition of masked and degraded stimuli. Psychonomic Science, *13:* 83–84.

Haber, R. N. and Standing, L. G. (1969a). Direct measures of short-term visual storage. Quart. J. exp. Psychol., *21:* 43–54.

Haber, R. N. and Standing, L. G. (1969b). Direct estimates of apparent duration of a flash followed by visual noise. (in preparation).

Hershenson, M. (1969). Stimulus structure, cognitive structure and the perception of letter sequences. J. exp. Psychol. (in press).

Hershenson, M. and Haber, R. N. (1965). The role of meaning on the perception of briefly presented words. Canad. J. of Psychol., *19:* 42–46.

Hunter, W. S., and Sigler, M. (1940). The span of visual discrimination as a function of time and intensity of stimulation. J. exp. Psychol., *26:* 160–179.

Kahneman, D. (1968). Method, findings and theory on studies of visual masking. Psychol. Bull., *70:* (in press).

Liss, P. (1968). Does backward masking by visual noise stop stimulus processing? Paper presented at the Eastern Psychological Association Convention, Washington, D.C., April.

Lorinstein, I. B., Haber, R. N. and Standing, L. G. (1969). Counting dots of masked and degraded presentations. (in preparation).

Miller, G. A. (1956). The magical number seven, plus or minus two. Psychol. Rev., 63: 81–97.

Natsoulas, T. (1967). What are perceptual reports about? Psychol. Bull., 67, 249–272.

Neisser, U. (1967). Cognitive psychology. New York: Appleton-Century-Crofts.

Sales, B. D. and Haber, R. N. (1968). A different look at perceptual defense for taboo words. Percept. Psychophys., 3: 156–160.

Sperling, G. (1960). The information available in brief visual presentations. Psychol. Monogr., 74: (Whole No. 498), 1–29.

Sperling, G. (1963). A model for visual memory tasks. Human Factors, 5: 19–31.

Sperling, G. (1967). Successive approximations to a model for short-term memory. Acta Psychologica, 23: 285–292.

Standing, L. G., Haber, R. N., Cataldo, M. and Sales, B. D. (1969). Two types of short-term visual storage. Percept. Psychophys., 5: 193–196.

Standing, L. G., Sales, B. D. and Haber, R. N. (1968). Repetition versus luminance as a determinant of recognition. Canad. J. Psychol., 22: 442–448.

Weisstein, N. (1968). A Rashevsky-Landahl neural net: simulation of metacontrast. Psychol. Rev., 75: 494–521.

DISCUSSION

WEISSTEIN: Apparently you assume that the mask reacts with the target only at the moment the target is presented. But there are experiments in which effective masking occurs at some 40 msec. after presentation of the target. And this estimate would be for simple targets, much simpler than the letters you have used; one would expect, for letters, an even greater duration over which a mask would have an effect. In any case, all through some short duration, a mask interferes in varying degrees with a target; "process-stopping" seems an oversimplification. In addition, if you estimate a processing time of, say, 20 msec. per item, then the item should already have been processed when the mask affects it. This contradiction cannot be explained, moreover, as due to a latency effect.

HABER: The interaction between target and mask occurs at the instant when the two neural representations get to the same place and that depends among others on the nature of the target and intensity of the mask. If target and mask have the same energy, I assume they will take the same time to travel from the retina to wherever masking occurs. We can then take the difference between the onset of the two stimuli as the available processing time for the target. But you are asking the "nitty-gritty" question which refers to the fine grain of the processes involved and for which we do not have the answer at present.

LEIBOVIC: To get down to the "nitty-gritty," one will presumably have to consider at what stages of the visual pathway the various processes take place and what these processes are. For example, at the retinal level alone there might be interference of image projections or interference of "read out" or interference in some part of the short term memory.

PETER H. SCHILLER

Massachusetts Institute of Technology
Cambridge, Massachusetts

8 · *Behavioral and Electrophysiological Studies of Visual Masking*

In the attempt to understand the temporal characteristics of visual perception, the investigation of visual masking has played a rather prominent role. The literature is surprisingly extensive on this topic and so are the theories which confront us (Eriksen and Collins, 1965; Kahneman, 1968; Kolers, 1962; Raab, 1963; Sperling, 1965). Attempts to deal with the behavioral findings in physiological terms have been most pervasive in theorizing, most of which so far has been based on rather scanty physiological evidence (Alpern, 1953; Fry, 1934; Weisstein, 1968; Werner, 1935).

In order to gain a better understanding of temporal interaction, I have undertaken to investigate visual masking phenomena using both behavioral and electrophysiological techniques. Behavioral work was obtained mainly in man (Schiller, 1965, 1966; Schiller and Smith, 1966), although we have done a series of studies in monkeys, as well, which have shown that, in this species, masking effects are similar to those in man (Bender, *et al.,* in preparation). The electrophysiological work was obtained primarily in cats, recording with microelectrodes in the optic tract, the lateral geniculate nucleus, and, more recently, in the cortical area 17 (Schiller, 1968).

My presentation is divided into two parts. In the first part, I will summarize the basic behavioral observations we have made on masking. In the second part, I will deal with the single unit characteristics of the visual system obtained under conditions typically used in masking situations.

I. Basic Behavioral Observations

The bulk of the evidence collected in the area of visual masking shows that several different kinds of interference must be discerned. Failing to do so can only result in confusion when one attempts to explain these phenomena. I believe that one must distinguish at least three different kinds of masking. Two of these occur with contour interaction and one without contour interaction.

A. Masking Without Contour Interaction

Masking without contour interaction is obtained with superimposed stimuli under conditions where the target is any small stimulus to be detected or identified and the mask is a large homogeneous patch of light the outer edge of which is not in close proximity with any part of the target (Boynton, 1961; Schiller, 1965; Sperling, 1965).

Fig. 1 is a schematic representation of the kinds of effects that are typically obtained with such stimuli. This figure shows the following:

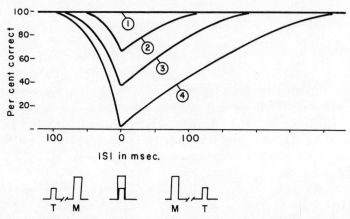

FIGURE 1. Schematic representation of forward and backward masking effects as a function of intensity and interstimulus interval ISI. ① Both stimuli of equal intensity; ②–④ Masking stimuli of increasing intensities, range approximately 2 log units. Order of stimulus presentation shown below graph: T = target, M = mask.

1. Masking is optimal when the two stimuli are presented simultaneously, or when their onset is simultaneous, and decreases as the interval between the stimuli (ISI) is increased.

2. Increasing the masking stimulus intensity, as designated in the figure by the circled numbers 1 through 4, increases the extent of masking.

3. Interference occurs both proactively and retroactively. The proactive effect, at higher intensities, is more prolonged in time.

4. With equal intensity stimuli, masking is generally not obtained under this condition.

Studies investigating this phenomenon have also shown that this effect is primarily monocular; interocular presentation, with the target presented to one eye and the mask to the other, produces only a small rise in threshold and is independent of intensity (Boynton, 1961; Schiller, 1965).

B. Masking With Contour Interaction

Masking with contour interaction occurs when the contours of the target and masking stimuli are in close proximity. With such stimuli two distinctly different kinds of masking can be obtained. I will refer to these two effects here as pattern masking and metacontrast.

1. Pattern Masking

This kind of masking is obtained with a large array of different stimuli. The target and mask may both be letters or patterns which are superimposed, or they may be stimuli which are adjacent to each other but have some of their contours contiguous (Kolers, 1962; Schiller, 1965, 1966; Sherrick and Dember, 1968).

With pattern masking, the extent of the interference increases as the mask and target become more similar. Masking appears to be optimal when the two stimuli are identical or when the contours of the target are in very close proximity to some of the contours of the mask. Masking, in contrast to the previous type, can also be obtained when the stimuli are of equal intensity provided superimposed stimuli are used. As we shall see, with nonoverlapping configurations equal intensity stimuli produce a different kind of effect.

Pattern masking also produces a monotonic function, with greatest influence at simultaneity. However, in contrast to masking without contour interaction, the effect occurs both with monocular and interocular modes of presentation. On the basis of this, it has been frequently inferred that pattern masking occurs at or beyond the point where the two eyes have common representations.

Pattern masking and masking without contour interaction frequently occur conjointly. In the case of the former, the effect hinges on the fact that the intensity of the mask is greater than that of the target. Since most studies employing stimuli with contours in close proximity have also used more intense masking stimuli, we find masking occurring both because of differential intensity and because of contour interaction. In order to separate these, it is desirable to study masking when the two stimuli are of equal intensities as well.

Some of the important features of masking with and without contour interaction using superimposed patterns can perhaps be clarified by a study which we recently completed (Schiller and Johnson, in preparation). The target was a homogeneous disk of .21°, .47° and .99°. Each of the paired stimuli was presented for 6 msec. at a constant ISI of 10 msec. Both monocular and interocular modes of presentation were employed using three

masking stimulus intensity levels. In the first case, the target and the mask
were of equal intensity; in the second, the target was 1/2 log unit less intense than the mask; in the third, the target was 1 log unit less intense than
the mask. The task of the subject was to detect the presence of the target.

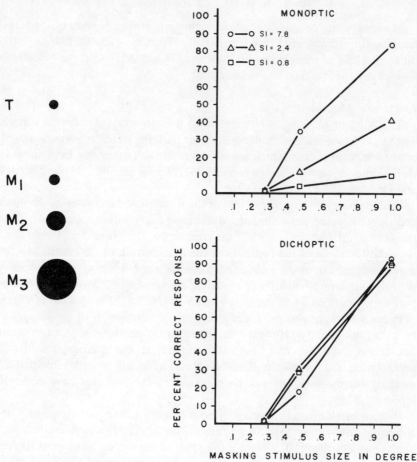

FIGURE 2. Backward masking with superimposed stimuli under conditions of
monoptic and dichoptic presentation, using three masking stimulus sizes and
three target stimulus intensity levels. The stimuli are shown on the left. Masking stimulus intensity constant at 7.8 mLamb. The three target stimulus intensity
levels, as shown in the figure are 7.8, 2.4 and .8 mLamb.

For control conditions we used catch trials in which only the masking
stimuli were presented without being preceded by the target. The results are
shown in Fig. 2. As can be seen, masking with equal intensity stimuli increases under both monoptic and dichoptic conditions as the size of the
mask is decreased. Varying the intensity has no effect dichoptically but a

pronounced effect monoptically. Curiously enough, it appears that under dichoptic conditions of presentation, the target stimulus is not degraded by the mask unless its contour falls in close proximity with that of the target.

This study, which complements the findings of Kandel and Boynton (Boynton, 1961,) and Kolers (1962) demonstrates that pattern masking and masking without contour interaction indeed produce different kinds of effects suggesting that separate mechanisms may underlie them.

2. Metacontrast

The third type of masking occurs with patterns which are adjacent to each other (Alpern, 1953, Werner, 1935; Schiller and Smith, 1966). This effect, generally referred to as metacontrast, is the most puzzling and least understood of the three types of masking.

Typical figures used in metacontrast are disks and rings where the contour of the disk, which appears first, overlaps or is adjacent to the inner contour of the ring. The effect is also obtainable with symmetrical figures such as two half-disks, but the interference is less pronounced.

Metacontrast is readily obtained with stimuli of equal intensity. In contrast to the other two types of masking, the suppression is optimal at intermediate ISIs. When the two stimuli are simultaneous, there is little or no interference at all. As the ISI increases, the target becomes dimmer and less apparent, with maximal effects around 60 to 100 msec. At longer ISIs the target becomes evident again. The whole phenomenon, it is important to note, is more drastic extrafoveally. The effect is primarily a retroactive one. This is especially clear when the stimulus configurations are symmetrical. Under such conditions, it is always the first stimulus which is suppressed.

A typical metacontrast result is shown in Fig. 3. The U-shaped function here was obtained using a brightness matching procedure in which a comparison disk was matched in brightness to the disk followed by a ring (Schiller and Smith, 1966). As can be seen, the disk is barely perceptible at ISIs between 60 and 100 msec.

The curious thing about this effect is the paradoxical nature of the brightness suppression. I want to enumerate four findings here to highlight this. First of all, as also shown in this figure, detection under forced choice conditions is immune to metacontrast: subjects thus can always detect the presence of the disk. Secondly, it has been found by a number of investigators that reaction time is unaffected by metacontrast (Fehrer and Raab, 1962; Schiller and Smith, 1966). An example of this is shown in Fig. 4. Reaction time is the same throughout the metacontrast sequence. However, when a single disk is shown at intensities which correspond to the brightness matches made, as shown in the previous figure, reaction time, as expected, increases with decreasing intensity.

Thirdly, when subjects are instructed to observe the afterimage of the disk, we find that the afterimage is also immune to metacontrast. Finally,

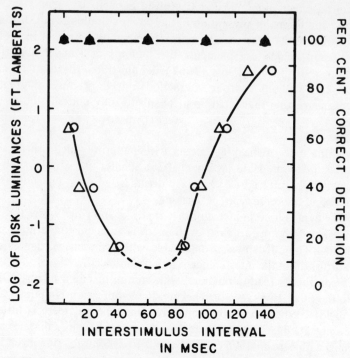

FIGURE 3. Metacontrast effects obtained with a disk-ring sequence using two different tasks: 1) Brightness matching, left ordinate and open figures, and 2) Forced choice detection, right ordinate and solid figures. The data for each of the two subjects used is shown by the circles and triangles.

when the interval between the disk and ring is set constant at 60 msec., and we now begin to speed up the recycling rate, the disk becomes brighter again. When the rate is such that the interval between ring and disk is the same as between disk and ring, the two stimuli appear equally bright (Schiller and Smith, 1966).

C. SUMMARY OF BASIC BEHAVIORAL FACTS

Let me now summarize the basic observations I have made so far.

1. Three different types of temporal interference phenomena have been discerned. The first has been termed masking without contour interaction, the second, pattern masking, and the third, metacontrast.

2. Masking without contour interaction increases with increasing intensity of the mask and with decreasing temporal separation. The effect does not take place dichoptically. Masking occurs both proactively and retroactively, with the former being more prolonged in time with high intensity masking stimuli.

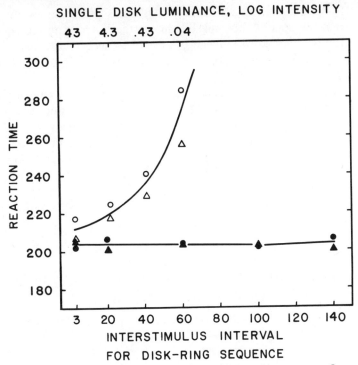

FIGURE 4. Reaction time in msec. with and without metacontrast. Open figures show reaction time to a single disk of different intensities (top abscissa). Solid figures show reaction time to disk in the disk-ring sequence at various ISIs in msec. (bottom abscissa).

3. Pattern masking is also monotonic, with greatest effect at simultaneity. Masking inceases with increasing stimulus similarity. The interference occurs both monoptically and dichoptically.

4. Metacontrast is largely confined to the perception of brightness. The effect is primarily retroactive and is U-shaped. Reaction time, forced choice detection and target afterimage are immune to metacontrast suppression. Increasing recycling rate eliminates the interference.

II. Electrophysiological Studies

Next I would like to turn to the single unit recording work I have undertaken in the attempt to understand these phenomena. The recordings were obtained in the optic tract, the lateral geniculate nucleus, and area 17 of the cat. The recording conditions were quite similar to those described by Hubel and Wiesel (1961) and Bishop (1962), using tungsten wire microelectrodes and conventional recording methods. For all stimulus presentation conditions, post stimulus time histograms (PSTH) were obtained (Gerstein and

Kiang, 1964), generally for 30 repeated stimulus presentations. Animals were operated on under thiopental sodium anesthesia and were subsequently immobilized by continuous infusion of flaxedil or succinylcholine chloride. They were maintained under nitrous oxide anesthesia during the experiment. The pupils were dilated with atropine and were protected with contact lenses. Using a slit retinoscope, the eyes were refracted on a tangent screen approximately 57 in. from the eye. Most of the experiments were done under low background illumination with the tangent screen intensity being less than .01 ft.L. The stimuli were projected on a Polacoat Projection Lens Screen using a Xenon arc lamp source. Electromagnetic shutters were used, providing rise and fall times of less than 1 msec. Stimulus intensity was varied with Kodak Wratten filters. The general procedure was to plot the receptive fields of the units studied and to follow this by stimulation of the field with flashing stimuli of very brief duration. Typically the stimuli were disks and rings of various sizes.

A. Response Characteristics of LGN Units to Brief Single Flashes of Light

Let me first consider the response characteristics of units to single stimuli of very brief duration. A 10 msec. flash of light elicits responses, even at very low intensities, which exceed the duration of the stimulus to a considerable degree. At 3 to 4 log units above threshold, such a brief flash may produce responses lasting 1 or 2 seconds. An example is shown in Fig. 5. The post stimulus time histograms were here obtained by stimulating the center of an ON and an OFF center unit in the cat LGN with a brief, 10 msec. flash of light at different intensities.

When light is presented to the center of ON units, a vigorous response is produced. The same light presented to an OFF unit first produces inhibition, which is then followed by a burst of activity. The discharge latency of ON units decreases with increasing intensity from about 70 to 25 msec. The discharge latency of OFF units, by contrast, increases with increasing intensity. The OFF burst is preceded, of course, by the inhibitory OFF response, the duration of which gets longer and the latency of onset shorter with increasing intensities. At high intensities, the OFF response may last longer than 500 msec.

The latency changes which we can observe appear to occur primarily in the retina, as similar relationships have been found there (Kuffler, 1953). Furthermore, it has been reported that when the optic tract is stimulated electrically with different intensities, the response latency of lateral geniculate units can be influenced only over a range of about 8 msec. (Bishop, *et al.*, 1962). Thus, processing rate in the retinal elements prior to the ganglion cells seems to be primarily responsible for the latency of spike activity

UNIT 31-1-2   UNIT 44-1-2

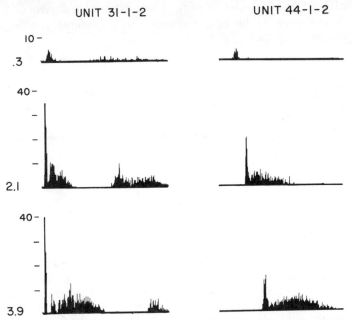

FIGURE 5. Post stimulus time histograms obtained from an ON (31–1–2) and an OFF (44–1–2) center unit in the cat LGN to single 10 msec. flashes of light presented to the center of the receptive fields. The stimuli were presented at three intensities, as indicated in the figure, .3, 2.1 and 3.9 log units above unit response threshold. Thirty stimulus presentations per histogram. Abscissa, time. Ordinate, number of unit discharges. The sweep of each histogram is initiated by the onset of the stimulus. The total time for which unit responses are analyzed is 1 second (analysis time). Each bar in the histograms of this figure and all subsequent ones represents a 5 msec. time sample.

in the visual system. The characteristics of ON and OFF units to negative flashes of light, that is, to dark spots presented on a light background, reverses the situation. The OFF unit now fires as the ON unit did to a light flash. The onset of the dark spot, in turn, inhibits the ON cell, and when this stimulus terminates, we obtain the analogue of the OFF burst. On the basis of such observations, it has been suggested that ON units carry information about light increment and OFF units about light decrement. Whether or not this is a valid assessment remains to be seen. From now on, however, I will concentrate primarily on ON center units.

The next point I want to emphasize has to do with lateral inhibition. It has been shown that the center and surround of receptive fields in retinal ganglion cells and in the lateral geniculate nucleus behave in an antagonistic manner (Hubel and Wiesel, 1961; Kuffler, 1953). Stimulating the center of the field produces a vigorous response. Stimulating the entire field produces a greatly attenuated response. This applies, in particular, to brief flashes of light, as shown in Fig. 6. There is a high degree of center-surround antagonism in this case, but units vary considerably in the degree of antagonism.

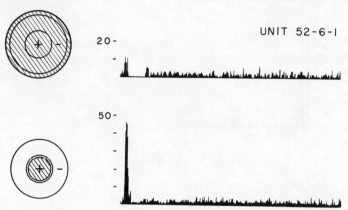

FIGURE 6. Post stimulus time histograms obtained from a cat LGN ON center unit to single 10 msec. flashes presented, 1) to the entire field, and 2) to the center of the receptive field. Both stimuli of equal intensity, presented .9 log above threshold, 30 trials, 2 second analysis time.

B. MASKING WITHOUT CONTOUR INTERACTION

Next, I would like to turn to the question of what happens under conditions of masking. Let me begin by showing two basic examples. The first of these is shown in Fig. 7. In this case, stimulation was restricted to the of 60 msec. The masking stimulus, a 2° disk, presented 3 log units above threshold, when presented alone, produces a response with a peak latency of 60 msec. The masking stimulus, a 2° disk, presented 3 log units above threshold, produced a more extensive response with an initial peak latency of 25 msec. As the interval between the stimuli is shortened, the response to the second stimulus begins to infringe on the first. At ISIs shorter than 50 msec., only the response to the second stimulus is apparent.

There are two noteworthy things here. One is the differential response latency to the two stimuli, on the basis of which it may be said that the second, more intense stimulus overtakes the first. Thus, although physically the two stimuli are successive, physiologically they are not. Secondly, it is apparent that when the masking stimulus is intense, there is very little summation at short interstimulus intervals. In other words, the response to the target plus mask is indistinguishable from the response to the mask alone.

How this occurs as a function of masking stimulus intensity is shown in Fig. 8. In this case the interstimulus interval was kept constant at 0 msec. A somewhat different array of stimuli were employed in order to make

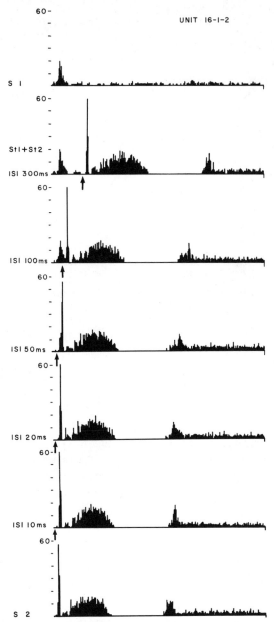

FIGURE 7. Post stimulus time histograms for single and paired presentations, ON center unit, cat LGN. Stimulus 1: 1° disk, 0.3 log units above threshold, 10 msec. duration. Stimulus 2: 2° disk, 3 log units above threshold, 10 msec. duration. Two second analysis time, 30 trials. Ordinate: number of spikes. Arrows show onset for stimulus 2. S1 = stimulus 1, S2 = stimulus 2.

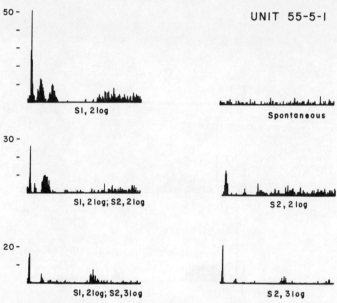

FIGURE 8. Post stimulus time histograms obtained from a cat LGN ON center cell to single and paired stimuli. Stimulus 1 presented to the center of the receptive field, stimulus 2 to the entire field. Paired stimuli were presented with an ISI of 0. Intensities as shown in the figure. Stimulus duration 10 msec. each, 30 trials, 1 sec. analysis time.

an additional point. The target, a 1° disk, was restricted to the center of the receptive field of a cat LGN neuron. The mask was a 15° disk, encompassing both center and surround. The intensity of the target was constant at 2.0 log units above threshold. The masking stimulus was presented at the same intensity and 1.0 log above this level. Histograms are shown both for paired and single presentations. As can be seen, the responses actually decrease as masking stimulus intensity is increased. The bottom PSTHs show that the response to the target and mask is essentially identical to the response to the mask alone. This example is different from the previous one in that the large masking disk, stimulating the entire field, produces an attenuated response. In spite of this, these response characteristics override those given to the first stimulus. In general, then, when the masking stimulus is of a high intensity, the responses to the target plus mask, at short ISIs, are indistinguishable from the responses given to the mask alone. This applies even when each of the single stimuli produces very different responses. It is interesting that practically no summation is observed. However, it must be remembered, that even with stimuli of equal intensity and size, summation is not that pronounced. Doubling light intensity, or doubling stimulus duration, produces an average increment in the number of discharges of 10–20 per cent. Units vary a great deal with respect to this. In some of them, the number of responses even decreases. What applies throughout, however, is that the extent of summation decreases as the intensity of one stimulus is increased.

With these considerations in mind, I want to pursue this problem further. A patch of light stimulates, not only the receptive field of one unit, but has an effect on many of them. Let us proceed with this analysis by looking at the next figure, Fig. 9. I want to draw attention to units which have their

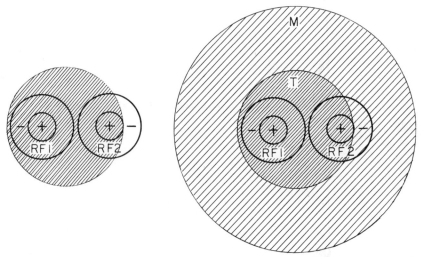

FIGURE 9. Circular receptive fields considered for a target and target plus masking stimulus.

receptive fields (RFs) entirely within the target stimulus as shown by RF 1, and units which have their fields near the borders of the stimulus as shown by RF 2. When the target is presented alone, units having their fields in position RF 2 will discharge more vigorously than those in position RF 1 because less of the antagonistic surround is stimulated.

Next, consider what happens when the target is followed right away with a masking stimulus, say of equal intensity. The majority of units with receptive fields in position RF 1 might discharge slightly more in accordance with what would be expected on the basis of summation effects. By contrast, units with receptive fields in position RF 2 may be affected very little, or may fire less, because that portion of the inhibitory surround which previously fell outside the target is now stimulated by the mask. One of the effects of the masking stimulus thus has to do with decreasing the responses which occur at the borders of the target stimulus. The outcome of this is the observable degradation of the target contour. When the intensity of the mask is increased, this effect is magnified, and eventually a point is

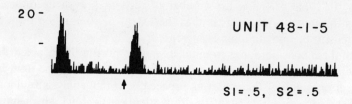

UNIT 48-1-5

SI = .5, S2 = .5

SI = 1.5, S2 = .5

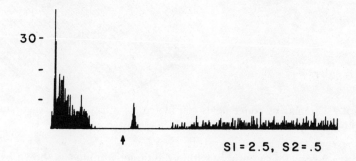

SI = 2.5, S2 = .5

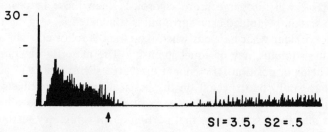

SI = 3.5, S2 = .5

FIGURE 10. Post stimulus time histograms to paired stimuli presented to the center of an ON center cell in the cat LGN. ISI = 500 msec. Intensity of second stimulus is constant at .5 log units above threshold. Intensity of first stimulus increased in 1 log unit steps. Stimulus duration 10 msec. each, thirty trials per histogram, 2 second analysis time.

reached where the responses to the masking stimulus for neurons falling both inside and at the edge of the target no longer produce a differential response to target plus mask.

As I have already noted, masking also occurs proactively, that is, when the mask appears first and is followed by the target (Boynton, 1961; Schiller, 1966; Schiller and Smith, 1965). This kind of interference is perhaps less interesting than the retroactive kind. Proactive effects appear to be due to the relative insensitivity of units to stimuli presented shortly after an intense masking stimulus. In contrast to retroactive masking, proactive masking may produce effective interference at ISIs longer than 500 msec. An example of this is shown in Fig. 10. The unit was obtained in the cat LGN. The ISI was held constant at 500 msec. When the two stimuli are of equal intensity each produces a clear response. As the intensity of the mask is increased the response to the target decreases until no response is obtained at all.

C. Pattern Masking

Before considering discharge characteristics of single units to paired stimuli with nearby contours, I want to restate what cues may be used to detect the target. The target may be detected because it is seen separately from the mask; that is, the subject perceives two stimuli. Alternatively, he may infer the presence of the target because the target and mask look brighter or different than the mask alone. Seeing a target separately from a mask would seem to necessitate a discernible neural response to each of the stimuli. Perceiving target and mask brighter than mask alone would seem to necessitate a greater number or different pattern of discharges to the paired stimuli than to a single stimulus.

Basically, what appears to happen on the single-unit level is that, when two borders fall very close to each other in rapid succession, the receptive fields near these borders fail to respond differently to paired stimuli as compared to a single stimulus. Observing the response characteristics of units near the border of the target, while varying the size of the mask, demonstrates this in Fig. 11. The size of the masking stimulus in this case was made progressively smaller until it approximated the size of the target stimulus. Let us consider what happens when both stimuli are of equal intensity. This is shown in Fig. 12. For the sake of clarity, two different ISIs were employed, one at 0 and one at 500 msec. The units were obtained in the lateral geniculate nucleus of the cat. At an ISI of 500 msec., the response to each of the paired stimuli can be seen separately. With a large masking stimulus, the response to the mask is both smaller and different than it is to the target. As the masking stimulus is made smaller, the response to it increases. With identical stimuli, the responses are highly similar, of course. When the ISI between the paired stimuli is 0, the response to the target is modified by the large masking stimulus; there are fewer discharges and the temporal distribution of the responses is different. As the size of the mask is decreased, the responses become more similar to those obtained to the target alone. With identical stimuli, there is only a

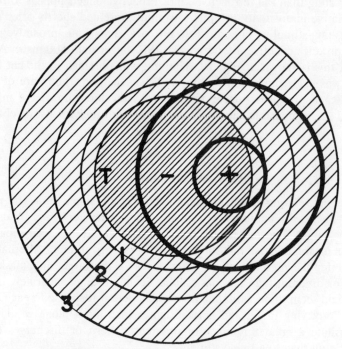

FIGURE 11. Circular receptive field considered in relation to a target and to masks of different sizes.

small degree of summation. The response to the paired stimuli in this last case is not very different from the response obtained to the target alone.

These findings show that as the two stimuli become increasingly similar, the differences in the responses to them near the borders of the stimuli decrease. Once the contours are very close, they stimulate closely adjacent or identical receptive fields which consequently fail in generating clearly distinct signals to each of the borders. With identical stimuli, a small degree of summation will occur; however, since the summation is rather small, it follows that with equal intensity stimuli, the target plus mask is difficult to differentiate from the mask alone. As the interstimulus interval between the paired stimuli is increased, the number of responses also increases and eventually two separate clusters of discharges can be seen, which then provide adequate information for the detection of two flashes.

In the beginning of this paper, I pointed out that masking with patterns is an effect which occurs interocularly. One may infer a contradiction here, in that, just now I tried to explain the interference at the geniculate level

UNIT 53-1-2

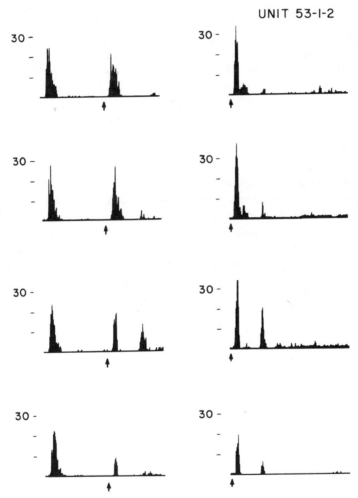

FIGURE 12. Post stimulus time histograms obtained from a cat LGN ON center unit to paired flashes. Column 1, ISI = 500 msec., column 2, ISI = 0. In the top row, the two superimposed stimuli are identical in size and intensity. Rows 2–4 show responses to the same target paired with masking stimuli of increasing size as shown in Fig. 11. Stimulus duration 10 msec. each, 30 trials, 1 second analysis time.

or even earlier. I believe, however, that there is no inconsistency here. Interference with patterns may occur at the cortical level under interocular conditions of presentation and earlier under monocular conditions.

To study this, I recorded from cortical cells in area 17, which have binocular receptive fields. I have started this only recently and so what I report here is still rather tentative. After plotting the receptive fields of units for each eye, I employed two kinds of stimuli. One was typically a slit so placed as to produce an optimal response. The other was a large patch of light encompassing the whole field. The stimuli were of the same intensity.

When the slit is presented to either eye alone a vigorous response is produced. A large patch of light superimposed on the slit produces a very much attenuated response, provided both stimuli are presented to the same eye. By contrast, when the slit is presented to the receptive field of one eye and the large disk to the receptive field of the other, the response appears to be the same as to a single slit. This finding corresponds to the observed failure of interocular effects with a large patch of light.

On the basis of these data, I would conclude that pattern masking may take place either at the cortical level or earlier. Where it happens appears to depend on the mode of presentation. Under conditions of interocular presentation, the interference occurs at the cortex; under monoptic or binocular conditions of presentation, it may occur at earlier stations.

Before turning to metacontrast, I would like to consider an interesting set of findings pertinent to pattern masking. It has been found (Robinson, 1966, 1968; Dember and Purcell, 1967) that under certain conditions, the introduction of a third stimulus following the mask results in improved detection of the target. A number of hypotheses have been advanced to account for such findings. One prevalent view proposes a "disinhibitory" process initiated by the third stimulus.

Robinson, in his studies, used three superimposed disks of increasing diameters. We have found that the facilitatory effect can be greatly improved when a ring is used for the third stimulus, the inner contour of which has the same diameter as that of the masking stimulus. I believe that these effects can be readily understood without recourse to a disinhibitory process. The effect of the third stimulus, most clearly seen with a ring, is that the responses of units having their receptive fields near the border of the mask are attenuated.

As a result, responses to the target suffer less interference. In other words, when the ring follows the mask we essentially remove the contour of the mask as an effective source of interference. Thus, we have a situation which is similar to a large masking stimulus, which, as we have seen in Fig. 2, produces less interference than a masking stimulus having its contour in close proximity with the target.

The same considerations apply when the third stimulus is a large superimposed disk, because such a stimulus also attenuates the contour of the mask, although to a lesser extent, of course.

D. METACONTRAST

Finally, I want to turn to metacontrast. This is the point, I am sad to say, where my story is far from satisfactory. Single unit activity under conditions of metacontrast raises serious problems in the attempt to try to explain this phenomenon. On the positive side, the reaction time and forced-choice results which I considered in the beginning, correlate well with the physiological data. On the other hand, the U-shaped effects obtained with brightness assessment do not seem to have this direct analogue in the visual system, at least up to area 17.

The simplest approach in the attempt to study metacontrast at the unit level is to stimulate the center of a receptive field with a disk and the surround with an equally intense ring. When this is done, one obtains results which seem to bear no direct correspondence to any perceptual experience. An example of this, obtained in the cat lateral geniculate, is shown in Fig. 13. These data show that, as the ISI is shortened, the total number of responses decrease monotonically, as would be expected if the effect was due to center-surround antagonism. Perceptually, by contrast, when the stimuli are simultaneous, they look equally bright while at intermediate ISIs the disk is suppressed. Since a disk and ring obviously do not stimulate a single receptive field but a large number of them, it might be more fruitful to consider the activity of units on the basis of how they are distributed over the stimulus figures. Units to be considered are shown in Fig. 14.

The discharge characteristics of receptive fields in positions 1 and 2 are not altered at all as the interval between the disk and ring is varied, except, of course, for the temporal delay in their respective discharges. On the other hand, units at the borders of the disk and ring are very much influenced by varying the ISI. The effect is similar to that shown in Fig. 13 except, of course, for the fact that it is much less drastic. When the two stimuli are simultaneous, the response of units in positions 3 and 4 is small, since the entire field is stimulated. As the interval is increased, the responses of these units also increases. Since the responses of units in position 2 are not influenced by the second stimulus, the information available from them can be utilized for detection. This may explain why forced-choice and reaction time are unaffected by metacontrast suppression. The characteristics of units in positions 3 and 4 explain how a border is gradually perceived as ISI is increased. None of the unit characteristics, however, account for the basic metacontrast effect of the paradoxical darkening of the disk at ISIs 50 to 100 msec.

Since none of the unit characteristics provide a ready explanation of metacontrast, one can only resort to inferences. It is likely that this phenomenon is related to processes depending on attention and judgment. The

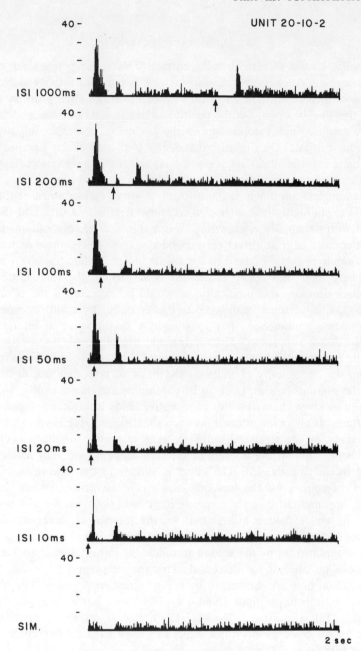

FIGURE 13. Post stimulus time histograms obtained from a cat LGN ON center unit. Stimulus 1: 2° disk, 1.3 log units above threshold, 10 msec. duration. Stimulus 2: Ring, 2° i.d., 9° o.d., same intensity and duration as stimulus 1. Two second analysis time, 30 trials.

fact that, foveally, metacontrast is drastically reduced may be interpreted as having to do with improved attention. Fixating centrally makes it easier to attend to the critical stimulus. When this is made more difficult by having the stimuli located extrafoveally, the tendency may be to make the judgment of the center at the time the ring is shown, that is, when the center is indeed dark.

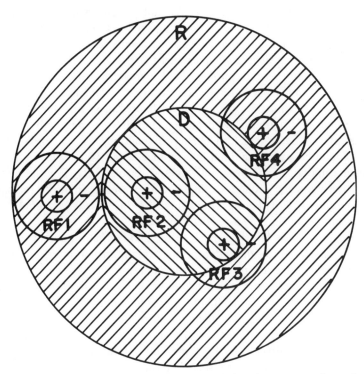

FIGURE 14. Circular receptive fields considered for the presentation of a disk and a ring.

That different conditions of viewing grossly affect this phenomenon, also supports this view. Unsuspecting subjects fail to perceive the first stimulus while sophisticated ones, at times, can see it clearly. When the sophisticated subjects relax and become inattentive, the effect becomes drastic again. When subjects are asked to describe the metacontrast effect, they frequently refer to a sensation of movement at those intervals at which the effect is optimal. They see the disk jump out to become a ring, thereby leaving the center dark. The fact that metacontrast suppression disappears when the recycling rate equals the interstimulus interval, also suggests that this phenomenon is not one that takes place early in the visual system.

These considerations make it evident that events in the nervous system which give rise to the perception of metacontrast, are of a degree of complexity which is, at this time, not amenable to single unit study. Perhaps when we better understand the coding mechanisms involved in this system, we might succeed in solving this puzzle.

Let me briefly summarize:

Behavioral analysis of visual masking discloses three different kinds of interference phenomena: (1) Masking without contour interaction, which is obtained with intense masking stimuli not having their borders in close proximity with the stimulus that is being masked. Masking is almost entirely monoptic and declines as the interval between the stimuli is increased. (2) Pattern masking, which occurs when the borders of the figures are in close proximity. In this case masking is also greatest at the shortest interval between the stimuli, but interference occurs dichoptically, as well. (3) Metacontrast, which occurs with adjacent figures of similar luminance and affects primarily brightness perception. The effect varies with the interstimulus interval according to a U-shaped function, less at very short and very long intervals, with maximal interference at 60–100 msec.

Masking may occur both proactively and retroactively. For the first two types of masking, the proactive effect becomes greater than the retroactive one as the intensity of the masking stimulus is increased. Metacontrast, on the other hand, is primarily a retroactive effect.

Single unit analysis of visual masking has shown that a number of factors must be considered in the attempt to explain visual interference phenomena. Backward masking without contour interaction occurs primarily because the responses to the second, more intense, stimulus overtake the responses to the first stimulus. This appears to occur already in the retina. The masking stimulus degrades the contour of the target through increased inhibition produced by stimulating the surrounds of receptive fields near the borders of the target. At high masking stimulus intensities, unit responses to target plus mask are, therefore, indistinguishable from responses to mask alone.

Pattern masking is brought about primarily by a failure of units, whose receptive fields lie near the contours of the figure, to respond differentially to target plus mask and mask alone. It appears that this effect may take place either cortically or at earlier levels in the visual pathway depending on the mode of stimulus presentation. Under dichoptic conditions, the effect occurs at the cortical level, while under monoptic or binocular conditions, it may take place earlier.

Metacontrast brightness suppression does not appear to have any direct correlates in the unit activity of the visual system in the retinal ganglion layer and the lateral geniculate nucleus. The discharge characteristics under conditions of metacontrast correspond, however, with forced choice, reaction time, and other related measures. The findings suggest that brightness suppression occurs elsewhere than in these structures.

REFERENCES

Alpern, M. (1953). Metacontrast. J. Opt. Soc. Amer., *43:* 648–657.

Bender, D., Gross, C. G. and Schiller, P. H. Visual masking in man and monkey. (in preparation).

Bishop, P. O. (1962). The determination of the projection of the visual field onto the lateral geniculate nucleus in the cat. J. Physiol. (London), *163:* 503–539.

Bishop, P. O., Burke, W. and Davis, R. (1962). The identification of single units in central visual pathways. J. Physiol. (London), *162:* 409–431.

Boynton, R. M. (1961). Some temporal factors in vision. In W. A. Rosenblith (ed.), Sensory communication. New York: Wiley.

Dember, W. N. and Purcell, D. G. (1967). Recovery of masked visual targets by inhibition of masking stimulus. Science, *157:* 1335–1336.

Eriksen, C. W. and Collins, J. F. (1965). Reinterpretation of one form of backward and forward masking in visual perception. J. Exp. Psych., *70:* 343–351.

Fehrer, E. and Raab, D. H. (1962). Reaction time to stimuli masked by metacontrast. J. Exp. Psych., *63:* 143–147.

Fry, G. A. (1934). Modulation of the optic nerve current as a basis for color vision. Amer. J. Physiol., *108:* 701–707.

Gerstein, G. L. and Kiang, N. Y.-S. (1964). Responses of single units in the auditory cortex. Exptl. Neurol., *16:* 1–18.

Hubel, D. H. and Wiesel, T. N. (1961). Integrative action in the cat's lateral geniculate body. J. Physiol. (London), *155:* 385–398.

Kahneman, D. (1968). Method, findings and theory in studies of visual masking. Psychol. Bull., *70:* 404–425.

Kolers, P. A. (1962). Intensity and contour effects in visual masking. Vis. Res., *2:* 277–294.

Kuffler, S. W. (1953). Discharge patterns and functional organization of mammalian retina. J. Neurophysiol., *16:* 37–68.

Raab, D. H. (1963). Backward masking. Psychol. Bull., *60:* 118–129.

Robinson, D. N. (1966). Disinhibition of visually masked stimuli. Science, *154:* 157.

Robinson, D. N. (1968). Visual disinhibition and binocular and interocular presentations. J. Opt. Soc. Amer., *58:* 254–257.

Schiller, P. H. (1965). Monoptic and dichoptic visual masking by patterns and flashes. J. Exp. Psychol., *69:* 193–199.

Schiller, P. H. (1966). Forward and backward masking as a function of relative overlap and intensity of test and masking stimuli. Percept. and Psychophys., *1:* 161–164.

Schiller, P. H. (1968). Single unit analysis of backward visual masking and metacontrast in the cat lateral geniculate nucleus. Vision Res., *8:* 855–866.

Schiller, P. H. and Johnson, N. Visual masking with and without contour interaction. (in preparation).

Schiller, P. H. and Smith, M. C. (1965). A comparison of forward and backward masking. Psychon. Sci., 3: 77–78.

Schiller, P. H. and Smith, M. C. (1966). Detection in metacontrast. J. Exp. Psych., 71: 32–39.

Sherrick, M. F. and Dember, W. N. (1968). Configurational factors in visual backward masking. Proceedings of American Psychological Association, 3: 111–112.

Sperling, G. (1965). Temporal and spatial visual masking. I. Masking by impulse flashes. J. Opt. Soc. Amer., 55: 541–559.

Weisstein, N. (1968). A Rashevsky-Landahl neural net: Simulation of forward and backward visual masking. Psych. Rev., 75: 494–521.

Werner, A. (1935). Studies on contour: I. Qualitative analysis. Amer. J. Psychol., 47: 40–64.

DISCUSSION

LEIBOVIC: Perhaps it is worth commenting that both in "forward" and "backward" masking we witness the interaction of successive stimuli, and any asymmetry in the effects is due to which we label the target and which the mask.

SCHILLER: You get symmetrical effects with similar stimuli. There are, however, different effects with dissimilar stimuli. For example, in forward masking an intense stimulus will produce a refractory state in the nervous system and, thus, reduce the effect of a following stimulus. In backward masking, on the other hand, the interference of an intense stimulus following a less intense one, is presumably due to the shift of the temporal representations of the two stimuli in the nervous system.

LEIBOVIC: When you were talking of one stimulus representation overtaking another one in relation to your LGN recordings, it could be interpreted that the stimulus interference took place in the LGN. Do you exclude that masking could be due primarily to processes in the retina?

SCHILLER: Most of the interference effects I have described appear to take place in the retina. The data on response latency alone would bear this out.

HABER: Would you agree that in the interval between the stimuli, the response to the first stimulus is unaffected by the second, as I have maintained? Some of your single unit records did not seem to be in accord with this.

SCHILLER: Let me answer this by saying that you have to look at different levels of the nervous system. For example, if you consider flicker, retinal cells can follow flicker more rapidly than LGN cells, and the latter more rapidly than cortical cells. So, in this sense, the further you get into the CNS the less sensitive it is.

BOYNTON: I should like to make one comment, Peter, if I may, with respect to a statement that you made which I think is not quite accurate, although you qualified it in your written paper. There is, certainly, a dichoptic effect under your No. 1 condition.

SCHILLER: Very, very small.

BOYNTON: Well, it's a factor of two or three, which means that if you started out with a stimulus just barely seen 100 per cent of the time, you could reduce visibility from 100 per cent down pretty close to zero, by using a mask in the other eye. That is, you could make the effect look large if you picked your conditions appropriately. I think this may be of some theoretical importance, too, so it ought not to be overlooked completely.

R. M. BOYNTON

Center for Visual Science
University of Rochester
Rochester, New York

9 · *Temporal Summation During Backward Visual Masking*

In this paper, I plan to talk about the latest in a series of experiments on visual masking which were done over the past several years at Rochester. Peter Schiller's very lucid presentation (P. H. Schiller, this volume) provides an excellent background for this, and gives one something to think about in the electrophysiological domain, which might be helpful in trying to explain our results. The present experiment was actually carried out by Robert Kintz, a graduate student at Rochester.

The first figure introduces the concept of the experiment. The bottom panel (c) on this figure represents a simple temporal summation experiment. We have two flashes of light, each lasting a little bit less than 2 msec., whose onsets are separated by 15 msec. in time. They are presented as small flashes on a large field. Although this is not yet a masking situation, the paradigm is the same one used in the masking part of the experiment, described below, which corresponds to masking condition type one, as defined by Peter Schiller.

Under these conditions, one can show that Bloch's law holds; in other words, that the only significant parameter for predicting the effectiveness of the double stimulus is the total amount of light in the double flash. If, for example, this represented a threshold condition, we could keep the combined stimulus at threshold by increasing the intensity of one flash (say the first one) and eliminating the other one altogether; or this could be achieved by adjusting them in any ratio that would give the same total sum of their intensities. This is the sort of thing that we did in the experiment to be reported.

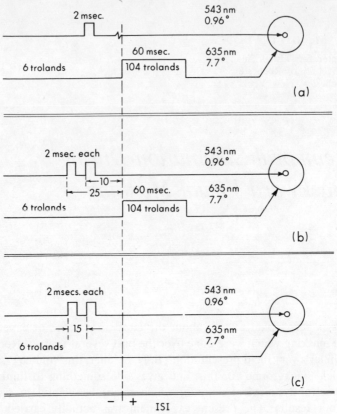

FIGURE 1. The temporal and spatial configurations of the stimuli used in the experiment. Their meaning can be illustrated by reference to Experiment 2 (Panel b). A steady background of 6 trolands suddenly increases to 104 trolands at time zero, defined by the vertical dotted line. 60 msec. later, it resumes its original level. This provides a masking stimulus of 98 trolands, superposed upon a steady adapting background of 6 trolands. Two test flashes are delivered. Each lasts for less than 2 msec. (not shown) and they have onsets at 25 and 10 msec. before the masking flash. The background and mask are 7.7° in diameter, and red. The green test flash, subtending 0.96° of visual angle, is superposed upon the background of 6 trolands.

The question to which we mainly addressed ourselves in this experiment was this: what would happen if we presented the double stimulus under the conditions of backward masking? In panel (b) of Fig. 1 we have two test stimuli, the first one presented 25 msec. before the onset of a masking flash, and the other one only 10 msec. before the onset of the masking flash, for the conditions as otherwise specified on the figure. In the normal situation, where we are dealing with a steady state, the rule of combination is simply that Bloch's law holds. But what is going to happen here, when we are dealing with a visual system whose sensitivity is changing very rapidly during this period?

Whereas Peter Schiller talked almost exclusively about a decrease in the probability of seeing that occurs when the test stimulus (or what he called the target) approaches closer and closer to the mask, we are looking at it the other way around, in terms of the increase that occurs in the threshold (that stimulus intensity required for 50 per cent chance of seeing) as we move the target temporally closer to the masking stimulus. The threshold goes up very rapidly during this period. We can evaluate this by doing the usual single flash masking experiment, shown at the top [panel (a)] of Fig. 1. We find that over this period of negative masking intervals (between -25 and -10 msec.), the threshold rises quite a bit—about 0.6 log unit, or a factor of four. In the figure, the target flashes are drawn fatter than they really are in time. These are actually very brief flashes, less than one fifth as long as the ones that Peter Schiller described, so they are essentially instantaneous in time (or nearly so) relative to the rate of change in sensitivity that is being evaluated.

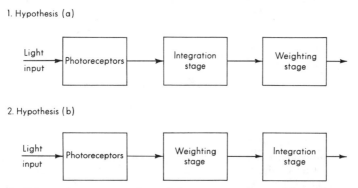

1. Hypothesis (a)

2. Hypothesis (b)

FIGURE 2. Schematic representation of the two experimental hypotheses under test.

The second figure illustrates two hypotheses which can be advanced about the rules of combination under this condition, where the double test stimulus is presented prior to the mask. It is possible that the initial responses occurring in or near the photoreceptor level (the double response to the two flashes) might somehow be integrated first, and then weighted according to a weighting function that would be described by the single stimulus masking function [hypothesis (a)]. Bear in mind here that, at the photochemical level, there will be separate events associated independently with each of the two stimuli. Conversely, it might turn out that each of the independent target stimuli is weighted according to the single target masking function, which may be considered to describe the changing sensitivity of the eye during this time interval, with the integration stage following this [hypothesis (b)].

The purpose of our experiment was to test these alternative hypotheses. Hypothesis (a) is a rather ambiguous one, in that if we assume that summation occurs first and weighting occurs second, it is hard to know exactly at what point in time (between −25 and −10 msec.) to pick off the appropriate value for the weighting factor. For the data which I will present, the calculations were done at the midpoint of this interval. We have also done it for other points all along the way, and it does not change the conclusions at all, because it turns out that hypothesis (b) is very exactly confirmed by the data of the experiment.

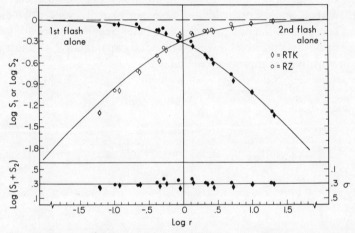

FIGURE 3. Outcome of Experiment 3 (Panel c in Fig. 1), where double flashes are presented upon a steady background. The abscissa values represent $\log_{10}$ of the ratio of the flash intensities, where a unit value is assigned to the intensity required for threshold perception, when each flash is presented alone. Solid symbols represent the scaled intensity S_1 of the first flash; open symbols represent the scaled intensity S_2 of the second flash, when the combined flash is at threshold. The solid curves represent the prediction made by Bloch's law of complete linear summation of effect of the two flashes. The same data are represented at the bottom, where the $\log_{10}$ of the sum of the scaled intensities of the two flashes is plotted; here Bloch's law predicts a horizontal straight line.

The third figure shows a way of describing the steady state condition, which can also be applied to the masking condition. Here we plot two functions of log r, where r is the ratio of the intensities of the two component stimuli in the double flash, expressed in terms of threshold units. The individual threshold amounts are equal in this case, since there is no essential difference between the two flashes. Each is being delivered to the eye in an identical state of sensitivity. On a logarithmic ordinate, we have the intensity of each component flash. The solid lines show what would

be predicted on the basis of perfect linear summation. This is a methodology originally worked out by Stiles, and used by him, Ikeda and myself
(1964) for describing some chromatic interaction data that we obtained
a few years ago.

The intersecting point of the two solid curves is perhaps the easiest to
understand: it occurs at 0.3 log unit below the threshold value for either
flash alone. This means that, if we use the flashes together in an equal
ratio of their threshold intensities, exactly half of the intensity of each flash
is required at threshold for the combined flash.

The third figure shows a set of summation functions for the steady-state
experiment, where a double flash is seen against a dim and steady background: it is simply a verification of Bloch's law, for the range of conditions covered. These two curves must cross above the ordinate value where
the logarithm of the ratio is zero. In other words, we have for this special
case an equal amount of intensity of the two component flashes. The figure
shows that the experimental data fall quite closely along the predicted
functions.

The prediction accounts for 96 per cent of the experimental variance in
this case, so we have confirmed Bloch's law for various ratios of the two
flash intensities. The horizontal line drawn through the points at the bottom of the graph shows the total amount of light in the double flash at
threshold, and the prediction here is that this value should be a constant.

Now let us look at the masking experiment. Fig. 4 shows the experimental
data obtained for single test flashes presented at various intervals (ISI)
with respect to the onset of the masking stimulus. The masking stimulus
comes on at time zero. We collected data here at a very large number of
time intervals, mostly negative, but also extending over to the positive side.
This was done by the "method of adjustment." These are very easy judgments to make, so we can get away with using this method, whereas a more
elaborate procedure might be required for more difficult judgments. And
here you can see that, between −25 and −10 (the values we are going
to use as a double flash), the threshold rises approximately by 0.6 of a
log unit. Visual sensitivity is thus changing rapidly during this period.
Another point to be made with respect to this figure, is that the variance
of these data (vertical bars) does not seem to change much across the
range of times investigated. This means that, in some sense, the visual
system must be keeping very accurate track of its sensitivity change during this period. (We had very good control over the timing; a little bit of
timing error, if allowed, would add a considerable, spurious variance to
the experimental data.) This figure describes a weighting function. We
are going to pick off two points from it, at −25 and −10 msec.

Fig. 5 shows what happens if we calculate the summation functions on
the assumption that hypothesis (a) is correct, i.e., that summation occurs
first, with the summated result then weighted according to the sensitivity

of the system at the midpoint of the time interval which we are talking about. The prediction is very poor. The predicted functions in this case account for 64 per cent of the experimental variance, but this is artifactual, resulting from the built-in correlation between what this model predicts and what is predicted by hypothesis (b), which turns out to be the correct one.

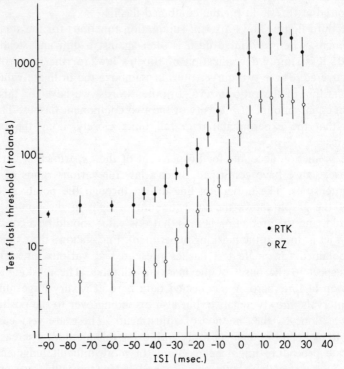

FIGURE 4. Threshold of single flashes at threshold (Panel a of Fig. 1) as a function of ISI, the inter-stimulus interval between flash onset and masking stimulus onset. Vertical bars represent the dispersion of settings. Data are for two subjects; those of RTK have been elevated one log unit from their true values.

Fig. 6 shows the results of the experiment plotted according to hypothesis (b). We express the intensity of the individual components according to the thresholds as determined by the single flash experiment at −25 and at −10 msec. We weight these according to what the threshold values are at these times, and then present double flashes having various ratios of these intensities. The results are remarkably like those for the steady state, two flash masking experiment. (I should point out here that one never sees two flashes in this experiment, any more than under steady state condi-

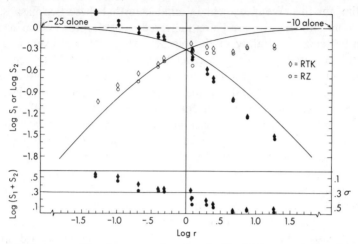

FIGURE 5. Same as Fig. 3, except for the double-flash experiment. Here the units of intensity of the flashes are scaled the same for both test flashes, according to the sensitivity of the eye at −17.5 msec. determined from the data of Fig. 4.

tions.) Here, 96 per cent of the variance is accounted for by the hypothesis under test.

We can conclude, without much difficulty, that hypothesis (b) is confirmed: that somehow, the visual system reacts to the individual flashes according to its sensitivity at the time the flash is introduced (as determined by the single flash masking function). We now have the problem of ac-

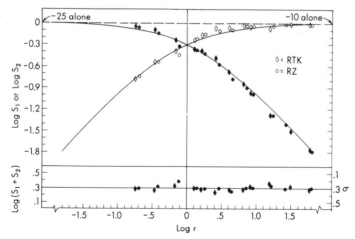

FIGURE 6. Same as Fig. 5, except that the units of intensity of the test flashes have been scaled separately according to the sensitivity of the eye at the time of presentation of each flash, as determined from the data of Fig. 4.

counting for this. We must bear in mind here that these two flashes, when they come into the eye, are being delivered to a receptor system which, at the initial stage (certainly in the receptor stage, at the level of the late receptor potential), is going to react fully and completely to each of the component stimuli, just as if no masking stimulus had followed. This is because the masking stimulus cannot work retroactively at that level. One hypothesis, *post hoc* (and, therefore, not too valuable) will be offered. It is difficult to justify on the basis of Schiller's single unit data, although we must keep in mind that we are dealing here with very large populations of units underlying the psychophysical experiment which makes such comparison difficult. The hypothesis is generally consistent with gross electrode experiments by Sturr and Battersby, who also stimulated cats in a masking experiment. The basic idea would be to assume that, as Schiller (Schiller, this volume) says (Sturr and Battersby make the same claim, and Haber made it also [Haber, this volume]), that, for the backward masking situation, the essential effect of the masking stimulus is to terminate the activity which is generated by the test stimulus before it has had an opportunity to run its normal course. Now, if one were to make the gross oversimplifying assumption that the responses are rectangular in shape, and that the height of the response is directly proportional to the intensity of the stimulus, then it would follow that the weaker stimulus at −25 msec. would generate a smaller response, but one which is allowed to go on for a fairly long time before the masking stimulus cuts it off. The more intense second stimulus, although it generates a larger response, does not have very long to run before the mask chops it off. Thus, the area under the two response functions would be about the same.

Of course these two assumptions that I have made are absurd—neither of them could be expected to hold exactly—and we are left then with the problem of how to account for the impressive precision with which hypothesis (b) is confirmed under our particular experimental conditions. I might conclude by saying that we have not checked this under any other conditions, so I cannot answer any questions about the generality of the finding.

REFERENCES

Boynton, R. M., Ikeda, M. and Stiles, W. S. (1964). Interactions among chromatic mechanisms as inferred from positive and negative increment thresholds. Vis. Res., 4: 87–117.

Sturr, J. F. and Battersby, W. S. (1966). Neural limitations of visual excitability. VIII: binocular convergence in cat geniculate and cortex. Vis. Res., 6: 401–418.

DISCUSSION

RUSHTON: What do you really mean when you assume the responses to be of rectangular shape?

BOYNTON: It could be that if you consider the aggregate total activity in many individual units, that the response could be approximately represented by a square wave, perhaps of impulse frequency as a function of time.

WICKELGREN: I thought you said that responses could not overlap due to delay in overtake of the test by the mask at the receptor level. What is the evidence for that?

BOYNTON: I was thinking in terms of the late receptor potential, whose latency is simply too short—a couple of msec. at the most. The response, therefore, occurs too soon to allow it to be influenced by any effect of a masking stimulus presented 10 or 25 msec. later. That is all I had in mind.

LEIBOVIC: Bob Boynton's intriguing presentation, as well as the results which were given earlier by Peter Schiller and Ralph Haber, bring to mind once more the question: where in the visual pathway do these phenomena take place?

I should like to suggest, as I have done elsewhere, that we look at the evidence for periodic activities in the visual pathway and their characteristic periods. For instance, in rough averages, electrophysiological recordings show there is a periodicity of 20 to 30 msec. in the retina, another of 100 to 200 msec. in the LGN and so forth. Correlated with these figures, there are various short term memory spans and some psychophysical data. For example, an average figure for critical flicker fusion might be 20 to 30 flashes per second.

Comparing such data with involuntary eye movements and retinal receptor dimensions I have suggested that, to a first approximation, one can consider the input at the retinal level to consist of some six "frames", as it were, which are transmitted as a package from the LGN stage.

On the basis of such a model one can look at the time course of various interference phenomena, such as in visual masking and use these as a probe to further elucidate the function of different stages in the visual pathway.

For example, on the basis of the figures I have quoted, it would seem to me that the weighting and integration described by Dr. Boynton for two flashes 15 msec. apart would be of retinal origin. Similarly, I would place interference of stimuli within a 100 to 200 msec. period as perhaps at the LGN or beyond.

BOYNTON: I think by periodicity you mean temporally integrated periods. I think, as you know, that I would generally agree with this point of view. It is a mistake to suppose that, because a temporal discrimination cannot be made in the context of one experimental situation, the integration occurs at the peripheral level, for we have a stagewise procedure, as the data I presented demonstrate. Under those particular conditions, it is clear that a careful record of the change of sensitivity as a function of time is kept in the visual pathway. In another experiment, which we did about 10 years ago, we demonstrated the same kind of thing in a different way. We showed that if you use a flickering masking stimulus at a rate just barely above fusion, then the subject sees this as if it were a steady uniform field. You can, nevertheless, demonstrate that an increment threshold measured at various times during the cycle waxes and wanes in phase with the flickering stimulus. This once again makes the point that, by one criterion—namely, the usual subjective fusion judgment—you are looking at a steady stimulus, and yet by another criterion—involving a mechanism which presumably reacts at some earlier stage of visual processing—you can show that the visual system is not responding as if the stimulus were continuous.

MANFRED CLYNES

Research Center, Rockland State Hospital
Orangeburg, New York

10 · *Toward a Theory of Man:*

PRECISION OF ESSENTIC FORM IN LIVING COMMUNICATION *†

Here on this island, friend, you find
The order of nature has no inner, has no outer—
Centered nowhere, yet everywhere
. . . Touch it and be touched!

I. Introduction

As we find out more about brain function, events in the brain associated with being and experience become amenable to description in terms of ordered, lawful processes and relationships, and so the division of the world into observer and the observed is transformed and needs to be re-examined.

This division of knowledge was nurtured by scientific thought of the last few centuries out of necessity. At the basis of the objective edifice of principle admittedly lay ultimately subjective axioms, but this was regarded as a necessary evil; it was attempted to reduce the number of subjective concepts to the minimum possible. This made the ordered basis of the subjective at once less obvious and more obvious. Most aspects of subjective experience were excluded from the objective world—but the ordered basis of these few subjective intuitions were made all the more apparent by their million-fold application in the universe.

Inherent order and precision of processes of the brain are clearly manifested in non-verbal communication processes. Two years ago, in the house of Pablo Casals in Puerto Rico, the Master was giving cello classes. On this occasion, an outstanding student played the theme from the third movement

* This work was supported in part by NIH grants, numbers NB06124FR00268 and MH07292. The author gratefully acknowledges the help of Michael Kohn, Don Litchfield and Robert Saron in the preparation of this paper.

† Thanks are due to the publishers of Zygon and to McGraw Hill Book Co. for permission to include some of the material in this chapter.

177

of the Haydn Cello Concerto, a graceful and joyful theme. Those of us who sat there could not help admiring the grace with which the young master cellist played—probably as well as one would hear it anywhere. Casals listened intently. "No," he said, and waved his hand with his familiar clear, definite gesture, "that must be graceful!" And then he played the same few bars—and it was graceful as if one had never heard grace before—100 times more graceful—so that the cynicism melted in the heart of the people who sat there and listened. That single phrase penetrated all the defenses, the armor, the hardness of heart which we mostly carry with us, and with its power transformed us into people who were glad to be alive.

What was the power that did this? A slight difference in shape between the phrase as played by the young man, and by Casals. A slight difference— but an enormous difference in power of communication, evocation, and transformation.

From where did Casals derive his precise shape? The function and meaning of such purity of expression in relation to the CNS is the subject of this paper.

It is clear that the function of the CNS cannot be understood solely from the knowledge of cell functions and their possible interrelations. The programmed organization of the brain in terms of function algorithms cannot be predicted from cell theory. Among the brain processes which form part of human nature are the algorithms concerning emotions and the expression of emotions. The precision of operation of these algorithms and the characteristic space-time forms associated with them will be examined in the following. We shall also note the aspects of the stability of these dynamic algorithms which confers on them an existence not to be regarded as necessarily less real than that of structural forms and relationships.

An object of such studies is also to discover what aspects of function are inherently programmed in man and to what extent he is able to uncover and also to disregard these algorithms in himself. In these experimental studies of central nervous system behavior, the behavior is the output, and the brain is, in a sense, the input.

II. Precision of Brain Responses to External Stimuli–Evidence of the Physiologic Language Code

Before we examine the precision referred to in the introduction, let us briefly examine the precision of the brain output to an environmental input.

Evidence concerning a one-to-one-to-one correspondence that exists between a sensory stimulus, its spatio-temporal representation in the brain (as measured by evoked potential electric activity) and the perception, as well as some aspects of how this correspondence arises through the design of the CNS data processing, have been previously discussed (Clynes & Kohn, 1967, Clynes, 1968a, b). Here we will only mention some of the evidence of this physiologic language code, that responses to different forms and to colors can be identified as uniquely corresponding spatio-temporal patterns of the electric brain activity (Figure 1 and Table 1). The

Table 1

Computer recognition of the brain responses to a visual stimulus test pattern of a dim line circle or square of 6″ or 12″ size. Largest correlation shows correct identi-fication. The computer identified both correct size and shape as the largest corre-lation; as second largest correlation it picks the other member of the same family of shapes, of different size. The computer can identify about 100 different visual stimulus patterns of color and form, from the brain responses alone. Numbers shown are summed correlation indices for the four leads (max. correlation 4).

IDENTIFICATION OF CIRCLES AND SQUARES, AND THEIR SIZES

Master	Test 1 Sm. Cir.	Test 2 Lg. Cir.	Test 3 Sm. Sq.	Test 4 Lg. Sq.
Small Circle	2.785	1.948	1.039	1.849
Large Circle	2.181	2.474	1.001	1.782
Small Square	1.389	0.912	2.860	2.254
Large Square	2.092	1.375	2.061	2.669

responses show evidence of similar coding across individuals in terms of the specific sequence and timing of regions of brain activation, displaying in this respect a similar algorithm.

Clynes et al. (1964) and Spekreijse (1966) have described the dy-namics of certain components of these spatio-temporal entities to consist of unidirectionally rate sensitive channels. More generally, physiologic op-posites are considered to be transmitted by a pair of unidirectionally rate sensitive (URS) channels—these combine in a manner that we have called rein control (Clynes, 1961, 1969a). It appears in this view that physiologic opposites of a single variable (e.g. hot and cold—light and dark) are represented in the brain by two different channels and that the quality of the information is distinguished from the quantity through the spatial or-ganization of these two channels.

A hierarchical combination of three channels which may be considered conducive to concept formation was recently discovered. We have called it the R-M function. It is manifested in a brain response (Figure 2) ob-servable at the vertex, which occurs when a variable enters into a state of motion from rest (Clynes, 1969b, Clynes & Milsum, 1969). Such a

Comparison of responses of different individuals to red-black stimulus

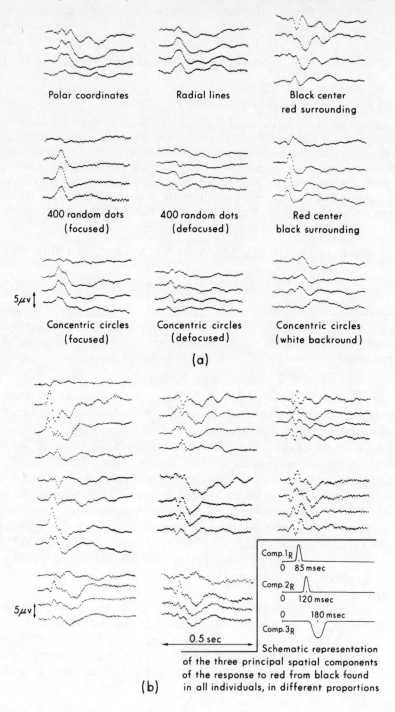

Polar coordinates   Radial lines   Black center
                                                 red surrounding

400 random dots   400 random dots   Red center
(focused)   (defocused)   black surrounding

5μv

Concentric circles   Concentric circles   Concentric circles
(focused)   (defocused)   (white backround)

(a)

5μv

0.5 sec

Comp. 1R
0   85 msec
Comp. 2R
0   120 msec
0   180 msec
Comp. 3R

Schematic representation
of the three principal spatial components
of the response to red from black found
in all individuals, in different proportions

(b)

combination behaves as a higher level URS channel with respect to the opposites of rest and motion for certain sensory variables of various modalities.

One may consider that a specific physiologic basis is present for the formation of concepts of qualities based on the nature of the data processing design of our nervous system. Within each sensory modality there are a distinct number of qualities which may be considered as separate physiologic data processing channels (e.g. color and intensity).

We should, therefore, ideally expect that the words in natural language for qualities should correspond to the number of distinct physiologic sensory quality channels. Further, we should distinguish between primary qualities and mixtures and combinations of these. Let us briefly examine language from this point of view.

III. Precision and Language: Words as Translations of the Physiologic Code

Let us first consider color as an example. In English we have "red," "green," "blue," "white," "black," as words denoting internal entities, not words referring to outside objects such as "orange," "turquoise," etc. These simple names refer to the separate internal entities which could not be imagined if they did not exist—other colors can be imagined as mixtures of these—their components can be directly sensed (e.g. "greenish blue" is sensed to contain green and blue, "purple"—blue and red).

The same is true of taste—"sweet," "sour," "bitter," are simple names not outer-related, such as "nutty". On the other hand the taste "salty" does

---

FIGURE 1. Each group of 4 traces are averages of 200 responses at $0°$, $45°$, $90°$ and $135°$ respectively, of a rosette lead configuration 3 cm in diameter in left occipital position, constituting a spatial differentiation of the electric vector. From Clynes and Kohn, 1967.

(a) Examples of varieties of shape obtained from various visual field structures of lines and shapes. Lines are projected on black background except at bottom right. Amplitude of responses drops sharply when images are defocused. Color differentiation is marked for the defocused images, and is relatively masked by the edge sensitive responses to the focused images. With these response shapes, component analysis reveals the existence of four main independent spatial components of different latency; this is also largely evident from visual inspection.

(b) Comparison of responses of eight adult males to same stimulus: red from previous black. Three principal components, 1_R, 2_R, 3_R, may be distinguished in each of these response groups. Relative amount of these components is different, but their sequence and timing is similar for different individuals. (Standard deviation of peak timing of the average responses across individuals is 4%, within the same individual better than 1%.) Note similarity of two groups of responses at right and also bottom two groups.

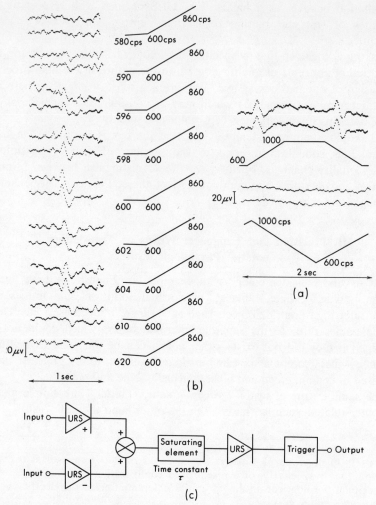

FIGURE 2. (a) Changes in pitch of sound of constant intensity (40 db above threshold). Note the absence of responses for triangular frequency modulation, and presence of two RM responses for trapezoidal modulation.

(b) Gradually increasing inhibition of the R-M response to pitch modulation by previous changes of pitch in either direction. Note the very sharp inhibition produced by small previous changes in pitch.

(c) Block diagram for the R-M function. Two URS channels are combined as inputs to a saturating element with time constant τ. The saturating element might be a self-inhibiting synapse such that the output inhibits the input, preventing any further input increase from being effective. The output of this synapse or saturating element is a URS channel which triggers the output transient. The two input URS channels may be "increase in pitch" and "decrease in pitch" respectively, but may also be other combinations of two variables belonging to the same sense.

have an outer-related name, which is an error of language from the point of view presented here. Sweet-sour has no name but is felt to be compounded of two tastes, sweet and sour, as is bitter-sweet and so on.

In hearing we have not developed quite as good a word translation of the physiologic code. We have loudness, pitch, timbre, smoothness, consonance, and dissonance, but some of these words are not "pure"—i.e. there is not a good one-to-one-to-one correspondence between the physiologic language code, the word, and the perceptual sensation. For example, consider "timbre." There is particularly lacking a word descriptive of the transient onset of the sound which has a very important effect on its character and is inadequately or impurely represented by the word "timbre." Adaptation or rate sensitivity enters into the quality perceived. We do not know how the different rates of adaptation at different frequencies affect the quality related to "timbre."

In many instances, language correctly translates the physiologic code (Clynes, 1969c), distinguishing between single unidirectionally rate sensitive sensory channels and those where two such channels combine to provide physiologic opposites: we have a word for smell, no word for no smell (a single channel system); a word for touch, but no word for no touch (also a single channel system); but we do have words for hot and cold, light and dark (two channel systems).

There are many (and important) sensory qualities, however, which have no words, such as, for example, many qualities related to touch and to sound, to sexual sensations, etc., as well as many words that denote mixed qualities. Very few words innately denote the time course of their quality sensations (e.g. sigh, caress), although forms in time are, in a sense, as substantive as forms in space.

The words that do translate the physiologic code may be arranged in the form of a short dictionary (Clynes, 1969c). The words of such a dictionary can give us useful hints in exploring the functions of the brain and also indicate where there is need for greater discrimination in our psychologic attention to experience.

We may similarly make a list of adjectives which denote various shades of feeling, and we may see whether such an assembly of words will lend themselves to be grouped according to certain basic "colors" of feeling, which may exist as separate entities emerging from a continuum. One may arrange adjectives denoting shades of feeling into categories so that each word shades gradually between its neighbors. One obtains an impression and estimate of the independent dimensionality of feelings in a way analogous to those translating sensory qualities. Osgood (et al., 1957) has independently shown that his use of the "semantic differential" is consistent with dimensional analysis.

Recently, Ekman, et al., (1969) have shown evidence in agreement with Darwin (1872) "that facial expressions of emotion are similar among humans, regardless of culture, because of their evolutionary origin," and they support the existence of "primary affects." There is doubt, however, as to precisely what affects are necessarily primary.

IV. Idiologs

We shall now introduce a concept to distinguish a thought or idea of a quality and the associated brain processes as distinct from the perception of it—the idea of a pitch, as compared with hearing it. We propose the term idiolog for the idea or thought or fantasy of a quality as a distinct psycho-physiologic reality, and further, that there are primary idiologs (corresponding to red, or sweet, say) and also combined idiologs. We use the term idiolog in a more restricted sense than "idea"—too inclusive a concept to be unambiguously used. An idiolog is an element of imagination which can be created in a moment, and has physiologic brain concomitants. We may say that the idiologs constitute a meta-language of natural language insofar as the words of natural language are a correct translation of the physiologic code. We may further distinguish three kinds of idiologs— sensory, affective, and motor idiologs.

NON-VERBAL COMMUNICATION OF IDIOLOGS: SOURCES OF PRECISION

Considering idiologs (and words) for various shades of feeling, the question is how these feelings are communicated in a non-verbal manner and what is the source of the precision which underlies both the feelings and the communication.

There is a prevalent notion, which permeates the fabric of the thought of our age, that feelings and other mental categories are somehow vague, ill-defined, even arbitrary. This is a false notion and a seriously damaging one. The vagueness does not lie in the described, but in the method of description. Associated with a lack of precise description, there is a corresponding lack of discrimination and control, giving rise to two further degrees of vagueness. We shall see in this section that there is evidence of great precision in the sphere of feelings and that this precision may be measured in terms of physiologic outputs. More generally, there is innate precision in the translation of idiologs into a physiologic output, when this is feasible.

As an introduction to this, consider what happens when one throws a ball at an object in order to hit a point in space. Conceiving the idea to hit the object, this idea determines the spatio-temporal dimensions of the execution. Imprecision in thought leads to imperfect execution. Learning here constitutes how to think clearly and execute with coordination. The potential capacity to think clearly (i.e. well-defined idiologs) in such a maneuver is not itself subject to learning, but is a function of the central nervous system processes or, we may say, it is an algorithm. What we are learning is how to use this potential capacity. Having learned it, we can then choose any object within a certain range, think of hitting it, and a spatio-temporal form will appear corresponding to the idea. Some internal factors (e.g. "concentration") may help in producing greater precision of the idiolog, but other internal factors (e.g. "fear") may disturb the precision. Similarly, a pianist can think of a distant note or group of notes, and the hand may accurately place itself.

Let us now take another example of the transfer between idiologs and the physiologic output. Consider the problem of matching the pitch of two tones separated in time. There is a rather nice and simple experiment here which demonstrates the precision of the idea of pitch itself. Let us take two single rectangular pulses, say of 0.5 msec. width, separated by 3 msec. One hears this as a knock with an associated pitch sensation. Varying the interval between the pulses changes the pitch sensation, but not the knock sensation. Attempting to match the pitch sensation in successive trials can only be done to about 5% resolution of the time interval between the pulses. However, in hearing one such pulse pair, one obtains a pitch sensation which can subsequently be matched with a continuous tone from another generator. Now repeating the matching of the single, remembered pitch sensation can be done to 0.3% resolution—the same as matching continuous tones! This illustrates that the remembered pitch sensation is more precise than the phenomenon which gave rise to it—i.e., that once a sensation is produced it necessarily is precise (Clynes, in preparation).

It is not necessary to have "perfect pitch" to do this (perfect pitch incidentally is equivalent to a long memory for the idiolog). Since the human voice can produce sounds, we also have the possibility of matching a sound pulse subsequently with a voice produced pitch, involving the processes of memory and stability of idiologs. (This leads also to the question of mimicry, which we will encounter later in this chapter.)

Consider now the constancy of the idiolog "red." While a particular object may look more or less red depending upon the context, the illumination and adaptation, the basic idiolog "red" itself (the concept or idea of red) stays the same, essentially over a lifetime, even under conditions involving fever, drugs, etc. (i.e., red may be more intensely red, but not something else—as one ages the sensitivity of the eye many change, i.e. a particular red may be less red, but not the redness of red). The same is true of sweetness, and of other idiologs. This constancy requires an explanation which is not available at present (in terms of any conceivable long term stability of possible interpretive, representational neuronal configurations—as distinct from the stability of a memory trace *per se*).

Another form of idiolog, involving time, is a rhythmic pattern. A rhythmic pattern can be repeated once it is "grasped," i.e., once an idiolog is established. In the course of repetitions one finds that inaccuracies are not cumulative but are deviations from a mean that corresponds to the "idea" of the rhythmic pattern (it may be a wrong idea!). Figure 3 illustrates the deviations and their self-correcting tendency.

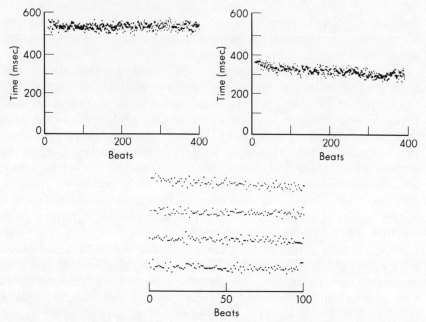

FIGURE 3. Distribution of intervals between consecutive beats when required to tap a constant even rhythm (top right) and when tapping according to a steady musical rhythm (Beethoven Waldstein Sonata) showing a gradual drift in the direction of faster beating in the absence of a musical thought and greater stability of the mean beat frequency with a musical thought. Lower portion of the figure illustrates detail of 400 beats showing deviations from the mean tend to be self correcting rather than cumulative. For steady tapping, in general, analysis of the statistical distribution of the differences indicates that their distribution is not Gaussian but that there are preferred values.

If one now takes a rhythmic pattern and replaces it with a meaningful "musical phrase," the stability and precision of the idiolog is increased as the idiolog is enriched. Repetitions of thinking and beating a popular theme such as the theme known as the Lone Ranger Theme (actually by Rossini) may have an overall stability of 1% or better, for an average individuals. If one attempts, mentally, to time a period of say two minutes, it can be done more accurately by using a musical theme or portion of a piece.

An idiolog has quality and also a quantitative dimension which places it in a relation to a range of possibilities—e.g., a pitch sensation has the quality of pitch but also is a particular pitch. Sweet has quality and intensity. Similarly, a rhythmic pattern has both tempo and a pattern, i.e., a basic speed and a relationship within the group. (But note: do not confuse idiologs of different sensory dimension; e.g., pitch and loudness, color and position.)

The following section describes data which document the extraordinary precision of idiologs that is possible and can be found.

STABILITY OF IDEA AND EXECUTION IN MUSICAL PERFORMANCE

Because of recorded music it is feasible to compare the performances of the same composition by the same individual separated by a long period of time. The stability of the performance is primarily a function of four influences: 1) stability of the idea and concept (i.e., idiologs and their organization); 2) stability of execution; 3) influence of physical environmental factors (e.g. acoustics, temperature, humidity) in their effect on the idiologs and their execution, as well as in their effect on musical instruments; and 4) the presence of noise elements with respect to idea and execution (e.g., inattention, anxiety, fatigue, lack of concentration, etc.). Knowing the possible sources of variability of a complex musical piece, one would estimate a relatively limited possibility of stability.

To estimate what is humanly possible in this regard, we examined the recordings of Arturo Toscanini, a legendary figure for precision, which he produced over a period of many years (Table 2). The published timings of these, in some instances, varied so little over many years that they aroused both our interest and doubt. With the help of the conductor's son, Walter Toscanini, access was gained to the original master tapes of the performances, in order to eliminate errors in timing due to transfer from the master, variability of pauses introduced, and confusion due to splicing of different tapes. Comparisons were confined to entire, continuous, "live" performances recorded in the same NBC studio with the same orchestra (although the personnel of the orchestra varied slightly). Here data are presented of three performances of the Brahms-Haydn variations OP 56b. This work is taken as an example because of the number of variations that allow convenient comparison of both the total length of time and of the times of individual sections, i.e. variations. There were three performances in 1935, 1936, 1948, respectively. The total timing of two of these differed by only 0.5 seconds in 16 minutes 50 seconds, or about 1 part in 2,000, although recorded 12 years apart! Comparisons of individual variations show most of them to be within one second of each other, illustrating that we are not dealing with a coincidence. (This is also in accordance with the property mentioned in the previous section according to which deviations from a pattern in time tend to correct towards a long term stability.) Major

Table 2

Timings of three performances of the Brahms Haydn Variations by Arturo Toscanini and the NBC Symphony Orchestra in Studio H in 1935, 1938, and 1948, respectively. A great similarity exists in the sections from the theme to variation 6 in the last two performances, total time 9.28 and 9.29, respectively, while the section from variation 5 to variation 9 is very similar in the first two performances, both having a total time of 9.18. The difference in the timings in the other variations are considerably greater and are consistent with a change in concept. Variation 7 has two time markings, the second one for a repetition. The changes in variations 7, 8, and 9 of the last two performances are mutually compensating, so that the total time of the performance differed by less than 0.5 sec. Accuracy of the timing system was about two times greater than this deviation.

BRAHMS HAYDN VARIATIONS OP. 56 A
TOSCANINI AND NBC SYMPHONY ORCHESTRA
STUDIO H. CONCERT PERFORMANCES. TIMINGS FROM
ORIGINAL MASTERS, IN MINUTES AND SECONDS

	1935 (Cum. Time)	1935	1938 Feb. 26 (C.T.)	1938	1948 Feb. 21 (C.T.)	1948
Theme		1.56		1.52		1.53
Var. 1		1.08½		1.11		1.10
	—3.04½—		—3.03—		—3.03—	
2		.51½		.53½		.54
	—3.56—		—3.56½—		—3.57—	
3		1.33		1.35½		1.37
	—5.29—		—5.32—		—5.34—	
4		1.57		2.01		1.59½
	—7.26—		—7.33—		—7.33½—	
5		.48		.48		.48½
	—8.14—		—8.21—		—8.22—	
6		1.07		1.07		1.07
	—9.21—		—9.28—		—9.29—	
7		2.01		2.03		1.58
		1.01		.59		.58
	—12.23—		—12.30—		—12.25—	
8		.55		.55		.52
	—13.18—		—13.25—		—13.17—	
9		3.26		3.25½		3.33½
Total		16.44		16.50.6		16.50.3

(var. 5 to 9) portions of the 1935 performance also coincide with the 1938 performance, further confirming the stability—and when there is a deviation, it is relatively substantial.

The timing data are in accordance with the principle that, if the concept or idea of the piece or section of a piece remained the same, timing does not vary significantly, but if there was a change in concept, timing varied considerably, by 5 to 10 per cent. In those variations where there is change, it would amount to at least an order of magnitude greater than the variability of the other variations. Other performances show similar results. Toscanini indicated his own metronome marks in his score; however, he was an order of magnitude more accurate than the resolution of the metronome steps!

That the idea and concept should remain the same over so many years, during which time there was a major world upheaval and 13 years of aging of the conductor as well as members of the orchestra, is quite a remarkable fact. Astonishing as it is, we must thank the recording techniques for being able to demonstrate this. The stability of the idea—the concept and its execution demonstrated here—is a remarkable proof of the precision of feelings and idiologs. There can be no question of Toscanini trying to remember how he did it ten years ago: a good artist always feels the work anew—besides, remembering would hardly allow such accuracy! Such precision is probably present in all great art, whether it is a line in a Raphael painting or an eloquent phrase from the cello of Pablo Casals. The source of this precision are the human qualities and corresponding idiologs and not a stability of repetitiousness due to rote learning. These assertions will be examined in more detail in the following sections.

V. Theory of Actons

Let us examine the nature of voluntary movement. While there has been much physiologic work done on the action of muscles and their innervation, and on system behavior with respect to tasks such as tracking, less attention has been paid to the voluntary initiation and control of single movements. The study of separate voluntary eye movements show that they take about 180 msec. to complete. During this time the movements are not subject to voluntary modification, i.e., they are preprogrammed.

The behavior is similar for the single (natural, not deliberately slowed) movement of a finger or other limb or facial musculature. Even the simplest voluntary movement, such as moving a finger, involves programmed starting, accelerating, and decelerating. In order to do this, two sets of muscles acting for each movement must come into operation at the appropriate times and to the appropriate extent to start, and more difficult, to stop the motion at the right time and place as intended. We observe the physiologic fact that the course of a simple movement is preprogrammed by the brain before it begins. The work of J. C. Eccles reported in this volume deals with the role of the cerebellum in supervising and modulating the transient course of the action. There is no time in the 200 msec. for feedback to affect the decision. In all these movements there is an element of decision which precedes the beginning of the movement. This decision is of a precise nature and controls the subsequent movement according to the program it has set (i.e., the decision event preprograms the subsequent course of the movement). The preprogramming is of the nature of an algorithm. During approximately 200 msec. after a programming decision is made, another programming decision affecting the same limb or muscle cannot be made. Movements begun under such a decision cannot be reversed or controlled within this time. It is clear that a single movement and its decision constitute an existential unit integrally combining the physiologic and conscious aspects. We call such a preprogrammed voluntary movement having a clear beginning and end an "acton." An acton is the combination of an action idiolog and its execution.

The minimum duration of an acton is related to what we experience as the "present moment." In this minimum time a decision cannot be reversed.

Consider once more our example of a person deciding to hit a particular spot with a ball. To do so he has an idea, which is a "command," and his arm and body execute this "command" in a more or less precise way, involving accurate programming. To act satisfactorily, he has to have both a clear idea (or action idiolog) and an accurate execution.

In the acts of emotional expression there is a similar, related process. The difference between a "mechanical" movement and an expressive movement is that the form of the latter is modulated by a state of feeling, or "sentic state" as we shall call it, functioning as an algorithm. (This modulation may increase the duration of preprogramming depending on the sentic state.)

EXPRESSIVE ACTONS

Let us briefly consider the various types of motion. In the continuing motion of matter in the inorganic world there are no moments of causal events, but a stream of flow in accord with an existing changeless order. In the lives of individuals, however, the order manifests itself also, disturbingly, in the ability of the individual to make decisions and to begin actions. His actions may be in relation to changing the distribution in the material world, or they may be expressive of the individual's state. (We may remark here, that the proportion of motion in the world under the direction of brains appears to be increasing, and we are heading in the direction where the movement of matter in space is increasingly controlled by information and decision rather than by exchanges of energy alone.) Actions of the latter kind are communication and art, while the former represent his ability to build, destroy, and transform the world around him as well as himself. (Another class of actions involves a rather different process of initiation: these are reflexive unconscious actions.)

We are especially concerned here with the initiation of action which mirrors the inner state of the individual.

Expressive actons, like other actons, have a beginning and also an end.

There is a moment of initiation. In this moment, the individual makes a choice or decision to express or not express. In that moment he must open all those gates in his data-processing system which will allow the program of expression to command the expression, if the expression be "faithful" or "sincere." The degree to which this is done determines the faithfulness of the expressions to the inner command shape—and gives rise to the impression of "depth of feeling." At the moment of initiation, the shape of expression is already determined, that is to say, the contour between the beginning and end of the expressive unit of action is designed. This moment is then of great importance. The process which takes place in the brain during this time determines the nature of the entire expressive action.

VI. Expressively Modulated Action: Sentic States and Essentic Form

Expressive action has no other aim than to respond and correspond to an inner state. Such action is composed of actons but the shape of these actons (E-actons) is modulated by the state commanding or seeking expression which we call the "sentic state." We say that the sentic state (or the idiolog of the sentic state) requires the E-acton to have a certain characteristic shape, e.g. sadness will change the shape in time-space of an unidifferentiated movement to a new shape if we allow it to express sadness. The shape expresses and communicates the sadness. We call this the "essentic form." Similarly, joy will cause the movement to be modulated to a different characteristic form corresponding to joy.

Essentic form is basic to the expressive act in gesture, touch, dance, song, music, and in the tone of voice of speech. In all these, the essentic form is the basis of communication—constitutes the basic element of language.

Anyone who has observed and attempted to analyze that which we call expression in a gesture, or other mode of expression, is aware that the nature of the expression is contained in the form or space-time shape of the particular gesture of mode of expression. The specific part of the body used matters less than the manner of movement. It is possible, for example, to mime actions of individuals using movements of the fingers only. The tone of voice and the shape of the mouth are other dynamic systems responsive to the internal shape of the modes of expression.

In all of these modes, the eloquence or power of communication of the expression depends, in the first instance, on the precision with which it corresponds to the inner, required space-time shape. Even small departures from such shape give the impression of unnatural or insincere expression. What is implied by this is that there exist a) defined internal states determining particular space-time expression, and b) these internal states are precise and can become "truly" communicated to the degree to which their precision is both sensed and carried out in the act of expression.

Experimental Determination of Essentic Forms

Standardization

Since the commands of the brain determine the expressive shapes, it becomes possible to eliminate the difficult and varied measurement techniques presented by the different output possibilities (e.g., a smile, head movement, eyebrow movement, etc.) by standardization the output as the transient pressure touch of a limb (middle finger) on a two-dimensional pressure transducer (Figure 4). If this is done, results are in fact consistent and comparable, indicating the stability of the brain phenomenon giving rise to the shape. This was a crucial step in making measurement possible.

The subject in sitting position, as shown in Figure 4, presses on the pressure transducer with his finger. (The particular limb chosen does not essentially matter—the essentic form is a brain program, and can be executed by various effectors, e.g., the foot. For standardization, however, one should always use the same finger to eliminate secondary effects; cf. handwriting and footwriting; the character of the writing is similar.) Two components of this pressure are recorded (vertical and horizontal) giving time profiles of instantaneous pressure. This is our measure of the essentic form. Also recorded for study are muscle potentials, evoked brain potentials, as well as heart rate and respiration. The arm as a biologic filter eliminates activity not concerned with the form of the expressive act.

The subject is told to express with the greatest precision the quality of a sentic state given in word approximations (e.g., hate, anger, grief, love, sex, joy, reverence) by pressing the pressure transducer. The time at which he is to express a given state is given to him with a soft click occurring randomly at 2–8 sec. intervals. The corresponding essentic form outputs, i.e., the transient shapes recorded, are averaged on a CAT computer.

In this measurement process, we ask the individual, by suggesting an approximate word, to generate in himself an algorithm—an idiolog of a sentic state—and repeatedly express this with each acton in as precise a manner as possible.

It turns out that the act of expressing essentic form itself has an effect on the sentic state. This is a direct, positive feedback which teaches the subject both to increase the precision of his essentic form and to be more aware of the quality of the sentic state. This means that the process is self-teaching and self-refining. In doing it we appear to learn to sense a pure or "ortho-essentic" form toward which we practice as a reference. While the conventional meaning of the word "learning" involves newly formed memory, this appears more like discovering what we already inherently are, and have perhaps neglected to cultivate (cf. the Platonic sense). At first, the subject usually imagines particular situations to focus on a certain sentic state; but he is soon able to experience and express the state without specific situa-

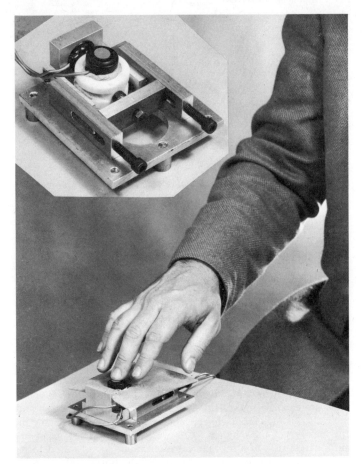

FIGURE 4. Touch transducers and arm position for the measurement of essentic form. Insert on top left shows details of construction. Two pressure transducers are mounted at right angles to one another. The transducers are mounted so as to have no cross interference. The transducer measuring horizontal force is biased with a constant pressure so that the horizontal pressure measured may be either positive or negative without losing contact. The pressure transducers are of the type used for pulse pressure measurement and are coupled into a FET high impedence input stage providing a frequency response essentially 50 cycles to DC. Strain gauges may also be used.

tional imagery—and in doing so, new imagery may also spontaneously arise.

Figure 5 shows the stability of essentic forms measured in the same individual at different times, and Figure 6 shows comparisons of different individuals. The stability and uniqueness of the forms indicate that, like the colors of the spectrum, there apparently exist within us basic or "proto-

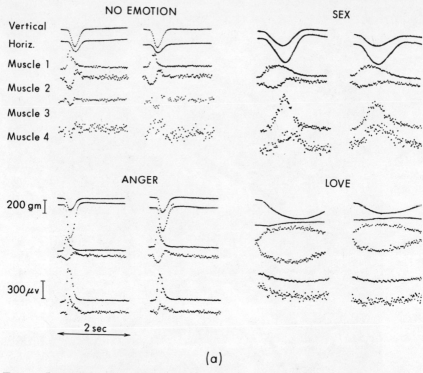

(a)

FIGURE 5(a). Recordings of essentic form as vertical and horizontal components of finger pressure; also four groups of muscle potentials integrated and rectified with a time constant of 0.01 sec. Each group is the average of 50 actons. Muscle potentials are recorded from the forearm, upper arm, front shoulder, and back respectively. Groups represent repeated recording from the same individual showing the stability of the patterns.

"No emotion" consists of a mechanical movement, such as used for typewriting. In "anger" there is a marked accentuation of the horizontal component indicating a tendency for the acton to be outward, away from the body. The type of anger illustrated here is more akin to irritability than to resentment. The "slow, burning" type of anger has a different pattern which is not illustrated here. The characteristic shape for "love" (not sexual) shows a longer curved acton often with a slightly reversed horizontal component indicating a pulling inward or embracing mode of behavior. The muscle actions reflect the differences of the essentic form. The preprogrammed time of the acton for love is considerably longer.

The characteristic form for sex shows a strong secondary thrust with emphasized late muscle activity. This secondary thrust is a characteristic of the purely sexual expression and is analogous to the vocalized expressive effect of the syllable ur*nh*.

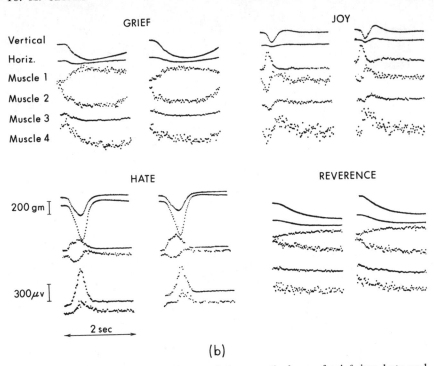

FIGURE 5(b). Typical response shapes of the essentic form of grief, joy, hate and reverence respectively. Note the strong outward (negative horizontal) component of hate, the late muscle acceleration in muscle 2 indicating a secondary thrust, a characteristic of passion. The response to grief has similarity to the love form, but is flatter and slightly outward. Muscular action of grief is related to an induced general lassitude and the subject does not actively lift the released pressure, the opposite of joy. In joy there is rebound with overshoot, related to a floating sensation, a "jumping for joy" effect. Reverence has general similarity to love but, on a longer time scale. The preprogramming of the acton is extended in time. Respiration is slowed and the acton is preferrably carried out on expiration. The latter is also true of hate and grief, but not of joy, which may be frequently done on inspiration.

sentic" states giving rise to the corresponding "proto-essentic" forms. These essentic forms are not arbitrary, but fall into biologically determined discrete shapes (Table 3).

The words of natural language which have developed to fit the corresponding states are approximate and not unique. However, the state and its ortho-essentic form are very precise. Communication through essentic form also exists in animal, man-animal, and animal-man communication. Some higher animals (mammals) appear to have certain similar proto-essentic forms. (Fairly recently, I visited the zoo and was watching a bear. Suddenly this bear yawned; within two or three seconds I found myself yawning also!) Having measured the human forms, one also notes apparently

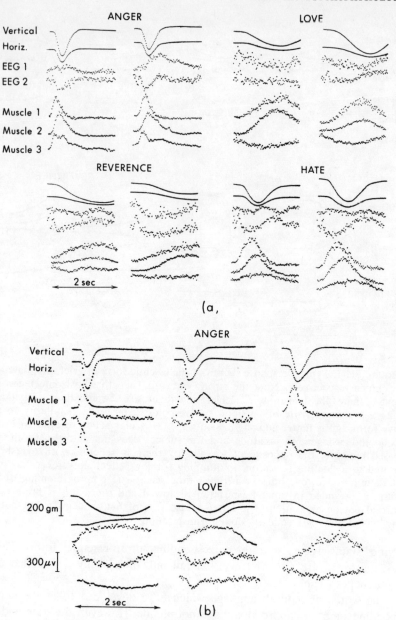

FIGURE 6. Sentic forms in various individuals in similar sentic states. Note the general similarity of corresponding essentic form with, also, features of individual differences. Each group represents a different individual.

(a) The responses of one subject on different occasions are compared. The figure also shows evoked potentials and muscle potentials.

(b) The responses of different individuals are compared.

Table 3

Correlation of vertical components of essentic forms of E-actons for the same individual on two different occasions (left) and between different subjects (center and right column). Note the small correlation of "anger" in the second column. This subject displayed a different form of anger—which we may call "slow burning type of anger" as compared with the "irritability" type of anger—a different essentic form, but commonly described by the same word. Cross correlations between different essentic forms were generally lower than 0.300.

	MC2/MC1	EN/MC1	GB/MC1
Anger	.927	−.224	.928
Hate	.824	.973	.779
Grief	.769	.815	.775
Love	.951	.827	.702
Sex	.966	.779	.867
Joy	.994	.827	.917

similar expressive forms of affection, sexual activity and anger in monkeys, for example.

The non-verbal communication of feeling exists through essentic forms —we react to other individuals' sentic states through their ortho-essentic expression; we cannot react to each other's sentic states if we do not express or perceive the true or ortho-essentic form—a form that has meaningful existence and can be experienced in itself.

If we are to sum up now some of the principles we have discussed, we note:

1) Sentic states may be various combinations of basic or proto-sentic states.
2) There are a rather small number of proto-sentic states.
3) At any one time an individual can only express one sentic state.
4) To each sentic state there is a corresponding essentic form.
5) Essentic forms are biologically programmed and genetically preserved.
6) Essentic form acts as a communication depending on the degree of precision to which it conforms to the ortho-essentic form.
7) We communicate feelings with others through their recognition of essentic forms. The essentic form, like a key, will work in the data processing lock in individuals who sense that form, whether that form is produced in themselves or in others. Higher empathy is a relationship with an individual's pre-sentic control rather than his sentic state alone. We perceive the relative fluidity or rigidity of his sentic state.
8) Sentic states may be self-generating through the essentic form production.

INTERNAL PULSE SHAPES OF MUSIC

Examples of uniqueness and stability of essentic forms are given by the language of music. To an important degree, thinking in music is a succession of expressive actons which have beginning and ends and precise shape.

In music there exists a recurrent initiation of action which provides a possibility of measurement with modern techniques. This recurrent form of action is also basic to music itself. It is that which propagates music through time—that which subdivides the continuum of time into building blocks of characteristic shape. That is to say, it quantizes the music time into repetitive quanta of action, but these quanta themselves have characteristic shapes in space-time or essentic form. We have called this the "inner pulse" of music. That such a thing exists is very clear from observations of conducting and of rhythmic beating of time. The internal pulse shape, however, is not identical with meter, rhythm, or beating time. The same meter or notated rhythm may have entirely different essentic forms.

When we talk of recurrent events of action, this concept necessarily involves two states. The musical pulse is not to be considered as an alternation between something and nothing, but an alternation of two states which might be called active and resting phases. The shape of the pulse is determined by the relative ratio of the two phases and their dynamic onset and decline. The phenomenon is similar to the dynamics of the gesture or dance in which the relative acceleration and deceleration phases are programmed to result in the particular expressive shape.

The living alternation of internal states of the musical pulse corresponds mentally to idiologs of alternations of states in space or of sensation. Music mostly is related to either a) movement in space (dance, march, procession, gesture, that is, alternation in space of limbs and the corresponding alternate activation and sensations of the musculatures); or b) song or speech (alternation of degrees of tension and relaxation of the throat, vocal and respiratory muscles); or also, rarely, c) existential music (played essentially without vibrato, without pulse, generally in the forms of sustained chords or notes). In the third category of musical elements, the existential music, the inner musical pulse, representing a human, personal "presence" is suspended (e.g. Var. No. 20 from Diabelli Variations by Beethoven.

An expressive motion, such as a caress or gesture or dance step, has clear relationship to the nature of the musical pulse. The successive states of the musical pulse are related to the dynamic elements of motion of a caress, or gesture, or dance step.

EXPERIMENTAL MEASUREMENT OF ESSENTIC FORM IN MUSIC

The experimental measurement of essentic form is basically similar whether measuring within the language of music or not, with some necessary modification.

Considering music as a language, we measured aspects of essentic form as the inner pulse of music. For this measurement, a musical composition is thought by the subject in real time as if singing or performing it. The physiologic output chosen is a transient finger pressure. As before, the subject presses on a pressure transducer with his finger and records the pulse which corresponds to the type of movement that would occur if he were to conduct the piece. (A counter is used as a visual synchronizing agent, but no auditory synchronization should be used.) To find meaningful essentic form in terms of the language of music, sensitive musicians were selected as subjects. Fifty pulse shapes (at approximately 1 sec.) are averaged with a CAT computer, for each musical piece.

It became clear that these shapes were related to the personality of the composer in a highly intimate manner. It was found that with some care we could reliably determine pulse shapes, characteristic of individual composers, regardless of the particular piece chosen (Figures 7, 8, and 9). No sound is used. The music is entirely thought. One thinks not about music, but the music. Only musicians capable of intimate understanding of the composers could produce their characteristic pulse shape.

The Significance of the Stability of the Internal Pulse Forms for Particular Composers

A relation between the internal pulse and a given musical phrase is that the internal pulse determines the precise contour of the phrase; the notation is only a rough approximation. The "living" character of the music as compared with dead, "mechanical" shape lies in the faithfulness to the inner musical pulse, the essentic form, rather than to the notation only. The notation may be regarded as a guide to the essentic form which has an inner precision not represented by the notation.

This does not mean that there is only one way to perform a given piece, but rather that they should all be living ways, i.e., faithful to some essentic form. There are many possible "living" forms based on sentic states and essentic forms, but the class of "dead" forms is infinitely greater. The interpretive choice of a given musical phrase or section consists of what essentic forms to choose—what sentic state and its ortho-essentic form—and to follow that form with greatest faithfulness, or inner precision.

Considering now a given composer, say Beethoven, a meaning of a particular piece is possible only in terms of idiologs of certain sentic states and ortho-essentic forms, e.g., love, courage, and joy and not others like hate, anger, jealousy, sensuality. It is somewhat like a sentic jigsaw puzzle: certain combinations will fit, others cannot possibly. Within a given sphere various combinations can exist, but others are excluded. The matrix of such combinations is contained in the personality of the composer. This means that the shape of the internal musical pulse (as measured by an average of, say, fifty pulses) in a given piece is an image (albeit only a shadow of a shadow)

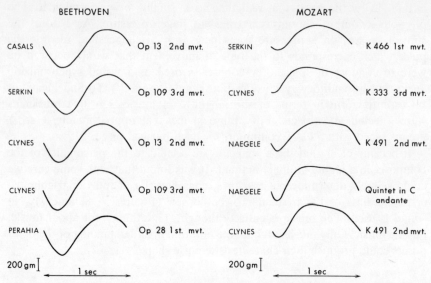

FIGURE 7. Essentic forms of the inner pulse: slow movements of Beethoven (vertical component). Different movements are compared, as well as the same movement for different interpreters. The lowest trace is of a first movement in triple meter whose pulse is considered comparable on an appropriate time scale (one pulse per bar in this case). The pulse shape continues into periods of rest and, considered as a second order dynamic system, it has a damping equivalent to approximately 0.2, indicating about three after-beats before the cessation and a comparatively high inertia. The high inertia tends to give both an inherent propulsion and a comparatively late down (negative) peak. There is a prolonged initial acton preprogramming as compared with the low inertia pulse of Mozart.

The essentic form of the inner pulse of Mozart shows considerably lower inertia than that of Beethoven. The down peak occurs much earlier and there is a small overshoot with damping of the order of 0.7. The Mozart pulse, thus, has no more than one after-beat compared with several for Beethoven. Its relatively light and buoyant character is related to the low inertia term coupled with slight underdamping and a response time corresponding to a normally preprogrammed free acton. In that sense the Mozart pulse is freer than the Beethoven pulse and we may see how it could well be associated with such descriptive terms as a "cosmic pulse" as compared with a "Promethean pulse" of Beethoven. The pulse shape is only secondarily dependent upon the character of the piece so that the tragic and joyful Mozart have basically similar internal pulse. It may be that this is because in Mozart the joyful and the tragic are implicit in each other and subsumed in a higher synthesis.

of the composer's personality, as seen by the interpreter. The process is similar to the dream process in which one dreams of a person and that person continues to retain his or her personality during the dream. It is the dreamer who creates this consistent continuity. Just as in the dream the dreamed person retains his or her identity so the personality of the composer is retained in the character of the continuing musical pulse. In fact, the absence of the characteristic musical pulse is immediately recog-

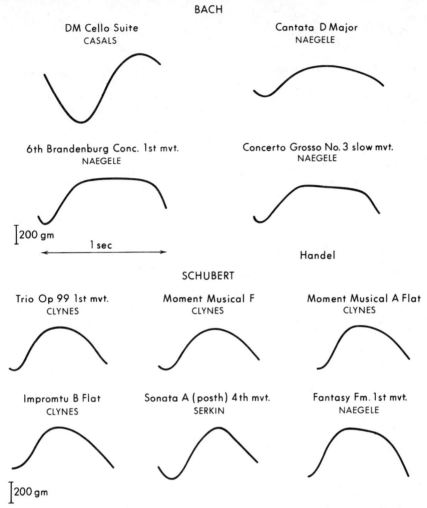

FIGURE 8. Baroque music, as conceived in the customary Baroque style, has a pulse which is primarily time beating and not charged with essentic form. Not so for Cassals, whose interpretation of Bach has more aspects of a super-Beethoven pulse. It is interesting that differences in interpretive approach are so clearly brought out by the measure of essentic form of the inner pulse.

Essentic form of the Schubert pulse illustrated here shows a generally very early down peak and low inertia. But, characteristic of Schubert is a fast rise leading to overshoot. There is a characteristic upward deflection which may be simulated by an added predictor term related to aspects of hope and longing. But this characteristic Schubert rise is very different from the romantic, sexual rise, accompanied by higher inertia. The Schubert pulse is relatively highly damped. (Lyric Brahms has a high inertia and low damping.)

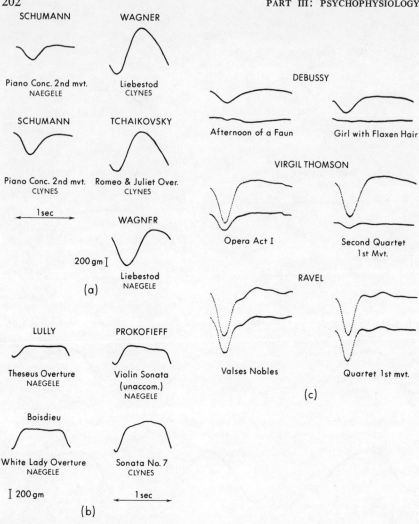

FIGURE 9. (a) Examples of inner musical pulse forms of romantic composers. (b) Eighteenth Century French music showing a sharp overdriven, rapier-like, disdainful or "cynical" pulse form, to a certain extent similar to Prokofieff. (c) A living composer, Virgil Thomson, performing his own compositions (center) and Debussy and Ravel (top and bottom). Both vertical and horizontal components are shown. His compositions are regarded as being somewhere in between Debussy and Ravel in character by connoisseurs.

nized as an absence of the "living presence" of the composer. The composer, in creating the piece, is representing himself as an individual—consistently and integrally—as is also a person in one's dream, regardless of whatever the specific action might be. This means further that a given musical phrase is not interchangeable from one composer to another even if the notes are identical; for the internal musical pulse is not!

As Becking (1928) already recognized so clearly, one cannot take a musical phrase from Mozart and put it into Beethoven without stumbling over the beat when one arrives at the phrase: there are different underlying musical pulses involved even if the phrases are identical, note by note. The change from one pulse form to another involves a major change of algorithmic program in the brain—e.g., switching from a Beethoven pulse to a Chopin pulse. The switching of such a program is accomplished by a function of the brain which we call pre-sentic control. The stability of the essentic forms indicates that those who have recognized the character of the composer's personality see him in a similar way. It does not mean that they are equally good at performing, but merely that they share certain ideas about the nature of the composer. These ideas might have been regarded as "intuitive," but we are now able to relate them to the performer's discovery of the type of idiologs and essentic forms that "fit" (again somewhat in the manner of the sentic jigsaw puzzle).

Such discoveries are readily made even by talented children and often even better by these, before sentic fluidity is blocked as they grow up. The music itself implies the forms. The manner of implication has not yet been analyzed, so that one still depends on individuals at this time to have the "sensitivity" to perceive these implications. The stability, however, shows that, like red, the personality of Beethoven as revealed in his music has a precise existence that continues on.

The stability is not a result of tradition or of style. Mozart and Haydn have very different internal musical pulse shapes and so have Debussy and Ravel. On the other hand, the changes in pulse shape with the history of music is interesting as an indication of the change in sentic matrix, the inclusion of sexual longing, of disdain, of anger, of despair, or hope, of enthusiasm, etc. as important elements at various times and with various composers. The "sentic charge" of the musical pulse is also not necessarily a general musical phenomenon—certainly it appears to predominate European music of the late eighteenth and nineteenth centuries. Earlier music, such as a great deal of baroque and Renaissance music appears to have a beat which merely is marking time and has no expressive meaning in itself. This music depends on other dimensions for its expressiveness. (One may say that here the music is, as it were, a super-structure on top of the basic beat, and is not sentically integral with the beat—the phenomenon of "brio" is absent.) But we cannot go into this question here in detail.

SENTIC CYCLES

As one conducts these experiments with a succession of sentic states, which constitute a sentic cycle, a cumulative effect may be observed over and above the effect of each single state. The possible relation of this effect

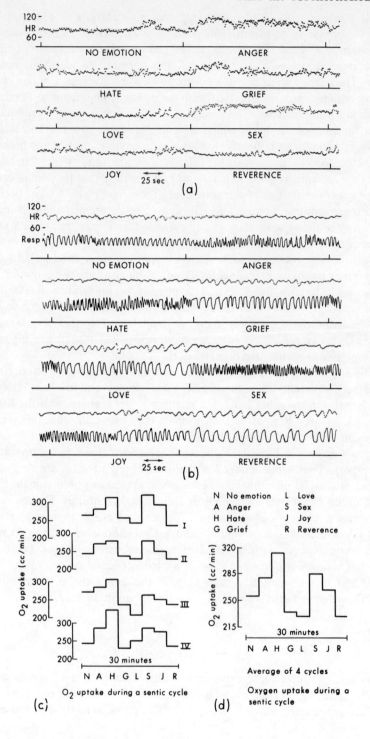

(a)

(b)

(c)

O₂ uptake during a sentic cycle

N	No emotion
A	Anger
H	Hate
G	Grief

L	Love
S	Sex
J	Joy
R	Reverence

(d)

Average of 4 cycles

Oxygen uptake during a sentic cycle

to creative mental processes and to therapy, as well as some sociological implications are presented elsewhere (Clynes & Milsum, 1969).

Sentic Cycles provide an experience which is to some extent similar to that of an artistic performance—a musical, dramatic, or dance performance. But the expressive acts are not tied to a particular work of art, but requires that the individual employs his own imaginative processes. Physiologic changes which accompany the succession of sentic states, such as systematic changes in heart rate, respiration and oxygen consumption, are shown in Figure 10.

THE ORIGIN OF ESSENTIC FORM

Assuming we know the inherent communicative shape of, say, love, as measured and identified by our method of measurement, we may ask a new question, namely why love, as expressed, has this particular shape—i.e., why is love experienced and evoked through these forms?

To this question we have no answer, and it is difficult to know how to consider the question. Why does anger have the form it does? True, there is clearly a tendency for anger to push away—to reject—and for love to enfold, and the essentic forms we obtain reflect such movements. But the problem is that not all outward movement expresses anger—there is a pure form of anger as there is for love. We shall have to be content at this time to ascertain the essentic forms of love, sex, anger, etc., and derive satisfaction from knowing that we are dealing with forms independent of particular physical realizations.

FIGURE 10. (a) Variations of heart rate during a sentic cycle showing marked increases in heart rate, especially during anger and sex.

(b) Changes in respiration and heart rate during a sentic cycle. Respiration accelerates during anger and hate. During grief the respiration has a gasping character, with rest periods at the expiratory end of the cycle. Respiration slows during love, speeds up markedly for sex. It is particularly noteworthy that during reverence there is a marked slowing down of respiration with resting phases at the inspiratory phases of the cycle (cf. at the expiration phases for grief). Heart rate cycles in the subject are related to respiration. This subject shows otherwise less deviations in heart rate than the subject in the lower figure.

(c) Oxygen consumption for four sentic cycles of the same subject show consistent changes in oxygen consumption between the various sentic states. Changes in all four cycles are in the same direction for corresponding states, except for one step between grief and love, cycle 4. Passionate states tend to show greater oxygen consumption. Respiration rate and oxygen consumption are related.

(d) Average of the four cycles shown in part (c).

REFERENCES

Becking, G. (1928). Der Musikalische Rhythmus als Erkenntnisquelle. Augsburg: B. Filser, pp. 216.

Clynes, M. (1961). Unidirectional rate sensitivity—a biocybernetic law of reflex and humoral systems as physiologic channels of controls and communication. Annals of the New York Academy of Science, *92 (3):* 546–969.

Clynes, M., Kohn, M. and Lifshitz, K. (1964). Dynamics and spatial behavior of light evoked potentials, their modification under hypnosis, and on-line correlation in relation to rhythmic components. Annals of the New York Academy of Sciences, *112(1):* 468–509.

Clynes, M. and Kohn, M. (1967). Spatial visual evoked potentials as psychologic language elements of color and field structures. The International Conference on Evoked Potentials. Siena, Italy, July 1966. Electroenceph. Clin. Neurophysiol. Suppl. 26, 82–96.

Clynes, M. (1968a). Essentic form—aspects of control, function and measurement. The 21st Annual Conference on Engineering in Medicine and Biology. Houston, Texas.

Clynes, M. and Kohn, M. (1968b). Recognition of visual stimuli from the electric responses of the brain. Proceedings of the 3rd International Psychiatric Congress. Madrid, September 1966. In: N. S. Kline and E. Laska (eds.), Computers and electronic devices in psychiatry. New York: Grune and Stratton, Inc., 206–237.

Clynes, M. (1969a). Cybernetic implications of rein control in perceptual and conceptual organization. Symposium on Rein Control of Unidirectional Rate Sensitivity, a Fundamental Dynamic and Organizing Function in Biology. Annals of the New York Academy of Sciences, *156(2):* 629–670.

Clynes, M. (1969b). NASA conference on evoked potentials. E. Douchin (ed.), dynamics of vertex evoked potentials: the R-M brain function.

Clynes, M. (1969c). A dictionary of words that translate the physiologic code. In preparation.

Clynes, M. (1969d). On being in order. Symposium on Computers and Religion. Zygon: Journal of Science and Religion, Sept. 1969.

Clynes, M. and Milsum, J. (1969). Biomedical engineering systems. New York: McGraw-Hill Book Company. In press.

Darwin, C. (1872). The expression of the emotions in man and animals. London: Murray.

Ekman, P., Sorenson, E. R. and Friesen, W. V. (1969). Pan-cultural elements in facial displays of emotion. Science, *164(3875):* 86–88.

Osgood, C. E., Suci, G. J. and Tannenbaum, P. (1957). The measurement of meaning. Urbana: University of Illinois Press, 335.

Spekreijse, H. (1966). Analysis of E.E.G. responses in man evoked by sine wave modulated light, Amsterdam: University of Amsterdam, 157.

Part IV

NEUROPHYSIOLOGY

H. B. BARLOW

Department of Physiology-Anatomy
The University of California
Berkeley, California

11 · Trigger Features, Adaptation and Economy of Impulses*

I. Redundancy Reduction and Economy of Impulses

About ten years ago I became fascinated by the notion that a very important part of sensory information processing consisted of recoding messages into a less redundant form at sensory relays and centers (Attneave, 1956; Barlow, 1959, 1961a, b). This is a suitable opportunity to have another look at this notion in the light of more recent advances. First, I will briefly recapitulate the idea.

It is an obvious fact that animals with higher nervous systems are capable of responding selectively to a vast number of specific combinations of sensory stimuli. The number of possible combinations rises exceedingly rapidly with the number of inputs, and even though many combinations are presumably not discriminable from each other, it is still a task of almost incredible difficulty to pick out a specific and apparently arbitrary combination of activity among some three million sensory fibers, each capable of transmitting hundreds of impulses per sec. The essence of the notion is that the nervous system does not form associations directly with the input, but first recodes the input into a less redundant form suitable for associating directly with actions and responses. This greatly simplifies the associative task, because the raw input must be enormously redundant. The peripheral sense organs are subjected to physical stimuli that may vary over an enormous range of values, but these stimuli are not received at random. The same sense organ will very often receive the same physical stimulus at one instant as it did at the preceding instant, and neighboring

* Supported by USPHS Grant NB–05215.

209

sense organs will often be excited at a similar level, either simultaneously or in succession. These are the simplest forms of redundancy, but there are innumerable other more complex regularities and patterns in our sensory stimuli. Thus, great economies can be achieved by recoding the information contained in the physical stimuli and representing it less redundantly.

If one extends the idea, and supposes that different codes are found and utilized in different environments of sensory stimulation, then the task of redundancy reduction seems to go deeper than simply preprocessing information for pattern recognition. Probabilities of sensory events and joint probabilities of groups of events are required to select a code, and the selection made reflects in some manner this store of information. A redundancy reducing code selected for a particular environment of sensory stimulation thus represents much stored information about that environment, and it might correspond to the model of it that Craik (1943) and others have postulated. Furthermore, the operations required to find a less redundant code have a rather fascinating similarity to the task of answering an intelligence test, finding an appropriate scientific concept, or other exercises in the use of inductive reasoning. Thus, redundancy reduction may lead one towards understanding something about the organization of memory and intelligence, as well as pattern recognition and discrimination.

In the nervous system, information is carried by all-or-nothing impulses in nerve fibers. Clearly the number of nerve fibers in a sensory pathway is unlikely to change during the life of an animal; one might have to qualify this during the early stages of development, where disuse seems to lead to atrophy or failure of proper development, but one cannot suppose that adaptive redundancy reduction is achieved by eliminating nerve fibers. Now the informational capacity of a nerve pathway depends not only on the number of fibers, but also upon the mean rate of nerve impulses in the fibers, and this is something that certainly might be varied adaptively. Thus, the notion of coding to reduce redundancy can be epitomized in the phrase "economy of impulses": one expects to find genetically determined patterns of synaptic connections that will enable the animal's typical sensory environment to be represented by low average activity in sensory centers. If the environment is changed, the average activity should rise, but changes in those synaptic connections should occur and again enable the new environment to be represented economically, *i.e.* the low mean firing rate of the nerve cells should be restored. Of course, this economy of impulses must occur with the minimum sacrifice of information; it would be trivial to reduce the firing rate if the code then became non-reversible.

When I first wrote up this idea, Attneave (1954) had already adduced a considerable background of psychological evidence for it, but there were only two physiological mechanisms that seemed to fit well. As Adrian

(1928) had pointed out, the adaptation of sensory discharges might serve the function of reducing the flow of impulses from a maintained stimulus, thus making it easier to detect the onset of an important new stimulus. Lateral inhibition in the visual pathway might also be regarded as a mechanism to reduce the flow of impulses from spatially uniform stimuli, and comparable mechanisms are found in other pathways. Moving stimuli, causing sequential stimulation of neighboring sensory receptors, are another obviously redundant feature of the physical stimuli in most sensory environments, and though they had not at that time been described, Lettvin, *et al.* (1959) obligingly found single nerve cells in the frog retina that were selectively sensitive to movement of the image, and Hubel and Wiesel (1959) found similar cells in the cat cortex. Since then a good deal more evidence has come to light, and this really fits in surprisingly well with the general idea of redundancy reduction and economy of impulses. I shall first show how these notions provide a good framework for understanding some of Hubel and Wiesel's, and our own, subsequent discoveries in the cat cortex, and how the concepts enable predictions to be made, at least to a limited extent. Secondly, I want to talk about the mechanisms for achieving pattern selectivity that have been proposed. Thirdly, I shall describe some of the conclusions that Levick and I have reached from our study of adaptation in the cat's retina. Finally, I want to take another glance at the whole problem of sensory information processing in the light of this evidence.

II. Trigger Features of Neurons in the Cat's Cortex

Let us suppose that lateral inhibition in the retina and lateral geniculate has done its job very well, so that activity in nerve fibers is restricted to those from the positions of contours and edges in the visual field. Redundancy has been reduced, because activity in one unit tells one less about the probable activity in neighboring units than it did before, but much redundancy remains. We are now all familiar, through Xerography, with the appearance of pictures in which the second spatial derivative of luminance is emphasized and the luminance itself scarcely represented. A prominent feature of such reproductions is the common occurrence of linearly connected regions of blackening; thus, if one region is black, there is a high probability that a pair of neighboring regions will be black, though we have no way of guessing which pair. Orientation selective cortical neurons (Hubel and Wiesel; 1959, 1962) seem just what is required to detect such oriented sets of excited points, and the particular neuron activated will signal the orientation.

For a detector of such a specific feature to be informationally useful, the specific feature must, in spite of its specificity, occur frequently, as lines and edges do in Xerox copies. To anticipate, I think our work on the coding of intensity in the cat retina (Barlow and Levick, 1969) brings out another aspect of this, for we conclude that the main benefit of lateral inhibition is to enable the retina to signal small departures from uniformity with great sensitivity. Small departures from the mean are more common than large departures; thus, both for Hubel and Wiesel's pattern detectors, and for our change of intensity detectors, the neural connections are such that the discriminatory power of the system is best for a particular range of stimuli, namely the stimuli which occur most often.

Having coded an image into a representation of the positions and orientations of lines and edges, what is the next appropriate type of redundancy to code for? It is hard to visualize images coded in this form, partly no doubt because there is no Xerography process to mimic it. Attneave (1954) has argued that informative events occur when expectations are *not* fulfilled, as when a line or contour changes direction or comes to an end. His picture of a cat (Fig. 1) emphasizes that these discontinuities really are in-

FIGURE 1. Attneave's sleeping cat, made by abstracting 38 points of maximum curvature from its contours and joining them by appropriate straight lines. Discontinuities in edges carry much information. Reproduced from Attneave (1954).

formation bearing. It was made by abstracting 38 points of maximum curvature from the contours of a sleeping cat, and connecting these points appropriately with a straightedge. I am a bit unhappy about how the "appropriate" connections of points were distinguished from inappropriate ones, but obviously 38 points describe the cat quite well.

Just as a contour is a discontinuity in an area of nearly uniform illumination, so one is led to expect "discontinuity in edge" detectors, and this is a reasonable description of Hubel and Wiesel's (1965) next level of unit. However, many details of their results are not predicted, and one can reasonably question whether the hypothesis leads to predictions that are specific enough to be helpful. To counter this, we shall shortly describe a case where it predicted a specific detail that was not in agreement with Hubel and Wiesel's results, but which was, nevertheless, found upon reinvestigation. First, however, let us look at possible types of analysis beyond the "discontinuity in edge" detectors.

It seems improbable that Attneave's cat would be recognized in one step by a group of thirty-eight corner detectors making a cat detector. Instead, I suppose one expects units responsive to assemblies of vertices, for such assemblies will often correspond to real solid objects that move in a co-ordinated fashion. They will also undergo perspective transformations, and generalization at this level might be over the set of allowable distor-tions due to perspective. The next level would be assemblies of these assem-blies of vertices, and thus, one might define or detect a cat as follows: a pentagon with concave top edge, and a large rounded blob with four sup-ports, and a curved appendage. This indicates the sort of way in which corners and curvatures might be grouped, and the groups of features fur-ther grouped. Furthermore, a cat detector of this sort might still recognize Attneave's sleeping cat when it awoke and stood up, but these predictions are obviously very speculative and difficult to test. If one knew more about the patterns present in the output of corner detectors one might fumble less, but I prefer to move on to a prediction to which the concept led us and which has turned out to be correct.

In an animal in which the visual fields of the two eyes overlap extensively, as in the cat, monkey, and man, one obvious type of redundancy in the messages reaching the brain is the very nearly exact reduplication of one eye's message by the other eye. Following the principle that has emerged from the initial concept and the previous examples, one would expect to find units that respond preferentially to binocular stimulation of corre-sponding parts of the visual field in both eyes. This is precisely what Hubel and Wiesel (1959, 1962) found among the "simple" cells of the cat cortex; a high proportion (75–90%) have identical trigger features for both eyes, and respond best when both eyes are stimulated rather than one alone. So far, one might interpret this as the reduction of redundancy by eliminating reduplication, possibly at the same time improving the signal/noise ratio. However, parallax resulting from the slightly different positions of the two eyes makes the reduplication not quite exact. There is much information in the differences between the two images, just as there is in the departures from spatial and temporal uniformity, the orientation of edges, and dis-continuities in orientation. In the examples so far described, information on these matters was preserved, as it should be in a redundancy-reducing but non-destructive code. However, if the cat's simple cortical cells did no more than pool messages from the two eyes, the information carried by

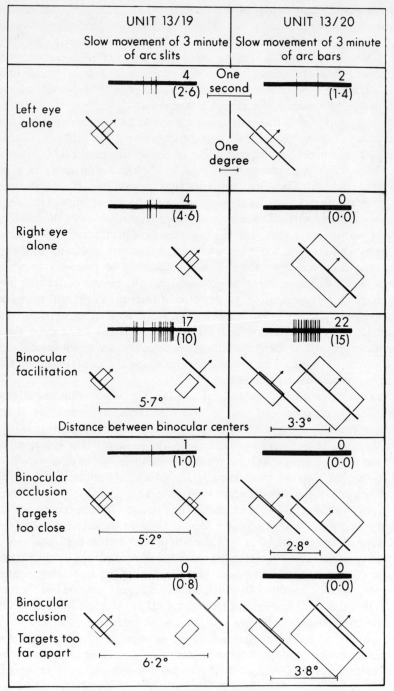

Binocular interaction in two units with different horizontal disparities

the small differences would be lost: it would appear to be an exception to the rule that the discriminatory capacity is greatest for the range of information bearing characteristics that occur most frequently. Reduction of redundancy should not lead to loss of discrimination of non-redundant features. Thus, in the present case, we were lead to investigate the possibility that cortical neurons discriminate the small differences between the two retinal images caused by binocular parallax (Barlow, *et al.,* 1967; Nikara, *et al.,* 1968; Pettigrew, *et al.,* 1968a, b). The question was: "Do all neurons that connect to both eyes connect to exactly corresponding retinal regions? Or do neurons connect to retinal regions that do not correspond exactly, but lie over the range of noncorrespondence expected in retinal images because of binocular parallax?" In the latter case, different units would respond selectively to different amounts of parallax, and thus one would have a mechanism for discriminating distance.

Fig. 2 shows that this is what happens. The eyes of an anaesthetized cat were fixed at an angle of about $6.4°$ divergence. A neuron was found in the primary visual cortex, and the appropriate position and orientation of target found by moving slits, bars, and edges around in the visual field. Responses were recorded for each eye alone, and for the two eyes together at various separations of the paired targets. After these results had been obtained, the electrode was advanced a little, a second unit was picked up, and more records taken. For each unit, there was a particular separation of the paired targets that gave a much bigger response than any other separation, and this was a remarkably sharp peak as shown by the fact that changing the separation by $1/2°$ in either direction reduced response to practically zero—less than with stimulation of either eye alone. Now the interesting point is that the optimal separation was different in the two units: one responded optimally when the targets lay $5.7°$ apart in the visual field, corresponding to about $0.7°$ of convergent disparity, the other when they lay $3.3°$ apart, corresponding to $3.1°$ of convergent disparity. Thus, one of these units would have been optimally excited by an object a little closer than the cat's fixation point where the parallax was $0.7°$, the other still closer where binocular parallax was $3.1°$. Notice also that for both units the change in disparity that reduces the response to zero

---

FIGURE 2. Cortical neurons combine the information from the two eyes, but the parallax required for binocular facilitation is different for different cortical neurons. In the preparation shown here, the visual axes diverged by about $6.4°$; optimum facilitation occurred at $5.7°$ separation of the targets for unit 13/19, $3.3°$ fo the next unit isolated 13/20. These would correspond to $0.7°$ and $3.1°$ of convergent disparity. Both units were obtained in the same penetration of the cat's left cortex. The number at the end of each record shows the number of impulses in that particular record, and in parentheses the average for five repetitions. From Barlow, *et al.,* (1967).

is much less than the separation of the units from each other, so there is no overlap in the range of distances for which each responds.

Fig. 3 shows the distances for optimal response of these two neurons and 19 others recorded from the same region of cortex in the one cat. For the purpose of making the diagram it was assumed that the cat's eyes were converged on a point 50 cm in front of him, and the points show the positions, projected onto the horizontal plane, of an object that would optimally excite each of the units. It is clear that the cells of the visual cortex correspond to elements peppering his visual space, each one responding optimally to an object at a specific distance; conversely, the units that are active give the cat information from which the relative distances of the stimulating features can be directly derived.

To summarize, the notions of redundancy reduction and economy of impulses provide a rather satisfactory framework for understanding the transformations that have been discovered in the visual cortex. There are a good many details that are not predicted, but many of the results are directly in line with the expectations, and in one case an important prediction has been confirmed. The hypothesis leads to rather vague ideas about the higher levels of analysis of the visual image, but even vague expectations are probably better than none.

So far, we have talked about the codes that are employed and said nothing about the neural mechanisms involved. These are discussed in the next section.

III. Mechanisms for Achieving Selectivity of Responsiveness

Sensory neurons respond to rather specific trigger features in their environment, and do not respond to stimulation, however massive and violent it is made, if it does not contain the trigger feature. Fig. 4 shows various proposals that have been made about how this specificity is achieved. Cajal's drawings of retinal ganglion cells and bipolar cells show that there is distinct stratification in the neuropile between bipolar and ganglion cells. Maturana, *et al.* (1960) suggest that different abstractions from the stimulus pattern are picked up by bipolar cells and represented at different depths in the external plexiform layer; these authors think that the form of the ganglion cell's dendritic tree shows how it dips to the appropriate depth to have access to these abstractions. The anatomical features of the cells must, of course, be related to their function, but this scheme does not really tell us how the bipolar cells form the abstractions represented in the different layers, nor how the ganglion cells combine them.

The middle figure shows Hubel and Wiesel's scheme (1962) to account for the "simple" and "complex" cells of the cerebral cortex. The essential operation here may be called selective summation. The simple cortical cells summate only from inputs that are connected to those particular

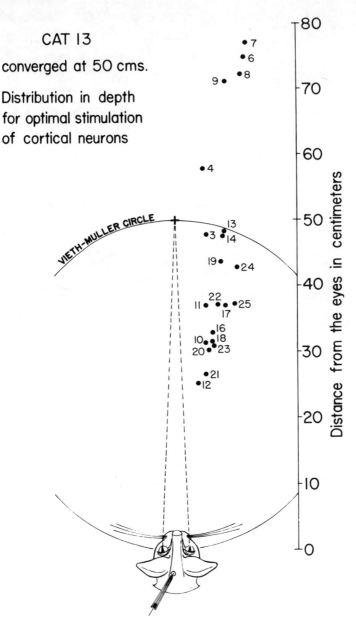

CAT 13

converged at 50 cms.

Distribution in depth
for optimal stimulation
of cortical neurons

FIGURE 3. Assuming the eyes were converged on a point 50 cm from the cat, the optimum parallax for the units of Fig. 2 would correspond to objects 42 cm and 30 cm from the cat. These are shown here projected onto a horizontal plane together with 19 other units from the same region of the cortex of the same cat. The cat's cortex peppers his visual space with units responding optimally to objects at different distances. From Barlow *et al.*, (1967).

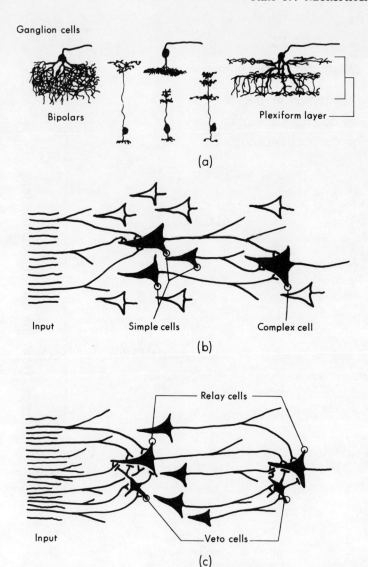

FIGURE 4. Possible ways of obtaining responses to specific trigger features. (a) Maturana, *et al.,* (1960) point out that the external plexiform layer is laminated, and they suggest that bipolars represent different abstractions of the input in the different layers, which are picked up in different combinations by the ganglion cells. (b) Hubel and Wiesel (1962) say that simple cells achieve their selectivity of response by summating from selected inputs from the lateral geniculate; complex cells then selectively summate from the simple cells. (c) Barlow and Levick (1965) suggest that inhibitory "veto" cells additionally restrict the range of response of selectivity summating cells at all levels. Figure from Barlow (1969).

retinal ganglion cells excited by the specific stimulus for the cell in question. Similarly, the complex cell connects to a specific selection of simple cells; in Hubel and Wiesel's case these are the simple cells that are excited by a target of the same orientation, but not necessarily the same position, in the visual field. This scheme has the very attractive feature that the final output is both specific, in this case for orientation, and non-specific or generalized, in this case for position; this is clearly a very important feature of the percepts into which we classify sensory information. Notice, however, that although the complex cell is "generalizing," while the simple cell is "specifying," both are said to be doing no more than summating the effects of a selected group of inputs. This does not seem quite right, because real specificity for a line or edge requires an operation more like a logical product than a union; it should respond only to the combined excitation of the appropriate ganglion cells, rather than simply the sum of their excitations. On the other hand, the operation of generalization by the complex cell is like a logical union, not a product, so we have the same neurophysiological operation ostensibly performing quite different logical operations.

The lowest figure shows a generalization of the mechanism Levick and I proposed for the directionally selective cells of the rabbit's retina (Barlow and Levick, 1965). As in Hubel and Wiesel's scheme, generalization is obtained by summating the inputs from a lower level, and specificity is achieved by restricting these to a particular class of inputs. But inhibitory cells, possibly representatives of the multitudinous "Golgi Class II," short-axon, cells of the central nervous system, restrict the range of response and thus confer further specificity. These "veto cells" are thought also to summate selectively the inputs from a specific set of neurons at a lower level, just like the neurons that they inhibit, though, of course, the specific inputs they summate will usually be different.

The evidence for this scheme is, very briefly, (a) retinal ganglion cells pick up from subunits, and it is these subunits which have the capacity to distinguish one sequence of receptor stimulation from the reverse sequence; (b) sequence discrimination involves inhibition, which must operate at the level of the subunit; (c) there is a second type of inhibition that appears to operate at the level of the ganglion cell. In the retina we have suggested that the subunits are bipolars, and that the two types of inhibitory or "veto" cells are horizontals and amacrines, but these identifications remain uncertain. Dowling's electron microscopy on the retina of the frog (Dowling, 1968) leads him to believe that the more complex types of feature extraction depend on structural specialization in the inner plexiform layer, rther than the outer plexiform as Levick and I proposed. His evidence suggests, though it does not prove, that amacrines are interneurons interposed between ganglion cells and bipolars; they might, therefore, be the subunits our evidence requires. On the other hand, Dowling's own results on the rabbit (Dowling, *et al.*, 1966) confirm the existence of the connections in the outer plexiform that we had previously postulated on physiological grounds in the face of vigorous objections from our histologically better informed colleagues. At this point we cannot be sure about the respective functions of horizontal cells and amacrines.

As a general model, the scheme of Fig. 4 is probably too restrictive in that both veto cells and the relay cells on the through-pathway only pick up from the single, preceding level of cells: it would seem advantageous, and by no means unlikely on anatomical grounds, that the hierarchy it suggests is not followed rigidly. However, the rigid scheme can readily be symbolized and will be convenient for discussion. Let E_n^ψ be the class of inputs that causes a neuron n to fire, where n is at a level in the nervous system such that ψ synapses have been passed since the receptors were activated. Then the class of inputs for a cell at the next level is related to those for cells at the previous level as follows ($\vee$ signifies inclusive "or", . ∞ signifies "and not"):

$$E_n^{\psi+1} = (E_a^\psi \vee E_b^\psi \vee E_c^\psi \ldots) . \infty (E_r^\psi \vee E_s^\psi \vee E_t^\psi \ldots) \tag{1}$$

This oversimplifies by representing all the variables as binary, but it indicates the outline of the suggested mechanism in the rabbit retina and it also seems capable of representing cortical units at successive levels. In their later work on "hyper complex" units, Hubel and Wiesel (1965) have also come to recognize that inhibition plays a role that cannot be adequately represented by mere subtraction from an excitatory drive or by interactions at a lower level.

The response of central sensory neurons is restricted to a range of highly specific sensory stimuli, and the neural mechanisms for achieving this are thought, in summary, to be as follows: (a) specificity is achieved by making selective, rather than comprehensive or random, connections to earlier elements in the chain of sensory neurons; (b) inhibitory connections, probably often from interneurons, prevent responses to certain stimuli; (c) generalization to a range of sensory stimuli is achieved by having several alternative excitatory pathways that can summate; (d) the organization is hierarchical. The following section describes some adaptive changes in the response characteristics of sensory neurons, but the mechanism of these changes is little understood.

IV. Adaptation in the Cat Retina

Measurements of the quantum efficiency of human vision (Rose, 1948; Barlow, 1962) show that the eye operates effectively over an enormous range of intensities. Television cameras and photocells rival its efficiency in specific ranges, but its versatility is hard to compete with and it is interesting to see how the eye's automatic adjustments achieve it. Levick and I have been studying this problem in the cat's retina, and we believe the secret of its success is the fact that there are two control mechanisms (Barlow and Levick, 1969). One of these controls the gain; this (or rather its inverse, the attenuation) is the relation between the number of input quanta and the number of output impulses—the quantum/spike ratio. But if this was the only variable, at a high luminance level there would either have to be a high maintained output from the ganglion cells, or the attenuation would have to be increased in proportion to adaptation level to hold the maintained discharge at a fairly constant value. In fact, we find that the maintained discharge of a typical "on-center" unit rises a little as adapting luminance is raised from a very low value, but thereafter it stays rather constant or even falls. To account for this near-constancy of the maintained discharge, the quantum/spike ratio should rise in direct proportion with adaptation level, whereas it actually rises much less rapidly. The explanation lies in the variable influence of the surround. At low levels this has little effect on "on-center" units, but at high levels it has the well-known inhibiting effect. We now believe that this is being constantly exerted and holds the maintained discharge down to a reasonable level, thus making it possible for the sensitivity in the receptive field center to be maintained at a high level.

Anatomically, it is tempting to place these two stages of control in the outer and inner plexiform layers. The horizontal cells would then have the function of controlling attenuation at the receptor-bipolar cell synapse, while amacrines pool activity over a larger area and inhibit the ganglion cell directly. This function of horizontal cells as gain controllers may seem incompatible with their previously suggested function in giving the rabbit's bipolar cells the power to discriminate one sequence from its reverse—but I do not think this is necessarily so. If the horizontal cells in rabbits pick up from receptors on one side of those that excite a bipolar, then a moving object will either change attenuation before changing the excitation, which would result in little change in output, or it would change attenuation after changing the excitation, which would result in a large but transient change in output. Thus the outline scheme at the bottom of Fig. 4 could fit both. Notice also that the inhibitory "veto" cells are removing redundant impulses in both cases; in adaptation this has the effect of improving sensitivity to small departures from the mean adaptation level; in motion selectivity responses to motion in one particular direction are prevented for one particular cell. In both cases good discrimination of a specific type results from the activities of the inhibitory interneurons as scavengers of unwanted impulses.

V. Another Look at Sensory Information Processing

Since Boole's "Laws of Thought," one has tended to think of a word, thought, or action as a logical function of certain variables which, to a physiologist, are the states of the raw sensory messages. To simplify the problem we will only consider present states of the input, though past states must really also be involved. If there are n sensory pathways each capable of m distinguishable grades of activity in a short interval of time, then there are m^n different possible states of the input within that time. The logical functions we are seeking to describe can be written in normal form as a union of a selection of these possible inputs states. Since one can make 2^x different selections of x different objects, the total number of possible logical functions of the m^n input states is 2^{m^n}. Now if this number was infinite, it would be fair to say that we still knew nothing at all about the relation between thought and sensory message, because restricting choice to one among infinity is no restriction. As it is, for any reasonable values of m and n, 2^{m^n} is so large that it is fair to say that we know almost nothing.

There is nothing wrong with trying to define the brain's responses as logical functions of the sensory messages it is receiving and has received, but the argument above shows that, in doing so, one tends to start off in a rather misleading direction. In a fully developed logical function written in normal form, the state of every input is specified in each term. This appears to be necessary because, under favorable conditions, change of a single input can probably change the meaning of the whole input message in an important way. But it is really very misleading to think of an exhaustive list of the possible input states, and of forming the logical functions as a union of items from this list. The only infallible way to make an exhaustive list is to describe the state of every element of the input, and go through all possible combinations, but this is quite inappropriate for the following reasons: (a) it is virtually impossible because of the large capacity of the sensory output; (b) it is uneconomical because nothing is gained by distinguishing terms which are promptly going to be combined in a union; and (c) it is undesirable because bare knowledge of the state of every element of the input does not tell one anything about what other stimuli are closely related to that particular input, and should be responded to positively or negatively like that particular one. In other words, the ordering of the list entries will not represent patterns of relationships among the causes of our sensations.

A very simple calculation shows the absurdity. If there are a mere 100 binary sensory inputs, if a lifetime is 100 years, and if a physiological "instant" is 1/4 second, then on the average, if they are equally probable, only about $1/10^{20}$ of the possible input states occurs even once in a lifetime! Obviously when the number of possible descriptions so vastly exceeds the number of things to be described, one is going very much too far to ensure that the descriptions are unique and unambiguous: it is as if the telephone companies arbitrarily insisted upon 20 extra digits in every telephone number.

Considering neural responses as logical functions has, in a sense, opened up too many possibilities. The logical functions we are interested in finding are not randomly or arbitrarily selected from this enormous number, 2^{mn}, of possible functions, and a sensible first step in narrowing the field is to consider what is required of the input to a device that can learn and form associations in the manner in which these occur in operant conditioning and the formation of conditioned reflexes.

A. Requirements for the Representation of the Sensory Input

First, the representation need only define the physical stimulus with sufficient resolution and precision for it to be separable from other stimuli that do not yield the conditional response after this response has first been established, that is, before any training to differentiate the reinforced stimulus from other stimuli. Secondly, there must be some inherent pattern of relationships between the stimuli causing activity in a given element, such that a learned response is initially generalized appropriately to other stimuli. This means that initially the resolution must be no better, as well as no worse, than that defined by the first requirement, but it also means that the confusions caused by poor resolution must be of a special kind. Third, there must be some way of changing the class of stimuli for which an element stands from undifferentiated to differentiated; initially the classes must be wide and overlapping, so that the appropriate generalizations occur, but after a differentiating regime of negative and positive reinforcements it must be possible for it to become extremely narrow and restricted, so that sensory stimuli can be discriminated up to the limit allowable by the sense organs. It is this third requirement that makes one think that an exhaustive list of the possible input states is required, but we now see that this high resolution is only attained in very special circumstances. I want next to show briefly that the end product of the type of coding described above and indicated by eq. (1) has many of the features required for the input to a learning device.

B. An Alternative to the Exhaustive Specification of the Sensory Input

The redundancy reducing codes described have the effect of reducing the number of impulses required to transmit sensory messages while reducing as little as possible the efficiency or accuracy with which the message is transmitted. Lateral inhibition does this by taking advantage of the high correlation between light intensities of neighboring points in the visual field, temporal adaptation by taking advantage of the correlation between stimulus strengths at succeeding intervals in time. Motion detectors and orientation detectors take advantage of sequential stimuli and the tendency for the edges of areas of uniform luminance to be arranged in lines. In these cases, there are several possible directions of motion or orientations of an edge or line, and, therefore, the representation has to be expanded into several different types of units corresponding to different directions. Similarly, when information from the two eyes is combined, nearly coincident pairs of features with different amounts of parallax cause excitation of different neurons. Thus, what seems to happen is that the number of neurons available to represent the information increases at the higher level, but these neurons have such highly specific trigger features that any given neuron is only activated infrequently: the information comes to be represented by fewer and fewer impulses among more and more fibers. It is as if the number of letters in the alphabet was being increased, and the number of letters per word decreased. If one thinks of the whole sensory input as corresponding to a word, then, extrapolating, we would expect to find the word represented by a single symbol, or activity in one single unit. In fact, the type of coding we are talking about is taking us in the direction of representing the whole or, at least, a large part of the sensory input by activity in one or a small number of neurons selected from among a very large population. The characteristic of the exhaustive list of input states is that one and only one item in the list defines the whole input; redundancy-reducing, impulse-economizing, codes seem capable of approximating a set of alternative, mutually exclusive descriptions of the input, but the number of alternative descriptions required is no longer m^n as it would be if one had used the brute force method of having an element for every possible combination of inputs. If the coding has been done as specified by our hypothesis, the number will certainly be enormously reduced. The exact lower limit cannot be stated without knowing the allowable probability of the representation failing, either by one output representing two inputs that are required to be discriminable, or by an input causing simultaneous activity in more than one output element; one would also need to know how much redundancy there was in the messages from the animal's sensory environment.

The first and second requirements for the input to a learning device were that it should initially have poor resolution, and as a result make similar responses to different inputs. Units whose responses are logical functions of the form of eq. (1) fulfill these requirements; if a conditional response was established for one element of the union represented in the first bracket, then it would automatically be generalized and a stimulus causing activity of any other member would also give the response. Notice that it is possible that there should be considerable complexity in the class of inputs to which generalization occurs; for, if the unit to which an association is made at a level ψ (*i.e.*, ψ preceding synapses), the level which is generalized is only one step earlier, level $\psi\text{-}1$, and can have all the complexity of elements at that level. However, once this is said, it is also clear that we know very little about the actual order and relationships here, *i.e.*, we can see there is room for complexity but we do not know any details.

The third requirement was that the code for a unit should be modifiable from the initial state where generalization occurs to a state where it occurs to a much more restricted class or not at all. If one conceives of negative reinforcement acting to enter, or render effective, terms in the second parenthesis of eq. (1), this condition is well fulfilled, for any term that appears in both parentheses will cause no response. Thus, it would be possible for the responsiveness of an element to be narrowed in the way that conditional responses can be made to occur for a narrow range of stimuli after a regime of differentiation.

VI. Summary and Conclusions

There is mounting evidence that sensory messages are recoded into a less redundant form at relays in sensory pathways, and this leads to economy of impulses rather than reduction of nerve pathways. In fact, the number of neurons seems to increase at higher levels, and it is suggested that the representation of the sensory message by fewer and fewer sensory impulses in a larger and larger number of highly specific neurons is a substitute for representation as one among an exhaustive list of all possible input states. It is pointed out that the input requirements for operant conditioning and conditioned reflexes would be well served in several respects by units having properties generalized from those found in the rabbit's retina and cat's cortex.

REFERENCES

Adrian, E. D. (1928). The basis of sensation. London: Christophers.

Attneave, F. (1954). Informational aspects of visual perception. Psychol. Rev., *61*: 183–193.

Barlow, H. B. (1959). Sensory mechanisms, the reduction of redundancy, and intelligence. Symposium on the mechanization of thought processes at the National Physical Laboratory, London: H.M. Stationery Office, Symp. No. 10, 535–539.

Barlow, H. B. (1961a). The coding of sensory messages. In W. H. Thorpe and O. L. Zangwill, (eds.), Current problems in animal behaviour. Cambridge: Cambridge Univ. Press, 331–360.

Barlow, H. B. (1961b). Possible principles underlying the transformations of sensory messages. In W. A. Rosenblith (ed.), Sensory communication. Cambridge: MIT Press, 217–234.

Barlow, H. B. (1962). Measurements of the quantum efficiency of discrimination in human scotopic vision. J. Physiol., *160:* 169–188.

Barlow, H. B. (1969). Pattern recognition and the responses of sensory neurones. Annals N. Y. Acad. Sci. Symposium on "Rein Control, or Unidirectional Rate Sensitivity." *156:* 872–881.

Barlow, H. B. and Levick, W. R. (1965). The mechanism of directionally selective units in rabbit's retina. J. Physiol., *178:* 477–504.

Barlow, H. B., Blakemore, C. and Pettigrew, J. D. (1967). The neural mechanism of binocular depth discrimination. J. Physiol., *193:* 327–342.

Barlow, H. B., and Levick, W. R. (1969). Coding of light intensity by the cat retina. Rendiconti della Scuola Int. di Fisica "Enrico Fermi," XLIII corso. New York: Academic Press. (in press).

Boole, G. (1854). Laws of thought. Reprinted ed., New York: Dover.

Craik, K. (1943). The nature of explanation. Cambridge: Cambridge Univ. Press.

Dowling, J. E. (1968). Synaptic organization of the frog retina; an electron microscopic analysis comparing the retinas of frogs and primates. Proc. Roy. Soc. (London) B. *170:* 205–228.

Dowling, J. E., Brown, J. E. and Major, D. (1966). Synapses of horizontal cells in rabbit and cat retinas. Science *153:* 1639–1641.

Hubel, D. H. and Wiesel, T. N. (1959). Receptive fields of single neurons in the cat's striate cortex. J. Physiol., *148:* 574–591.

Hubel, D. H. and Wiesel, T. N. (1962). Receptive fields, binocular interaction, and functional architecture in the cat's visual cortex. J. Physiol., *160:* 106–154.

Hubel, D. H. and Wiesel, T. N. (1965). Receptive fields and functional architecture in two non-striate visual areas (18 and 19) of the cat. J. Neurophysiol., *28:* 229–289.

Lettvin, J. Y., Maturana, H. R., McCulloch, W. S. and Pitts, W. H. (1959). What the frog's eye tells the frog's brain. Proc. Inst. Radio Engrs., *47:* 1940–1951.

Maturana, H. R., Lettvin, J. Y., McCulloch, W. S., and Pitts, W. H. (1960). Anatomy and physiology of vision in the frog (*Rana pipiens*). J. Gen. Physiol., *43:* (Number 6, Pt. 2) 129–176.

Nikara, T., Bishop, P. O., and Pettigrew, J. D. (1968). Analysis of retinal correspondence by studying receptive fields of binocular single units in cat striate cortex. Exp. Brain Res., *6:* 353–372.

Pettigrew, J. D., Nikara, T., and Bishop, P. O. (1968a). Responses to moving slits by single units in cat striate cortex. Exp. Brain Res., *6:* 373–390.

Pettigrew, J. D., Nikara, T., and Bishop, P. O. (1968b). Binocular interaction on single units in cat striate cortex; simultaneous stimulation by single moving slit with receptive fields in correspondence. Exp. Brain Res., *6:* 391–410.

Rose, A. (1948). The sensitivity performance of the human eye on an absolute scale. J. Opt. Soc. Amer., *38:* 196–208.

DISCUSSION

RUSHTON: If I may, I will ask Dr. Barlow the first question. One extrapolation of your idea, that there are a lot of comparatively idle and very specific lines as one goes up the visual pathway, might be that the meaning or significance of those lines might change. This could introduce the old and debated question of the centrifugal fibers in the optic tract. An economy in the design of such a system to avoid too many and idle lines, might be to change their significance. I should like to ask your views on that.

BARLOW: Well, I don't like the idea very much, as it would depend on conditional connections.

BROOKS: Did you find an anatomical relationship between the location of a cell in the primary visual cortex and the depth of field it was looking at?

BARLOW: Pettigrew was very keen on this idea when he first came to us. But we did not find consistent evidence that, e.g., units corresponding to greater convergent or divergent disparities were located deeper in a functional column. The only thing we could find was that, in some cases, successively recorded units with the same orientation selectivity seemed to correspond to the same visual direction but different depths of view. In other cases, units with the same orientation seemed to correspond to the same disparity but slightly different positions in the visual field. So there was some hint that visual direction and visual depth may be segregated in different columns.

ARBIB: It is interesting to note that after all the reduction of a stimulus pattern and the extraction of specific features, the number of channels for transmitting the information is not reduced but actually increased. That fits in with a problem in automata theory on time optimal computing networks on which my student, Spira, has worked. He found that the way to achieve the fastest computation, was to use a network with highly redundant coding, with different parts of the network computing some special features quickly.

WICKELGREN: Being prejudiced in favor of your finding for disparity detectors in the cortex, I should like to know why Hubel and Wiesel did not find them.

BARLOW: In one of their later papers they have two or three units which do show a disparity difference. But they were looking in a central region and they were interested in crosshemisphere representations. In this region the range of variation of disparities is relatively small, perhaps 2° or 3°, while at an eccentricity of 10° or 15° you get a range of variation of disparities of some 7°. This is in the cat. But in man the stereoscopic range also narrows down as the eccentricity is reduced. To be certain about disparity differences you have to be very sure that the eyes do not move.

LEIBOVIC: What are your views on the anatomical basis of the surround mechanism? I believe this is relevant to such matters as adaptation. Dowling has argued that some kind of lateral inhibition, mediated by the amacrine cells, is the mechanism for light adaptation. Rodieck, on the other hand, has told me that he believes adaptation occurs at or prior to the level of the horizontal cells.

BARLOW: I am inclined to the view that the change in sensitivity occurs as a result of the horizontal cells acting either on bipolar cells or on the bipolar-receptor synapse as one part of the mechanism; another part is anatomically in the amacrine cells. Now that puts me in a slightly difficult position, because we have already used the horizontal cells to account for motion sensitivity in the rabbit. However, it may well be that if the gain control works just from one side, you have motion sensitivity.

ECCLES: I should like to take up again your suggestion that the signals become more specific as they go up the visual pathway. How does this increasingly selective information get put together? For we—and the cat too—see a whole environment. Somewhere, there has to be some integration. So we have to think not only of more and more dispersion as you have described but of information coming together.

BARLOW: Well, I am not too happy about this bringing together again of the signals. It seems to imply that you are thinking of a pattern of activity similar to a pattern of light and shade in the visual field. Now, if a code means anything you need only get some kind of a unique representation.

ECCLES: Well, I am thinking that you can see such a thing as a triangle and it matches a unique concept of triangle.

BARLOW: Well, maybe there are a number of cells each responding to some specific triangle and all connecting with one master triangle unit.

ECCLES: Now, that is what I wanted you to say—but I don't believe that, you know, I believe this is the wrong way to look at the nervous system. Because you can't make, say, one lesion in the nervous system and then become aphasic to triangle.

BARLOW: Very limited replication of the "master triangle unit" would, I think, explain the fact that a lesion of, say, half the brain does not destroy half its concepts. For instance, if there was just one "master triangle unit" in each hemisphere, the perception of triangles could survive hemispherectomy. If there were, say, half a dozen master units widely scattered over the cortex, one or two of them would survive almost any localized lesion. The effects of lesion probably do show that some degree of redundancy is required in the neural representation of our perceptions: but such observations fail to disprove that single units represent complicated abstract concepts. Actually, I do not know of any other notion of how such concepts are represented that one would expect to be less disturbed by destructive lesions: this evidence may actually favor single unit representation.

(In further discussion it was pointed out that different stimuli may produce similar responses.)

BARLOW: Units do vary in their response to monocular and binocular stimulation. It is often difficult to get a really vigorous response, except by binocular stimulation at the right orientation and the right disparity. One problem that comes up here, is that we can see nearly as well with one eye as with two. But, if you look at some monocular and binocular records you find the largest response binocularly at the right disparity, a smaller response monocularly, but the smallest response binocularly at the wrong disparity, which suggests that the other eye will in many cases decrease firing rather than increase it. Once you have found the right stimulus, it is remarkable how vigorous the response can be.

BLUM: It seems to me that we are not really getting at the primitives of visual perception—elements that might be the equivalents of the phonemes in speech. Stopped edges, corners, and similar primitives are not likely to form an adequate base for understanding the visual process. There is still the preconception, here, of the organism as a Euclidean geometer, and, the serious question of finding what kind of a biological geometer the organism is, remains.

BARLOW: I think it is just these "primitives" which we are finding in the detectors of edges, discontinuities, and oriented segments. Now, it is very difficult to know how they are put together in the next stage. Perhaps there are detectors for groups of edges and segments which finally give us the sensation of, say, a cat.

HARTH: On the one hand, we have the activity of single cells which have been monitored extensively. Thus, Hubel and Wiesel have demonstrated that in a functional column, large numbers of neurons have identical, or nearly identical, receptive fields. Now, we also know from anatomy that these cells are tightly interconnected. So, one should perhaps look at this as a small net, and the activity in a single unit then reflects the level of activity within this net and, perhaps, this activity is the encoded form of sensory events.

ECCLES: I am told there are no anatomists present so I will be very brave and point out that when you are looking at the cortex with a microelectrode, you only see the big cells and you may get quite a distorted view of the total ensemble. I am sure, as we get more refined techniques, we shall get more and more of the smaller cells.

BOYNTON: Suppose it were true that the only place in the brain which responds to a photic stimulus is the visual cortex, and the only place which responds to an auditory stimulus is the auditory cortex. I know this is not so, but, for the sake of thinking about the problem, let us accept this proposition. Now, let us do an experiment and ask a subject to judge the temporal order of two stimuli—one light and one sound. This discrimination can be made within certain limits. Now the question is this: is it necessary to assume that the neural representation of these inputs must be brought together to a common point somewhere in the brain?

LEIBOVIC: This is one of the unsolved problems which has puzzled us on several occasions at this symposium: are discriminations—and other brain functions—represented in the activity of single neurons or the pattern of activity of cell assemblies? What relationship is there between the response specificity of single cells and the uniqueness of stimulus representations?—and, what is the significance of neurons receiving inputs from several sensory modalities and, perhaps, having a nonspecific response?

ECCLES: Some years ago, as others had done before, I made a count from the literature of the number of cells in the cerebral cortex which had been detected as receiving from more than one sensory modality, and I counted several hundred. There is no point in going on with this, you can find them particularly numerous in the temporal lobe, the silent areas, as long as you don't mind the response latency.

VERNON B. BROOKS

Department of Physiology
New York Medical College
New York, New York

12 · *Information Processing in the Motorsensory Cortex**

In order to discuss the processing of information in the motorsensory cortex, we need to know what information reaches this part of the brain, how it is processed, and to what purpose. We will begin by defining the motorsensory cortex, and by making some first guesses at the functions that it might serve. Next, we will consider the kinds of information that reach it, and how the target cells for these sensory inputs are distributed and grouped in the cortical tissue. After examining the motor outputs of these cells, we can formulate some input-output properties for cell groups that can be defined anatomically. Having established the minimal input-output building blocks of motorsensory cortex, we will then re-examine our guesses about its functions.

I. What Is the Motorsensory Cortex?

The term "motor cortex" was coined to define those parts of the cerebral hemisphere from which limb movements could be elicited by electrical stimulation (Phillips, 1966). It is the precentral cortex in humans (Penfield and Boldrey, 1937) and primates, and the pericruciate cortex in dogs and cats (see Terzuolo and Adey, 1960; Phillips, 1966). The name was amended to "motorsensory" cortex (MS1) when it was realized that it received sensory inputs similar to those reaching the somatosensory cortex (S1), located just caudally (Woolsey, 1958; Welt, *et al.,* 1967). The

* Supported in part by Research and Training Grants from the National Institute for Neurological Diseases (NB–05508 and NB–05544).

dividing line between these areas is the central fissure in primates and the postcruciate dimple in the cat (Woolsey, 1958). Large and small pyramidal cells in the motor cortex give rise to large and small fibers descending in the pyramidal tract (Patton and Amassian, 1960). The "motor" effects are mediated to the spinal cord most directly by the corticospinal tract (Patton and Amassian, 1960) and with increasing number of interneurons by the corticorubrospinal, and corticoreticulospinal tracts (Brodal, 1962). The cells of origin of these tracts lie intermingled in the cortex rostral to the dimple and so are many of their final target cells in the spinal cord (see Brodal, 1962; Patton and Amassian, 1960; Phillips, 1966; Tsukahara, et al., 1968; Welt, et al., 1967). Thresholds for stimulation to elicit movements within the cortex caudal to the dimple are more than 10 times those rostral to the dimple (Sakata and Miyamoto, 1968).

II. First Guesses at Functions of the Motorsensory Cortex

This part of the brain obviously has something to do with movement: its excitation produces muscular contractions (see Patton and Amassian, 1960; Terzuolo and Adey, 1960). Furthermore, it has recently been shown that during voluntary movements, pyramidal tract cells in monkeys discharge in relation to particular muscles, whose contraction follows the cortical events (Evarts, 1967). Yet, the motorsensory cortex is not essential for willed, voluntary movements: bilateral excision does not produce permanent paralysis but only a loss of the manipulatory use of the distal joints, particularly in fast movements. Pure bilateral pyramidal lesions deprive chronic primates of independent finger movements and slow them down generally, but acute lesions leave the coarse "motor map" obtained by electrical stimulation of the cortex essentially unchanged (see Lawrence and Kuypers, 1965; Paillard, 1960; Patton and Amassian, 1960). Properly controlled standing, walking, and positioning of the limbs depend on intact primary sensory areas as well as motor cortex in both primates and in lower species. It has been shown that these functions depend on integrative cortical reflexes, the "placing reactions," of which the "tactile" type generates hand or paw placement in response to skin input (Bard, 1938). The "instinctive grasping reactions" underlie exploratory behavior. They are pursuits of tactile stimuli; and in the natural state are balanced by the "tactile avoiding reaction," mediated through the supplementary motor area without participation of the pyramids (Denny-Brown, 1960). All these cortical reflexes are lost upon removal of motor cortex.

The question is thus raised again: to what extent do the motor cortex, and the corticospinal tract, in particular, initiate voluntary movement, on the one hand, and on the other how much do they merely control movements through sensory feedback (see Brodal, 1962; Evarts, 1967; Phillips, 1966; Towe, et al., 1968)? The old concept of the "upper motor neuron" must be brought into accord with understanding why the pyramidal tract, through collateral branches into afferent relay nuclei, modifies the flow of information to the cerebral cortex (Levitt, *et al.,* 1964; Adkins, *et al.,* 1966; and see Terzuolo and Adey, 1960). In the following sections we will assemble evidence that bears on this problem of functional significance.

III. What Information Reaches the Motorsensory Cortex?

The motorsensory cortex receives three kinds of inputs. The first reflects definite events: for instance, movement of a finger, of which we may be conscious, or the tensing of a muscle which may be unconscious. The information content of another kind of message may deal with less definite information. Examples for that would be the mixing of two converging inputs, like the two examples cited above. The response of the recipient target cell does not usually reflect which of the two inputs impinged on it. Such convergence occurs at all levels of the neuraxis projecting to motor-cortex, as well as in that tissue itself. Finally we must recognize the third kind: subtle modulating influences that diffuse from any focus of activity throughout the cerebral mantle. They apparently cannot signal distinct events because, in passing through a great number of cells, the wave is averaged to reflect mean levels of excitability of that network of cells. The first two types of input can bring cells in the motorsensory cortex to all-or-none discharge, or at least generate strong synaptic drive. The third type usually cannot, and it is best grasped by statistical analysis of population excitability (Burns, 1968). We will neglect it in our present consideration.

We thus limit our definition of "information" to the content of messages related to definite inputs, whose intensity and degrees of specificity can be measured at the cortical level. Using this guide line, we can now ask: what is processed in the motor cortex? It is information that deals with the exterior world as well as the world within us. Distant events are signalled to motor cortex through the visual and auditory systems (see Buser, 1966; Terzuolo and Adey, 1960; Welt, *et al.,* 1967). Knowledge of the orientation of the body in space converges to motor cortex through the vestibular system (Kornhuber and Aschoff, 1963). These inputs reach cells that also receive the main message traffic in motor cortex, namely exteroceptive input from the skin and proprioceptive inputs from the joints and muscles.

Let us deal with the skin input first. The incoming, or afferent, messages from various parts of the body surface reach the motor-cortex topographically organized according to their origins on the body surface. This is similar to the "somatotopic" projection of the body surface on the primary sensory cortex: there is the same alignment with representation of the head lateral and (hind) feet medial (Penfield and Boldrey, 1937). In primary sensory cortex (S1) nearly all neurons respond to messages from only one adequate stimulus delivered in one specific, local receptive field on the contralateral side (see Rose and Mountcastle, 1959). In the motor-cortex (MS1) there is multiple representation, however, so that one could draw several body images, one next to the other, on the cortical surface. This evidence is derived from responses of single cells to natural stimulation of the skin (Terzuolo and Adey, 1960; Towe, 1965; Towe, *et al.*, 1968; Welt, *et al.*, 1967). Cells as specific as those in area S1 also form the majority in MS1, but their relative proportion decreases in the rostral part of the brain. There is a concomitant increase in the number of cells that receive convergent input from more than one local skin area. The "peripheral receptive fields" become larger, they may be discontinuous, and include the ipsilateral side. Such fields may cover one or several limbs like a stocking, or be as large as half or the whole body surface. Three quarters of the cells in the cat's motorsensory cortex can be brought to vigorous "all-or-none" discharge by inputs from "local" fields and one quarter from "wide" fields. Local fields are smallest distally, near the tips of the extremities where innervation is densest.

The adequate natural stimuli are hairbending, touch, tap, and pressure. About half of all cells in MS1, and three quarters in S1, of the cat are driven by superficial stimuli. Passive movement of joints can excite about one third of the cells in MS1, and these cells are not excited by skin contact, except about one tenth of the total population that can respond to both "somesthetic" and "kinesthetic" messages (Asanuma, *et al.*, 1968; Welt, *et al.*, 1967). These ratios differ somewhat for different investigators (Towe, 1965; Towe, *et al.*, 1968). In the monkey, joint input seems to outweigh that from skin (Albe-Fessard and Liebeskind, 1966). All inputs may, of course, be excitatory or inhibitory. Information about static muscle length appears to reach all brain areas that receive joint and skin inputs (Rosén, 1968, personal communication), while information about changes of muscle length, *i.e.*, velocity of contraction, is channelled to only a narrow strip of MS1 at the border to S1 (Oscarsson, 1966). Study of the cortical integration of messages from joints and muscles has hardly begun. It will be of the greatest importance, because in voluntary movements many pyramidal tract (PT) cells govern muscles according to the force of movement exerted or some function of it (Evarts, 1967)—or, as Phillips has put it, PT-cells discharge according to the resistance that the limb encounters in its movement.

The input pathways to the motorsensory cortex are reasonably well established. The medial lemniscal system carries input from muscle sense organs (Oscarsson, 1966), as well as that from skin (Towe, *et al.*, 1968) and joints (Perl and Whitlock, 1961). The spinocervical tract is an important component (Oscarsson, 1966). The thalamic nucleus ventralis lateralis (VL) (Buser, 1966) projects more to the rostral end, the ventralis postero-lateralis (VPL) more to the caudal end of the cat's motor cortex (Amassian and Weiner, 1965). Thus, there is a gradient across MS1, reflecting the greater incidence of wide peripheral fields for cells in the rostral area versus local fields in the caudal end.

Visual and auditory signals reach "polysensory" motor cortex cells through the thalamus and the midbrain reticular formation discharging into the posterio-medial (PM) and ventro-lateral (VL) nuclei. Most of the visual and auditory input comes in through cortico-cortical connections, however, because it has been shown that visual and auditory convergence can be abolished by depressing the primary visual and auditory areas, without affecting the usual somatic responsiveness of the cells in motorsensory cortex (Buser, 1966, and personal communication).

IV. Distribution and Grouping of Cells in Motorsensory Cortex

Do the various types of input projections described in the previous section impinge preferentially on particular cell species, such as interneurons as opposed to corticofugal cells? Testing of several hundred cells in the cat's cortex with natural stimuli revealed no special preponderance of any particular adequate input stimulus for corticospinal, or pyramidal tract (PT) cells, (identified by backward or "antidromic" stimulation of PT-cell axons in the brain stem). There was, however, a trend for less specific input to select large PT-cells (see Welt, et al., 1967). Statistical analysis of responses to electrical skin stimulation of nearly two thousand cells showed that from 60 to 90 per cent of the PT-cells (with increasing proportion rostrally) had wide skin inputs driven predominantly by hair bending. The large, fast-conducting PT-cells lying deep in the cortex were outstanding targets for this input; but the smaller, slowly conducting PT-cells lying more superficially were also reached. Input from local fields to superficially located intracortical interneurons may be through another separate channel. (Towe, et al., 1968; and also see Phillips, 1966).

How are the cells with related topographic input grouped in motorsensory cortex? Do they form radial columns, as has been found in primary somatosensory cortex (Rose and Mountcastle, 1959)? This expectation was indeed confirmed by systematic, serial, examination of receptive fields of neurons in MS1 (Welt, et al., 1967). It was found that cells within radial columns have overlapping topography. What this means is that the local and wide receptive fields overlap one another, and that the wide fields always contain as their focal points the local fields belonging to cells within those radial columns. In other words, neurons with local input provide a radially oriented somatotopic framework which also contains many cells that receive less specific input. The diameter of the radial columns with common inputs was established histologically: the number of changes of the origin of the messages, i.e., of the topography of receptive field, were measured against the angles of penetrations made by the microelectrode.

The mean tangential diameter of the radial columns thus established was about 0.2 mm (0.1–0.4 mm), when changes of topography were defined as receptive fields with less than one-half overlap. These columns grade over one into another, as judged by the foci of their activation: there is "shifting overlap" just as is found in sensory cortex (see Rose and Mountcastle, 1959; Terzuolo and Adey, 1960; Welt, et al., 1967). Within the columns of motor-cortex, cells with different adequate stimuli are always mixed together, but inputs from skin, deep receptors, and joints originate from the same limb (Welt, et al., 1967). This stands in contrast to the unimodal nature of topographically homogenous columns in primary sensory cortex (Rose and Mountcastle, 1959).

The polymodal columns in MS1 contain mixtures of all cell species: PT-cells and non-PT-cells (Welt, et al., 1967). The latter include intracortical interneurons as well as cortico-rubral cells (Tsukahara, et al., 1968). Evidence presented in the previous sections indicate that the nature and intensity of the adequate stimuli influence the proportion of output cell species activated within any one column. There are also intracortical modulations. A careful statistical timing of the arrival times of various inputs has shown that a specific small field projection activates first interneurons without cortical output. There is much evidence to suggest that these cells with local input facilitate PT-cells receiving less specific input (Towe, et al., 1968). This facilitation reaches cells within about one third mm distance, particularly those aligned in the radial direction. This integrative action provides a basis to the finding that foci of wide fields have the size and location of local fields of neurons in the same radial columns (Welt, et al., 1967). To put it another way, one quarter of the cells in a radial column receive fairly non-specific input, but the information content of their output can be modulated to become more specific by cells within that column which receive local specific inputs. Thus, dynamic properties are added to static field overlap.

The excitability of motor cortex is also modulated by a sustaining projection from the sensory cortex (see Bard, 1938). It has been shown that the main inputs to S1, namely VPL and in a minor measure also VL, activate S1 first, which then facilitates MS1. The cortico-cortical linkages between these adjacent areas appear to be primarily between radial columns with equivalent peripheral inputs (Thompson, et al., 1969). The primary sensory cortex thus facilitates the motorsensory cortex, but it does not constitute an obligatory firing pin for it.

V. How Is the Output
of the Motorsensory Cortex Organized?

Our first guesses at the function of this tissue were introduced by the relationship between individual PT-cells and particular muscles during voluntary movement (Evarts, 1967). This result suggests a detailed representation of muscles in motor cortex; perhaps the existence of nuclei of "upper motoneurons" analagous to those of spinal "lower motoneurons." The variation of use to which these nuclei could be put would, of course, be greater for cortex than for cord. Such fine-grained representation has not been found, however, until very recently—although all experiments with electrical stimulation of motor cortex have indicated the existence of some form of "motor map" with successive overlap of focal points.

Does the motor cortex normally, in natural function, produce highly integrated movements, or spinal reactions, or contractions of individual muscles? The question has been much debated on the basis of experiments using electrical stimulation of the brain, and the answers obtained hinge largely on the experimental methods used (Denny-Brown, 1960; Evarts, 1967; Paillard, 1960; Phillips, 1966; Preston, et al., 1967; Terzuolo and Adey, 1960; Welt, et al., 1967). For instance, surface stimulation of the baboon's and cat's cortex has revealed "best points" with lowest thresholds for activation of individual muscles. Even at threshold, however, thousands of cortical cells were activated (Phillips, 1966). Such extreme convergence from cortex to cord seems surprising as the natural pattern of organization, because it would make the motor cortex a rather cumbersome instrument. This result is probably dependent on the use of single surface shocks. The recent introduction of repetitive stimulation within the cortex has revealed a finer mosaic of muscle representation (Asanuma, et al., 1968). Cat's PT-cells were localized with a microelectrode through which current pulses could be passed to excite nearby cells. Threshold for facilitation of a spinal motoneuron pool by such local intracortical repetitive stimulation, mediated by the pyramidal tract, was $1/100$ of that needed with single surface shocks. These threshold currents ($10\mu A$ at the electrode tip) excited about 28 neurons of which probably less than 10 were PT-cells. Such direct excitation of only a very few PT-cells sufficed to produce measurable muscle twitches.

Systematic exploration of cat's motor-cortex with local intracortical micro-stimulation revealed that PT-cells lying in radially aligned efferent zones of about 1 mm diameter (0.5–2 mm) mostly excite the same spinal motor nucleus. There is successive overlap between low threshold zones for different muscles, which may be the reason why nearly one half of all local stimulations excite more than one muscle, usually at lower a threshold for one muscle than for the others. Corticofugal cells with different spinal targets may be mixed within columns, or within their afferent subunits of 0.2 mm diameter. Mapping of the motor cortex revealed that many columns with common output exist in relatively diffuse groups in the pericruciate cortex (Asanuma, et al., 1968). As a first approximation, we can therefore say, that the "nuclei" of "upper motorneurons" consist of many separate radial columns of 1 mm diameter. These columns each contain "pools" of

0.2 mm diameter. The scatter of the columns, or the porosity of the nuclei, contrasts with the relative compactness of spinal motor nuclei.

VI. Minimal Input-Output Building Blocks of Motorsensory Cortex

In the foregoing, we have defined minimal cell aggregates both with common sensory inputs and with common motor outputs. Both were found to be anatomically organized in radial columns of neurons. What are the functional and anatomical relations between the smaller input columns and the larger output columns? Some answers have been provided by experiments with intracortical microstimulation. Modes of natural peripheral activation and motor effects following intracortical microstimulation can be studied for individual cortical neurons in awake animals. This has been accomplished (a) with cats acutely tranquilized by initial injection of one tenth anesthetic dose of pentobarbitol (Asanuma, et al., 1968) and (b) with chronically implanted cats (Sakata and Miyamoto, 1968). The most reliable results were obtained in the acute experiments where cortical threshold activation of individual muscles could be checked by electromyography. It was found that proprioceptive input reaches radially aligned efferent zones mainly from the distal joint involved in the action of the muscle under study (Asanuma, et al., 1968). This relation is not precise enough, yet, for further analysis, but it will have to be a starting point for relating these experiments to others with voluntary movements (Evarts, 1967). Study of input from the skin, however, has yielded results of great immediate significance.

Muscles with simple action—like dorsiflexion of the paw, for instance—are activated from cortical neurons with peripheral receptive skin fields largely on the dorsal surface of the paw and digits. By the same token, cortical neurons activating muscles for paw ventroflexion have receptive fields on the ventral surface of the paw and forearm. Muscles with more complex actions—such as dorsiflexion and lateral deviation of the paw, for instance—are driven from efferent zones containing neurons with peripheral receptive fields on both the dorsum and lateral side of the paw. Conversely, efferent zones projecting to more than one muscle, arising out of zone overlap as described in the previous section, receive the greatest input from skin areas intermediate to those of the constituent single muscles.

For each muscle there is one skin area with the densest overlap of peripheral receptive fields projecting to the cortical cells activating that muscle (Asanuma, et al., 1968). This would produce the most intense synaptic bombardment for that efferent zone; and, therefore, the skin area of densest overlap is likely to be the preferred skin trigger zone with the lowest threshold for the efferent column governing that muscle. The trigger zone always lies in the path of muscle action and reflects it in most detailed fashion, although parts of many constituent receptive fields do not. A reliable input-output relationship can therefore only be established by systematic study of many neurons in various efferent cortical zones at thresholds below those for gross, compound movements. Asanuma, et al., (1968) have shown that, cortical efferent zones receive cutaneous inputs predominantly from skin regions which lie in the pathway of limb movement produced by contraction of the muscle to which the zone projects. In other words, cortically activated muscles contract so as to move the peripherally stimulated skin area towards further contact with the initial stimulus: there is positive feedback.

The overlap of skin receptive fields is, of course, equally dense in the small afferent columns and in the larger efferent columns, inasmuch as these columns are parts of the same cortex. The input to efferent columns, however, covers more skin surface; several contiguous afferent columns are represented in it, each defined by topographic homogeneity to the extent of half-overlapping receptive fields. The relative skin areas projecting to afferent and efferent columns fit well with their respective mean diameters of 0.2 and 1.0 mm (Asanuma, et al., 1968; Welt, et al., 1967). One efferent column, governing mostly one muscle, thus contains about 25 afferent columns. The radial orientation and size of the physiologically determined input-output columns are indeed supported by histology. The extent of branching of the afferent fibers is less than 0.5 mm, and so is that of the dendritic trees of efferent cells. Furthermore, interneurons with radially running dendrites and axons, link cells heavily into radial columns of less than 1 mm diameter (see Colonnier, 1966).

Successively shifting overlap applies as much to the afferent subcolumns which provide detailed information, as to the recipient efferent columns. Output columns are thus provided with a range of inputs whose relative importance shifts with the locus of peripheral focal stimulation. Each point on the skin is in the focus of the peripheral receptive field of some neuron and, at the same time, is in the less potent fringe of the receptive fields of some nearby cells (Rose and Mountcastle, 1959; Welt, et al., 1967). Similarly, each point on the skin is in the preferred trigger zone for some efferent column influencing one particular muscle, while, at the same time, this skin point is also in the less potent fringe of nearby columns. A "cortical reflex," set off by local touch to the skin, therefore activates a particular combination of muscles—analogous to "local sign" in the spinal flexion reflex.

The less potent fringe of receptive fields may yield weak discharge of cortical neurons, or its influence may be subliminal. Such gradients are useful in input-output adjustments at the level of cells or of columns, as has been elaborated above. The nervous system, however, usually poises one graded device against another one working in the opposite direction, to give even finer "vernier" control. Our examples are no exception: diffuse edges of input, be they in space or time, are trimmed by "surround inhibition." This may be fed forward to the motorsensory cortex from afferent paths (Rose and Mountcastle, 1959) or fed back from recurrent axon collaterals in intracortical and subcortical loops. Such collateral inhibition involves PT- and non-PT-cells, including corticorubral cells, and it has been shown to cause edge trimming of peripheral receptive fields and of their foci (Brooks and Asanuma, 1965; Tsukahara, *et al.,* 1968). Cortical interneurons with tangential process of lengths and connectivity appropriate to distribute this inhibition in columns, have been described (Colonnier, 1966). Collateral inhibition can, thus, sharpen the definition of the outer shell of input-output columns. This inhibition also acts as an anticonvulsant, helping to keep the positive skin-muscle feedback from spiralling out of control. Such limiting function is also under voluntary control and, most likely, under the sway of the cerebellum as well.

VII. Functions of Minimal Building Blocks

In the first two sections it was pointed out that the motorsensory cortex is an executor rather than an initiator. "Decisions" to move, or even how to move, are apparently made elsewhere and passed on to the corticofugal systems for processing (see Evarts, 1967; Paillard, 1960). The minimal building blocks, namely, input-output columns serving mostly one muscle, might therefore be expected to deal mostly with cortical reflexes. Skin input reaches the columns predominantly from skin regions that lie in the pathway of limb movement produced by contraction of the target muscle. Each efferent zone thus receives continuous inputs mainly from a skin region, which is likely to be excited further during movement when the target muscle contracts. This positive feedback may be active in the "tactile placing reactions" that help to position the limbs accurately in standing and walking.

When we consider a moving target that is being handled, the cortical muscle drive generated by skin contact can function as a tracking system which tends to cause the limb to follow the source of stimulation and keep it on target (Asanuma, *et al.,* 1968). This feedback provides the neural substrate for the functional plasticity of the motor cortex: its coarse grid, "wide" input is under the sway of attention-drawing fine-grid "local" messages. Here we have a neural basis for the "instinctive tactile grasping reactions" that form part of simple exploratory movements (Denny-Brown, 1960).

Another possible function for input-output columns is to facilitate preset cortical action patterns residing in more complex circuits. Examples can be found in voluntary actions of man and primates. The act of accurate stepping is concluded in too short a time for interplay of sensory feedback (Watt and Jones, 1968). Reasonably well controlled fine movements can also be executed after removal of afferent (dorsal) spinal roots supplying the limbs of young monkeys (Taub, *et al.*, 1965; also see Paillard, 1960). The analogy made previously to spinal reflex "local sign" is relevant to this consideration of integrative feed-forward function of columns in the "upper motor neuron key board" (Paillard, 1960).

In conclusion, it should be emphasized that the description of tight preferential input-output coupling for cortical cells activating forepaw muscles reveals only minimal building blocks, from which cortical function is thought to be synthesized. Normally, many such building blocks are activated together, to produce coordinated function. Input-output columns thus channel the flow of information through the motorsensory cortex. While they individually act as focussing devices for single muscles, they collectively integrate execution of movements and of appropriate sensory feedback.

REFERENCES

Adkins, R. J., Morse, R. W. and Towe, A. L. (1966). Control of somato-sensory input by cerebral cortex. Science, *153:* 1020–1022.

Albe-Fessard, D. and Liebeskind, J. (1966). Origine des messages somato-sensitifs activant les cellules du cortex moteur chez le singe. Exp. Brain Res., *1:* 127–146.

Amassian, V. E. and Weiner, H. (1966). Monosynaptic and polysynaptic activation of pyramidal tract neurons by thalamic stimulation. In D. P. Purpura and M. D. Yahr (eds.), The thalamus. New York: Columbia University Press.

Asanuma, H., Stoney, S. D., Jr. and Abzug, C. (1968). Relationship between afferent input and motor outflow in cat motorsensory cortex. J. Neurophysiol., *31:* 670–681.

Bard, P. (1938). Studies on the cortical representation of somatic sensibility. Bull. N.Y. Acad. Med. *14:* 585–607.

Brodal, A. (1962). Some anatomical considerations of the cortico-spinal tract and corticofugal fibres to the brain stem. In M. Bax and R. Mitchell (eds.), Acute hemiplegia in childhood. London: William Heinemann.

Brooks, V. B. and Asanuma, H. (1965). Recurrent cortical effects following stimulation of medullary pyramid. Arch. Ital. Biol. *103:* 247–278.

Burns, B. D. (1968). The uncertain nervous system. London: Edward Arnold.

Buser, P. (1966). Subcortical controls of pyramidal activity. In D. P. Purpura and M. D. Yahr (eds.), The thalamus. New York: Columbia University Press.

Colonnier, M. (1966). The structural design of the neo-cortex. In J. C. Eccles (ed.), Brain and Conscious Experience. New York: Springer-Verlag.

Denny-Brown, D. (1960). Motor mechanisms—introduction: the general principles of motor integration. In, Handbook of Physiology-Neurophysiology. Vol. 2. Chapt. 32. Washington, D.C.: Amer. Physiol. Soc.

Evarts, E. V. (1967). Representation of movements and muscles by pyramidal tract neurons of the precentral motor cortex. In M. D. Yahr and D. P. Purpura (eds.), Neurophysiological basis of normal and abnormal motor activities. Hewlett, New York: Raven Press.

Kornhuber, H. H. and Aschoff, J. C. (1963). Somatisch-vestibuläre konvergenz und interaktion an neuronen des motorischen und des somatosensiblen cortex der katze. Pflügers Arch. Physiol., *278:* 72–73.

Lawrence, D. G. and Kuypers, H. G. J. M. (1965). Pyramidal and non-pyramidal pathways in monkeys: anatomical and functional correlation. Science. *148:* 973–975.

Levitt, M., Carreras, M., Liu, C. N. and Chambers, W. W. (1964). Pyramidal and extrapyramidal modulation of somatosensory activity in gracile and cuneate nuclei. Arch. Ital. Biol., *102:* 197–229.

Oscarson, O. (1966). The projection of group I muscle afferents to the cat cerebral cortex. In R. Granit (ed.), Muscular afferents and motor control. New York: John Wiley & Sons.

Paillard, J. (1960). The patterning of skilled movements. In Handbook of Physiology-Neurophysiology. Vol. 3. Chap. LXVII. Washington, D.C.: Amer. Physiol. Soc.

Patton, H. D. and Amassian, V. E. (1960). The pyramidal tract: its excitation and functions. In Handbook of Physiology-Neurophysiology. Vol. 2. Chap. 34. Washington, D.C.: American Physiol. Soc.

Penfield, W. and Boldrey, E. (1937). Somatic motor and sensory representation in the cerebral cortex of man as studied by electrical stimulation. Brain, *LX:* 389–443.

Perl, E. R. and Whitlock, D. G. (1961). Somatic stimuli exciting spinothalamic projections to thalamic neurons in cat and monkey. Exp. Neurol., *3:* 256–296.

Phillips, C. G. (1966). Changing concepts of the precentral motor area. In J. C. Eccles (ed.), Brain and conscious experience. New York: Springer-Verlag.

Preston, J. B., Shende, M. C., Uemura, K. (1967). The motor cortex pyramidal system: patterns of facilitation and inhibition on motoneurons innervating limb musculature of cat ad baboon and their possible adaptive significance. In M. D. Yahr and D. P. Purpura (eds.), Neurophysiological basis of normal and abnormal motor activities. Hewlett, New York: Raven Press.

Rose, J. E. and Mountcastle, V. B. (1959). Touch and kinesthesis. In Handbook of physiology-neurophysiology. Vol. 1. Chap. 17. Washington, D.C.: American Physiological Society.

Rosén, I. (1968). Personal Communication.

Sakata, H. and Miyamoto, J. (1968). Topographic relationship between the receptive fields of neurons in the motor cortex and the movements elicited by focal stimulation in freely moving cats. Jap. J. Physiol. *18:* 489–507.

Taub, E., Ellman, S. J. and Berman, A. J. (1966). Deafferentation in monkeys: effect on conditioned grasp response. Science. *151:* 593–594.

Terzuolo, C. A. and Adey, W. R. (1960). Sensorimotor cortical activities. In Handbook of physiology-neurophysiology. Vol. 2. Chap. 33. Washington, D.C.: American Physiological Society.

Thompson, W. D., Asanuma, H. and Stoney, D. (1969). Organization of connections between sensory and motor cortex in cats. Fed. Proc. *28:*456.

Towe, A. L. (1965). Neuronal population analysis in the cerebral cortex. In P. W. Nye (ed.), Proc. Symp. Information Processing in Sight Sensory Systems. Pasadena, California: Cal. Inst. Techn.

Towe, A. L., Whitehorn, D. and Nyquist, J. K. (1968). Differential activity among wide-field neurons of the cat postcruciate cerebral cortex. Exp. Neurol. 20: 497–521.

Tsukahara, N., Fuller, D. R. G. and Brooks, V. B. (1968). Collateral pyramidal influences on the corticorubrospinal system. J. Neurophysiol. 31: 467–484.

Watt, D. and Jones, G. M. (1968). Observations on the neuro-muscular control of purposeful movements. In Proceedings of the annual scientific meeting of the aerospace medical association, Bel Harbor. 174–175.

Welt, C., Aschoff, J. C., Kameda, K. and Brooks, V. B. (1967). Intracortical organization of cat's motorsensory neurons. In M. D. Yahr and D. P. Purpura (eds.), Neurophysiological basis of normal and abnormal motor activities. Hewlett, New York: Raven Press.

Woolsey, C. N. (1958). Organization of somatic sensory and motor areas of the cerebral cortex. In H. F. Harlow and C. N. Woolsey (eds.), Biological and biochemical bases of behavior. Madison, Wisconsin: University of Wisconsin Press.

Note: The references are largely chosen from reviews rather than research papers to orient the non-specialist reader.

DISCUSSION

HARTH: Within each functional column, as you have described it, there exists information more specific than the column as a whole, and there are also strong interconnections within each column. Does the latter tend to wipe out the specificity within a column?

BROOKS: No. There is a kind of titration: Towe suggests that higher lying cells tend to have more specific information than lower lying ones; thus, some cells know a lot about a little of the outside world, and vice versa.

ECCLES: How widely does the inhibition spread?

BROOKS: Intracortical recurrent axon collaterals of large PT-cells are inhibitory and focus the response of their target-cells, e.g., small PT-cells. Peripheral receptive fields shrink during inhibition but not enough to convert "wide" receptive fields into "local" ones. Collonier's data suggest that the collaterals spread for about 1/2 mm.

BARLOW: Are there direct somatic, auditory and visual inputs to MS1?

BROOKS: There are no direct columnar, teleoceptive inputs. They come from cortico-cortical loops. But there are direct exteroceptive inputs via the thalamus—there are two sets of thalamic nuclei—and, in addition, there are cortico-cortical loops from S1 to MS1. Thus, teleoceptive and exteroceptive inputs are superimposed within columns.

J. C. ECCLES

Department of Physiology
State University of New York
Buffalo, New York

13 · The Dynamic Loop Hypothesis of Movement Control*

It is generally believed that in some way the cerebellum functions as a type of computer that is particularly concerned with the smooth and effective control of movement. It is assumed that in the cerebellum there is integration and organization of the information flowing into it along the various neural pathways and that the consequent cerebellar output either goes down the spinal cord to the motoneurones—and so participates directly in the control of movement—or else is returned to the basal ganglia and to the cerebral cortex, there to modify the control of movement from these higher centers.

I. The Neuronal Machinery of the Cerebellum

Fig. 1 gives a schematic illustration of the principal neuronal pathways in the cerebellum. There is a full account of these anatomical pathways and of their physiological operation in a recent book (Eccles, Ito, and Szentágothai, 1967). Fig. 1 shows the two afferent pathways that convey information to the cerebellum—namely, climbing fibers (Cl) and mossy fibers (Mo.)— and also the only pathway out of the cerebellum, which is via the Purkinje cell axons. A Purkinje cell is supplied by a single climbing fiber which exerts a powerful excitatory action. On the other hand, the mossy fiber input is characterized by the enormous divergence documented in Table 1, and it

* Acknowledgment: The author wishes to acknowledge the NIH grant. Number NB 08221–01.

245

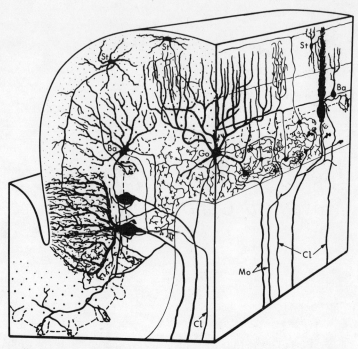

FIGURE 1. Perspective dawing of a section of a folium of the cerebellar cortex. Further description in text.

Table 1

MOSSY FIBER PATHWAY IN CEREBELLAR CORTEX

	Excitatory			Inhibitory	
	Divergence number	Convergence number		Divergence number	Convergence number
Mossy fibers	600	4	Mossy fibers	600	4
↓			↓		
Granule cells			Granule cells		
↓			Parallel fibers		
Parallel fibers			↓		
↓	300	200,000	Basket cells	~30	~20,000
Purkinje cells			Basket cell axons		
			↓		
			Purkinje cells	~50	20

CLIMBING FIBER PATHWAY

Climbing fibers		
↓		
Purkinje cells	~10	1

has both excitatory and inhibitory actions on Purkinje cells. For our present purpose it is sufficient to outline the two major pathways. The excitatory pathway is by mossy fibers to granule cells which discharge impulses along their axons, the parallel fibers, that give excitatory synapses to Purkinje cells, the approximate divergence and convergence numbers being given in Table 1. The inhibitory pathway is by mossy fibers to granule cells to parallel fibers to basket cells (Ba) that give a dense array of inhibitory synapses on the bodies of the Purkinje cells. The approximate divergence and convergence numbers are also given in Table 1 for the sequential neuronal links in this inhibitory pathway.

In contrast, the climbing fiber pathway is very restricted in its distribution as documented in Table 1. Each Purkinje cell receives synapses from only one climbing fiber which exerts such a powerful excitatory action that the Purkinje cell responds by a brief repetitive discharge at high frequency. It is generally believed that the climbing fibers are axons of cells in the inferior olive, but the cell counts there show that the population is less than 10 per cent of the Purkinje cells. Hence it is assumed that there is a limited branching along the pathway of the inferior olive cell axons. Evidence for this branching has been provided by the axon-reflex responses evoked by climbing fibers in the selachian cerebellum (Eccles, Táboříková and Tsukahara, 1968, unpublished observations). As yet, there has been no report of comparable observations in the mammalian cerebellum. However, it is possible that the scattered patches of climbing fiber responses (cf. Fig. 4) may be, at least, in part attributable to the distribution of the axonal branches from single inferior olive cells. Possibly, too, the sagittal strips that Oscarsson (1967) has discovered for the distribution of climbing fibers to the anterior lobe may be produced by a fan-like branching of climbing fibers in sagittal planes.

It is remarkable that all Purkinje cells receive in this way, two quite different inputs. Yet these two inputs convey information from approximately the same peripheral receptors in skin, joint, muscle and fascia, for example. Moreover, the pathways from any particular zone of these receptors have an approximately congruent distribution of climbing fiber and mossy fiber input to the cerebellar cortex (Eccles et al., 1968a; Eccles, Faber, Murphy and Táboříková, 1968, unpublished observations). The output from the cerebellum is via the Purkinje cell axons that terminate synaptically in the cerebellar nuclei and Deiters' nucleus and probably in some sites of the brain stem reticular formation. It was a remarkable discovery of Ito and his colleagues (Ito and Yoshida, 1966; Ito, et al., 1966) that all cerebellar Purkinje cells have an inhibitory synaptic action upon the target neurones, as illustrated schematically in Fig. 2.

When considering the processing of information by the cerebellar cortex it is usual to consider quite a limited distribution of information as in Fig. 2. The treatment is restricted to the sequential synaptic actions resulting from

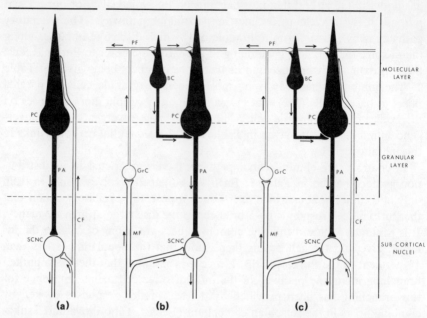

FIGURE 2. Diagram of neuronal pathways in the cerebellum. PC, Purkinje cell; BC, basket cell; PA, Purkinje cell axon; GrC, granule cell; MF, mossy fiber; CF, climbing fiber; SCNC, subcortical nuclear cell. The directions of impulse flow are shown by arrows.

the mossy fiber and the climbing fiber input and the Purkinje cell output. In this way, one can obtain quite interesting concepts with respect to the processing of information, there being, for example, feed-back and feed-forward inhibition, disinhibition, and the like. Thus, the Purkinje cell output to the target neurones is inhibitory, but these target neurones receive, in addition, excitatory inputs from climbing and mossy fibers (cf. Eccles, Ito and Szentágothai, 1967); hence there is a background excitation upon which the Purkinje cell inputs exert a sculpturing effect, so producing spatio-temporal forms in the patterns of discharge of these target neurones. Fur-thermore, it has been shown that this inhibitory depression of neuronal dis-charge can be handed on from these neurones to neurones next in sequence as a silence or a diminished discharge, which is called disfacilitation, and which can be transmitted indefinitely through the nervous system. Another aspect of this neuronal wiring diagram concerns the inhibitory action of basket cells, which can silence the background discharges of Purkinje cells and so can diminish the inhibition of the target neurones, a disinhibition, which is equivalent to an excitatory action, and this in turn can be transmit-ted along the neuronal pathways from the cerebellum.

If we consider a mossy fiber input that is sharply focussed, as it can well be by the negative feedback pathway through Golgi cells (Go in Fig. 1), it will give rise to impulses in parallel fibers traveling in a beam for about 3 mm in total length along the cerebellar folia. The basket cells excited by this beam give lateral inhibition extending to about 1 mm at either side. Hence, the mossy fiber action is effected in the rectangular lattice that is determined principally by the parallel course of the parallel fibers for about 3 mm along a cerebellar folium and by the basket cell axons that spread for up to 1 mm orthogonally thereto (cf. Fig. 3). A sharply focussed

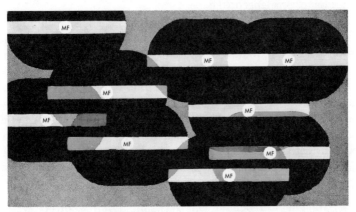

FIGURE 3. Diagrammatic representation of a map of the cerebellar cortex showing symbolically (excitation light, inhibition dark) the levels of excitation and inhibition of the Purkinje cells under the influence of nine focussed MF inputs. The MF inputs are shown by circles, and stemming transversely therefrom will be the beams of excited parallel fibers that extend for about 1.5 mm and excite the Purkinje cells along these trajects. Extending for about 1 mm orthogonally to the beams there are the basket cell inhibitions of the Purkinje cells. Interactions between the inhibitory and excitatory influences on Purkinje cells are shown by the gray shadings.

mossy fiber input would give a "beam" of parallel fiber impulses that results in a 3 mm strip of excited Purkinje cells "on-beam," and, by action of the basket cells, a zone of inhibited Purkinje cells 1 mm "off-beam" on either side. It will be appreciated that this arrangement gives excellent opportunities for the integration of the inputs by the various mossy fibers that have overlapping excitatory and inhibitory actions, these arbitrary zones of potential interaction being limited to a few square millimeters. In Fig. 3 the ranges from uninhibited excitation to deep inhibition are indicated by light gray to black. Even with these sparse and arbitrarily distributed foci of MF action, there is opportunity for much excitatory and inhibitory interaction. The Purkinje cells excited on-beam by one focus may receive convergent inhibitory action from adjacent foci. But this diagram illustrates merely an extremely simplified static view. Under what we may call "real life" operation during conditions of extreme muscular activity there would be an unimaginable complexity and intensity of rapidly changing patterns of excitatory and inhibitory interaction, there being many completely different patterns even during one second.

We can envisage that each Purkinje cell is subject to a bombardment by a large fraction of the 200,000 excitatory synapses it receives from parallel fibers and by the very powerful convergent action of the inhibitory synapses from about 20 basket cells (Table 1). It has a resting discharge of about 30/sec, and even during mild activity this rate can be accelerated up to 100/sec or so, or silenced (Thach, 1968).

It can be assumed that there is no significant transfer of information from each small zone to another in the cerebellar cortex because the only association pathways would be by the Purkinje axon collaterals that are weakly inhibitory. On the assumption that Golgi cell inhibition has a very effective focussing action, it is likely that a train of impulses passing to some focus in the cerebellar cortex via mossy fibers may influence at most only a few square millimeters of cerebellar cortex (Fig. 3). The absence of excitatory association paths gives for any particular input an areal restriction that must be considered in relation to the mode of operation of the cerebellum in the integration of information from diverse inputs.

II. The Cerebellum and Dynamic Loop Control of Movement

A distinction can be made between this relatively simple approach to the processing of information in the cerebellar cortex and a more composite manner of looking at the cerebellum. The simple approach that is usually adopted serves quite well in a limited manner, but it fails to recognize the amazing complexity of the task of the cerebellum in integrating information from an immense array of receptors of widely different modalities. It is not sufficient for this purpose to restrict the examination to a small element of the cerebellar cortex. Rather a more global concept of cerebellar action is needed. In the first place it is essential to study as far as possible the input to wide areas of the cerebellar cortex using for this purpose comprehensive samples of the total information inputs to which it is subjected. This experimental approach has shown that in the anterior lobe of the cerebellum disparate selections of the input are arranged in a mosaic-like manner to a large number of ill-defined patches. This is illustrated diagrammatically in Fig. 4, where stimuli applied to various afferent nerves at a relatively weak strength evoke very diverse climbing fiber responses of Purkinje cells at different recording sites through the depth of the cerebellar cortex. This section is constructed from a series of microelectrode tracks in a transverse plane projecting antero-ventrally through the anterior lobe from a site just anterior to the fissura prima (Eccles, *et al.*, 1968b). All eight of the various inputs were tested at each of the recording sites, and the sizes of the CF-evoked responses are represented in coded form at each site.

In Fig. 5 no distinction is made between the different spatial distributions of the CF and MF inputs to the cerebellar cortex which are shown diagrammatically in Fig. 5 along with the efferent pathways from the cerebellar

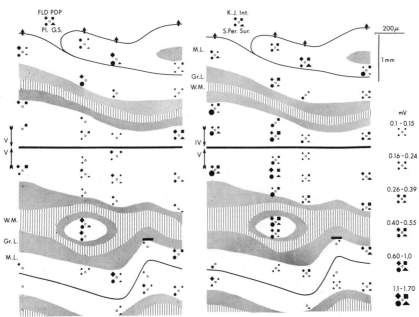

FIGURE 4. Fine grain discrimination of CF inputs from 8 different afferents. As shown by the arrows at the top, recordings were made along 4 tracks passing rather obliquely from the lateral vermis to the pars intermedia, and from the 5th into the 4th lobule. These tracks have been reconstructed from serial sections and are shown in a plane passing anteroventrally. At each site the sizes of the climbing fiber responses evoked from the various nerves (shown by the symbols at the top of the right-hand column) have been plotted in a coded form for size as shown by the right-hand column in millivolts. White matter, WM; granular layer, Gr.L.; molecular layer, ML, can be seen with standard shadings. Fissurae are shown by continuous lines and the arrows at the top show the point of emergence of the microelectrode track from the anterior surface of the cerebellum. The length scales show that the plotting has been enlarged transversely. (Eccles, Provini, Strata and Táboříková, 1968b).

vermis to the spinal cord. Experimental investigation on the mosaic distribution of subsets of information has been concentrated on the CF input, but it appears that the MF distribution is approximately congruent (Eccles, et al., 1968a; Eccles, Korn, Táboříková, and Tsukahara, unpublished observations), though somewhat different concepts have been developed by Oscarsson (1967).

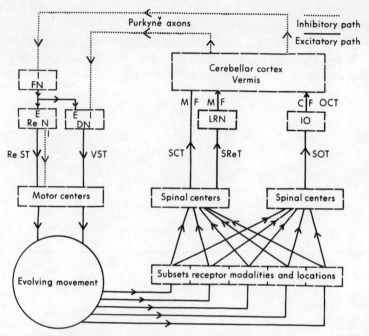

FIGURE 5. Diagram showing in detail the pathways involved in the cerebello-spinal circuits, the continuous and the dotted lines showing respectively the excitatory and inhibitory neural pathways. Spino-olivary tract, SOT, to inferior olive, IO, with climbing fibers, CF, in olivocerebellar tract, OCT; MF, mossy fibers of spinocerebellar tracts, SCT; FN, nucleus fastigeus; ReN, reticular nucleus with reticulospinal tract, ReST; DN, Deiters' nucleus with vestibulospinal tract, VST; LRN, lateral reticular nucleus.

In Fig. 6 there is shown, schematically, the flow of information to and from the cerebellar cortex during the carrying out of some movement, which can, for example, be initiated by the motor cortex via the pyramidal tract (cf. Eccles, 1967). The upper diagram gives the flow of information from the moving limb early in the evolving movement. The different thick-nesses of lines symbolize the intensities from these various modalities and receptor sites. The crossing lines symbolize the flow of information from these various inputs to subsets of the cerebellar cortex that has been observed experimentally (cf. Fig. 4), namely, diverse distributions of subsets of in-formation in a patchy manner that gives opportunity for a widely differing integration of actions. It has been shown that there is a transfer of informa-tion from the Purkinje cells of the cerebellar cortex to the spinal motor centers via the pathways of Fig. 5. Diverse line thicknesses in Fig. 6 again symbolize the intensities of the various outputs from these subsets of the cerebellar cortex. It will be seen that in the diagram each subset of the cerebellar cortex is integrating its own particular inputs of information;

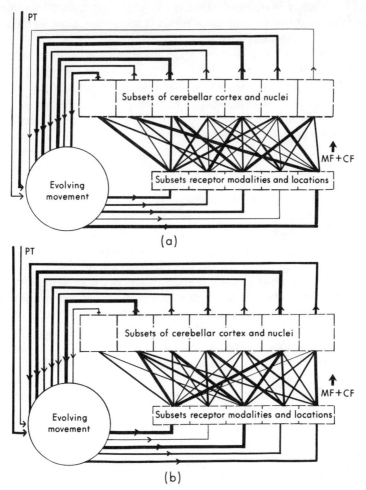

FIGURE 6. Diagrams of the circuits proposed for the flow of information from a hind limb to the vermis of the anterior lobe of the cerebellum and thence down the spinal cord to effect some modification of the evolving movement. (a) Onset of a movement in response to activity in some other descending pathway such as the pyramidal tract (PT). This movement evokes the discharge of impulses in various receptors, as is signalled by the lower horizontal arrows, and in accord with observations, each class of receptor is shown with various intensities of input (symbolized by line thicknesses) on some integrational patches of the cerebellar cortex, but not on others. This input of information into the cerebellum results in the discharge of impulses down the various cerebellospinal pathways, and so induces a change in the evolving movement. (b) illustrates that, as a consequence of the input of revised information (note line thicknesses) to the cerebellum via the sensory receptors of the limb, there is a modification in the output from the cerebellum (note the line thicknesses), so completing the first sequence of the dynamic circuits of cerebellar control.

and, as has already been noted, there is virtually no transfer of information between these various subsets. Each subset is, as it were, blind to the operations of the other subsets.

It can now be asked: How are these numerous and diverse subsets of integration themselves integrated to give some coherent control of a movement? In answer, it is postulated that the integration actually occurs in the total movement process (the evolving movement in Fig. 6) that is evolving under control from the impulses discharged from motoneurones to the muscles. The integrational mechanisms of the spinal cord and, more particularly, the interplay of muscle contractions with the consequent movement of the limb must give some unity or coherence to the evolving movement.

It can be asked: If the movement as so evolving under control by motoneurone discharges is "off-target," how is it corrected? The evolving movement will give a change in receptor activation and it is postulated that the input of this "revised" information into the cerebellar cortex in turn gives "corrective" information in the efferent discharges from the cerebellar cortex down the descending pathways, and so changes the evolving movement. This is illustrated in the lower diagram of Fig. 6 by the changed intensities of the various afferent and efferent lines as symbolized by line thicknesses.

In summarizing the postulates diagrammed in Fig. 6, it can be stated that there is a dynamic control of an evolving movement by feedback loops up to the cerebellar cortex. It is important to recognize that in the resting state before a movement begins, there is a background discharge of impulses along all the components of these loops, and that the evolving movement merely heightens or lowers or even silences these discharges (cf. Thach, 1968). Furthermore, there is a continuous on-going operation of these loops, not merely a brief burst of efferent discharges, then a pause for the return messages, then a revised efferent output, and so on. Nevertheless, consideration of the operational sequences in an imaginatively isolated loop is essential for the understanding of the temporal effectiveness of the postulated dynamic loop control of movement.

The total conduction times in the afferent and efferent pathways and in the cerebellar cortex (cf. Fig. 5) probably would be no more than 10 and 20 msec. for cat forelimb and hindlimb, respectively. However, the operational time of the loop also must include an appreciable fraction of the muscle contraction time, because meaningful feedback can occur only when there is some evolution or change in the ongoing movement. If 10 msec. be allowed for this phase of the dynamic loop, the total loop times in the cat would be of the order of 20 msec. and 30 msec. for the cat forelimb and hindlimb respectively.

The curiously patchy distribution of any particular input gives opportunity for a virtually unlimited piecemeal integration of diverse information inputs. The postulate of dynamic loop operation can account for the synthesis of all these multifarious integrations into a harmonious control of muscle movement. More complex operational circuits are concerned in the cerebro-cerebellar inter-relationships in the control of movement that depends primarily on cerebro-spinal discharges via the pyramidal and other descending

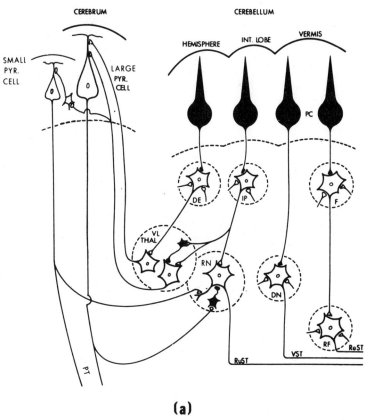

(a)

FIGURE 7. (a) Diagram showing the various efferent pathways of Purkinje cells (PC) in the vermis, intermediate lobe, and hemisphere of the cerebellum. All inhibitory cells are shown in black. F, fastigial nucleus; IP, interpositus nucleus; DE, dentate nucleus; RF, reticular formation; DN, Deiters nucleus; RN, red nucleus; VL THAL, ventrolateral nucleus of thalamus; PYR, pyramidal cell; ReST, reticulospinal tract; VST, vestibulospinal tract; RuST, rubrospinal tract. The pathways are shown from small and large pyramidal cells to the VL thalamus and red nucleus.

pathways. The pathways from the Purkinje cells of the cerebellar hemisphere to the pyramidal cells of origin of the pyramidal tract are shown in Fig. 7(a). In Fig. 7(b) there are the pathways from the cerebral cortex to the pontine nuclei (PN) and so to the mossy fibers (mf) with excitatory collaterals to a cerebellar nucleus (IP) as in Fig. 2. In addition, there are the pathways from the motor area of the cerebral cortex to the inferior olive and so by the climbing fiber pathway to the cerebellum (Jansen and Fangel, 1961; Armstrong and Harvey, 1966; Provini, *et al.*, 1968).

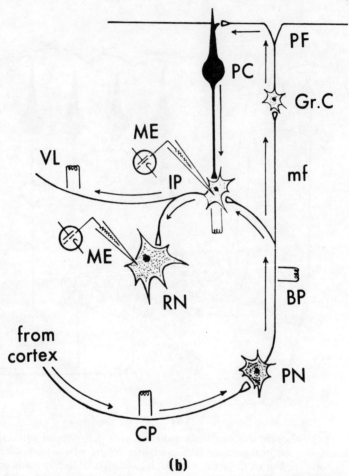

(b)

FIGURE 7. (b) Diagram showing the pathways from the cerebellar peduncle (CP) through the pontine nucleus (PN), brachium pontis (BP) to the granule cells (Gr.C) via the mossy fibers (mf) and to the interpositus nucleus (IP) from which axons pass to the red nucleus (RN) and to the VL thalamus. PC shows a Purkinje cell and PF parallel fibers. (Tsukahara, Korn and Stone, 1968.)

In Fig. 8 there are shown the essential features of the reciprocal connections between the pyramidal tract neurones of the cerebrum and the Purkinje cells of the contralateral cerebellar hemisphere. This diagram embodies the recent discovery of Oshima, *et al.* (1968) that axon collaterals

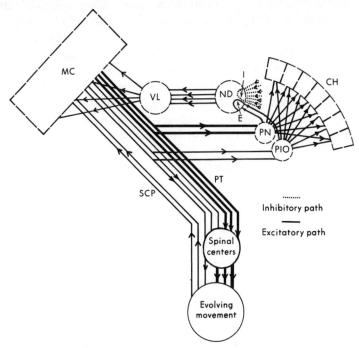

FIGURE 8. Diagram as in Fig. 5 showing cerebro-cerebellar pathways concerned in the operation of the cerebellar hemispheres, CH. ND, nucleus dentatus or lateralis; VL, ventrolateral nucleus of the thalamus; PN, pontine nuclei; PIO, principal inferior olive. E and I symbolize excitatory and inhibitory synapses. Note that the control of the evolving movement occurs only via the motor cortex, MC, and the pyramidal tract, PT. SCP, spinocortical pathways for information flow from movement to the cerebrum.

from the large and fast pyramidal tract (PT) fibers activate the mossy fiber input from the pontine nuclei (PN), while collaterals from the small and slow PT fibers activate the climbing fiber input from the inferior olive (PIO). The diagram further shows the excitatory collaterals to the cerebellar nuclei (ND) from cells of the PN and PIO nuclei, and the convergent inhibitory input to ND from the Purkinje cells, just as in Fig. 2.

In general, the MF input has a wide origin from the cerebral cortex as shown by anatomic investigations and is distributed widely to the cerebellar hemisphere of the opposite side. However, it should be recognized that the physiological investigations of these pathways are still at a very early stage. More is known now about the CF input from the cerebrum, there being a monosynaptic activation of cells in the principal olive that in turn projects to the cerebellar hemisphere of the opposite side (Armstrong and Harvey, 1966). It is postulated that integration likewise occurs there in subsets resembling those of Fig. 3(a). The output from the cerebellar hemisphere is solely by Purkinje cells that inhibit the neurones of the nucleus dentatus, which are excited by collaterals from the mossy fiber and climbing fiber pathways, as indicated. From the nucleus dentatus the pathway leads via the ventrolateral (VL) nucleus of the thalamus back to the cortex, where it makes monosynaptic connections with the PT cells. Thus the neuronal pathways of Fig. 8 are designed so that the cerebellum receives precise and immediate information of the discharges down the pyramidal tract. As a consequence it can return appropriate corrective information to the cerebral motor areas before the PT discharge has caused any muscle contraction.

We may regard the cerebellum as in this way giving to the cerebrum an ongoing comment on its PT discharges. Considerably later there will be the feedback to the cerebrum along the spino-cerebral pathways (SCP in Fig. 8) of information resulting from the muscle contractions evoked by the PT discharge. This pathway is fairly expeditious, being via fast conducting fibers of the dorsal columns or the spino-cervico-thalamic tract, and it acts monosynaptically on PT cells as well as by more delayed and integrated cortical pathways. In this way the cerebellum receives information indirectly from the evolving movement via the changes in the PT discharge and it is, of course, continually modulating the PT discharge by virtue of its computation from its own input along the PT collaterals. Thus, again we can envisage that all PT discharges are provisional and are unceasingly subject to revision both by the feedback from the periphery as a consequence of the evolving movement, and more expeditiously via the cerebro-cerebellar loop. Presumably the cerebellum carries an immense store of information coded in its specific neuronal connectivities so that, in response to any pattern of PT input, computation by the integrational machinery of the cerebellum leads to an output to the cerebrum that appropriately corrects its PT discharge, and corrective information via this dynamic loop operation must be continuously provided during all movements deriving from pyramidal tract action. Fig. 8 is, of course, greatly oversimplified. It may be presumed that there are many other dynamic loops forming complex interacting patterns with it and involving such structures as the caudate nucleus, the globus pallidus and the substantia nigra.

As shown in Fig. 9, the intermediate lobe of the cerebellum combines the operational pathways of Figs. 6 and 8. The MF and CF inputs are both from the cerebrum as in Fig. 8 and from the spinal afferents as in Fig. 5 (Provini, et al., 1968). It has been shown that this spinal input is distributed to the intermediate zone in integrational subsets just as in Fig. 6 (Eccles, et al., 1968b). The output resembles in part that for the cerebellar hemisphere (Fig. 8) in that it projects from the subcerebellar nucleus (the interpositus nucleus, IP) to the .contralateral cerebral cortex via the VL thalamic nucleus (cf. Fig. 7b), but, as shown in Figs. 7(b) and 9, the axons from IP also innervate the neurones of the red nucleus, and so the output projects down the spinal cord in the rubrospinal tract to participate more directly in the evolving movement in addition to the more indirect path via the cerebral cortex and the pyramidal tract.

In Fig. 10(a) and (b) a diagrammatic summary is given of the essential features of the circuits concerned in cerebro-cerebellar control of movement. It is seen that in (a) (cf. Fig. 8) the cerebellar hemisphere does not receive information directly from the various spinocerebellar pathways (Jansen and Brodal, 1954). The flow of information from the movement

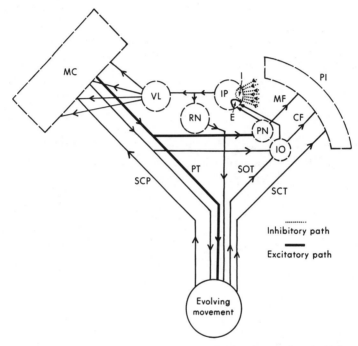

FIGURE 9. Diagram as in Fig. 5 of the complex pathways involved in the operational linkages of the pars intermedia, PI, of the cerebellar cortex both to the motor cortex, MC, and to the spinal cord, and so to the evolving movement. RN, red nucleus; IP, nucleus interpositus; IO, inferior olive. Other symbols as in Figs. 5 and 8.

is represented as occurring via the cerebral cortex and is given in the modification of discharge from pyramidal cells. Thus the evolving movement can project sensory information to the cerebellar hemisphere by the following pathway: from the sensory receptors to spinocerebral pathways to cerebro-cerebellar paths through the pontine nuclei and the principal olive. The integration of the presumed diverse subsets of cortico-cerebellar information will occur in the evolving movement as in Fig. 6, but of course it will also occur in the immense and complex association paths in the cerebral hemispheres.

Fig. 10(b) shows diagrammatically the more complex circuitry that is postulated to operate in movement control by the intermediate zone of the anterior lobe in the cerebellum (cf. Fig. 9). It will be seen that there are three locations at which integration can occur in the cerebral and cerebellar contributions to the control of movement: in the cerebral cortex with expression in the pyramidal cell discharge; in the cerebellar cortex with

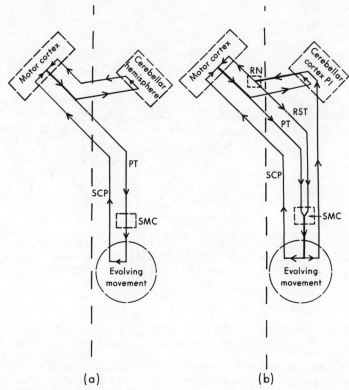

FIGURE 10. Simplified operational circuits of the situations shown in more detail in Figs. 8 and 9. The vertical broken line shows the midline, and hence the various decussations are revealed. Symbols are as in Figs. 5, 8 and 9. SMC, spinal motor centers; RST, rubrospinal tract.

expression in the Purkinje cell discharge; and in the spinal cord where the motoneuronal discharge finds expression in the evolving movement.

Ito (1968) has recently proposed a theory of cerebello-cerebral control which, in its essential features, attempts to do what has been built into the dynamic loop control theory. He is likewise impressed by the existence of projections from the pyramidal tract via axon collaterals to the relay nuclei and so to the cerebellum. He points out that the cerebellum may function as a kind of "dummy" with respect to the cerebral motor control. As illus-

trated in Fig. 11(a), the original loop for a voluntary movement is closed
through the evolving movement in the external world, by which he means
external with respect to the central nervous system. He assumes that a
voluntary action starts from the association cortex and then goes in the
conventional manner through the motor cortex to the lower motor centers
and so is expressed in a movement which is checked back via the sensory
system to the association area. In Fig. 11(b) it will be seen that he repre-

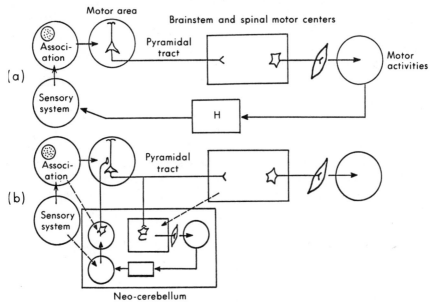

FIGURE 11. Diagrams of cerebello-cerebral control as postulated by Ito. H represents the processing of information in the sensory pathway. In both diagrams
the pyramidal tract is shown ending in a rectangle which symbolizes the spinal
cord mechanisms leading to synaptic action on motoneurones which are shown
with their axons passing out to a muscle. In (b), the whole pathway in (a)
from pyramidal tract back to sensory system is shown in miniaturized form in
the neocerebellum in order to symbolize the proposal that the cerebellum functions essentially as a miniaturized image of the loop through the external world.
(Ito, 1968).

sents the side loop through the cerebellum as a miniaturized image of the
loop through the external world. The essential feature of his concept is that
the cerebellum, by virtue of its trained performance in respect of learned,
skilled movement, can make continuing predictions to the cerebral cortex
of the movement that is being programmed by the discharges down the
pyramidal tract before this movement actually has occurred and so, of
course, before any sensory feedback can reach the association area of the
cerebral cortex. He further goes on to suggest that other connections to

the neocerebellum may be assimilated into this general schema. Just as is suggested above for the dynamic loop control theory, he envisages that there are many other components in parallel to the oversimplified schema that he diagrams in Fig. 11(b), and which he indicates by the interrupted lines and arrows.

III. Movement and Tremor

It has been suggested above that the dynamic loop time for the cat would be about 20 and 30 milliseconds for forelimb and hindlimb respectively. Longer pathways are involved in the postulated dynamic loop in human motor control. These loop times would be much longer and it was suggested that the order of 100 milliseconds could be an appropriate figure, particularly because human muscle contractions are much slower than the contractions of cat muscles. The best figures for human muscle contraction times have recently been published by Slomic, *et al.* (1968). They give values of about 65 msec. for the time to summit of twitch contractions of small muscles in the human hand. Probably arm muscles would be slower than this, hence the estimate of about 100 msec. for the whole loop time.

This suggestion was made before a search had been made in the literature for movement tremors that could be related to the dynamic loop control. It was therefore of great interest to discover that muscle tremors of about 10 per second were discovered as long ago as 1884 by Schaefer and, since that time, have been investigated on many occasions. Fig. 12, for example,

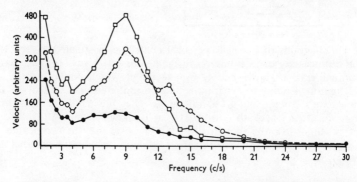

FIGURE 12. Plotting of tremor measured as velocity versus frequency in cycles per second averaged for the movements of the terminal phalanx of the fingers of 26 normal men. With the unloaded fingers (filled circles) and with 50 g (circle) and 100 g (square) strapped to the terminal phalanx. (Halliday and Redfearn, 1956).

plots the tremor spectra for 26 men under various conditions of loading of the terminal phalanx of their fingers. It is seen that, particularly under loaded conditions, when a steady muscular contraction was required, there was a dominant tremor of about 9 per second. Various attempts have been made to explain this tremor, particularly by reference to the servo-motor control operating via muscle spindles and the gamma loop. However, these explanations have been rejected in a recent investigation by Merton, *et al.* (1967).

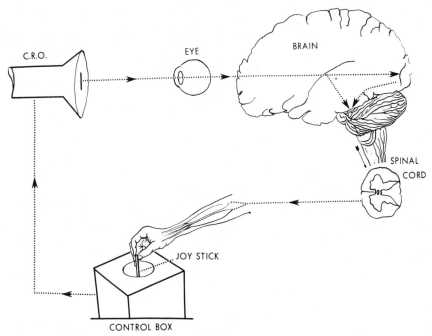

FIGURE 13. Circuits in the manual centering of the spot on the C.R.O. screen. Diagram showing the arrangements employed by Sutton and Sykes (1967); Merton, *et al.* (1967). Full description in text.

Fig. 13 gives an example of the dynamic loop pathway that would be proposed in experiments such as those of Sutton and Sykes (1967) and Merton, *et al.* (1967). The essential features are that the subject holds with his fingers a joy stick mounted on a control box and at the same time has some deflecting weight that he has to resist by contractions of his fore-arm muscles, his forearm being supported in a horizontal trough so that only his wrist movements are being investigated. The subject has to con-centrate upon a moving spot on a CRO screen which he attempts to fix at some mark on the screen. He does this by the control box arrangement operated through the joy stick. He must concentrate upon the spot dancing about the screen and the fixation mark to which he should bring it. As shown in Fig. 13 the pathways are essentially through the eye to the brain and then via various brain mechanisms eventually down the spinal cord to the motoneurones controlling the forearm muscles.

In trying to understand the mode of operation of the loop illustrated in Fig. 13, it is convenient to consider the corrective operation when there is a rather large perturbation of the spot movement. It will be seen that, in response to such a perturbation, the pathway runs around the loop in the direction of the arrows, so calling forth the appropriate corrective muscular contraction and movement of the joy stick with a consequent return of the spot towards its target position. However, such corrective movements usually would be imprecise and result in some other pertubation such as over-correction, under-correction, and the like, and these in turn will evoke through the loop further corrective action, and so on. It will thus be appreciated that, following any large perturbation, there would be a series of subsequent perturbations due to imperfections of correction and that these give a brief tremor with a frequency corresponding to the total loop time of the system. In this way we can explain how there tends to be a dominant tremor of about 9 per second if the dynamic loop time is about 110 msec., which is of the order that has been estimated. It will be appreciated that all of this time would be occupied in pathways from the eye to the joy stick control and thus be entirely a property of the subject.

The experiments of Merton, *et al.,* are of particular interest in relationship to this explanation of the tremor because, as shown in Fig. 14(a), when a delay is put on the path between the joy stick operation and the spot movement of the CRO, there is a corresponding slowing of the tremor frequency, approximately as would be predicted from the length so produced in the loop time. Actually the cycle times of the tremors in the curves displayed in Fig. 14(a) reveal that there is an appreciable deviation from this prediction. The tremors have a periodicity which is faster than would be expected, the lengthening of the cycle usually being about 70% of that expected if there were a simple addition of the delay on to the original dynamic loop time. Thus, the results are in general, but not precise, agreement with the prediction. Moreover, there is an additional deviation that can be seen in Fig. 14(a) with delays of 75 and 100 msec.; namely, there still is evidence of a tremor at the original frequency—at 9.9 and 9.6 per sec., respectively.

Dymott and Merton (1968) have further investigated this phenomenon (Fig. 14b,c) and shown that, when the eyes are closed, some subjects give a tremor of less amplitude than when their eyes were opened but having much the same frequency (Fig. 14c). This tremor is of course to be expected when it is realized that the subject is sensing his movement of the joy stick not only by its effect on the visually observed dancing spot on the CRO, as in Fig. 13, but also by impressions from his fingers, joints and muscles that are affected by his controlling movement. In Fig. 13, therefore, there should be introduced another pathway that goes from the various receptors of his forearm to the spinal cord up to the brain, and this pathway would supplement the visual pathway. The dynamic loop control theory

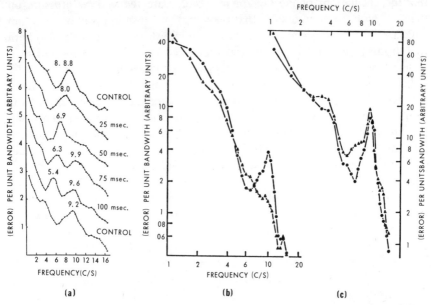

FIGURE 14. (a) Power spectra of hand tremor with the various time delays shown inserted between the joystick and the display cathode ray tube. Each recording run lasted 30 sec. The series began and ended with a control run and the runs were made in the order shown, starting at the top. To avoid overlap, consecutive spectra are displaced one log unit downwards. The frequencies of the main peaks are given above them in cycles per second. The data were digitized, punched onto paper tape, and the power spectra computed on Edsac II in Cambridge (Merton, Morton and Rashbass, 1968).

(b) and (c) Power spectra of hand tremor with the eyes open (filled circles) and with the eyes shut (filled triangles). In (b) the wrist was straight and in (c) it was cocked up. Each recording run lasted 36 sec. The four runs were made consecutively with 1 min rest between each. The arbitrary units are the same for (b) and (c). (Dymott and Merton, 1968).

thus is capable of explaining not only the tremor induced when there is a visual control, but also the tremor induced in the absence of visual control.

In view of this proposed explanation, experiments are now being undertaken in which either cutaneous or joint receptors are to be utilized by the subject in sensing the steadiness of his movement, and hence in evoking tremor by the postulated dynamic loop mechanism. In our initial experiments we propose to use sensing by cutaneous receptors in order to restrict the loop operation to arm and brain or leg and brain circuits. We thus avoid the complexity of visual sensing of limb action. The most suitable stimulation of cutaneous receptors is provided by a vibrator (Goodman) that is driven by a sine-wave generator and that can have both the frequency and the amplitude of vibration set to desired levels. Frequencies of 150 to 200 per sec probably are in the best range. It has been found that the oscillations of the Goodman vibrator are reduced by pressure on the skin, with the consequence that the vibratory sensation is at a maximum with a mild pressure and decreases with diminished contact and also with too strong a pressure. The forearm of the subject will be supported in a trough, and a weight hanging from the wrist or finger has to be resisted by a steady muscular contraction in order that the subject's finger or hand can be held in contact with the vibrator at some steady position that the subject recognizes by virtue of the steady sensation of vibration. Since the amplitude of the vibration is changed by the pressure on the subject's skin, this amplitude modulation will be utilized in the initial attempt to obtain a record of the expected tremor in the movement. Alternative methods of recording the tremors would be to use a Statham strain gauge suitably mounted, or to cause the tremulous finger to obscure a light beam to various degrees and employ a photoelectric cell as a detector. This initial experiment can be developed in many ways for different muscular movements and for foot and leg as well as for hand and arm. Further developments would be to experiment with joint sense instead of vibration, because it, too, like vibration, is virtually free of adaptation so that the sensation remains steady for long periods.

Various further tests can then be envisaged such as, for example, the attempt to produce artificial rhythmic perturbations to discover if there is resonance in the tremor mechanisms as would be predicted by the loop control theory. It is of course evident that investigations of this kind would be particularly valuable in the study of human tremor when it is pathologically increased as occurs in paralysis agitans, multiple sclerosis, cerebellar lesions, and other severe muscular disorders. The pathways concerned in these various tremors are, of course, very largely unknown. It would be expected that the very complex systems of loop control that normally are operative can be destroyed or damaged at various sites, and hence would arise the various types of tremor in neurological disorders. For example, in multiple sclerosis the lesion essentially is in the long medullated pathways up and down the spinal cord. It is evident that severe damage to these pathways would result in an ineffectiveness of the ordinary dynamic loop control with consequent amplification of tremor. In paralysis agitans the lesion is in the basal ganglia, but the manner in which the tremor is produced is not understood. Undoubtedly investigations on the neural mechanisms concerned in the production of tremor would be very valuable in the attempts to account for the disabilities arising from the various neurological lesions.

REFERENCES

Armstrong, D. M. and Harvey, R. J. (1966). Responses in the inferior olive to stimulation of the cerebellar and cerebral cortices in the cat. J. Physiol., *187*: 553–574.

Dymott, E. R. and Merton, P. A. (1968). Visually and non-visually determined peaks in the human tremor spectrum. J. Physiol., *196:* 62P–64P.

Eccles, J. C. (1967). Circuits in the cerebellar control of movement. Proc. Natl. Acad. Sci., *58:* 336–343.

Eccles, J. C., Ito, M. and Szentágothai, J. (1967). The cerebellum as a neuronal machine. Heidelberg-Berlin-Gottingen-New York: Springer-Verlag.

Eccles, J. C., Provini, L., Strata, P., and Táboříková, H. (1968a). Analysis of electrical potentials evoked in the cerebellar anterior lobe by stimulation of hindlimb and forelimb nerves. Exp. Brain Res., *6:* 171–194.

Eccles, J. C., Provini, L., Strata, P., and Táboříková, H. (1968b). Topographical investigations on the climbing fiber inputs from forelimb and hindlimb afferents to the cerebellar anterior lobe. Exp. Brain Res., *6:* 195–215.

Halliday, A. M. and Redfearn, J. W. T. (1956). An analysis of the frequences of finger tremor in healthy subjects. J. Physiol., *134:* 600–611.

Ito, M. (1968). The cerebello-vestibular interaction in cat's vestibular nuclei neurones. Proc. 4th Symposium, The role of the vestibular organs in space exploration. Pensacola (In course of publication.)

Ito, M., Obata, K. and Ochi, R. (1966). The origin of cerebellar-induced inhibition of Deiters neurons. II. Temporal correlation between the transsynaptic activation of Purkinje cells and the inhibition of Deiters neurones. Exp. Brain Res., *2:* 350–364.

Ito, M. and Yoshida, M. (1966). The origin of cerebellar-induced inhibition of Deiters neurones. I. Monosynaptic initiation of the inhibitory postsynaptic potentials. Exp. Brain Res., *2:* 330–349.

Jansen, J. and Brodal, A. (1954). Aspects of cerebellar anatomy. Oslo: Johan Grundt Tanum Forlag.

Jansen, J. and Fangel, C. (1961). Observations on cerebro-cerebellar evoked potentials in the cat. Exp. Neurol., *3:* 160–173.

Merton, P. A., Morton, H. B. and Rashbass, C. (1967). Visual feedback in hand tremor. Nature, *216:* 583–584.

Oscarsson, O. (1967). Functional significance of information channels from the spinal cord to the cerebellum. In M. D. Yahr and D. P. Purpura (eds.), Neurophysiological basis of normal and abnormal motor activities. Hewlett, New York: Raven Press.

Oshima, T., Provini, L., Tsukahara, N. and Kitai, S. T. (1968). Cerebro-cerebellar connections mediated by fast and slow conducting pyramidal tract fibers. Proc. of the Intl. Union of Physiological Sciences, *7:* 332.

Provini, L., Redman, S. and Strata, P. (1968). Mossy and climbing fiber organization on the anterior lobe of the cerebellum activated by forelimb and hindlimb areas of the sensorimotor cortex. Exp. Brain Res., *6:* 216–233.

Schaefer, E. A. S., Canney, H. A. L. and Tunstall, J. O. (1884). On the rhythm of muscular responses to volitional impulses in man. J. Physiol., *7:* 111–117.

Slomic, A., Rosenfalck, A. and Buchthal, F. (1968). Electrical and mechanical responses of normal and myasthenic muscle. Brain Res., *10:* 1–78.

Sutton, G. G. and Sykes, K. (1967). The effect of withdrawal of visual presentation of errors upon the frequency spectrum of tremor in a manual task. J. Physiol., *190:* 281–293.

Thach, W. T. (1968). Discharge of Purkinje and cerebellar nuclear neurons during rapidly alternating arm movements in the monkey. J. Neurophysiol., *31:* 785–797.

Tsukahara, N., Korn, H. and Stone, J. (1968). Pontine relay from cerebral cortex to cerebellar cortex and nucleus interpositus. Brain Res., *10:* 448–453.

DISCUSSION

KILMER: If we look at the possible role of the cerebellum in movement control we must also look at other brain centers involved with movement: the spinal cord, the brain stem, the midbrain, the basal ganglia and cortex. What strikes me is that the projection patterns of these brain centers onto the cerebellum are quite different. If the cerebellum is concerned with fine movement control then it will be comparing the positions of some body parts with others, and one way to exercise such control is through a correlation computer. Now the cerebellar anatomy is quite uniform, so one asks how can the computations be mediated by the projections onto the cerebellum. The timing becomes quite crucial here. The cerebellum will be told, as it were, what is to be done and then it will compute the correlations, taking account of ongoing movement. During this time the information is presumably held within an inhibitory loop. What is the circuitry of the cerebellum which would mirror this function?

ECCLES: I must correct some possibly mistaken impressions: The cerebellum does not hold information for any length of time. There are no loops going around. The cerebellum only computes ongoing effects of movements. It is not programming, but being purely servile. The initiative for control is elsewhere. The cerebellum only modifies the timing or instructions for movement, as the latter develops. Throughout life, moreover, we learn how to use to the utmost the capabilities of this structure, which is not naïve but becoming extremely skillful.

BROOKS: I want to comment on an experimental finding which has a bearing on what has been said here. We have trained Cebus monkeys to move a lever into a target area which the monkey cannot see and the target area has no mechanically detectable borders; but when the monkey is in the target area a light goes on or a buzzer sounds, so that he has an exteroceptive cue. Correct performance is rewarded with juice. We have implanted a cooling probe in the dentate nucleus enabling us to turn part of it off, and thus to interfere with cerebello-cortical transmission. The monkeys perform well in the absence of cooling, anticipating the target areas correctly, presumably by using joint and muscle senses from the arm. But with the dentate nucleus turned off the arm accelerates too long, causing overshoot, until the monkey suddenly sees the target—or hears the buzzer and then he decelerates too late and overcorrects. The point I want to stress is that the monkey has lost anticipatory control. It is a direct demonstration of the role of the cerebellum in anticipatory control by reversible sub-cerebellar block.

LONGUET-HIGGINS: Is there any evidence for learning in the cerebellum?

ECCLES: No. But then where is learning represented in the brain and what is the neural mechanism involved in learning? This is a problem for the future.

LONGUET-HIGGINS: There is an interesting piece of work by Mickie and Chambers in the area of artificial intelligence which may be of some interest here. They have constructed a computer consisting of a large number of independent computing elements in parallel to control the balancing of a vertical pole. Each computing element is concerned with one particular state of the motion. Whenever that state motion arises, within some limits, the appropriate computer is brought into play and the computer has to decide e.g. whether to accelerate the pole to the right or the left. This decision is based on the statistics of what happened on previous occasions—both when it was called into play and when it was not so called—such as the mean length of time the pole has stood up and the mean length of time when it was accelerated to the right or left. I am intrigued by the analogy between this array of independent computing elements and the anatomy of the cerebellum.

Part V

MODELS AND THEORY

K. N. LEIBOVIC AND N. H. SABAH

Center for Theoretical Biology
Department of Biophysical Sciences
State University of New York at Buffalo
Buffalo, New York

14 · On Synaptic Transmission, Neural Signals and Psychophysiological Phenomena*†

I. Introduction

This paper is concerned with the "neuronal machinery" which is at the basis of observed psychophysiological phenomena. The "building blocks" are synapses, nerve fibers, and some simple nerve nets, since ultimately all psychophysical observations and, beyond that, all behavior mediated by the nervous system, must be explicable through the operations of these "building blocks."

With regard to information processing, the most significant aspect of the state of a neuron is the distribution of potential across the membrane. We propose the existence of a signal which has not been considered before. It is intermediate between electrotonic depolarization and the "all-or-none" spike and we will call it a "graded pulse," or "g-pulse," for short. This signal can be flexible and reliable with respect to information processing. It may give rise to waves of polarization in nerve nets, and the state of a neuron assumes a new richness of possible representations.

We consider signal transformations at synapses, in nerve fibers, and some simple network structures and we briefly touch on some implications for psychophysiology.

* Thanks are due to Tom Mathieson for his help in some computations on synaptic transmission.

† This work has been supported by NIND grant R03-NB-06682 and in part by NASA grant NGR 33-015-016.

II. Synaptic Relationships of Stimulus and Response

Consider a chemical synapse with the presynaptic terminal containing a transmitter substance which is released on stimulation; e.g., by nerve impulses or by graded depolarization. The chemical transmitter diffuses across the gap to the postsynaptic membrane where it initiates a response in the form of a depolarization (or hyperpolarization).

Let S = stimulus strength (e.g., mV presynaptic depolarization)

C = strength of transmitter signal (e.g., number of transmitter molecules impinging on the postsynaptic membrane per unit time)

R = response strength (e.g., mV postsynaptic depolarization)

The problem is to find the relationship between R and S as mediated by C.

A. THEORY OF DRUG-RECEPTOR INTERACTION AND EMPIRICAL DATA

According to drug-receptor interaction theory (Ariens, for a review see Triggle, 1965), there are a number of receptor sites on the postsynaptic membrane which form a drug-receptor complex with an appropriate stimulating drug, and the membrane depolarization is proportional to the concentration of drug-receptor complex. The rate of formation of drug-receptor complex is assumed to be given by

$$\frac{d[CX]}{dt} = k_2[C] \times [X] - k_1[CX] \tag{i}$$

where $[CX]$ = concentration of drug-receptor complex

$[C]$ = concentration of drug

$[X]$ = concentration of active receptors

When $\dfrac{d[CX]}{dt} = 0$

$$[CX] = \frac{k_2}{k_1}[C] \times [X] = \frac{1}{K}[C] \times [X] \tag{ii}$$

Let $[X_\infty]$ = maximum possible value of $[X]$, corresponding to the total number of receptors

then $[X] = [X_\infty] - [CX]$.

Substituting in (ii),

$$[C] = \frac{1}{K}[C] \times ([X_\infty] - [CX])$$

$$\therefore [CX] = \frac{[X_\infty] \times [C]}{K\left(1 + \frac{[C]}{K}\right)} = \frac{[X_\infty][C]}{K + [C]} \tag{iii}$$

The response being proportional to $[CX]$, by hypothesis, and the strength of transmitter signal to $[C]$, then

$$R = \frac{\alpha C}{\beta + C} \tag{iv}$$

with α, β being defined in the obvious manner. This equation applies only when $\frac{d[CX]}{dt} = 0$.

If R is plotted versus ln C one gets an S-shaped curve. It is also observed that a plot of R versus S gives an S-shaped curve (e.g., Katz & Miledi, 1967). This would be expected from (iv), if S were related to C as

$$C = k \exp (cS) \tag{v}$$

with $k, c =$ constant.
But this is precisely the empirical relationship which can be obtained, e.g., from data of miniature end plate potentials versus presynatic depolarization (Katz, 1962), at least over an initial range of depolarization. Thus, from (iv) and (v) R is of the form

$$R = \frac{a \exp (cS)}{b + \exp (cS)} \tag{vi}$$

An attempt to fit this equation to experimental data (Fig. 9, Katz & Miledi, 1967) gives the equation

$$R = \frac{58 \exp (0.25S)}{3.63 \times 10^5 + \exp (0.25S)} \tag{vi,a}$$

The fit is, however, only approximate, as shown in Fig. 1, and suggests that the theory itself can only hold as an approximation.
It may be observed that for values of S for which $\{\exp (cS)\}/b \ll 1$, (vi) is approximated by

$$R = \frac{a}{b} \exp (cS) \tag{vii}$$

and for values of S, such that $b \exp (-cS)$ is small, one gets approximately

$$R = a\{1 - b \exp (-cS)\} \tag{viii}$$

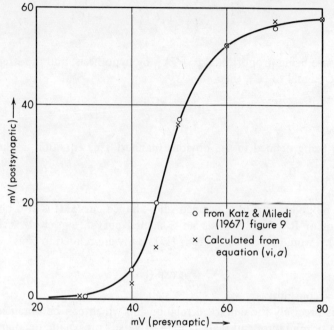

FIGURE 1. Postsynaptic vs. presynaptic depolarization.

while for small cS, such that $\exp(cS) \sim 1 + cS$, one may approximate R by

$$R = \left(\frac{a}{b+1}\right)\left\{1 + \frac{bc}{b+1}S\right\} \tag{ix}$$

Both forms (vii) and (viii) are frequently found as approximations to the initial and final segments, respectively, of S-shaped curves, while (ix) refers to the middle portion. Equation (v) may, in fact, be presumed to be an approximation like (vii). For, clearly, the maximum obtainable end plate potential is limited and sooner or later the steeply rising curve of end plate potential versus depolarization will saturate, giving an S-shaped curve. However, it can easily be shown that if (v) were written in a form like (vi), the general form of equation (vi) for R would remain the same and, thus, the above discussion remains qualitatively correct.

Any one of the three forms (vii)–(ix) may be an appropriate approximation depending on the operating range of the S-R relationship.

B. THEORY OF COOPERATIVE INTERACTIONS: AN ALTERNATIVE DERIVATION OF THE STIMULUS-RESPONSE RELATION

The occurrence of an S-shaped curve, so frequent in biology and physical chemistry, suggests the presence of cooperative phenomena. In terms of stimulus and response, the latter increases slowly at first, as if working against some barrier, but then there is a rapid increase, as if some cooperative interaction had set in, and finally the response approaches saturation.

Instead of drug-receptor complex on the postsynaptic membrane, we may use the notion of active receptor sites. There will be a maximum possible number of such sites, but the actual number which is active at any one time will depend on stimulus conditions and, in general, on the state of the membrane. The response R will be assumed to be proportional to the density n of postsynaptic active sites. An increase of presynaptic stimulus strength δS will lead to a corresponding increase of postsynaptic response δR. Suppose, then, that for small changes:

1. $\delta R \propto \delta S$
2. $\delta R \propto (n_\infty - n)$, where n_∞ is the maximum possible value of n. This is based on the idea that the number of additional receptor sites, which can be activated by a given amount of transmitter is proportional to the number not yet active.
3. $\delta R \propto \delta n$. This is simply a restatement of the hypothesis that $R \propto n$.
4. There is a cooperative interaction between active receptor sites, such that the increase of active receptor sites δn, following a stimulus increase, is proportional to n.

It then follows, due to the proportionality of R and n that

$$\frac{dR}{dS} = kR(R_\infty - R) \qquad \text{(x)}$$

The solution of (x) is of the same form as (vi), namely

$$R = \frac{R_\infty \exp\left[kR_\infty(S - S_0)\right]}{\dfrac{R_\infty - R_0}{R_0} + \exp kR_\infty(S - S_0)}$$

where R_0 is the response when $S = S_0$, or if $S_0 = 0$, then R_0 is the spontaneous response in the absence of stimulation. It should be noted that (x) can be deducted from (iv) and the generalization of (v) which is

$$C = \frac{\gamma \exp(cS)}{\mu + \exp(cS)} \qquad \text{(v,a)}$$

from which,

$$C_0 = \frac{\gamma}{\mu + 1} \qquad \text{when } S = 0$$

$$C_\infty = \gamma \qquad \text{when } S = \infty$$

$$R_0 = \frac{\alpha C_0}{\beta + C} = \frac{a}{b + 1}, \text{ from (vi)}$$

$$R_\infty = \frac{\alpha C_\infty}{\beta + C_\infty} = a$$

Then, in (x),

$$k = \frac{c}{a}$$

As a further test of this relationship, if $\frac{dR}{dS} \div (R_\infty - R)$ is plotted against R on a log-log graph, one should get a straight line of slope 1. This is approximately the case, as may be seen from Fig. 2, which is derived from the data of Katz and Miledi (1967, Fig. 9). Clearly, however, the accuracy of the data is not very good, since they are some stages removed from the original data and thus additional tests will be required.

Tentatively, we may summarize the synaptic stimulus-response relationship by our model in which

a) the amount of transmitter released is related to the presynaptic stimulus strength by the equation

$$C = \frac{\gamma \exp (cS)}{\eta + \exp (cS)}$$

b) the response is related to transmitter C and presynaptic stimulus S by

$$R = \frac{\alpha C}{\beta + C} = \frac{a \exp (cS)}{b + \exp (cS)}$$

c) an increase of S leads to an increase of R, which is governed by a process of cooperative interactions between active receptor sites, such that the rate of increase of the latter with S varies as the concentration of active sites.

The features of this model to emphasize are firstly, the way in which *b*) is derived and given a physiological interpretation and secondly, the proposal of the "cooperative interaction" contained in *c*).

Brief mention should also be made of non-chemical transmission: There is direct electrical transmission, which is well established for tight junctions between opposing membranes. But there are many synaptic structures which look neither like chemical nor electrical synapses, such as, for instance, the horizontal cells in the retina, whose end bulbs at their fiber processes may not only receive, but also transmit signals. We propose that in these cases the end bulbs may act as a source or sink for a relatively mobile

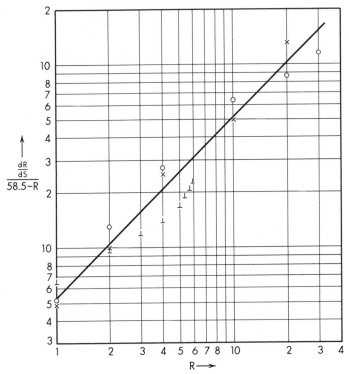

FIGURE 2. Test of Equation (x) using Fig. 9 of Katz and Miledi (1967). The graph has been split into three parts so as to get it *onto* one figure.

× for these points $0.1 \le R \le 10, 0.00001 \le Y \le 0.001$
○ for these points $1.0 \le R \le 100, 0.0001 \le Y \le 0.01$
⊥ for these points $10.0 \le R \le 1000, 0.001 \le Y \le 0.1$
$R = \log (mV \text{ postsynaptic})$
$S = \log (mV \text{ presynaptic})$

where

$$Y = \frac{\dfrac{dR}{dS}}{58.5 - R}$$

ionic species, perhaps K^+ in the following sequence of events: the polarization transmitted to the end bulb increases its permeability to the ionic species and either augments or depletes the concentration in the intercellular gap; this in turn affects the membrane polarization of an adjacent cell, which is permeable to the same ionic species. This mechanism has recently been considered by Lebowitz (1967) in connection with the axonal action potential and the Hodgkin and Huxley membrane equations.

III. Signal Transmission in Nerve Fibers

It is well known that axons transmit nondecremental pulses and it is generally thought that dendrites do not sustain such pulses, and instead conduct electrotonically. However, there is evidence that not all electric events in dendrites are electrotonic (Lorente de Nó, 1947; Fatt, 1957; Eccles, 1959; Lorente de Nó and Condouris, 1959; Andersen et al., 1966) and recently Llinás, *et al.* (1968) have recorded signals in Purkinje cell dendrites which are reminiscent of impulses, as shown in Fig. 3. The theory

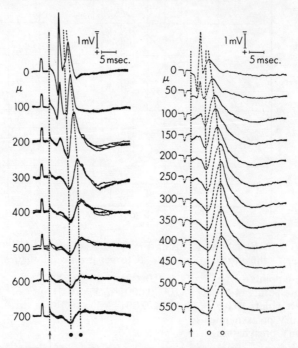

FIGURE 3. Recordings from Purkinje cell dendrites of alligator cerebellum (from Llinás, *et al.*, 1968). The numbers at the left of each set of records indicate the depth of the recording electrode. The first dotted line marks the stimulus artifact; the second, the foot; and the third, the peak of the dendritic compound potential. The set of records on the left shows four superimposed traces, that on the right shows the average of 16 responses.

of pulse propagation has been developed by Hodgkin and Huxley (1952), Cole (1968), and others, and the theory of electrotonic, dendritic conduction has been treated by Rall (1964). It would appear on the basis of electrotonic conduction, as predicted by classical, passive cable theory, that the signals impinging on the periphery of a large dendritic tree would have little effect on the cell body, where integration of neural signals takes place and pulse propagation is initiated. Also, the mode of signal transmission in many nerve cells without pulse propagating axons are in doubt. Among these may be the cells in the retina, such as the horizontals, amacrines and, perhaps, the bipolars, in which relatively weak and diffuse electronic signals might scarcely be expected to produce precise discriminations and such specific responses as are actually found.

It is therefore appropriate to reconsider signal propagation in neural membranes.

It is well known that the nondecremental impulse depends on a trigger-like mechanism: when a certain threshold depolarization is exceeded, the sodium conductance increases sharply and, after reaching a maximum value, it declines to its resting level. Also, there is a delayed increase of the potassium conductance which aids in returning the membrane potential to its resting level. While the course of ionic conductances in axonal membranes is relatively stereotyped, at chemical synapses, on the other hand, the permeability of the postsynaptic membrane to different ionic species can be affected in a variety of ways, depending on the transmitter and the properties of the postsynaptic membrane. Thus, ACh leads to depolarization in a muscle fiber, but in another situation, in the heart pacemaker, the same substance produces hyperpolarization (Katz, 1962). The sodium, potassium or chlorine permeabilities can be altered selectively at synapses, as has been shown by the elegant work of J. C. Eccles and others (Eccles, 1964). Yet, at the neuromuscular junction there is evidence that the release of ACh produces a nonspecific increase of both sodium and potassium conductances (Katz, 1962): the membrane potential is driven towards a point which is -10 to -20 mV, negative inside, which is different from the usual nerve impulse, where the potential is driven initially towards the sodium equilibrium potential of $+50$ mV. At the neuromuscular junction, moreover, an impulse in a muscle fiber can be produced either through the action of ACh or by direct electrical stimulation.

The burden of the above remarks is that:

a) the properties of the membrane are crucial in determining changes of ionic permeability;

b) electrical stimuli can have similar effects to chemical stimuli;

c) changes of ionic permeability determine the state of polarization of the membrane and records, such as those of Llinás, suggest that this applies to at least some dendritic membranes, as well as to axonal membranes where it is already well established;

d) purely passive membranes, in which ionic conductances are constant, are perhaps the exception rather than the rule in the central nervous system.

Prompted by such considerations, we propose considering a new mode of signal propagation. This is based on a cable model in which the ionic conductances depend on membrane depolarization, but are so balanced that purely nondecremental pulses or normal spikes are ruled out.

As is well known electrical responses are not restricted to electrotonic signals and spikes. In their 1952 paper containing the mathematical analysis of their work, Hodgkin and Huxley considered subthreshold oscillations in a space clamped axon. Mention should also be made of the work of Cooley and Dodge (1966), who used the nonlinear, partial differential equations of Hodgkin and Huxley to calculate the membrane potential following point stimulation. Of special interest in the present context is their calculation for what they call a "narcotized axon" in which the sodium and potassium conductances are decreased to a quarter of their normal values. A "subthreshold wave of depolarization," as they call it, is propagated with decreasing amplitude and increasing temporal spread (Fig. 8A of Cooley and Dodge), as shown here in Fig. 4. But, as we will show,

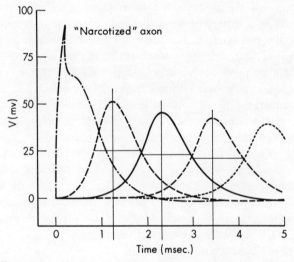

FIGURE 4. Decrementally propagated impulse (from Cooley & Dodge, 1966) plotted at $x = 0$, 1, 2, 3, 4 cm when a very strong stimulus was applied at $x = 0$. g_{Na}^0 and g_K^0 are reduced to $\frac{1}{4}$ their normal values.

this is in fact what we will call a "graded pulse," which is intermediate between an electrotonic signal and the "all–or–none" spike.

Taking as a starting point the Hodgkin and Huxley equations (Hodgkin and Huxley, 1952), there are several possibilities for the mechanism underlying the generation of such pulses: one is that the sodium conductance has a slower time course or τ_m is greater than in the usual axonal membrane; another is that the potassium conductance changes more rapidly. A third possibility, arises from an increased RC time constant of the membrane. The latter is given by

$$\tau = C/g \qquad \text{(xi)}$$

where C is the membrane capacitance and g its conductance. In fact, from the Hodgkin and Huxley equations

$$g = g_K + g_{Na} + g_L = g_K^0 n^4 + g_{Na}^0 m^3 h + g_L$$

Then a decrease of g_K^0 and g_{Na}^0 will decrease τ, slowing down the depolarization, and this can lead to decrementally propagated pulses.

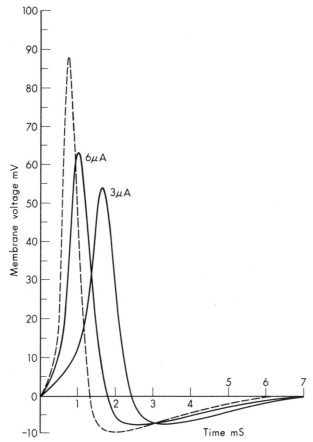

FIGURE 5. Graded pulse response at a distance of 0.4 cm from the point of stimulation. Dotted curve is for a normal membrane and shows the usual spike, in response to a stimulus of 6μA amplitude and 1 mS duration. When the sodium activation time constant (τ_m) is increased by a factor of two, graded pulses are obtained, as shown by the solid curves, which represent responses to stimuli of amplitudes 6μA and 3μA, respectively, and 1 mS duration. The parameters correspond to a temp. of 20°C.

The leakage conductance g_L will also be of some importance and, depending on its magnitude relative to g_K and g_{Na}, the propagated pulses may attain either some nonzero or zero asymptotic value.

We were fortunate to obtain from Dr. Cooley his computer program (Cooley and Dodge, 1966) and we have modified this for our computations of "graded pulses." Fig. 5 shows the results for the case when τ_m is increased by a factor of 2. Similarly, Fig. 6 shows the effect of increasing the RC time constant (xi) by reducing g_K^0, g_{Na}^0 and g_L by a factor of 4.

Compared to the normal spike (shown dotted), the "graded pulses" have a slower time course and a longer duration, and they are much more sensi-

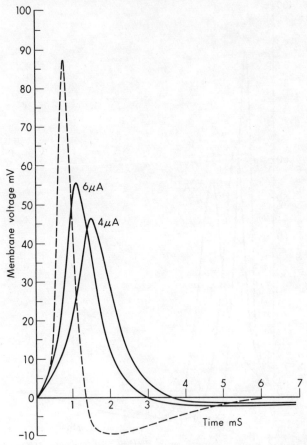

FIGURE 6. Graded pulse response at a distance of 0.4 cm from the point of stimulation. Dotted curve is for a normal membrane and shows the usual spike in response to a stimulus of 6μA amplitude and 1 mS duration. When all membrane conductances are reduced by a factor of four, graded pulses are obtained. The solid curves show responses to stimuli of amplitudes of 6μA and 3μA, respectively, and 1 mS duration. The parameters correspond to a temp. of 20°C.

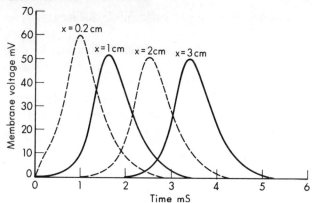

FIGURE 7. Propagation of a graded pulse along a Hodgkin-Huxley cable in which membrane conductances have been reduced to a quarter of their normal values. Stimulus: 6μA amplitude and 1 *m*S duration; temp. = 20°C; conduction velocity = 11.4 *m/s*. Hyperpolarizations not shown.

tive to stimulus strength. They have a threshold, which in this case is higher than that of a normal spike, and they propagate similarly to spikes.

For a stimulus well above threshold the amplitude of the pulse decreases at first and then levels off to a constant value as shown in Fig. 7. For smaller suprathreshold stimuli, the amplitude at first increases and then levels off to the same constant value as shown in Fig. 8. For the conditions of Figs. 7 and 8, the conduction velocity is about half that for a normal spike, as might be expected in view of the slower rate of rise of the potential. The fixed amplitude attained by the pulses at a distance sufficiently far from the point of stimulation, is consistent with the view that in a regenerative mode of propagation the signal is stably propagated in a fixed

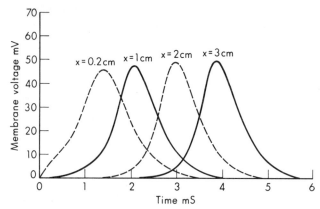

FIGURE 8. Propagation of a graded pulse along a Hodgkin-Huxley cable in which membrane conductances have been reduced to a quarter of their normal values. Stimulus: 4μA amplitude and 1 *m*S duration; temp. −20°C; conduction velocity = 10.8 *m/s*. Hyperpolarizations not shown.

form, and the energy input is just sufficient to balance the losses in the system.

We have not yet computed the "graded pulse" responses for other changes in the parameters, nor for other input stimuli. We may, however, mention that in the case of step inputs one may make a comparison with our computations for the Hodgkin-Huxley cable and its linearized form, shown in Fig. 9. The initial oscillations may be expected to be more damped in the case of "graded pulses," due to their slower changes of potential and reduced amplitude as compared to normal spikes.

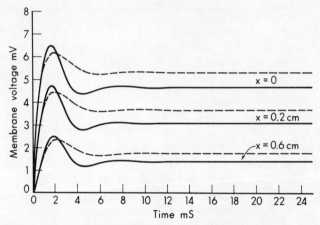

FIGURE 9. Response at different distances x of Hodgkin-Huxley cable of infinite length to a current step input of $1\mu A$ amplitude. Parameters correspond to a temp. of 20°C. - - - - - - linear cable ————— non-linear cable.

If one accepts that neural membranes in dendrites and fibers, such as in some retinal cells, may have the properties to produce "graded pulses," then some interesting consequences arise:

a) In dendrites, signals may be propagated for relatively long distances, without completely dying out.

b) Because of their slower time course and smaller amplitude, one may expect "graded pulses" to be less refractory than normal spikes, and as a result, they could then be summated. Unlike the reliable, but rigid "all–or–none" spike, on the one hand, and the flexible, but imprecise electronic signal, on the other hand, "graded pulses" could be reliable yet flexible. The interaction of such pulses could well have implications in the retina, with regard to periodic activities and psychophysiological phenomena. In this context a re-examination of the impulses recently found in the bipolar cells could be of interest (Tomita, 1967).

c) If one accepts the notion that the "all–or–none" spike in an axon is triggered by a rearrangement of polar groups in the membrane, as suggested by Hodgkin and Huxley, then the transition involved is very rapid. The varying amplitude of "graded pulses" depending on stimulus strength may be due, as we have shown, to a reduction of the ionic conductances or to an alteration in their time course. This would suggest that the switching mechanism in the membrane might also be transformed so as to have a slower transition and this could open new possibilities for examining the molecular events accompanying membrane polarization.

In summary, it is proposed that decrementally propagated pulses may be an important form of signalling in dendrites and other nerve fibers, which do not sustain "all–or–none" spikes and that this form of signal depends on the parameters of the ionic conductances.

A significant conclusion relating to electrophysiological work, is that some of the unclassified signals recently observed in numerous preparations could be traceable to "graded pulses."

To distinguish this kind of signal from electrotonic propagation, on the one hand, and the full-sized, nondecremental spikes, on the other, we propose calling them "graded pulses," or "g-pulses," for short.

IV. Simple Network Structures

We now turn to a consideration of some structures which are found at points of interaction of groups of neurons.

One of the earliest forms of neural interaction to be demonstrated, was lateral inhibition in the eye of limulus (Hartline, 1949). It is an example of simple summation of signals. More recently it has been proposed that a so called shunting inhibition should also be considered (Lettvin, 1962). This is presumed to occur when a patch of membrane on an active fiber is depolarized, so that some of the output is shunted through a low resistance path.

With constant network parameters one obtains linear equations for the case of simple summation (Leibovic, 1963; Furman, 1965). For two neurons this would typically be of the form

$$\text{or} \quad \left. \begin{array}{l} o_j = i_j - a_{jk} i_k \\[2mm] o_j = i_j - b_{jk} o_k \end{array} \right\} \tag{xii}$$

where i, o denotes input, output respectively for neurons j or k, with the indices taking the values 1 or 2, as appropriate. Similarly, shunting inhibition leads to expressions of the form

$$o_j = \frac{1}{1 + c_{jk}i_k}\, i_j$$

or
$$\left. \begin{array}{c} \\ \\ o_j = \frac{1}{1 + e_{jk}o_k}\, i_j \end{array} \right\}$$ **(xiii)**

The coefficients a_{jk}, b_{jk}, c_{jk}, e_{jk} are constant in (xii) and (xiii), and such a model may be adequate for representing simple network interactions. In general, however, it is not true that the network parameters are constant, as may be seen even in steady state voltage vs. current records (see e.g., Hodgkin, *et al.*, 1952, Fig. 13). If one is to take account, realistically, of membrane properties, the membrane conductance needs to be expressed as a function of potential and time. This soon leads to nonlinear differential equations, for which one usually resorts to numerical computations. Yet, it is possible to consider in a fairly elementary manner the functional significance of some simple structures—like reciprocal synapses or recurrent collaterals—which are of frequent occurrence in neural nets.

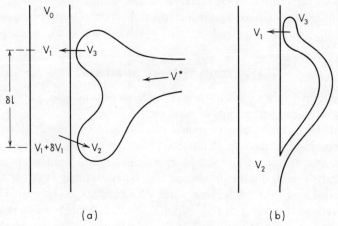

FIGURE 10. (a) Reciprocal synapse; (b) Recurrent collateral.

Consider, for example, the reciprocal synapse illustrated in Fig. 10a. Such a structure may be found in the retina between the bipolar and amacrine cells (Dowling and Boycott, 1967). The depolarization V_1 in a fiber, such as a bipolar cell, changes to $V_1 + \delta V_1$ a distince δl further. The first point is postsynaptic and the second presynaptic to (say) an amacrine cell, in which the corresponding depolarizations are V_3 and V_2. In addition, there is a depolarization V_0 upstream from V_1 and V^* transmitted along the amacrine process.

In the steady state, the membrane parameters along the length δl—and hence $V_1 + \delta V_1$—will depend only on V_1. Thus, one may write

$$V_1 + \delta V_1 = f(V_1) \tag{xiv}$$

Similarly, at the two synapses there will be a functional relationship between presynaptic and postsynaptic potential and

$$V_2 = g_{12}(V_1 + \delta V_1, V^*)$$

$$V_3 = h_{23}(V_2, V^*)$$

Hence, $$V_1 = g_{31}(V_0, V_3, V^*) = h(V_0, V_1, V^*) \tag{xv}$$

From the last relationship it is clear that, for fixed values of V_0 and V^*, there can be only one or at most a finite number of solutions for V_1. Thus, the steady state output is fixed and the reciprocal synapse is seen to function as a means for resetting the output to a constant level. If suitably connected, V^* can measure neighboring levels of activity and the output may then be modulated in accordance with these levels.

Similar considerations apply to recurrent collaterals, such as in Fig. 10(b) except that V^* is now zero.

V. Some Psychophysiological Implications

The source of many psychophysiological phenomena lies peripherally, and even when central processes are involved, they can generally be traced to a peripheral origin. Thus, in vision, retinal events contribute primarily to what is observed; e.g., in adaptation, flicker fusion, and masking.

As a result of his studies on adaptation, Rushton (1965) has proposed the existence of a variable "gain control"; Dowling (1967) has suggested that the network of amacrines and bipolars is the site where some adaptation, at least, takes place, while, according to Rodieck (1968), there is evidence of adaptation prior to the bipolar cell layer. Rodieck's observations may be relevant to Rushton's statement, that the bleached fraction of visual pigment transmits a signal into the adaptation pool. From our preceding consideration of reciprocal synapses, on the other hand, the amacrine and bipolar net would qualify well for the variable "gain control box," since the output can be modulated by the general level of activity through V^* in (xv). In this manner the bleaching and regeneration of visual pigment, as well as the activities of horizontal and amacrine cells, can contribute to adaptation. A detailed analysis of the process may require consideration of the synaptic events and propagated "g-pulses" discussed above.

Some of the more subtle effects in visual masking may depend on the interaction of "g-pulses," as they collide or summate in retinal cells. Presumably, the wave of depolarization in a "g-pulse" represents the smallest unit of information and the rate at which such waves can be transmitted would place an upper bound on the serial capacity, e.g., with respect to flicker fusion (Leibovic, 1969).

Accuracy of perception could be well served by "g-pulses," as already mentioned, and the synaptic input-output relation shown in Fig. 1. For, it will be seen from the latter, that along the steeply rising middle portion of the curve, a small stimulus change produces a large change in the response. Since the amplitude of the "g-pulses" depends on stimulus strength, this illustrates once again the flexibility and accuracy of a system subserved by such synaptic mechanisms in conjunction with "g-pulses."

REFERENCES

Andersen, P., Holmquist, B. and Voorhoeve, P. E. (1966). Entorhinal activation of dentate granule cells. Acta Physiol. Scand., *66:* 448–460.

Cole, K. S. (1968). Membranes, ions and impulses. Berkeley: University of California Press.

Cooley, J. W. and Dodge, F. A. (1966). Digital computer solutions for excitation and propagation of the nerve impulse. Biophys., J., *6:* 583–599.

Dowling, J. E. (1967). The site of visual adaptation. Science, *155* (No. 3760): 273–279.

Dowling, J. E. and Boycott, B. B. (1967). Organization of the primate retina: electron miscroscopy. Proc. Roy. Soc., *166* (B): 80–111.

Eccles, J. C. (1959). The properties of the dendrites. In D. B. Tower and J. P. Schadé (eds.), Structure and function of the cerebral cortex. Amsterdam: Elsevier.

Eccles, J. C. (1964). The physiology of synapses. New York: Springer-Verlag.

Fatt, P. (1957). Electric potentials occurring around a neuron during its antidromic activation. J. Neurophysiol., *20:* 27–60.

Furman, G. G. (1965). Comparison of models for subtractive and shunting lateral inhibition in receptor-neuron fields. Kybernetik, *2:* 6. 257–274.

Hartline, H. K. (1949). Inhibition of activity of visual receptors by illuminating nearby retinal elements in the limulus eye. Fed. Proc., *8:* 69.

Hodgkin, A. L. and Huxley, A. F. (1952). A quantitative description of membrane current and its application to conduction and excitation in nerve. J. Physiol., *117:* 500–544.

Hodgkin, A. L., Huxley, A. F. and Katz, B. (1952). Measurements of current-voltage relations in the membrane of the giant axon of loligo. J. Physiol., *116:* 424–448.

Katz, B. (1962). The transmission of impulses from nerve to muscle and the subcellular unit of synaptic action. Proc. Roy. Soc., *155* (B): 455–477.

Katz, B. and Miledi, R. (1967). A study of synaptic transmission in the absence of nerve impulses. J. Physiol., *192:* 407–436.

Lebowitz, R. M. (1967). Analysis of the electrophysiological implications for single cells of a limited extracellular space in the CNS. U.C.L.A. Ph.D. Dissertation, Physiology. Ann Arbor, Mich.: University Microfilms.

Leibovic, K. N. (1963). Information processing systems, mathematical mappings and self-organizing systems. Bull. Math. Biophys., *25:* 189–201.

Leibovic, K. N. (1969). Some problems of information processing and models of the visual pathway. J. Theoret. Biol., 22: 62–79.

Lettvin, J. Y. (1962). Form-function relations in neurons. M.I.T. Research Lab. for Electronics. Quarterly Progress Report, 66: 333.

Llinás, R., Nicholson, C., Freeman, J. A. and Hillman, D. E. (1968). Dendritic spikes and their inhibition in alligator purkinje cells. Science, 160 (No. 3832): 1132–1135.

Lorente de Nó, R. (1947). Action potential of the motoneurons of the hypoglossus nucleus. J. Cell. Comp. Physiol., 29: 207–287.

Lorente de Nó, R. and Condouris, G. A. (1959). Decremental conduction in peripheral nerve. Proc. Natl. Acad. Sci., U.S.A., 54(4): 592–617.

Rall, W. (1964). Theoretical significance of dendritic trees for neuronal input-output relations. In R. F. Reiss (ed.): Neural theory and modeling. Proceedings of 1962 O.J.A.I. Symposium. Stanford: Stanford University Press.

Rushton, W. A. H. (1965). The Ferrier lecture 1962: visual adaptation. Proc. Roy. Soc., 162 (B): 20–46.

Rodieck, R. W. (1968). Personal communication.

Tomita, T. (1967). Seminar at Center for Visual Science. University of Rochester, Aug. 1967.

Triggle, D. J. (1965). Chemical aspects of the autonomic nervous system. New York: Academic Press.

DISCUSSION

MCCULLOCH: Lucas studied potentials in nerve poisoned with small quantities of alcohol. He found that velocity of conduction was slowed down, the potential wave spread out as it propagated and decreased in amplitude. Alcohol upsets the water structure and one would expect K^+ to be affected.

LEIBOVIC: I believe Lucas' work was on fiber trunks.

SABAH: We did find a slowing of "g-pulse" conduction velocity as compared to normal action spikes.

SCHILLER: How can one square the long latency of the ganglion cell response in the retina with the fast conduction velocity of pulses?

LEIBOVIC: This is one thing we do not know. It has been suggested (e.g., by W. K. Noell, personal communication) that inhibition is the first neural event in the retina following a light stimulus. Maybe, if one has "g-pulses" some wave-like activities arise in the retinal network prior to the ganglion cells and there are processes of interference and summation which may have implications for adaptation and similar phenomena.

BARLOW: There are some experimental recordings from the amacrine layer, which are similar to your "g-pulses."

LEIBOVIC: Yes; similarly, Tomita's records of bipolar "spikes" may fall into this category.

RUSHTON: Retinal recordings, which Dowling has shewn me, shew spikes only in the ganglion cell layer. As one penetrates the retina with a micro-electrode one finds the cone potentials of Tomita and S-like potentials in the remaining cell layers. But such pulses as these depend very much on the duration and intensity of the light stimulus.

SABAH: The shapes of our "g-pulses," prior to the steady propagation state, are very sensitive to the type of stimulus, e.g., whether it is a step or a pulse and how long the pulse is.

ECCLES: There is evidence for a K+ mediated mechanism in the cerebellum. This occurs in the slow potentials of the granular layer, where there are few glial cells and hence minimal cushioning of ionic flows. The authors' suggestion of K+ mediated interactions between cells is, therefore, of some interest.

WARREN S. McCULLOCH

Research Laboratory of Electronics
Massachusetts Institute of Technology
Cambridge, Massachusetts

15 · Of Digital Oscillators*

I want to talk about neurons, which I hold to be coupled nonlinear oscillators. Unfortunately, I lack the mathematics to handle them. Van der Pol (personal communication) opined that whether an ocean of them, like the cerebral cortex, given any constant coefficient of coupling, would lock in phase, as in a convulsion, depended only on the density of the Gaussian primes as one goes away from the origin. He died too soon to prove or disprove it.

There are two papers by Eduardo Caianiello (1966; Caianiello, *et al.,* 1967) in "Kybernetik," published a few years ago, that have some bearing on such problems but are of no use to Kilmer and me in the present context. We have been trying to understand how a part of the central nervous system, its reticular core, could commit the whole organism to one of several incompatible modes of behavior like fighting, sleeping, making love and running away. We turned naturally to Hennie's (1961) theory of iterated nets, in which he proved that many interesting questions were recursively insoluble. Kilmer did it for the rest and we were forced to digital simulation (see Kilmer, this volume).

Our computer simulation now does all we originally asked of it and will soon be able to associate a signal that is separated by some intervening events from that for which the signal stands. But to have a good model is not quite as nice as to have a good theory—and, clearly, our model is an iterated net of coupled, clocked, digital oscillators.

So I looked at a simple spontaneously active neuron as a simple oscillator not biased to cutoff, and gave it a pulsed output that would stop it

* This work was supported in part by the National Institutes of Health (Grant 5 RO1 NB–04985–06) and by the U.S. Air Force, Aerospace Medical Division (Contract AF 33(615)–3885.

for one pulse. It could only have one mode of oscillation. Two such neurons properly coupled have 24 modes of oscillation. For six, I found more than a thousand and asked Carl Schnabel (1966) to look at it, and the next day he had found out how to compute them for any number of neurons, say n.

There are $M = \sum_{k=2}^{2n} (k-1)! \binom{2n}{k}$ modes, and all M can be elicited from a single net of n neurons by $\log_2 M$ input lines, as was shown by Roberto Moreno-Diaz (1966a) using Manuel Blum's (1962) constructive proof. This was the first step for me in the theory of closed loops since Part 3 of Pitts' and my "Logical Calculus for Ideas Immanent in Nervous Activity," in 1943.

After Norbert Wiener's early work on nonlinear filters, cybernetics has been hindered chiefly by these difficulties. It was not until 1955 that David Huffman (1955, 1956) taught us how to look at shift registers. I mean those that are composed of delays linked in one direction, with the last back to the first and with one or more zero sum adders fed from between delays. His theory made use of prime polynomials over Galois fields. These shift registers are used to produce pseudo-random sequences of zeros and ones. R. Silver (personal communication) has tabled approximately 50 of the simplest, i.e., with one zero sum adder. The longest has 95 delays and will spit them out at, say, 1/nsec. for the square of Hubble's age of the universe measured in nanoseconds. A few years ago, James Massey (1967; Massey and Lin, 1964a, b) came to work on these problems at Massachusetts Institute of Technology and devised an algorithm to build the shortest linear shift register to embody a given sequence of zeros and ones. At that time, Jose Simões da Fonseca (McCulloch and Fonseca, 1967; Fonseca and McCulloch 1967a, b, c, d) was with me studying them, and he managed to handle the nonlinear ones, which are never longer and sometimes shorter than those for a given string of zeros and ones. They consist of delays, each of which has an input to a logic box housing any Boolean function whatsoever. Access to this box by similar signals makes the whole device manageable from outside. If we think of a neuron as, at fastest, a msec. device, then 17 in a row would be of sufficient length to store a symphony. The breadth might be 100, and the algorithm tells us how to make it; in short, how to learn the sequence.

At that time, also, Roberto Moreno-Diaz and I began discussing the possibility of a net representing a universal Turing machine. A universal net should do what any net can do. Just as the first part of the tape of the universal Turing machine tells it what it is to compute, so an encoder should tell the net what net it is to simulate. The universal net can be constructed and it is trivially easy. Roberto (Moreno-Diaz, 1966b; Moreno-Diaz and McCulloch, 1968) first stacked a state transition matrix for each input. Then he structured them and projected them onto the plane below the inputs that produce these transitions, thereby producing a functional state transition matrix. Notice, please, that while the net proper is Boolean, determinate, all-or-none, with every neuron firing, the input need not be so —in fact it can be continuous or probabilistic. The encoder is free of loops, so probabilistic affairs make no trouble. The universal net is determinate and Boolean, with all circles permitted and manageable. By passing the output through a decoder without loops, that samples all neurons in the universal net, we can form all permutations. This theory is sufficiently powerful for me to feel that eventually we shall be able to have a theory of the reticular core of the nervous system which has, without itself evolving, defended all vertebrates, including man.

REFERENCES

Blum, M. (1962). Properties of a neuron with many inputs. In H. von Foerster and G. Zopf (eds.), Principles of self organization. London: Pergamon.

Caianiello, E. R. (1966). Decision equations and reverberations. Kybernetik, 3: 2, 98–100.

Caianiello, E. R., de Luca, A. and Ricciardi, L. M. (1967). Reverberations and control of neural networks. Kybernetik, 4: 1, 10–18.

da Fonseca, J. L. S. and McCulloch, W. S. (1967a). Synthesis and linearization of nonlinear feedback shift registers—basis of a model of memory. Research Laboratory of Electronics, M. I. T., Q. P. R. 86: 355–366.

da Fonseca, J. L. S. and McCulloch, W. S. (1967b). Neural nets of connectivity that forms closed loops without external inputs. Do. 367–369.

da Fonseca, J. L. S. and McCulloch, W. S. (1967c). Decidability in shift register theory. Do. 370.

Hennie, C. P. (1961). Iterative arrays of logical circuits. New York: Wiley & Sons.

Huffman, D. A. (1955). The synthesis of linear sequential coding networks. In C. Cherry (ed.), Information theory. London: Butterworths.

Huffman, D. A. (1956). A linear circuit viewpoint on error-correcting codes. IRE Trans., IT-2: 20–28.

Massey, J. L. (1967). Shift-register synthesis and applications. Research Laboratory of Electronics, M.I.T., Q.P.R., 85: 239–240.

Massey, J. L. and Lin, R. (1964a). Equivalence of nonlinear shift registers. IEEE Trans., IT-10: 378–379.

Massey, J. L. and Lin, R. (1964b). Application of Lyapunov's direct method to the error-propagation effect in convolutional codes. IEEE Trans., IT-10: 248–250.

McCulloch, W. S. and Pitts, W. H. (1943). A logical calculus of the ideas immanent in nervous activity. Bull. Math. Biophys., 9: 127–247.

McCulloch, W. S. and da Fonseca, J. L. S. (1967). Insight into neuronal closed loops from shift-register theory. Research Laboratory of Electronics, M.I.T., Q.P.R., 85: 325–327.

Moreno-Diaz, R. (1966a). Realizability of a neural network capable of all possible modes of oscillation. Research Laboratory of Electronics, M.I.T., Q.P.R., *82:* 280–285.

Moreno-Diaz, R. (1966b). Stability of networks with loops—state transition matrix of a neural network. Research Laboratory of Electronics, M.I.T., Q.P.R., *83:* 165–171.

Moreno-Diaz, R. (1967). A comment on shift registers and neural nets. Research Laboratory of Electronics, M.I.T., Q.P.R., *87:* 191–193.

Moreno-Diaz, R. and McCulloch, W. S. (1968). Fiorello, Research Laboratory of Electronics, M.I.T., Q.P.R., *88:* 337–339.

van der Pol, B. Personal communication.

Schnabel, C. P. J. (1966). Number of modes of oscillation of a net of N neurons. Research Laboratory of Electronics, M.I.T., Q.P.R., *80:* 253.

Silver, R. Personal communication.

DISCUSSION

EDITORIAL NOTE: If any suitably defined state, say of a biological system, can be represented symbolically by a string of 1's and 0's, then it is of interest to consider the transitions from one state to another and the generation of a succession of states when starting from some given initial or "lead in" state. For, we know that biological systems are not static, but generate such "state sequences", often—if not always—cued by some suitable "initial state." McCulloch's concern with shift registers is motivated by this problem and more particularly, how to construct a device which will generate sequences of reasonable length without going into repeating cycles. Kilmer's question following, is of some interest in this context.

KILMER: What is the longest song a bird can learn which is not species specific?

McCULLOCH: Pick was a starling. He fell out of a nest and was picked up by a friend of mine in Chicago. He gave it to his wife, who raised him on a dropper. She is always playing music—mostly Mozart—and her husband, when he cooks—and he loves to cook—always sings a Hungarian song. That bird can give you 15 minutes of Hungarian music and 15 minutes of Mozart. That is the longest bird song I know—and nobody thought that starlings were good at music. Pick died in his ninth moult last year. I was there at the time.

W. KILMER

Michigan State University
East Lansing, Michigan

W. S. McCULLOCH

Massachusetts Institute of Technology
Cambridge, Massachusetts

16 · The Reticular Formation Command and Control System

No animal can fight, go to sleep, run away, and make love all at once. We have therefore listed mutually incompatible modes of vertebrate behavior as follows:

1. sleep
2. eat
3. drink
4. fight
5. flee
6. hunt (prey or fodder)
7. search (curiosity)
8. urinate
9. defecate
10. groom

11. engage in sex
12. lay eggs or give birth
13. suckle or hatch
14. build nests
Possibly, also:
15. migrate
16. hibernate
17. engage in certain special forms of instinctive behavior

Some may challenge this classification, but the important thing is that there will never be more than, say, 25 modes. An animal is said to be in a mode if the main focus of attention throughout his central nervous system (CNS) is on doing the things of that mode. We hypothesize that the core of the reticular formation (RF) is the structure in vertebrates that commits the animal to one or another mode of behavior (Fig. 1).

The notion of a mode is somewhat subtle, so a little explanation is needed. An animal fleeing in fear may urinate, but he is not in the urination mode. Some of his 13 or more spinal, brain stem, and cerebral urination

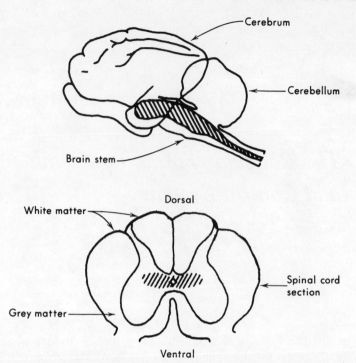

FIGURE 1. Cat brain and section of spinal cord. RF regions hatched in. The RF extends from the head of the brain stem throughout the core of the spinal cord. (Kilmer, *et al.,* 1969a.)

reflexes have been accidentally released in sympathy with his fleeing actions; yet the animal's total attention is directed towards escape. Many birds and fish include components of fighting and fleeing behavior in their courtship rituals when the mode is sexual engagement. Animals can flee in many ways. For example a duck may "flee" by standing still, running, swimming, flying, or using the broken wing trick to lure a predator away from its young in a ground nest. In the last case, it is "fleeing" for itself and also vicariously for its young.

Not all major behavioral patterns are modal. For example, vomiting is not a mode, but an eating trick. This can be seen by noting, for example, that cows use regurgitation as a normal part of their feeding pattern: most birds feed their young by regurgitating; African hunting dogs gulp down prodigious amounts of food after a kill and then return to their burrows and feed the pups and guards that stayed behind by regurgitating; owls often swallow their prey whole and then regurgitate the unwanted bones and hair or feathers; horses almost never regurgitate, nor do reptiles or fish.

If the core of the RF commands the mode of behavior, the RF as a whole serves this command by issuing signals that effect integrated behavior among the various organs and brain parts. An animal's total systemic physiology is known to be very different in sleep, fighting, sexual activity or parturition, and probably also differs considerably among the other modes. This difference is not only autonomic, affective, motoric, and glandular, but perceptual and cognitive as well. In fighting, for example, the visual system sacrifices spatial acuity to gain a slow motion picture of the world, the pain system nearly shuts down, long-range planning is stopped, vocalization is ejaculatory, rage is felt, and movements are stereotyped total action patterns. There is also an almost complete autonomic changeover. RF efferents command all of these things, and participate in the gross control of most of them.

Mode decisions have three important characteristics: (1) The crucial knots of information which prompt them must always get through the sensory filters on which the command system sits. A sleeping mother herring gull is wakened by the new call of its young, but undisturbed by the calls of others. In this case, doubtless cerebral auditory analyzers urge the RF core to wake the gull, and if no other information overwhelmingly conflicts, the gull is wakened. (2) The most important mode decisions are often the most urgent. For example, if a very hungry dolphin is closing in on a fish in the deep ocean and his air supply runs low, the moment-by-moment decision as to whether to continue the hunt or flee to the surface for air, becomes extremely urgent as well as important. Also, the duration required for many fight or flight decisions cannot exceed a fraction of a second—about the duration of Stroud's third of a second moment for humans. Thus, a logically deep serial computer such as man's frontal lobes is ruled out; only a shallow anastomatic one of sufficient scope and economy will suffice. (3) Mode decisions must use a redundancy of potential command in which information constitutes authority. The various regions in a command system that recruit most strongly for a consensus on a mode must be those that have the most exceptional information (compared to a shifting norm) with respect to the ongoing needs and situation of the animal, and vice versa. The other side of this is that no modal command system can allow one of its centers to bully the rest, because the modes and reasons for going in to them are organized as a largely unpredictive heterarchy and not as a predictive hierarchy. Strongly predictive systems are not generally sufficiently open to slight but vitally important information to be reliable mode commanders, especially in unexpected emergencies. Also, most animals at one time and place usually have one set of mode priority relations and at another time and place an entirely different set: a pair of Cichlidae fish chasing each other back and forth out of their respective territories early in a breeding season, but mating and defending a pair-held territory later on (no intervening change in coloration, etc.) is an example of this. State changes in both animals and their environments are generally responsible for such things, of course, but these are best thought of, in the present context, as changes in the kinds of logic performed by brains in different modes and changes in the inputs and intrinsic variables computed by those brains. This only allows a heterarchical ordering of modes, and it requires modal decision systems with a redundancy of potential command.

The oft-cited urgency hierarchy:

1. physical support (recovery from fall)
2. catching breath
3. correcting body temperature and providing shelter, including withdrawal from painful stimuli
4. restoring water balance
5. reducing hunger

is worked out through intra-modal variations on modal themes.

Modal command systems with potential command redundancy are the least vulnerable to fits and deaths among their components, and this vulnerability decreases as the size of the system increases.

Elsewhere (Kilmer, *et al.,* 1969b) we have justified our RF modal hypothesis in the following ways:

a) The RF appears to have direct or monosynaptic two-way connections with every other part of the CNS. Since no other structure has this property, the RF is neuroanatomically best situated to serve as the CNS modal command center. The already demonstrated RF controls over the rest of the forebrain as to consciousness and attention bolster the case.

b) Rats with complete transection of the brain stem just posterior to the thalamus and hypothalamus show well integrated (though not sophisticated) behavior except for losses due to blindness, lack of temperature control, and disruption of hormonal regulation. These rats are capable of impoverished versions of most modes of behavior, but are not well tuned in to their surroundings. This suggests that the RF is the modal integrating center, because all the brain such rats have left consists of sensory and motor systems, cerebellum, some basal ganglia, and RF. The cerebellum is considered essentially as an interval clock and cross correlator of relative positions of body parts. It subserves tonic functions, and controls the smoothness and precision of movements. The basal ganglia insure the proper body relationships in posture and motion, especially during well learned sequences of actions. The integrating center in mesencephalic rats thus, is probably the RF.

c) Local electrical and chemical stimulation of intact animals in descending pathways just anterior to the RF has switched them into sleeping, eating, drinking, fighting, fleeing, urinating, searching, grooming, sexual, and nest building modes. Apparently any mode can be entered in this way under the proper physiological conditions. The important thing is that such stimulated behavior of animals is specific as to mode but dependent upon social relationships, memories, and environmental cues for details. Thus, the mode is what is activated.

d) The main effects of debilitating temporary or permanent lesions in the RF are of two types: firstly, formerly integrated behavior disintegrates, as when the sleep of the brain and the body get out of step, or when the physiological concomitants of paradoxical sleep dissociate; secondly, switching from mode to mode is pathological, as when cats awake frequently out of deep sleep and pass immediately into extreme rage or fright, or when akinetic mutes cannot get out of the sleep and resting mode.

e) It is becoming increasingly clear that an animal's feeling states and drives to action originate mostly in the periventricular system of the brain stem and hypothalamus. The RF core neurons which constitute most of this region are morphologically identical from shark to man. Since the lower in phylogeny the animal, the more sharply modal its behavior, the core of the RF would seem to be intrinsically organized for operation in one or another stable mode. Rioch (1954) noted that in mammals the stereotyped behavior patterns mediated by the paleocortex and the highly differential functions performed by the necortex could probably not have evolved unless the underlying brain stem integrative patterns were stable and modal.

The main plastic behavior found in the RF relates to development (almost entirely prenatal), habituation, and classical and avoidance conditioning on modes and autonomic responses.

We conceive, then, that the RF core commits an organism to a mode with a number of relatively undifferentiated neurons which is estimated to be less than the number of afferent peripheral neurons, or bipolars, and greater than the number of efferent peripheral neurons, or motoneurons. This number is about three quarters of a million in frog and perhaps two million in man. Jointly, these sample all signals from the bipolars and all signals ascending or descending in the neuraxis, including those from all other parts of the nervous system, each neuron receiving, perhaps, a thousand of these, selected almost at random. The axon of each divides into an ascending and a descending branch, often having, in addition, a collateral that ends on or among its dendrites and those of its neighbors. By these axons, the reticular core not only controls all other parts of the nervous system but many other neurons of its own system (Figs. 2 and 3). Our primary concern is with its intrinsic organization. How, in a fraction of a second, can a million or more computing components reach a workable consensus as to the proper mode of total commitment? This is our problem.

Since neurons are nonlinear oscillators, we would have liked, for verisimilitude, to have used the mathematics of oscillator coupling, but it was inadequate because it dealt only with steady states and not transient computations. Since the reticular core is an iterated net of sorts, we would also

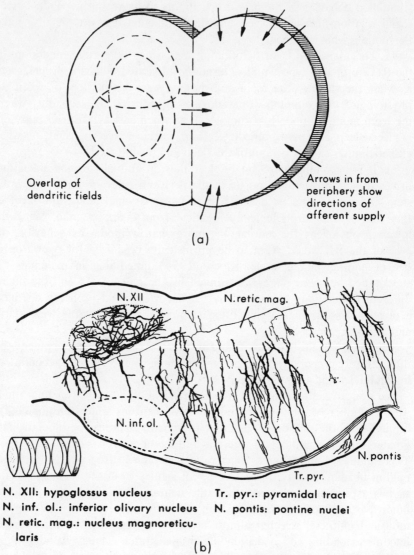

(a)

N. XII: hypoglossus nucleus   Tr. pyr.: pyramidal tract
N. inf. ol.: inferior olivary nucleus   N. pontis: pontine nuclei
N. retic. mag.: nucleus magnoreticu-
        laris

(b)

FIGURE 2. RF dendritic organization. (a) RF cross section, showing dendritic organization on left, and input organization on right. (b) Sagittal section through the lower half of the brain stem of a 10-day-old rat. Collaterals from the pyramidal tract (Tr. pyr.) and from a single reticular cell axon illustrate the tendency toward organization of the afferent terminals in planes approximately perpendicular to the long axis of the stem. The organization of reticular dendrites appears to parallel these terminals—in contrast to the dendrite organization of the adjacent hypoglossal (XII) nucleus—so that the reticular core might be considered as a series of neuropil segments (insert diagram). (Scheibels 1958; their captions.)

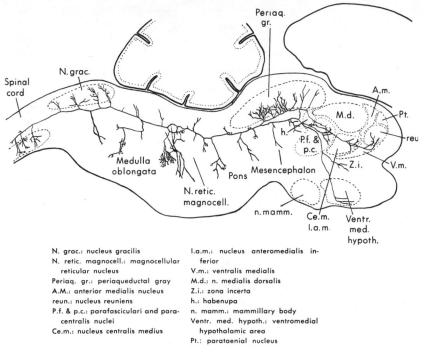

N. grac.: nucleus gracilis	I.a.m.: nucleus anteromedialis in-
N. retic. magnocell.: magnocellular	ferior
reticular nucleus	V.m.: ventralis medialis
Periaq. gr.: periaqueductal gray	M.d.: n. medialis dorsalis
A.M.: anterior medialis nucleus	Z.i.: zona incerta
reun.: nucleus reuniens	h.: habenupa
P.f. & p.c.: parafasciculari and para-	n. mamm.: mammillary body
centralis nuclei	Ventr. med. hypoth.: ventromedial
Ce.m.: nucleus centralis medius	hypothalamic area
	Pt.: parataenial nucleus

FIGURE 3. Sagittal section of 2-day-old rat, showing a single large reticular cell of the magnocellular nucleus. It emits an axon which bifurcates into a caudal and rostral segment. The caudal segment gives off many collaterals to the adjacent reticular formation, to the nucleus gracilis, and to the ventral nuclei of the spinal cord. The rostrally running segment gives off collaterals to the reticular formation and to the periaqueductal gray substance, and then appears to supply the parafascicular and paracentral nuclei, the centromedian and interanteromedian nuclei, the reuniens nucleus, and the ventromedian hypothalamus, as well as the zona incerta. (Scheibels 1958; their captions.)

have liked to use iterated net theory, but every question we thought worth asking proved recursively insoluble.

The only remaining course was through the art of combinations which multiply rapidly as the number of related items increases by a single step. Therefore, we decided to deal with small numbers of possible inputs and computing modules, using modules that were loosely coupled. Five modules did not give us room for a probabilistic distribution of functions of the input, but at six modules the computation got out of hand. So we were forced to use computer simulation. Still there was too little room, and we finally had to go to twelve modules. We decided to settle, for the time being, on four incompatible modes of behavior and ended with our present S-RETIC model (Fig. 4).

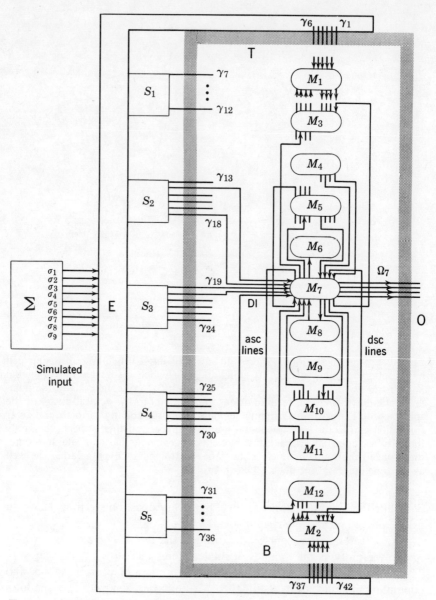

FIGURE 4. S-RETIC Simulation model. Connections are shown only about M_7. Each M_i is a caricature of a poker chip region, or neuropil segment, in Fig. 2b. The S_i are input systems and the Ω_i comprise S-RETIC's output. E generates S_i values by computing functions of the irredundant set of binary variables out of Σ. S-RETIC is said to have converged on a mode if more than half of its M_i indicate that mode with probability (preference) greater than .5. (Kilmer, *et al.,* 1969a.)

Each module of S-RETIC, pictured as a neuronal computing chip, receives a few channels which inform it well of a few and poorly of most of the functions computed on the inputs at other modular sites. Each module, then, computes the best guess it can about the probability of the proper mode and informs a random group of other modules of what it thinks the odds are on the mode to be selected. It also receives the guesses of some other modules chosen at random. It then forms a new opinion and repeats the process. Clearly, a module that regards all modes as equally likely to be right should have little weight, whereas one that has a strong preference shoud be heard because it probably has the necessary evidence to warrant it. Hence, the value of a mode preference should be rated in a nonlinear manner representing the intensity of preference. Only trial and error on the computer could tell us what the nonlinearities should be to always ensure convergence to a workable consensus among the modules as to proper mode within a small number of interchanges of opinion, for instance less than 25. (In the reticular core this would take less than a third of a second.)

Note that unless there is some strong reason for changing its opinion, a module gives less and less attention to its more extreme inputs as a mode persists. This, if left unmodified, would have prevented S-RETIC from being too distractible, but would have made it pigheaded and allowed an entrenched mode to persist even when some modules had significant new inputs that demanded a change of mode. We remedied the situation by arranging for each module to uncouple from its fellows upon the presentation of a new input to a degree that increases with both the significance of the new signal received and the degree to which the old mode had been entrenched. The degree of decoupling cannot be simply proportional to either or both. The proper nonlinear function could be found only by trial and error. Fortunately, here again the exact form of the nonlinearity need not be optimal, provided it is of the right kind and never too great. In fact, there may be no optimum function for all real contingencies.

The continual reverberation of signals among the modules of S-RETIC constitutes a distributed memory which is just sufficient to form conditioned reactions, provided nothing intervenes between the conditional and unconditional stimuli. Its time-binding ability can be sufficiently increased to yield conditioning with short intervening events by introducing short delay lines. (For longer delays we could use shift registers, and for these, Jose da Fonseca (1967), has given us the algorithm for making the shortest nonlinear ones to produce a given sequence.)

We should add that our model does what it is supposed to do, that it has been enlarged to simulate habituation, classical conditioning and extinction, and avoidance conditioning. It also can be enlarged to accommodate a selection of one of a dozen or more modes, and its number of modules can be increased indefinitely without markedly increasing the duration of "conversation" among the modules to reach consensus. In so doing, it becomes more reliable, not less, because of its redundancy of potential command.

Our simulation of S-RETIC and its successors was not devised to be the most economical, but to be thoroughly transparent and easily modified. We are indebted to Richard Warren for the appropriate philosophy and to Jay Blum for the programming. They have made it possible for us to think, not merely about, but with the computer, in a kind of dialogue in which each helps the other to enrich and revise his processes. Without that dialogue we would never have been able to make or explain a model that does in a logical sense what we believe the vertebrate reticular core does in a phenomenal sense. The reticular core is not supposed to usurp the role of the forebrain in perception in forming propositions and in long-range planning, for these are inductive processes. It is not to supplant the executive organs of the rest of the nervous system in programmed and controlled activities, for such logic as they enjoy is basically deductive. They know that they have a case to be handled under a given rule and proceed to perform their proper acts.

The reticular core cannot invent new modes and it cannot perform what it commands. Its logic is abductive, the Apagōgē of Aristotle. Given the rules, it must, when confronted with the fact, guess which rule applies. This, S-RETIC does; and, since it is a logical model, it is not restricted as is its nervous counterpart, but is applicable to the command problem of a battle fleet, the deliberation of a grand jury, or the patient classification problem of a diagnostic clinic. Greater verisimilitude to the vertebrate reticular core, making it better for devising experiments, will only limit its scope.

It is one thing to have a working model, and quite another to have a clean theory. For the first inkling of that theory we are indebted to Roberto Moreno-Diaz (1969). The theory grew out of Peirce's (1933) logic of relations, and employs what he has called "functional state transition matrices." It can handle the behavior of neuronal nets, whether they are deterministic or probabilistic, or depend for their transitions upon continuous or discrete variables. Hopefully, we will have more to say on this in years to come.

In the meantime, our simulation work has led us to a new outlook on some RF experiments. The S-RETIC model shows that a nonlinear redundancy of potential command, and extensive decoupling of modules upon significant input changes, is sufficient for the operation of a command computer. The question arises as to what evidence there is for decoupling, or inhibitory quenching, of circulating signals in the RF core upon the appearance of a mode changing effect in the animal. Now, the Scheibels (1967) have found that most RF neurons apparently undergo cyclic shifts in their receptive field sensitivities. By investigating the entrainment of such cycles, one might shed some light on the decoupling question. If cycling entrainment exists, but only as a statistical coherence that changes with the behavioral mode of an animal, on-line data processing from electrodes in animals that move freely in fixed circadian environments might be revealing. Such experiments would pose grave technical problems but, if achieved, could give as a by-product much better data on the probabilistic character of mode transitions than is now available. One wonders if these transitions are in general governed by the simple time-varying Markov probabilities that Calhoun's (1968) data on rat sleep suggests. (In non-sleep modes, of course, environment cue schedules would have to be taken into account.)

Another question that our recent modeling work has raised is whether or not a RF response to a new input can be broken up into a short phase of novelty-detection superimposed on a long-period of coupled-circuit combinational computing. If so, the main significance of this would be suggested by our new H-RETIC model, which is now in a late design phase.

REFERENCES

Calhoun, J. B. (1968). Private correspondence.

Fonseca, J. de (1967). Synthesis and linearization of nonlinear feedback shift registers—basis of a model of memory. M.I.T., Quarterly Progress Report, 86: 355.

Kilmer, W., McCulloch, W. and Blum, J. (1969a). Embodiment of a plastic concept of the reticular formation. Proc. Symposium on Biocybernetics of the Central Nervous System. Boston: Little and Brown.

Kilmer, W. and McCulloch, W. (1969b). The biology of the reticular formation, to be published as a Michigan State University Division of Engineering Research Report under Grant No. AF-AFOSR-67-1023B.

Moreno-Diaz, R. (1969). On a calculus of relations. Proc. Symposium on Biocybernetics of the Central Nervous System. Boston: Little and Brown.

Peirce, C. S. (1933). Collected papers of C. S. Peirce. Vol. III. Exact logic. Cambridge, Mass.: Harvard University Press.

Rioch, D. M. (1954) In E. D. Adrian, Brain mechanisms and consciousness. (Eds.) et al. London: Oxford University Press.

Scheibel, M. E. and Scheibel, A. B. (1958). Structural substrates for integrative patterns in the brain stem reticular core. In H. H. Jasper et al. (eds.). Reticular formation of the brain. Boston: Little and Brown.

Scheibel, M. E. and Scheibel, A. B. (1967). Anatomical basis of attention mechanisms in vertebrate brains. In G. Quarton et al. (eds.), The neurosciences, a study program. New York: Rockefeller University Press.

RICHARD F. REISS

Linacre College
Oxford, England

17 · "Autonomy" and "Dominance" in Neural Systems: Two Examples of Dynamic Properties Defined on Finite State Models

During the past twenty years, microelectrode measurements have generated a complex picture of the individual neuron. The neuron is seen to have marked inertial properties; it is not a massless shuttlecock driven from state to state by the blows of input signals. Rather its behavior is a resultant of impinging external forces and ongoing internal processes which reveal themselves in phenomena such as facilitation, adaptation, rebound and "spontaneous" activity.

What is true of the individual neuron is, in this respect, true of the group. A group of interconnected neurons, viewed as a unit, need not respond slavishly to signals from without the group; this would be true even if neurons were the simple shuttlecock relays sometimes envisioned. Many reflexes provide rather extreme examples. Once initiated, a reflex action may go a characteristic course with little regard to concurrent activity in receptors or brain centers which at other times dominate the neuro-motor subsystem involved, i.e., a subsystem momentarily behaves as though it were an autonomous system.

The behavior of a neural system, whatever its size or composition, may be largely autonomous at one time but dominated by exogenous signals at another time. In large nervous systems the uncounted but undoubtedly massive assemblies of feedback loops, positive and negative, with effector-to-receptor as well as purely neural links, indicate that a varying and sometimes high

309

degree of autonomy is a commonplace phenomenon in subsystems at diverse levels. We are unlikely to understand the hierarchies of nervous function without some clear, quantitative concepts of—and methods of measuring— variable autonomy phenomena.

What concepts do we have? On the one hand, there is the stimulus-response formula which, for its successful application, depends upon the absence of autonomous behavior in the respondent. This severe limitation is often evaded by treating an entire episode of autonomous action as a single, unitary "response," but of course we are not going to understand autonomous activity by theoretically evading it. On the other hand, there is the fuzzier concept of "spontaneous" activity, so often put within quotation marks because it is so often ambiguous and philosophically suspicious. In its simple sense it denotes the extreme condition where the subject, whether a single cell or a whole nervous system, acts independently of all impinging stimuli, i.e., its behavior is entirely autonomous. Thus we have two extreme functional concepts: the S-R relation, where the subject's behavior is entirely dominated by exogenous stimuli, and the spontaneous case, where the subject's behavior is entirely "self-determined."

It is unlikely that anyone supposes that either of these extremes occurs in nature; the common supposition is that observed behavior, at whatever level, is a resultant of exogenous stimuli and endogenous processes in combination. But how can we measure the resultant—the degree of autonomy—and so discover how it is related to component states and connections? Indeed, how can we clearly conceive, much less measure, the continuum of functional relations extending from extreme dependence to extreme independence?

It should be noted that the concept of "feedback" does not define nor provide direct measures of degrees of autonomy; rather it provides a means (among others) for explaining autonomy phenomena in terms of the components of a neural system. The relation of feedback theory to variable autonomy phenomena may ultimately be comparable to the relation between particle dynamics and temperature-pressure measures of system behavior in thermodynamics.

The narrow objective of this paper is to define two particular concepts of functional relationship between a "subject" and its "environment"; it is proposed that these relationships provide approximate measures of the "degree of autonomy" of the subject under various conditions. The broader objective is to suggest, by way of these two examples, a general and conceptually simple method for defining a wide variety of new measures of system behavior.

Although these measures are easy to define, they may prove quite costly to apply even with the aid of currently available facilities for automated data recording and processing. The empirical difficulties will be sketched in the latter part of the paper.

Certain simple ideas and terminology will be drawn from the field variously known as finite state machine theory, sequential machine theory, or automata theory. What are called "sequential machines"—or often just "machines"—in the literature of that field will be called sequential functions or sequential models below. Furthermore, my treatment of sequential functions will be crudely statistical, not at all in keeping with the subtle mathematical analysis to which they are accustomed.

Sequential functions will be defined only on finite sets of states. On the assumption that most or all neural state variables are "really" continuously variable, finite sets of states can be considered no more than approximations. Thus, the sequential functions must always be considered approximate models of neural processes, perhaps very feeble approximations when small sets of states are used, and the measures called "dominance" and "autonomy" are defined only for such models of neural processes. If a particular sequential function is a poor model of a particular neural process, then the dominance and autonomy measures on that model will have little physiological significance.

I. Finite-State Models

The familiar McCulloch-Pitts (1943) 2-state model neuron provides a simple starting point, and a slightly more complicated 3-state model will supply adequate material for the introduction of the dominance and autonomy measures. Although these models are supposed to represent single neurons, they mights more accurately represent the behavior of a small patch of axon membrane, i.e., a part of a neuron, or they might less accurately represent a large group of neurons. It all depends upon the empirical interpretation given to the "states" of the models. Each state of such models might be identified with a "group-state," i.e., a particular combination of states of the components of some group, or with a set of group-states which are thereby treated as functionally equivalent.

Fig. 1a represents a neuron, x, with one excitatory input (left) and one inhibitory input (right). It is postulated that the "state space" of x, i.e., the set of all possible states of x, is the set $\{s_1, s_2\}$. The "environment" of x is

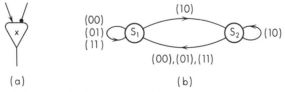

(a)   (b)

FIGURE 1. (a) A hypothetical neuron x with one excitatory input (left axon terminal) and one inhibitory input (right axon terminal). (b) A sequential function in graphical form showing the behavior of x for all possible combinations of (binary) input states when the threshold of x is one. The two states of x are S_1 and S_2.

postulated to be the two axon terminals, and each of these has just two possible states: the "inactive" denoted by "0" and the "active" denoted by "1." A state of the environment is represented by a pair of bits, e.g., the pair (10) denotes the state when the excitatory terminal is active and the inhibitory terminal is inactive. Thus the environment has four possible states: (00), (01), (10), and (11).

In Fig. 1b the entire behavior of this system is defined by a sequential function in the form of a directed graph. The directed lines represent transitions from one state to another; adjacent to each line are the conditions—states of the environment—which "produce" these transitions. Following the McCulloch-Pitts paradigm, time is quantized. Thus if x is in state s_1 and the environment in state (10) at time t, then x will be in state s_2 at time $t + \Delta$, where Δ is the time quantum. If the environment is in state (10) at $t + \Delta$ too, then x will still be in state s_2 at time $t + 2\Delta$, as indicated in the reflexive line.

Given the state of x at time t and the sequence of environment states at times $t, t + \Delta, t + 2\Delta$, etc., the behavior of the model can be predicted by inspecting the graph.

This is a conventional McCulloch-Pitts type of model neuron although there has been no mention of input summation or threshold. This equivalence can be seen, for example, by assigning the weights $+1$ and -1 to the active states of the excitatory and inhibitory terminals, respectively, and postulating that the threshold $= 1$. Then s_1 becomes the "resting" or "no output" state, and s_2 becomes the "firing" or "output" state.

It is essential to notice that the sequential function defined by the graph of Fig. 1b constitutes a model of more than a neuron; it is a model of a system composed of two parts: the subject (a neuron) and an environment of the subject (two axon terminals). The behavior of the neuron is explicitly described relative to all possible environment states. This may be less economical than the simple threshold definition of McCulloch-Pitts type 2-state models, but it is a far more general form and, as seen below, can easily accommodate models with any number of states and functions which cannot be summarized by threshold rules.

A peculiar property of this model may be noted: it is not necessary to know the state of x at time t in order to predict its state at time $t + \Delta$. All we need know is the state of the environment at time t. There is a simple mapping from the state space of the environment onto the state space of x. This property defines a special class of sequential functions. Furthermore, there is a way of assigning numerical weights to the states of the components of the environment (here the terminals) such that the effect of an environment state can be predicted by comparing the arithmetic sum of the component states with a single number called the threshold.

Thus the conventional 2-state threshold models are related to their environments (inputs) in a very special way. Such a model exhibits no autonomous behavior; its state at $t + \Delta$ is always determined entirely by the environment state at t. It is an ideal subject for stimulus-response experiments.

Suppose that the neuron x is given three states; call state s_3 the "inhibited" state. A reasonable sequential function for such a model is given in Fig. 2a. The environment states (00), (01), (10), (11) have been named

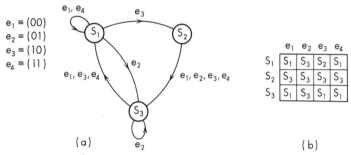

$e_1 \equiv (00)$
$e_2 \equiv (01)$
$e_3 \equiv (10)$
$e_4 \equiv (11)$

	e_1	e_2	e_3	e_4
S_1	S_1	S_3	S_2	S_1
S_2	S_3	S_3	S_3	S_3
S_3	S_1	S_3	S_1	S_1

(a)   (b)

FIGURE 2. (a) A sequential function which defines a hypothetical neuron having three possible states, S_1, S_2, S_3, and the same inputs as x in Fig. 1. The four combinations of input states are here labeled $e_1 = (00)$, $e_2 = (01)$, $e_3 = (10)$, $e_4 = (11)$. (b) The same sequential model presented in the form of a function table. Each row is labeled by a state of the subject, and each column is labeled by a state of the environment. If state e_i and S_j occur at time t, then the state of the subject at time $t + \Delta$ is that named in the cell of the ith column and jth row.

e_1, e_2, e_3, and e_4 respectively, but they have the same postulated significance in terms of terminal activity. These are called "group states," each representing a particular combination of states of a group of components (the terminals). Model state s_1 will be called the "resting" state, and s_2 will be called the "excited" state.

An informal account of this model's behavior might run as follows. The excited state s_2 can only be reached from the resting state s_1, and this transition will occur only if the environment is in state e_3 (excitatory terminal active, inhibitory terminal inactive). If the excited state occurs at time t, it will be followed by an occurrence of the inhibited state s_3 at time $t + \Delta$ regardless of the environment state at time t. Here is a situation in which the subject might be said to behave in a "highly autonomous" fashion; when the subject is in state s_2 the environment is momentarily without influence. The subject will remain in the inhibited state s_3 only if the environment state e_2 occurs; otherwise it will move on to the resting state. And so on.

A sequential function can be described in the form of a "function table." The function in Fig. 2a is shown in tabular form in Fig. 2b. From this function table we can read, for example, that if x is in state s_1 and environment state e_3 occurs, then the next state of x will be s_2.

Sequential functions can also be described by transition matrices and by lists of ordered triplets, but the function table will be the most useful here.

The first question we might ask about the model of Fig. 2 is whether it is in the same class as the McCulloch-Pitts model of Fig. 1. If it is, then we should be able to predict the state of x at time $t + \Delta$ given only the state of the environment at time t. Looking down the column under e_1 in the table we see immediately that this is not possible for that environment state; the state of x at $t + \Delta$ will be either s_1 or s_3, depending upon the state of x at time t. The behavior of this model is more complex than that of the McCulloch-Pitts type. It should be noted, however, that this difference is not correlated with the number of states in the state spaces of these models. It is possible to construct a 3-state—or n-state—model whose behavior can be predicted from a knowledge of its environment states alone; conversely, it is possible to construct a 2-state model which does not have this property.

II. Dominance and Autonomy

Further examination of the function table reveals that the e_4 column is identical to that of e_1. If we wished to make a physiological interpretation of this identity, it might be that the excitatory and inhibitory terminals are of the same "strength," and when they are both in the active state they cancel each other.

Environment state e_2 is striking; when it occurs this model behaves like the earlier model, i.e., if e_2 occurs at t, then the state of x at $t + \Delta$ can be predicted without knowledge of the state of x at time t. One might say that when the environment is in state e_2 it entirely "dominates" the behavior of the subject.

By comparison with e_2, state e_3 is quite feeble; if it occurs at t, then any state of x may occur at $t + \Delta$, depending entirely upon the state of x at time t. Given that e_3 occurs at t, our uncertainty about the future state of x is at the maximum; we can only say that all of the model's states have the same probability of occurring at $t + \Delta$.

Looking again at the physiological interpretation of the environment states, the sharp difference between e_2 and e_3 suggests that there is, after all, some difference between the strength or effectiveness of the excitatory and of the inhibitory terminals. When the inhibitory terminal is alone active, the next state of x can be predicted with certainty even though the present state of x is unknown; when the excitatory terminal is alone active, there is maximum uncertainty about the next state of x.

This method of comparing—or ordering—the environment states does not depend upon assumptions about the strengths of the axon terminals, numerical integration of such strengths, or parameters such as threshold.

There does not have to be any simple mathematical relationship between the state variables of the environment components, e.g., axon terminals, and state variables of the model neuron. On the contrary, this ordering of environment states, being independent of assumptions about quantitative relations between state variables of the system's components, sets the stage for discovering such quantitative relations.

The foregoing comparison of environment states was based upon their effects on the neuron over all of its possible states, i.e., upon the range and frequency distribution of states appearing in the columns under environment states. There are, of course, various ways of measuring the range and distribution, and I have chosen a very simple one that does not require a preliminary ordering of the model's state space, i.e., the names of the model's states can be assigned in any arbitrary way. Thus, the states of the model need have no quantitative significance; all that is required is a labeling that enables us to distinguish one from another. This is very important. It permits us to identify the states of the model with group states of some group of components, i.e., combinations of component states, when there is no known principle for assigning quantities to those combinations.

The measure proposed here will be called the "dominance," $\delta(e_i)$, of an environment state e_i. It will be defined for the general case where the neuron has n states, $s_1, s_2, \ldots, s_n$. Let d_{ij} be the number of times that s_j appears in the e_i column of the function table. The dominance of e_i will be defined by:

$$\delta(e_i) = \frac{1}{n^2} \sum_{j=1}^{n} d_{ij}^2 \qquad \textbf{(i)}$$

Division by n^2 normalizes the measure, and therefore the range of dominance is

$$\frac{1}{n} \leqslant \delta(e_i) \leqslant 1 \qquad \textbf{(ii)}$$

Application of this measure to the environment states of Fig. 2 yields the following:

$$\delta(e_1) = (2^2 + 1^2)/3^2 = 5/9, \quad \delta(e_2) = 1, \quad \delta(e_3) = 1/3, \quad \delta(e_4) = 5/9$$

The dominance of e_2 is the maximum possible in any model, and the dominance of e_3 is the minimum possible for a 3-state subject.

Dominance is a measure roughly—very roughly—comparable with that of "force" in physics. But it is a relative measure. Dominance is defined on sequential functions which describe a causal relation between a particular subject, e.g., the neuron x above, and a particular environment. A change in the coupling between these two entities will produce a change in the function and perhaps a change in the dominance of one or more environment states.

If the axon terminals in the model above were postulated to be the environment, also, of another neuron y, the dominance of state e_1, for example, might be quite different relative to neuron y.

In the given model the ordering of the environment states is (by increasing dominance values): e_3, (e_1, e_4), e_2. Written in terms of pairs of terminal states, it is: (10), ([00], [11]), (01). This shows the sharp difference between the effects of the excitatory and inhibitory terminals, a difference not easily perceived by examination of the function in graphical form (Fig. 2a).

Another way of looking at this result is that the dominance measure provides a meaningful ground for ordering environment states in a model that cannot be easily characterized by thresholds or similar parameters. It is only a partial ordering since $\delta(e_1) = \delta(e_4)$, but this is also true of the threshold function used in the McCulloch-Pitts type of model.

Returning to the function table of Fig. 2b, consider the distribution of states in the rows rather than the columns. The second row is the most interesting; it shows that the neuron state s_2 is followed by s_3 regardless of the environment state. If s_2 occurs at time t, we can predict with certainty that s_3 will occur at $t + \Delta$ even though we do not know what the environment is doing. In the case of s_3, if we do not know the environment state we are less certain about what state will follow, and in the case of s_1 there is still less certainty about the identity of its successor. Clearly one could calculate probabilities here, but that facet of the function table interpretation will be deferred until a later section of this paper.

The range and distribution of states in a row of the table provide grounds for defining a measure of the degree of independence (from the environment) which the model neuron enjoys when it is in the corresponding state. I have chosen the same mathematical form as that used for dominance.

Suppose the state-space of the environment contains m states. Let a_{ij} be the number of times that state s_j appears in the row of s_i. The autonomy, $\alpha(s_i)$, of the model state s_i is defined by:

$$\alpha(s_i) = \frac{1}{m^2} \sum_{j=1}^{m} a_{ij}^2 \qquad \text{(iii)}$$

Again, division by m^2 normalizes the measure, and the range of the autonomy measure is

$$\frac{1}{m} \leqslant \alpha(s_i) \leqslant 1 \qquad \text{(iv)}$$

This measure is proposed as a first approximation to the "degree of autonomy" of the subjects in finite-state models. Like the dominance measure, it is only meaningful relative to a particular coupling between the environment and the subject.

In the case of the neuron in Fig. 2, $\alpha(s_1) = 3/8$, $\alpha(s_2) = 1$, and $\alpha(s_3) = 5/8$. Ordering (by increasing values) the neuron states on the autonomy scale, we have: s_1, s_3, s_2. This is a different ordering than that expected if the states were quantified by assigning "degrees of depolarization" in the obvious way, i.e., the "inhibited" state s_3 having the lowest degree of depolarization, s_1 having an intermediate degree, and s_2 having the greatest depolarization. This might be the empirical interpretation of the states if the model were to represent a patch of axon membrane. There is no reason to expect the depolarization ordering to be the same as the autonomy ordering since the latter is based upon the functional relation between the modeled subject and its environment.

Autonomy, as defined above, falls well short of an ideal measure. This can be seen by examining the McCulloch-Pitts model of Fig. 1. If the function table of that model is constructed and measured, it turns out that the dominance of every environment state is 1. This matches the picture of a neuron whose behavior can be predicted from a knowledge of the environment states alone. One would also expect that the autonomy of that neuron's states is zero in every case. Instead we find that the autonomy of each state, s_1 and s_2, is $5/8$. This is larger than the autonomy of s_1 in the second model, a neuron which is far more independent of its environment.

As the range of the autonomy measure shows, the autonomy of a state can never be less than $1/m$, and since m is finite, the autonomy can never reach zero.

Thus this measure of autonomy is weak; it can be considered only a first approximation. It is reasonably clear that a better measure would involve the distributions of states in the columns as well as the rows, i.e., the dominance values of environment states would appear, directly or indirectly, in the definition of autonomy.

It is obvious that the dominance and autonomy measures are not independent of each other. For example, if two subject states have autonomy $= 1$, and they have different successor states, then no environment state can have a dominance $= 1$. And so on. No doubt a large number of theorems of this sort can be generated. They might prove important in empirical applications where known constraints could facilitate statistical inferences concerning the "true" function table of a system under imperfect observation. Like improvements of the autonomy measure, this is another direction of theoretical development that will not be pursued in this paper.

Autonomy might be considered an inverse measure of "responsiveness." The experimenter who is interested in finding regular stimulus-response functions will try to get his subject into a "responsive state," i.e., a state in which the subject will regularly respond to a chosen set of environment states. In the present context, the search is for states of the subject which have low autonomy relative to a specific set of environment states. Put another way, the experimenter searches for subject states such that his chosen environment states have high dominance values.

Strictly speaking, however, the foregoing account is incorrect. The autonomy of a state has been defined relative to all states of the environment, not any particular subset; similarly, the dominance of an environment state is defined relative to all subject states. Of course the definitions of autonomy and dominance could be easily changed to accommodate measurements over subsets of states. The question is: do the "relative dominance" and the "relative autonomy" measures produced by the use of subsets of states, have a different meaning than the measures defined by equations (i) and (iii)?

From a formal standpoint the answer is "no." By defining the measures over subsets rather than the full sets of environment and/or subject states, the reference has been changed, but not the concept; the interpretation would remain the same. However, if the model was not arbitrarily created but was constructed from observations of a real system, then the answer might be "yes." The autonomy measured relative to a subset of environment states may have a quite different value than the autonomy measured over all environment states. Therefore, the ordering of subject states on the autonomy scale might be quite different. If the ordering is being compared with quantified state variables of the system, the correlations may be appreciably different. Thus, what might be called "the correlation meaning" of the autonomy and dominance measures can be changed when the measures are defined over subsets rather than the full sets of model states.

It is possible that measures over subsets of states would produce, in the case of a particular model, more suggestive correlations than are produced by measures over the full state spaces. I see no a priori grounds for predicting that one form of the autonomy and dominance measures will be "better" than the other in models constructed from empirical observations.

III. Empirical Problems of Finite State Models

If measures on finite state models are to be of any direct value in uncovering principles of neural dynamics, then we must construct such models from observations of particular, real neural systems. The McCulloch-Pitts model was an imaginative creation based upon observations of many different neurons at different times; it was not a model of a particular neuron. It was intended to be a simple and very general representation of certain features of neurons, a model that would provide answers to general questions about hypothetical networks.

Given the ideal system—say a system composed of neurons which behave exactly like the McCulloch-Pitts model—and observational equipment to record the state of each neuron every Δ seconds, the construction of a sequential function which very accurately models the system would be a trivial (though perhaps time consuming) task. The system would be divided into a "subject" and the immediate "environment" of that subject; each would be a group of neurons. The group state of the subject and of the environment would be recorded every Δ seconds. Each pair of group states defines a cell in the initially blank function table, and if the pair (e_i, s_j) occurred at time t, whatever subject state s_k occurred at $t + \Delta$ would be entered into the ij cell. In this fashion the function table is gradually filled, providing a complete description of the environment + subject system. The model would provide very accurate—presumably perfect—predictions of the system's behavior for all possible environment state sequences.

Possession of such a model would not automatically confer "understanding" of the system modeled. We could make perfect predictions but understand nothing. Unless it was a very small system, the model—the sequential function table—would be very large, perhaps immense. In order to make any sense of the system, it would be necessary to make measurements on the table, i.e., measures of the dynamic properties of the system, and search for correlations with state and structural variables of the parts of the system. The dominance and autonomy measures are only two of the more obvious and intuitively appealing measures that one could make on the model.

The foregoing, then, is the ideal situation for empirical applications of the dominance and autonomy (and other) measures. But neural systems are not much like the ideal system presumed above. Digital computers and their relatives are about the only physical systems that closely resemble the above ideal.

In how many ways and to what extent do nervous systems depart from the ideal finite state sequential mechanism? At the time when McCulloch and Pitts (1943) and J. T. Culbertson (1950) created their various models and theories, the differences may not have appeared very great. But now we can make a long list. The neuron is seen to be a complex system of continuously interacting parts, not a point mass. Interactions between neurons may be dominated by the propagating spike, but it is complemented by electrotonic conduction, electric fields, chemical transport and who knows what, all crying for representation by continuous variables. Temporal relations appear to be very complicated; wide variations in propagation velocities, transmitter release and dissipation rates, and so on, all deny the concept of system-wide synchronization with a single time quantum.

Presumably, every departure from the ideal would be a source of error in finite state models. The errors would appear in the form of faulty predictions. It is very difficult to estimate the probable magnitude of errors in models of small or large neural systems; good estimates would require a thorough knowledge of the functional principles underlying the particular neural systems in question—and that is precisely what we do not have. If we could make good estimates, we wouldn't need the models in any case.

An obvious and apparently safe assumption is that the finer the partitioning of time and the ranges of continuous variables, the more accurate the model. If the model is to be constructed directly from observational data—the case of interest here—then minimization of model errors will be costly in at least two ways: the rate of sampling and recording variable values must be high (say 1000 per second?), and the state spaces of the environment and the subject (in the model) must be very large. It is easy to imagine that an accurate model of a system composed of only a few dozen neurons would require a time quantum Δ no larger than one msec. and a function table of several million rows and columns. Even with today's falling costs of automated recording, digitizing, storage, and data processing the construction of such a model could be very costly indeed.

But, as J. T. Culbertson once remarked, we must remain calm in the face of large numbers. Rather than imagining all sorts of error sources that could make the construction of an accurate finite state model impossibly costly, we might look at the way errors would appear and how bad they could be. So far as I know, no one has yet attempted to construct a sequential function directly from neurophysiological data. We simply do not know how "bad" a sequential model of reasonable size might be for this or that neural system. Only experiments will tell.

There are two ways in which a sequential model, i.e., a function table, can be "structurally" faulty. (1) One or more of its cells is blank. Let C be the proportion of cells that are not blank, and call C the "completeness" of the table. The range of C is zero to one. (2) One or more cells each contain the names of more than one state. Let A_{ij} be the number of different states appearing in cell ij, and call A_{ij} the "ambiguity" of cell ij. Let A be the average ambiguity over all the cells that are not blank. The range of A_{ij} and of A is 1 to n, where n is the number of rows (subject states) in the table.

For a proper function table, $C = 1$ and $A = 1$, i.e., there is exactly one state name in each cell of the table. If C is less than 1 or A is greater than 1, then the table is faulty. Let Q be the "quality" of the table, where $Q = C/A$; then Q ranges from zero to one.

These crude measures are presented only to show how easily structural faults in a finite state model can be quantified. A table constructed directly from a sequence of observations can be expected to contain both kinds of structural faults; indeed C will be zero initially—all cells will be blank. The effect of faults is to make predictions probabilistic or impossible. Suppose states e_i and s_j occur at time t; if cell ij is blank, then the table provides no grounds for predicting the state that will occur at time $t + \Delta$. If cell *ij* contains the names of more than one state, then a prediction can only be made on the basis of some probabilistic algorithm.

In order to construct a function table, the system (environment + subject) is observed at times t, $t + \Delta$, $t + 2\Delta$, etc. If e_i and s_j occur at t and s_k (as well as some environment state) occurs at $t + \Delta$, then the name of s_k is entered in cell *ij*. If the states e_i and s_j are never observed to occur simultaneously, then cell *ij* will remain blank. In order to produce a complete table, the system must be persuaded to pass at least once through all of its possible (quantized) states while it is under observation. The finer the quantization of continuous variables, the larger will be the system's state space and the function table, and the more difficult the achievement of completeness. Thus the value of C can be expected to vary inversely with the size of the table and directly with the number of observations. Therefore, this kind of fault is minimized by keeping the table small rather than large.

The ambiguity A_{ij} of cell *ij* is not only a measure of structural faults; it is also a measure of the empirical "accuracy"—or closeness of fit—of the model. Suppose the name of s_k is in cell *ij*, and that the states e_i and s_j occur together (for at least the second time) at time t. If state s_k occurs at $t + \Delta$, then the model is supported ("confirmed" would be too strong) in this particular detail; if some other state s_l occurs at $t + \Delta$, then the model is "opposed" in this detail, and the name of s_l is entered in cell *ij*. Thus each time the state pair $(e_i s_j)$ occurs, a part of the model is tested, namely the part represented by cell *ij*.

The probability that any given state pair will be observed repeatedly during a particular number of observations will depend partly upon the nature of the system and experimental conditions and partly upon the fineness of variable quantization, i.e. the size of the table. On the assumption that frequent testing of a model in all of its parts is highly desirable, small tables (crude quantization) are to be preferred over large tables. Other things being equal, the smaller the table, the greater the probability that any given state pair will be repeated.

Thus, there are two grounds for keeping function tables small; maximization of the table's completeness and of the testing rate. Of course, both of these grounds are fundamentally the same: minimization of the cost of construction and testing.

The crucial question remains: would the average ambiguity, A, of a small table be so high that the table would be useless? It is possible that for a given system under study, the value of A would not decrease monotonically with increasing size of the table. At certain degrees of quantization, the average ambiguity could be much smaller than at slightly cruder *or* slightly finer quantization; in effect, various kinds of quantization errors could cancel each other out. The argument behind this speculation is rather too complicated and tenuous to repeat here. In any case this crucial question cannot be answered without evidence from actual tests.

The prospect of model error is not so frightening when it is seen that such errors are continually detectable, indeed measurable, during the course of model construction. For each cell of the table, a frequency distribution of the state names in that cell could be maintained. Such distributions would be far better measures of ambiguity than the simple count of states named; sharp differences in frequency within a cell would point to a "most probable" entry. If time coordinates of entries are maintained, gradual shifts in the distribution would point to changes in the functional relation between parts of the system while it is under observation. One would also expect to find that the ambiguity of cells in some rows and columns is much less than that of cells in other rows and columns; these differences would point to specific quantization intervals that require further partitioning. And so on.

The foregoing sketch suggests two great advantages that sequential models would enjoy. First, the system observation and model construction and testing could be entirely automated. Second, the model is "spread out" over the state space of the system, not concentrated into a few special functions and their parameters, so that strong and weak parts (cells with low or with high ambiguity) are easily distinguished. Errors produced by the quantization of time and component state variables are not hidden until a complete and polished model is tested against reality; on the contrary, they show themselves in the midst of the construction process wherever state pairs occur repeatedly. Furthermore, since the model consists of many separate, independent parts (cells of the table), the error of each part can be separately evaluated.

The relation between the quality Q of a model (as defined above) and the cost of obtaining the model is not likely to be simple; it would, no doubt, vary greatly depending upon the nature of the system being modeled. As noted earlier, such economic questions can be answered only by experiments.

However, it is reasonable to suppose that models which cost less than a fortune will not be of high quality. What, then, would be the scientific value of a model whose Q is well below one? We do not know, at this stage, that measures such as dominance and autonomy on a perfect model would reveal significant correlations between the properties of a system and the properties of its components. It is to be expected that in a less than perfect model any such correlations would be fuzzier and more difficult to discover. I do not believe that we can reason much beyond that; again, the question can be resolved only by experiment.

The status of the dominance and autonomy measures can now be questioned. They were defined on function tables having $Q = 1$. Their status as theoretical concepts is not altered by the empirical difficulties of obtaining models with $Q = 1$. However, in view of those difficulties, it is clear that these measures must be redefined before they can be applied to empirical models. It must be assumed that in an empirical model, every row and column will contain blank cells as well as many cells with frequency distributions of names instead of a single state name. I do not have a rationale for redefining the measures to accommodate such tables. Obviously there are many ways to define measures on the distribution of states in the rows or columns of an incomplete, ambiguous table, and some of them might produce interesting correlations with the state variables of a system's components; but it appears to me that any weakening of the definitions of dominance and autonomy largely destroys their theoretical meaning. Of course this would not be a disaster; they are to a certain extent arbitrary definitions in any case, and in the absence of empirical models for testing the significance of proposed measures, arguments over the "meaningfulness" of various possible measures are probably pointless. At the present stage of the game, intuition is about the only ground for proposing particular measures, and the main value of the dominance and autonomy measures (unless they can be tested empirically) is their role of illustrating the possibilities of extracting dynamic properties of systems from finite state sequential models of those systems.

REFERENCES

Culbertson, J. T. (1950). Consciousness and behavior. A neural analysis of behavior and consciousness. Dubuque, Iowa: Wm. C. Brown.

McCulloch, W. S. and Pitts, W. H. (1943). A logical calculus of the ideas immanent in nervous activity. Bull. Math. Biophys. 9: 127–247.

DISCUSSION

KILMER: I want to question the relevance of some theory and models to biology. For example, one can construct an automaton with 32 states, which will faithfully reproduce human performance in tracking a point moving along a line or another which will reproduce records like EEG's. But, what does this tell us about the motor system or the activities of the brain?

REISS: Modeling is a matter of judgment. The size of a finite state model, *i.e.* the sizes of its state spaces, must have some reasonable relation to the size and complexity of the system modeled. That is the problem of judgment and it is relative to the objectives of the modeler. I would not expect much from a 32 state model of an extremely complex neuromotor system. Then, correlations between system properties—such as state autonomy—and component states are the sort of things that such models can tell us. That was the main point of my paper.

OTTO H. SCHMITT

Biophysical Science Group
University of Minnesota
Minneapolis, Minnesota

18 · *Biological Information Processing Using the Concept of Interpenetrating Domains*

In any meaningful discussion of information processing in the nervous system there will inevitably be aspects of theory, of experimental data or experiment and of ultimate application. Almost invariably, however, we will, without conscious plan, adjust the informational system in which we discuss the problem to be stationary in all aspects except that which we are exercising in our discussion. We may, for example, take a particular set of experimental facts and try to fit them into an existing theoretical framework or we may plan a new set of experiments to test an established or newly formulated theoretical idea. Alternatively we may use a body of experimental knowledge formulated in terms of available theoretical formulations to design a new laboratory technique or to achieve a "useful" social or economic purpose.

It is remarkable that an equally valid and very important class of stationarity occupies so small a part in our intellectual designs. We each have a limited repertoire of tried and true ways of thinking, mechanical skills, effective insights and persuasive techniques which taken together constitute our individual packages of expertise. This bag of tricks we exploit time and again and gradually enlarge, improve and weed out as an accidental by-product of our regular "legitimate" activities, theoretical, experimental, technological, educational or whatever.

Almost none of our attention is directed deliberately toward building a

325

new set of figures of thought in which to examine, efficiently and easily, our various technical, theoretical and experimental endeavors.

It is my desire here to make an initial effort toward gathering together a set of new figures of thought that seem to bear on the problem of information processing in the nervous system, in that they suggest new theory or experiment, they embody ideas clumsily expressed in conventional physical science formalisms, or they conform to known physiology, neuroanatomy, psychophysics or even to simple biological intuition at the perceptual level. Whenever possible they should embody the idea of meaningful quantitation; that is to say that the formalism should lend itself to computation at the engineering level of accuracy and precision. It should not be oversimplified into mere good-bad, true-false, nor should it be so ponderously exact as to be unwieldy.

We can begin with an examination of the ordinary, local space-time world in which we and all of our experiments are immersed. We very inflexibly formalize all of our representations of biological information processing in terms of a single time and geometric space coordinate set. We are, of course, at liberty to differentiate or integrate one of these with respect to another, to combine and to choose stretched or twisted metric scales, but we lose intimate intuitive understanding and degrade our information at each transformation. Are there manipulable dimensions and metrics in these representations which conform closely with the internal language in which we, as organisms, process our efferent and afferent information? One can generally assume that each linguistic translation or informational transduction or transformation should be avoided unless specially justified by system circumstances.

By direct analogy we see in our most powerful and readily available electronic computers the ghost of their genesis in accounting, record keeping, business and military management and physical science computing. Only recently have we been forced to design a somewhat different class of computer for on-line surveillance and control purposes and we have thus far evaded completely the requirement for major computer design more closely in the image of biological information processing that is to use it.

Consider the time history form of which we are so fond, $Y = f(t)$. Mathematically, $\int Y \, dt, \ dY/dt, \ d^2Y/dt^2, \ (\log Y)_t$ are all fully equivalent representations (given a starting point or constant of integration where needed) except that they assign the representation differently so as to emphasize different aspects of the time record. In the presence of limited sampling, inexact recording, or noise, these records deteriorate very differently. The derivative carries strongly the "what's new?" aspect, the function itself the "what's the present state of affairs?" idea, while the integral carries the "historical experience." Logarithmic scaling incorporates the "sense of proportion" we all admire.

Now what happens if we create a measuring variable that is simply a proportioned mix of the desired attributes? It is still mathematically legitimate, it can be modulated with just a tiny number of instructional bits to shift its emphasis according to a new set of prejudices, it requires only a change of parameters, not of form, and it conforms closely to the experimentally determined properties of neural transducers, visual, acoustic, proprioceptive, and thermal.

The suggestion, then, is that we consider a time scale of this form in building models of perception, of neurophysiological interaction, of neuroanatomy.

Let us turn now to our representation of spatial histories of environment. The spatial and temporal forms have almost one-to-one correspondence, except for the vectorial aspect of geometric space which permits direction to have a three component meaning. Derivative terms yield texture, function terms give position, integral terms give geography and compression gives perspective. Note that we can, by tagging temporal history on as an additional, formally equivalent component, provide a space-time symmetrical information processing domain in which to seek anatomical and physiological models.

Subjectively familiar to all of us, once it is pointed out, is an attribute of spatial-temporal perception which must have neurophysiological-neuroanatomic representation. This is the property of immediate and easy reresolution of a time history to a space history or the reverse. We need not resort to the formality of a wave equation $Y = f(x - ut)$ to explain to a student the idea that a spatial graph of an action potential impulse will have the same form for potential at successive positions at one time as it has for successive times at one place. It may take a little explaining to identify u, the velocity of propagation, as a scaling factor between the two patterns. It is very attractive to attach this mechanism to a time sequential, positioned residence of a perceived or recalled pattern in the nervous system. As one does in a class of bucket-brigade electronic filters, a short span of space-time can be processed at one instant and symmetrical past and future characteristics can be realized in almost real time.

A particular reason for examining this type of spatial-temporal representation is that it lends itself well to distributed holographic nervous system models and conforms to the continually running "blick" (viz., short sample) of space-time in which we all think. "Now" is not really a stop-motion sample of the environment but is a continually updated record of mostly recent spatial, temporal "happening." This principle yields a very useful device for applying human pattern recognition ability to data not already in familiar environmental form. By creating oscilloscopically a stereoscopic, colored, time varying, textured, visual geometric space, one can display a chosen path within a six dimensional hyperspace as an easily learned pattern. In this phase space display it is surprisingly easy to see otherwise very abstract relationships and to perceive patterns deeply immersed in statistical or natural noise.

Highly compatible with the family of traveling wave models just discussed are certain holographic principles. It is not good, however, to accept too much of the physical machinery of present day optical and sonic holography in incorporating these ideas into nervous system modeling. The big principle involved is that of dispersing spatial information widely within a two or, accasionally, three dimensional storage domain as an amplitude function. The dispersing rule must make systematic storage and retrieval simple, yet must make regions to which successive locations are assigned nearly random with respect to each other so that simple averaging of retrieved superimposed signals will quickly sort out signal from noise at the $\sqrt{n}$ rate associated with coherence.

It is not necessary or even desirable that dispersion be completely random for common factors of various related spatial-temporal patterns, for such commonality can be either more firmly or more economically represented by combination. It is easy to conceive of a patterned input into a neural net creating an associated unique time dispersed pattern, with an accompanying coherent coding input pattern, but an additional mechanism is required to store and make evocable this trace, its subcomponents and its subsequent modifications.

For this purpose certain representations that may be called interpenetrating domain models become very useful. Essentially the design is very similar to the pseudo-stationarity idea already mentioned in connection with problem reformulation in terms of conforming variables.

We realize that no computer we are ever likely to lay hands on will be big enough or versatile enough to imitate or represent cell by cell, molecule by molecule, hormone by hormone, nerve patterning by nerve patterning, the progress of a coordinated, biological, informational transaction even in the simplest organism. We must dissect by function, structure or organization all pertinent systems and then model representative elements, always using the largest feasible group of similar elements for lumping as one.

An easily examinable model of this type is one which mediates between the electrophysiological behavior of single active nerve or muscle cells or parts of such cells and the gross electrical field pattern in an entire organ or organism. We know enough about the detailed behavior of excitable cell membrane and of its neighboring conductive fluids, intracellular and extracellular, to calculate quite accurately the currents in and around such a cell, given its surrounding boundary conditions. A few seconds of large computer time will deal with the history of an impulse lasting a millisecond or two, so that a cell can be computed at about one thousandth of real-time rate.

We have similarly adequate transfer impedance and mutual impedance field models which will compute, at something like one hundredth to one thousandth of real-time rates, the gross potential and current contours in an organ or organism in which lumpable regions of changing activity are contained. It is obviously unreasonable to try to calculate a whole field pattern for even a few thousand cells for as little as a single second.

Let us introduce the notion of a local regional electrical vector impedivity representing cytoplasmic impedance of a neighborhood of like cells on a volume normalized basis and similarly represent regional interstitial fluid as an external impedivity with similar normalization and vectorial properties. Connect these two at every point by a distributed, scalar, non-linear admittivity, simulating typical active cell membrane.

We now have a model in which neighborhood fields can be calculated at reasonable computing cost and held momentarily stationary with respect to individual cell activity and regionally summed to gain gross statistical distribution. We have a difficult, but no longer insoluble, computing task.

If there is difficulty in comprehending this triple interpenetration of two impedivity and one admittivity domains, think of the following homely illustration. Imagine a three dimensional cubic fly screen of resistance wire as the first impedivity. Notice that another identical screen of perhaps different conductivity could be fitted completely within the first fly screen without touching it. A moderately conductive fluid poured into the fly screen system would, for all practical purposes, connect the two screens everywhere but only in a very limited neighborhood around each paired mesh cell would this conductivity be important. This model, while not exact in that it has preferred orientations, permits one to see how a body of cells coherently excited can build a converging, a diverging or a patterned field which will exert in a neighborhood a temporally as well as a spatially patterned inhibitory or excitatory influence quite different from ordinary cell to cell interaction and related to holographic strobing.

It is easy to see how interpenetrating domain representation can be extended to biochemical and possibly radiative modalities as well as to electric field and neurological pathway domains. In effect we divide the organism into regions of essentially similar structure, function or organization of an extent which for the modality in question can be considered uniform. We then let these regions be connected together into a network with respect to one modality, while being cross connected to each other modality with a minimal required frequency. It is important that the domains need not be uniform in size or shape. A circulatory hormone might for some purposes be considered as all pervasive and simply introduced and removed from a single pool, while its effect was concentration proportional but target selective strictly for those units responsive to it, so that many other hormones could be similarly endemic and individual target directed. In contrast, a synaptic path might be a strictly linear topological connection in a neural net domain. This domain interpenetration gives a very good framework for hierarchical structuring as it allows a single system to be simultaneously tightly structured in several very different patterns.

Little has been said thus far about coherency in the laser sense, as it was important to establish that holographic dispersion and retrieval into and from a storage and manipulative medium did not require this special phase-preserving, very specific frequency oscillation environment. Let us now consider whether there is in known or discoverable biology, particularly macro-molecular biochemistry, the machinery for implementing a far more versatile holography as well as a mechanism for incorporating biochemical structure and chemical genetics into electrophysiological pattern transduction and its inverse. In short, can we hope to find a biochemically-fueled, long-word, highly specific, coherently coupled mechanism which can control and be controlled by electrophysiological and cellular developmental factors?

Laser type systems are typically pumped from a gross pool of non-specific energy at a potential level high enough to more than support the emitted coherent signal. This is familiar biology in everything from muscle contraction to bioluminescence. Biological specificity lies in neighboring sequences of a few chemical groups strung together into partially redundant large words. Molecular resonances similarly depend on a local chemical structure, slightly but specifically modulated by near neighbors. Can local fields and field gradient patterns influence biosynthesis slightly or affect the pumping of a laser-like emission? It seems possible. Can specific, evoked radiation alter electrical cell polarization and, reciprocally, can polarization alter emissions? It is difficult to point at a specific frequency band or modality because the specific connection in question need not be far-field, ordinary electromagnetic radiation. Experimental search seems justified even if rather difficult development of transducers or indirect experimentation is required.

Unfamiliar and consequently unlikely to be incorporated in experimental designs is the fact that holographic variables need be represented only at minute levels of local probability if they are coherently summable from a large field. Thus a cellular bias that corresponds at fractional percent level with a biochemical sequence could firmly communicate that characteristic if only a few thousand coherent neighbors contributed to its message.

Perhaps we should examine in passing the properties of a key word distributed, strobable computer of the general class which would embrace the several models that have been proposed here. Remember that in a typical digital computer a single stylized word of from 12 to 64 bits can interchangeably represent the identity of the source from which a word comes, the information from that place, the identity of a place to which it is addressed, the action to be taken, the significance of the word at that place. In the speculatively proposed biocomputer the long words would have similar properties, but would interchange them quite liberally. Composite, associated words would be generated by coherent coincidence of strobe patterns. In particular there could be a "start up" program in a relatively simple net, containing key word molecular vocabulary and rudimentary input-output transducers with an external environment on which to experiment.

But enough of such free ranging speculation and wishful thinking! What constructive new ideas can we offer specifically toward a better understanding of information processing in the nervous system?

First, there is the real hope that we may be able to create deliberately a language and a set of meaningfully quantitative figures of thought in which nervous system processing of information becomes much more simple mathematically and more intuitively understandable. This is not a conventional procedure, for it deliberately allows synthesis to precede detailed analysis.

An interpenetrating domains representation offers a hope for computably incorporating several, simultaneously vital, different mechanisms and organizations of the nervous system, which we ordinarily examine separately. Very possibly, the phenomena we seek to understand in many cases depend on this interdisciplinary interaction and are totally missing from each system examined separately.

The notion of a constantly running "blick" of space-time as the dispersing variable in a distributed, holographic nervous system model is very attractive and fits well with much of the known picture of perception as well as the electrophysiology and neuroanatomy of the nervous system.

Coherent, long word, laser-like, distributed coupling between the biochemical informational entities and the nervous system and its electrophysiological components is so important in its possible implications, that exchange processes of this sort and the computer modeling of such processes deserve high research priority.

Part VI

FINAL SESSION

Final Session

The final session of the symposium consisted of general comments, principally from the session chairmen, and some discussion from the remaining participants. The topics of concern were information theory, neural coding, reliability of signal transmission, and the general problem of communication between specialized fields and the process of education.

I. Information Theory

K. N. LEIBOVIC: The title of our symposium is "Information Theory in the Nervous System," and we have heard relatively little about such topics as Shannon's theory of communication or Wiener's theory of filters which usually go under the name of "information theory." I think this is not surprising and without detracting from the value of these theories, it may be in order to point out some of their limitations. I submit that "information theory" in the sense of Shannon or Wiener is too restrictive for our purposes. Thus, the quantum theory of vision, the transformation of signals in nerve nets, memory and the thought processes which lead to the creation of "information theory" itself are all proper subjects for the study of biological information theory.

To Shannon—and to Hartley before him—the information content of an event is monotonically related to its probability of occurrence. But, if information content is to have anything to do with the significance of the information, such a definition leads to problems. Consider, for example, the case of the 1,000 monkeys typing away on 1,000 typewriters. It can be calculated, as someone has done, that in 10^N years there is a finite probability, depending on N, that the monkeys will produce a scientific paper on,

335

say, "Information Processing in the Nervous System." The probability that you and I might produce such a paper is, I hope, somewhat higher. But then, according to Shannon, the information content of our paper will be less than that of the monkeys', although the two papers may be identical. It is possible to get over the difficulties by introducing conditional probabilities. But this soon leads to intractable situations in specifying the appropriate data for the mathematical computations and the utility of the model is diminished.

Another example concerns the stored data, say, in log tables or in a book on quantum theory. Since these are set down in the form of certain knowledge—or with probability 1—their information content is zero.

I submit that a theory in which "information content" of a message increases with decreasing probability is a theory of news value and not a theory of information, since information is not only concerned with communicating new data. The statement "The earth moves around the sun" contains as much information now—in the sense of the "factual" relationships involved—as it did at the time of Galileo, although it had much more news value then.

Shannon's theory is, of course, quite relevant to problems of signal transmission, including channel capacity and coding. But, when one is dealing with biological information in the broad sense, it is well not to identify "information" with a narrow definition from engineering science.

LONGUET-HIGGINS: I suggest that programming theory is more useful than information theory for discussing the nervous system. For, in saying how a program works, one is providing an algorithm for transforming inputs into outputs in the light of data already stored. We know that in other areas of biology. For example, in molecular biology, information theory has not been as useful as programming theory: DNA and amino acids, operons, repressors and derepressors have to do with the organization of a process.

ARBIB: I should like to support the idea that programming theory may be relevant to our subject. We are making some progress in understanding sensory codes and some of the ways in which spatio-temporal patterns are filtered through different kinds of cells in sensory pathways. But in an organ such as the cerebellum, a cell may respond to information from different modalities, from different loci in the cortex and spinal cord which include feedback loops. One has to be careful about saying what the code is there. Perhaps it is better to say that the network is concerned with executing a complex program. Then, we must look for the instructions in the program, the really crucial computations which determine a complex pattern of action from the converging information.

RUSHTON: Two thousand years before Pythagoras, the Egyptians had tabulated particular solutions to numerous problems. Then the Greeks generalized—number could be manipulated independently of the objects enumerated. Then there were the generalizations of algebra and so on. Particular branches of mathematics have been developed to meet special problems, thermodynamics for steam engines, information theory for telecommunications. But now we have a new problem with regard to the brain, which is different in principle. It is not enough to develop machines which do something analogous to the brain. This model builder has to know about the brain—and then feelings, the analysis of emotions, is important, too.

II. Signal Coding and Reliability

WICKELGREN: I should like to take advantage of the combined presence of neural theorists and experimental neurophysiologists to discuss two issues on which I think there has been some implicit disagreement that ought to be made explicit. The two issues are: (*a*) Does any aspect of the pattern of firing of neurons, beyond sheer frequency of firing, matter for the functioning of the nervous system? (*b*) Is the firing of individual neurons substantially less reliable than behavior?

Firstly, with regard to pattern vs. frequency of firing: Many neural model builders and a few experimental neurophysiologists from time to time express the view that a single neuron might code many different events in a distinct manner by emitting different patterns of spikes in response to these events. For example, a particular ordered set of interspike intervals might be produced by a neuron in response to a slit of light oriented vertically, while a different ordered set of interspike intervals might be produced by the same neuron in response to a slit oriented horizontally, a third ordered set produced in response to a dot etc. Of course, for this to have any functional significance, each set of interspike intervals must be able to trigger a different response.

On the other hand, the dominant theory, for some time, has been that the only property of a spike train that has functional significance is the frequency of firing, with the proviso that the time period for determining frequency of firing must be specified before the frequency theory can be considered to be completely precise. If the frequency theory is true, then the spike output of a single neuron does not distinguish among different events, except along a single dimension of similarity to the one or more "ideal" events that produce the maximum frequency of firing from the neuron.

In the absence of any data on the manner in which neurons encode sensory or motor events, either the pattern or the frequency theory is tenable. From reading and listening to numerous discussions of this issue, I have gained the distinct impression that many people consider the issue unsettled. What puzzles me about considering the issue unsettled is that virtually all of the recent, very exciting, research on single neuron correlates of sensory or motor events has been done assuming that the frequency theory is correct. The principal effort has been to determine what event or set of events is associated with the maximal frequency of firing of the neuron, not what events are associated with one pattern of firing and what events are associated with other patterns. Either the neurophysiological evidence for the frequency theory is so compelling that there was no need to analyze temporal firing patterns in these studies, or else we must consider that there is a substantial probability that the results of these studies are completely misleading with respect to the coding properties of the neurons studied.

Personally, I am inclined to the view that the evidence for the frequency theory is quite compelling, though, of course, one cannot be absolutely certain that the frequency theory holds for all neurons in the nervous system until all types of neurons have been studied. If the pattern theory were true, it seems unlikely to me that such elegant results on the coding properties of single neurons would have been obtained making the false assumption that all one needed to look at was frequency of firing.

Of course, there are instances where other properties of a burst of spikes, besides frequency, are known to be systematically related to properties of sensory or motor events. The latency of a spike burst, produced in response to an appropriate stimulus, varies with the intensity of the stimulus in contrast to the background, but it is difficult to see how the nervous system could make use of this information. When the appropriate stimulus is itself a temporal pattern of more elementary events, such as a tone of a certain frequency, there is often some time locking of the spikes with the occurrence of the more elementary events. In the auditory case, the time locking which occurs at low frequencies may be of some functional significance in auditory discrimination of low frequency tones (only). However, it seems likely that the frequency information contained in the time locking of neurons at one level of the auditory system is transformed into frequency of firing of particular neurons at higher levels of the nervous system. A similar sort of transformation is known to occur in the inferior colliculus where phase or intensity differences between the stimuli delivered to the two ears are recorded into frequency of firing of particular neurons (Rose, et al., 1966). In any event, none of these cases constitutes a very extreme deviation from the frequency theory as no very exotic pattern coding is employed.

Thus, there seems to me to be considerable support for the frequency theory as the primary neural coding mechanism, with other characteristics of the firing sequence being of functional significance only in certain more peripheral parts of the nervous system that must be concerned with temporally distributed information.

The second question which I wish to consider is this: Are neurons substantially less reliable than behavior?

One of the concerns of many neural model builders has been to obtain reliable behavior from nets of unreliable component neurons (e.g., Mc-Culloch, 1959). The motivation for this work is that behavior is alleged to be remarkably reliable under certain drugs such as alcohol that are also alleged to have disastrous effects on the functioning of individual neurons. Of course, one could quibble about the need for more detailed studies of how behavior is affected by drugs such as alcohol. However, the more serious flaw in the motivation for this theoretical research is that there is no evidence that I know of to indicate that real neurons are very seriously affected by dosages of drugs that permit reasonably reliable behavior.

To my knowledge, it is not known whether a moderate dose of alcohol would greatly affect the receptive fields of neurons at different levels of the visual nervous system, for example. This sort of study needs to be done before we can consider the problem of obtaining reliable behavior from unreliable neurons to exist for the real nervous system.

Just showing that bathing a neuron in an alcohol solution affects the threshold of activation of the cell body by electrical stimulation is far from adequate to establish the unreliability of real neurons. To use such information, one must also know about blood-brain barriers and the effects of the drug on the natural chemical synaptic transmission, including possible presynaptic compensatory changes in transmitter release. The fact that single-threshold McCulloch-Pitts neurons have a severe reliability problem with changes in threshold does not mean that any analogous problem exists for real neurons, because under the conditions where behavior is relatively unaffected, "thresholds" of single neurons may also be unaffected or else there may be compensatory presynaptic changes.

However, we need not get involved in such detailed considerations to determine whether neurons are substantially less reliable than behavior. What needs to be done is to determine if the optimal stimulus for various neurons is altered by dosages of drugs that have only "mild" effects on behavior.

ARBIB: I should like to point out two things. Firstly, there is a considerable number of possible neural codes which the physiologist can distinguish in principle, but we do not know if they are biologically significant. These codes were discussed at a working session of the neurosciences research program. Secondly, with regard to reliability, this is much more difficult to achieve in a digital system than in a real neuron. In a binary representation, an error in one digit can falsify a complete message. But in a nerve impulse train with continuously varying time intervals a few random changes in the position of the spikes is not going to change the information content nearly that much. In addition, the nervous system has a great deal of reliability by virtue of the considerable overlapping of nerve nets.

ECCLES: Talking about nerve cells and how they pick up information and what information is interesting and what it means, one has to realize that the information converging on single neurons comes from the total activity of many parallel lines. For example, Purkinje cells in the cerebellum have 200,000 lines converging on them. The nerve cell is not concerned with the intervals on any one line but with the totality of the excitation and inhibition added up over reasonable intervals of time and its activity is constantly modulated against a background of maintained activity. This is what one has to keep in mind when building models. Then, there is inhibition for sharpening the message and for taking out the "noise." Rarely is there a one to one relationship between successive relays of neurons, for at each stage there is both some integration and some lifting of the signal out of noise.

BARLOW: In some cases, what we see and what we do is determined by single neurons. For example, in the fovea our acuity is limited by the separation of single receptors and the receptor to ganglion cell ratio is 1:1. Thus the behavioral and neural "graininess" are the same. Similarly, in the motor cortex, stimulation of single cells gives perceptible muscle movement. As regards coding, we look at the mean firing rate, because all other possible codes are too numerous to look at. This, however, does not exclude the possibility that they may be important.

REFERENCES

McCulloch, W. S. (1959). Agathe Tyche of nervous nets—the lucky reckoners. Mechanization of thought processes. Vol. II. London: Her Majesty's Stationary Office, 612–625.
Rose, J. E., Gross, N. B., Geisler, C. D. and Hind, J. E. (1966). Some neural mechanisms in the inferior colliculus of the cat which may be relevant to localization of a sound source. J. Neurophysiol., 29:288–314.

III. Communication and Education

ARBIB: One sometimes hears the statement from experimental physiologists: "The theorists are all parasites," or "What have the theorists ever done for us?" I think, by contrast, communication at this symposium has been good and for the following reasons. Very few of the speakers have been guilty of, what is to me, the cardinal sin at such meetings, namely give the sort of paper they would give to a meeting of their own specialists. Then, the theorists have put themselves onto the home ground of the neurophysiologists.

But still there is room for improvement. I will illustrate this by means of an example: consider a network in which each element has two inputs and one output. Perhaps one wants to find how the output is determined by the inputs; or one may have certain bounds on the complexity of the components and one asks how the inputs can be combined in some optimal way to give a specified output. We can prove certain theorems, e.g., that no network can compute certain functions in less than a certain time. But all this, we can do only for certain mathematical functions, using some mathematical operations like group multiplication and with network elements which are rather simple. Now, when we get onto the home ground of the neurophysiologist we may become somewhat apologetic, saying, "I am sorry, but I cannot apply this to your kind of neuron or your kind of input-output function." On the other hand we may turn round and say, "Here is a beautiful theory, if only you can give me the exact limits on the complexity of your components and will specify the input-output behavior of the network, I will tell you what is the best possible network and compare it with the real network and give you some clues in understanding its structure." We may turn to Sir John and ask him for an exact specification of the Purkinje cell and, quite reasonably, he will say "Are you not asking a bit much?" So I think we have to be satisfied at present with a twofold approach. The data of the neurophysiologist are still not enough to apply to much mathematical theory.

We need people who know something about the brain and try to widen the range of application of existing theory such as control theory or sequential machine theory. On the other hand we need people who gather the experimental data and who know something about the language of the theorists; and then there will have to be some who can go back and forth between the two camps bearing messages.

ECCLES: I am sure the theorists and experimentalists need each other and I welcome the association with theoreticians. Maybe sometimes they have not understood my problem and I have not understood theirs. But we are coming closer and I am sure the results are going to be most useful.

BOYNTON: Michael Arbib described himself as an individual with a foot in two camps: the theoretical and the experimental. We could code him— color him, if you will—1–1. If you do the same for me, it might come out 0–0. Being a visual psychophysicist, and not feeling a close identification with either camp, perhaps I have the advantage of being able to stand to one side and watch what is going on. About all I can do is to report to you some rather personal reactions to what has gone on here at this meeting.

I think the interchange has been fascinating. To watch people interact who come at the same problems with very different backgrounds is an inherently fascinating thing. It is not surprising to me that such strong differences of opinion should have been expressed here. Rather, it is remarkable that a symposium dealing with how the brain works can take place at all. There are some formidable problems of communication here that might have been anticipated ahead of time. I would like to describe what I think these problems are, and then elaborate a bit on them.

One problem is obvious—we are dealing with an inherently horribly complex problem: how the brain works. This is a problem which if it is ever solved (and this is probably not the right way to talk about it) is going to take a very long time, and it is a problem which is almost certainly beyond the bounds of our present capacities of imagination. It is a problem that is also difficult to discuss because we do not yet have the appropriate language to talk about it. Further advances in this field are going to include the development of this language. We have seen some straws in the wind here. For example, we have experienced trouble here with the words *code* and *information* which obviously mean many different things to different people. Yet we use them as though we can really communicate with one another. But we do not always communicate when we think we do, and this can lead to serious misunderstandings.

Another point I would like to make is that, in a multidisciplinary area where people come together and grapple with these very difficult problems, we are probably all suffering in various ways from the educational process by which we have been conditioned. I would include in this not only the formal education which goes on in schools, colleges and post-graduate work but also the kind of less formal education that goes on in the course of growing up in a particular culture. As I think back upon my own experience when I was in high school, for example, I am fairly well convinced that the educational process never succeeded in raising the curiosity of most of the students about the kinds of problems we have been discussing here today; what is worse, it sometimes succeeded in stamping out such curiosity whenever it spontaneously arose. How much is said about the question of brain function at the level of high school education? I wish more were said, because if we had a more common denominator of experience going back earlier into each of our backgrounds, it would have been helpful in the communicative process here today.

Now permit me to elaborate a little bit on some of these points. With respect to the educational process, I think that specialization—although it is obviously a necessary thing, in order to enable people to get down to details and break through the difficult frontiers with respect to problems—also breeds mutual fear and distrust, because some of this training, particularly as it goes on in graduate schools today, almost deliberately makes mutual understanding difficult if not impossible among people from disparate areas. Each of us must decide, somehow, how we are going to use our time; we cannot read all of the literature in which we might possibly be interested, or attend all of the meetings. An easy way to discard a good deal of it is to think about it as being worthless to begin with, and therefore not worthy of being considered. Some of the negative attitudes that particular groups of workers can develop with respect to others are exemplified in the conflict between the theoreticians and the empiricists here. I think it is unfortunate.

Another thing which is at the root of the difficulty in the educational problem concerns matters of perception (a subject area of particular interest to me). There are probably others who have made the attempt to teach the subject of visual perception, say to an introductory class in college. With a freshman student who otherwise is intelligent and perceptive, it is very difficult even to make him appreciate the fact that there is a problem about perception. You ask a student why he sees the chair and he says, "well, I see it because it is there." There is no problem for him; perception works well and easily, so what is the problem? To ignore the problems of perception in this way is the adaptive way to behave for most purposes. No animal in his right mind, in an environment where survival is important, is going to stand around and indulge in solipsistic thinking, or worry about the physics of the situation. The adaptive thing is clearly to know (correctly in some sense) that the threatening object is there and take evasive action. The perception of entopic phenomena (things that occur inside, rather than outside the eye in the real world) is stamped out. Most people do not perceive these events—although they can be observed easily—because this type of sensory input does not have any significant correlation with the meaningful objects in the outside world. Hallucinations are frowned upon and the outside reference is stressed over and over again as we learn the language to describe what we see and experience. Most people believe that seeing is believing.

Part of the problem of understanding perception involves language. We do not have the right words. The fact that, as language developed, most people did not understand that there were problems of perception, resulted in such absurdities in our language that a word like *light* standing on the one hand as a reference to a physical stimulus (something presumably capable of being described even if it existed in a world where there were no perceiving organisms) can also be used to specify sensation—a purely subjective experience. This is terrible, because in order to talk about perceptual problems clearly, it is absolutely necessary to have a clear separation of these concepts for analytical purposes. Although we try to do this it is easy to slip back into sloppy thinking because of the lack of the proper language and this does not make our educational process any easier.

Before leaving the subject of the educational process, as it impinges upon multidisciplinary problems, I would just like to comment on the fact that I teach a course which is called "Introduction to Visual Science." In this course, which incidentally has no pre-requisites (this I consider an important aspect of it although it is considered a graduate course) we have students who come from electrical engineering, psychology, physiology, brain research, and optics. It is fascinating at this stage of the educational process to try to create a respect on the part of these people for one another's strengths and ignorances. I feel this is a critical stage in the educational process, where a good deal of good can be done for graduate students from different disciplines with common interests, such as a study of the brain. It is valuable to get them together, and to begin to develop a mutual appreciation of one another and to a certain extent also a common language.

On the last point, the complexity of what we are talking about, I am concerned with the relationship between structure and function, a concern that has been with us throughout our discussion of these very problems. I think we talk about computers a lot when discussing the brain these days, because it is the best analogy we have got so far. Telephone switchboards were talked about in an earlier era, but certainly the computer is a much better analogy. If we talk about the relationship between structure and function in a computer, there are really many different physical structures which can parallel the required function. It does not matter whether the program is written for an I.B.M. computer or some other brand, or exactly what the hardware is; therefore it becomes easy to separate structure and function, so you can have experts in computer programming who do not know anything about the hardware. Conversely, the people who build the machines and understand how they work do not necessarily know how best to use them. Therefore, the structure and function can be separated and talked about in an abstract and profitable way. I wonder about this, however, when we talk about the brain and the sensory systems that lead into it, because these systems are so small and compact. For example, in the outer segments of the visual receptors it appears that the rhodopsin molecules, in addition to the very important function that they play in the absorption of light quanta, somehow leading to the generation of the initial visual signals, also make up an integral structure of the laminated outer segments of the receptors. In a computer there is a lot of metal and whatnot, which is a part of the structure, but has nothing to do with the function. But it seems to me rather clear that in a biological system as compact as the brain, with a huge number of elements crammed into a small structure, you cannot afford to waste too much space on the glue. So most of the system consists of functional as well as structural elements, and I wonder whether it does not really become impossible to talk about the one without talking about the other.

ARBIB: Do you have any mechanism in your course to make the students talk to each other and discuss their viewpoints or do you just get them to see how workers from different fields approach the area.

BOYNTON: I think this course provides the background for this, but a course which comes later serves the functions you are talking about more explicitly. We have a laboratory course where the idea is not to put the students through a series of exercises, but rather to try to get them to think out problems which, if carried out properly under the guidance of faculty members, can lead to publishable experiments. In this coming to grips on actual

experimental problems, the most genuine collaboration and mutual understanding of people from different disciplines comes to its full fruition. They
come to respect one another for their strengths and are a little less reluctant
than they were before to reveal their weaknesses. It is a very dangerous
thing in many high schools and colleges to ask questions, because of the
kind of reaction they produce from the teacher. Some teachers react, perhaps, defensively; they do not like to be asked deep questions. They may
react by saying, or at least implying, "that's a stupid question—go back and
memorize what I've told you and don't bother me." We should try to communicate to the students that they should not be afraid to reveal their ignorance.

Glossary

The following glossary of terms has been compiled at the suggestion of Professor Eccles as an aid in communicating with people from different specialties.

*Acton. The term acton is proposed for a unit of action consisting of the voluntary decision and physiologic execution in a single, simple voluntary act of movement. Duration of an acton is 0.2–0.3 sec under normal conditions. The space-time form of an acton is preprogrammed by the brain. It has a clear beginning and end. Under some emotional states, and conditions of trance the preprogramming period covered by the acton may be considerably lengthened. (mc)

Adaptation. The process by which a species adjusts to an environment, an individual to a change in its environment, the nervous system to different circumstances, or a sense organ to a different routine of stimulation. It is a very general term that is used to describe an apparently beneficial alteration in performance occurring in response to changes imposed upon the system. Examples are: the changes in perception that occur after wearing distorting spectacles; improvements in night vision that occur within about an hour of excluding bright lights; the decrease with time of the frequency of discharge of nerve impulses from a sense organ following the application of a steady stimulus. (hbb)

Afferent. Incoming to central nervous system (e.g., sensory inflow). (rml)

Allophone Rules. *See* generative grammar. (igm & aml)

Analogous Systems. Two systems are said to be analogous if they can be represented by the same set of dynamical equations; i.e., if there is a correspondence between them which preserves dynamical properties. Thus, an oscillatory RLC circuit is an analog of a purely mechanical oscillator. (rr)

Ascending Methods of Limits. A psychophysical procedure in which the stimulus is presented at an energy level below threshold and increased after each response until a correct response occurs. Threshold is defined as the mean

347

energy value averaged over several series which was just sufficient for a correct response. (RNH)

AUTOMATA THEORY is usually restricted to mean the study, by algebraic and combinatorial methods, of the information-processing capacities of computer-like abstractions, especially those related to finite automata (*q.v.*) and Turing machines (*q.v.*). (MAA)

AUTOMATON, FINITE a sequential machine (*q.v.*) with a finite number of states. (MAA)

AXIOMATIC THEORY. The prime example of an axiomatic theory is Euclidean geometry. An axiomatization of a topic comprizes a number of statements, the axioms, which are to represent the basic truths of a subject matter which one does not expect to reduce to a combination of simpler truths, and rules of inference hopefully so designed that if we use them to make an inference from a true statement, the resulting statement will also be true. A proof is a sequence of statements, each of which is either an axiom, or is deducible from earlier statements of the sequence by one of the rules of inference. A statement is then a theorem if it is one of the statements generated in the course of a proof.

An axiomatic theory is consistent if it can never have both a statement and its negation as theorems—otherwise the theory would be inconsistent. The theory is complete if every true statement about its subject matter is a theorem. The theory is decidable if there is an effective procedure to tell whether or not a statement is a theorem.

It is known that any axiomatic theory of the whole numbers is both undecidable and incomplete, if we demand that there be effective procedures for telling whether or not a statement is an axiom and for applying the rule of inference. (MAA)

BRIGHTNESS MEASUREMENTS. Intensity generally refers to the physical attribute of a stimulus while brightness designates the psychological counterpart of this term. This distinction is essential, as brightness and intensity do not necessarily vary in the same direction and do not have a one-to-one relationship.

In the study of vision and visual perception, the measurement of brightness has played an important role. A broad range of measures has been introduced. Subjective scales of brightness were developed by S. S. Stevens by having subjects make numerical estimates as a function of stimulus intensity. On the basis of this work a number of power functions were obtained not only for vision but for other senses as well.

Brightness measurement techniques of various sorts have also been used to investigate questions related to visual sensitivity, visual acuity, color vision, pattern perception and dark adaptation. In studying brightness thresholds, a typical method entails the presentation of a stimulus at different intensities with subjects giving a response after each presentation indicating whether or not the stimulus was perceived (see forced choice). Alternatively, a stimulus may be increased or decreased continuously until the subject sees it appear or disappear.

In studying brightness contrast and related topics, a brightness matching procedure is frequently used. In this kind of paradigm the subject is asked to vary the intensity of one of two stimuli until the two appear equally bright. Depending on the nature of the study, one of the two stimuli may be surrounded by another stimulus such as a ring, the intensity, size, wavelength, or contour proximity of which is varied. (PHS)

BOOLEAN FUNCTION. A function which assigns a value $f(x_1 \ldots ,x_n)$ to an n-tuple $(x_1, \ldots , x_n)$ is called Boolean if both the x_j's and the value of f may take one of only two possible values, which may be called "0" and "1," or "True" and "False." (MAA)

CLASSIFICATORY DISTINCTIVE FEATURE MATRIX. *See* generative grammar. (IGM & AML)

COLLATERAL FIBERS. The smaller branches given off the axon of a nerve cell (nerve fiber). (JCE)

COMPLETENESS. *See* axiomatic theory. (MAA)

CONSISTENCY. *See* axiomatic theory. (MAA)

CONTENT ADDRESSING. Method of retrieving stored information by the recognition of particular aspects of the information rather than by its physical location. (RML)

CONTEXT-FREE CODE. A spelling of words in a vocabulary by means of ordered sets of (context-free) symbols, where some symbols in some words give insufficient information concerning the adjacent symbols to determine them uniquely out of the unordered set for the word. (WAW)

CONTEXT-SENSITIVE CODE. A spelling of words in a vocabulary by means of unordered sets of (context-sensitive) symbols, where each symbol restricts the choice of its left and right adjacent symbols sufficiently to determine them uniquely out of the unordered set of symbols for any given word. (WAW)

CONVERGENCE NUMBER. The number of nerve cells that have a direct synaptic action on a nerve cell. (JCE)

CRITICAL DURATION. The upper limit of temporal integration beyond which no combination of effects will occur. (RNH)

CYBERNETICS. The current meaning, "The study of control and communication in the animal and the machine," was introduced by Norbert Wiener and his colleagues in 1947. In Europe and the U.S.S.R., it is often used in a broad sense which embraces all of control engineering, computer science, and operations research. However, it should really be reserved for mathematical studies of comparative aspects of control) computation and communication in nervous systems and in machines. (MAA)

DECIDABILITY. *See* axiomatic theory. (MAA)

DEEP STRUCTURE. *See* generative grammar. (IGM & AML)

DISCRIMINATION NETWORK. A network is said to discriminate between two stimuli (or two classes of stimuli) if it produces distinct responses to these stimuli (or to stimuli belonging to the classes being discriminated). (RR)

DISFACILITATION. The relatively depressed state of a nerve cell that accompanies diminution or cessation of a background of excitatory synaptic action. (JCE)

DISPARITY. The two eyes' view of a three dimensional scene from different positions; hence, binocular parallax causes small displacements in the relative positions of objects as seen by the two eyes. These displacements are called disparities, and their magnitude and direction depend upon the distance of the objects from the eyes; if the eyes are fixated on a point at, say, one meter, then objects closer than a circle through the fixation point and the anterior nodal points of the two eyes will have "convergent" disparity, because a convergent movement of the eyes, in addition to any conjugate lateral movements, would be required to fixate it. Similarly, points beyond the circle are said to have "divergent" disparities. (HBB)

DISTINCTIVE FEATURE MATRIX. *See* generative grammar. (IGM & AML)

DIVERGENCE NUMBER. The number of nerve cells on which a given nerve cell exerts a direct synaptic action. (JCE)

*E-ACTON. An acton whose transient form is modulated by emotional expression corresponding to a sentic state (e.g., an angry gesture, a smile). (MC)

EFFERENT. Outgoing from central nervous system (e.g., motor outflow). (RML)

ENGRAM. The, as yet unknown, organic substrate of a memory process in the nervous system. (RML)

*ESSENTIC FORM. The spatio-temporal output form of an expression of a sentic state. Essentic form is related to the sentic state in part as a fulfillment or output to a command, in terms of control systems theory. The essentic form has a precisely programmed spatio-temporal shape, but different output modalities may be utilized for its actualization (e.g., tone of voice or gesture, elements of communication of the arts: dance steps, musical phrases, and in a certain sense, the forms in visual art). The power of communication of a channel using essentic form is a form function. The gain increases as the precision of the form approaches the form required by the sentic state (i.e., the ortho-essentic form). (MC)

EXCITATORY. *See* McCulloch-Pitts neuron. (MAA)

EXISTENTIAL MUSIC. Music without an inner pulse, representing being rather than function or action. (MC)

EXTEROCEPTIVE. Pertaining to sensory information from the immediate external environment. (RML)

FACILITATION. (1) A process whereby a particular pathway between a pair of neurons in a neural net may be strengthened according to its past history; usually one assumes a pathway is strengthened by previous firings and weakened (or not strengthened) by the absence of previous firing. (RR)

2) The increased tendency for impulse discharge that is produced in a nerve cell when it is subjected to synaptic excitatory action. (JCE)

FILTER. A device with frequency dependent gain, often selective for certain regions of the input spectrum. (RML)

FINITE AUTOMATON. *See* automaton, finite. (MAA)

FORCED CHOICE. A psychophysical procedure which requires subjects to give a response following each trial in an experiment. A relatively simple procedure is one in which the task is to detect the presence or absence of a stimulus. The subject is requested to respond by saying "yes" or "no" after each trial. In other situations the task may be to detect the location of a stimulus so that the requested response may be "left" or "right," or to identify which of two or more stimuli were presented, requiring a response after each trial. Signal detection theory provides the rationale of this method, as worked out by J. A. Swets, W. P. Tanner, Jr., D. M. Green and others. (PHS)

FORMAL NEURON. 1) Mathematical and/or logical formulation of properties of components conceived as simplifications of real neurons. (WSM)

2) For example, a mathematical structure composed of the following data: (a) a finite set of positive numbers $\{A_1, A_2, \ldots, A_n\}$, the elements of which are called "input lines" each A_i represents the value of the input line when the latter is active; (b) an object B called an "output line"; (c) the two-element set $(0,1)$ whose elements represent the possible "states" of the input and output lines; (d) a non-negative integer h, called the "threshold"; (e) a discrete set of "instants," denoted by $t_0, t_1, \ldots$ The formal neuron operates as follows: denote the state of the ith input line at instant t_k by $\sigma(i, t_k)$. Then the state of the output line at instant t_{k+1} is 1 if and only if we have

$$\sum_{t=1}^{n} \sigma(i, t_k)A_i \geq h. \qquad \text{(RR)}$$

FREQUENCY THEORY OF NEURAL CODING. Single neuron coding of sensory or motor events by means of its frequency of firing, with frequency of firing increasing with increasing similarity of an event to one or more "ideal" events. (WAW)

GAIN. $\dfrac{A_o}{A_i}$ where A_o, A_i are the amplitudes of a waveform at the output and input, respectively, of a device. (RML)

GENERATIVE GRAMMAR. The following much oversimplified account may serve to illustrate the terminology of generative grammar, as developed by Chomsky and others. A sentence has both a *deep structure* and a *surface structure*. The deep structure, when interpreted by semantic rules, specifies the semantic value of the sentence; the surface structure, when interpreted by a set of phonological rules (the *phonological component*), specifies the phonetic value of the sentence.

The deep structure of a sentence can be represented by a *labelled tree* or branching diagram, for instance:

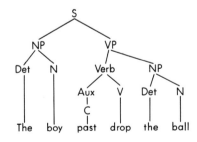

Each branching is equivalent to the application of a rewriting rule such as "$S \rightarrow NP + VP$," "$NP \rightarrow Det + N$," "$Det \rightarrow$ the, a $\ldots$," "$N \rightarrow$ boy, ball $\ldots$," and so on. 'The + boy + past + drop + the + ball' is a *terminal string*. *Boy, drop, ball* are *lexical morphemes; past* (likewise, *sing.* and *pl.*) is a *grammatical morpheme*.

The rules of the *transformational component* relate deep structure to surface structure by operations on the tree. These rules, stated with reference to nodes of the tree, rearrange its branches, insert new material and delete old material. If one applies the rule for the passive transformation:

$$NP_1 — Aux — V — NP_2 \rightarrow$$
$$NP_2 — Aux — be + past\ part. — V — by + NP_1$$

the terminal string above may become

The + ball + past + be + past   part. + drop + by + the + boy i.e. (after further transformations) :

\# The \# ball \# be + past \# drop + past part. \# by \# the \# boy \#

By virtue of other transformational rules, the same terminal string could have developed, at the level of surface structure, into

\# Do + past \# the \# boy\# drop \# the \# ball \#

or

\# The \# drop + pres. part. \# of \# the \# ball

or various other semantically equivalent strings.

The forms 'the,' 'boy' have been used for convenience above. Actually a lexical morpheme is represented by a *classificatory distinctive-feature matrix* which characterizes the morpheme phonologically. Thus *drop* (in phonemic transcription/drap/) might be represented with respect to the set of distinctive features used in English as

	d	r	a	p
vocalic	—			—
consonantal	+	+		+
high	—	—	—	—
back	—	—	+	—
..	.	.	.	.
..	.	.	.	.
etc.				

Only those features are specified which are necessary to define each phonological segment uniquely in the context of each lexical morpheme. The phonological component, operating on the surface structure, fills out the matrix according to redundancy rules and applies *allophone rules* which change the value of certain cells according to context. The phonological component also supplies a phonetic interpretation for the grammatical morphemes. The resulting specification of the utterance in *phonetic features* covers all the linguistically variable properties of speech, but not the physical properties common to all speech, or the physical variation from speaker to speaker.

For a full discussion of generative grammar, see N. Chomsky, *Syntactic*

Structures (The Hague: Mouton, 1957); N. Chomsky, *Aspects of the Theory of Syntax* (Cambridge, Mass.: M.I.T. Press, 1965); N. Chomsky and M. Halle, *The Sound Pattern of English* (New York—Evanston—London: Harper and Row, 1968); N. Chomsky and G. Miller, Introduction to the formal analysis of Natural Languages, in R. D. Luce, R. R. Bush and E. Galanter, eds., *Handbook of Mathematical Psychology* (New York-London: John Wiley, 1963), 2:269–321. (AML & IGM)

GRAMMATICAL MORPHEME. *See* generative grammar. (IGM & AML)

GRAMMATICAL TRANSFORMATION. A syntactic rule which converts abstract structures underlying sentences (phrase structures) into less abstract phrase structures (PSP)

HOLOGRAM. Photograph of the interference pattern between light from an object field interacting with a reference or background light source. Amplitude and phase image of an object. (RML)

HOLOPHONE. Analogue in temporal domain, at sound frequencies, of hologram (RML)

IDENTIFICATION PROBLEM. In systems theory, the problem of going from a description of the overt behavior of a system to the description of an internal mechanism which could mediate this behavior. (MAA)

*IDIOLOG. The mental and physiologic process associated with a specific, imagined sensory perception, feeling and action, including forms in space and time. Idiologs may be primary or combined. Primary idiologs are those which could not be imagined if they did not exist, e.g., "green," "sweet." An idiolog is not conerned with rational thought, such as a chess move. It is a special subclass of the more general concept "idea." (MC)

INCONSISTENCY. *See* axiomatic theory. (MAA)

INHIBITORY. *See* McCulloch-Pitts neuron. (MAA)

INSTINCTIVE GRASPING REACTION. Flexion of digits elicited by palmar stimulation and maintained by flexor stretch reflex. (RML)

*INTERNAL PULSE OF MUSIC. The internal music pulse is the form of the idiolog-actons as music is thought. An output expression of the inner pulse of music may be in the form of a conductors' gesture or beat. A good conductor modulates the form of the conducting gesture according to the essentic form demanded by the internal pulse shape of the music. The internal pulse is not identical with rhythm or meter, but is the living quality generating a precise shape in time, defining rhythm and the shape of a phrase more precisely than the approximate musical notation. In certain periods in musical history, composers appear to have their own characteristic internal pulse shapes. Aspects of the internal pulse shapes of music for different composers may be measured through their corresponding forms by means of tactile pressure transducers, *see* pp. 177–206, this volume. (MC)

LABELLED TREE. *See* generative grammar. (IGM & AML)

LATE RECEPTOR POTENTIAL (LRP). A component of the electroretinogram which reflects activity of the visual receptors. Although it has a very short latency, the LRP is preceded by the early receptor potential (ERP), believed to be associated with the photoisomerization of visual pigments. (RMB)

LATERAL INHIBITION. (1) In single neurons recorded in sensory pathways, it is very commonly found that an optimally located stimulus of the optimal type evokes a diminished response when neighboring points on the sensory surface are stimulated concurrently. This is attributed to inhibition conducted laterally from neighboring centripetal pathways. (HBB)

2) Lateral inhibition is very pronounced, for example, in the visual system. In the mammalian eye, stimulating the center of the receptive field of a retinal ganglion cell, for example, produces a vigorous discharge. If the surrounding area is also stimulated, as in the case of diffuse light, the cell will respond much less. It is assumed that this attribute of the visual system plays an important role in pattern perception. (PHS)

LEARNING NETWORK. A learning task for a network is the association of a particular network response to a particular stimulus. A learning network is one which is capable of improving its association of the desired response to the stimulus by repeated exposure to the stimulus. (RR)

LEXICAL MORPHEME. *See* generative grammar. (IGM & AML)

LOCATION. Internal storage position. (RML)

LOG UNIT. 1) Log_{10} (I_1/I_2), where I_1 and I_2 represent stimulus intensities. It is equivalent to 10 decibels and does not depend upon the units in which the stimulus intensities are specified. (RMB)

2) In this volume the term log units has been used primarily to specify the intensity of a stimulus, typically light, presented to the organism. Light intensity is generally varied using neutral density filters the transmittance of which is specified in logarithmic units. A .3 log filter transmits 50% of the light, a 1.0 log filter 10%, and a 2.0 log filter 1%. Conversely, presenting a stimulus .3 log units above threshold means that the light, which at threshold elicits a neural or behavioral response roughly half the time the stimulus is presented, has been doubled. (PHS)

MCCULLOCH-PITTS NEURON. A highly formalized neuron model. It has a number n of input lines, each of which can carry a signal 0 or 1 at any time t of a discrete time-scale. To the jth input line is assigned a weight w_j—if w_j is a positive number we say the jth input is excitatory, if $w_j < 0$ we call it inhibitory. Given that the jth input is $x_j(t)$ at tme t, the neuron "fires" at time $t + 1$ if the excitation exceeds the inhibition by a critical level called the threshold, θ. More precisely: the output of the neuron is 1 at time t if and only if

$$\sum_{i=1}^{n} w_j x_j(t) > \theta.$$

Such an element is also known as a "threshold logic unit." (MAA)

MASKING FUNCTION, in visual research, depicts the threshold intensity of a test flash, or probe, as a function of the inter-stimulus interval (ISI) between the probe and the masking stimulus. The test probe is typically smaller than, and is superposed upon, the masking stimulus. The rapid threshold variations in time that are produced by the mask are believed to reflect the reaction of the visual system to the masking stimulus. (RMB)

MATRIX, DISTINCTIVE FEATURE. *See* generative grammar. (IGM & AML)

METHOD OF ADJUSTMENT. In psychophysical research, is one of the standard psychophysical methods. It differs from most of the other methods in that the subject, instead of responding to stimulus conditions as fixed by the experimenter, is free to manipulate the intensity or some other aspect of the stimulus in order to produce a given result, such as a threshold percept, a match between two fields, or some other criterion response, depending upon the nature of the task and the instructions given to him. (RMB)

MORPHEME, GRAMMATICAL. *See* generative grammar. (IGM & AML)

MORPHEME, LEXICAL. *See* generative grammar. (IGM & AML)

NATURAL LANGUAGE. A communicative system only known to be possessed by humans, which is characterized by the properties of being unbounded (having an infinite number of different grammatical sentences), stimulus-free (the relationship between particular sentences and occasions appropriate for their use is not the behaviorist's relation of stimulus and response), and having an inner as well as outer form (possessing an abstract level of structure related to meaning as well as a concrete level related to pronunciation). (PSP)

NOUN PHRASE. That grammatical category containing as members all sequences consisting of a noun and its modifiers. (PSP)

NUCLEUS. An assemblage of nerve cells that have similar or related functions. (JCE)

*ORTHO-ESSENTIC FORM. Ortho-essentic form is the essentic form which the sentic state inherently commands or implies. To communicate the sentic state the essentic form must be true to this command. Inhibition and altera- tion of this shape is regarded as "insincere." The ortho-essentic form involves a number of different levels of nervous system control and the precise reali- zation of the form depends on the levels which participate or remove their respective inhibiting influence. (MC)

PATTERN THEORY OF NEURAL CODING. Single neuron coding of sensory or motor events by means of a pattern of interspike intervals, with different patterns corresponding to different events. (WAW)

PATTERSON FUNCTION. Autocorrelation of electron density in a crystal giving amplitude but not phase information. (RML)

PHONETIC FEATURES. *See* generative grammar. (IGM & AML)

PHONOLOGICAL COMPONENT. *See* generative grammar. (IGM & AML)

PHRASE STRUCTURE. A means of representing structural information about sentences; technically a directed, rooted, ordered, labeled tree. (PSP)

PLACING REACTION. Automatic positioning of the limb to support body weight, elicited by visual and tactile or tactile stimuli alone. (RML)

POST STIMULUS TIME HISTOGRAM. This term refers to a technique of data rep- resentation in electrophysiology introduced by G. L. Gerstein and N. Y. S. Kiang. The response of single neurons is assessed following the onset of a stimulus by determining their temporal discharge characteristics. Histograms of this sort are generally obtained with a computer. The abscissa in the histogram represents elapsed time following the onset of the stimulus, and the ordinate the number of discharges per histogram bar. These data are generally obtained using a number of repeated stimulus presentations. (PHS)

*PRESENTIC CONTROL. Presentic control is the brain function which allows one to switch sentic states at will, using the ability to sample sentic states as idiologs without the full physiologic concomitants that accompany the par- ticular sentic state. In depressive states, the presentic control is not functional. (MC)

PROPRIOCEPTIVE. Pertaining to sensory information from the internal environment, i.e., movement and position of the body in space. (RML)

*PROTO-ESSENTIC FORM. The essentic forms corresponding to proto-sentic states are called proto-essentic forms. (MC)

*PROTO-SENTIC STATE. There seem to exist a certain number of basic emotions which combine in various ways like colors of the spectrum. The sentic states corresponding to the basic emotions are called proto-sentic states. (MC)

*PURITY. The degree to which an expressive form approaches the ortho-essentic or command form required by the sentic state. Purity is an asymptotic concept. The impurity is a deviation from the required form. (MC)

RADIAL COLUMNS. Functional grouping (of cortical cells) into cylindrical assemblies perpendicular to the cortical surface. (RML)

RECEPTIVE FIELD. A single sensory neuron responds only to stimuli delivered to certain regions of the sensory surface. In vertebrates these regions are usually adjacent and form the single neuron's receptive field, a term first used by Hartline to describe the part of the retina that had to be stimulated to excite a particular optic nerve fiber. The receptive field may be uniform in that the same stimulus evokes the same response throughout its extent, or the responses evoked from different parts may be different or mutually inhibitory. Often the region adjacent to the excitatory receptive field (the "surround") is found to inhibit responses evoked from the "center," even though stimulation of the surround alone produces no detectable response. (HBB)

RECURRENT COLLATERAL. Axonal branches which turn back to influence directly or indirectly the cells of origin. (RML)

REDUNDANCY. The fraction of the capacity of a communication channel that is not utilized by the messages that it transmits, defined by Shannon (Bell System Technical Journal, [1948], 27:379), for a discrete noiseless source of symbols, as one minus the relative entropy. Relative entropy is the ratio of the entropy of a source to the maximum value it could have while still restricted to the same alphabet of symbols. Analogous definitions are possible in the continuous case and in the presence of noise, but redundancy here may be beneficial: if it is of the right type it will combat the effect of the noise, i.e., reduce equivocation. (HBB)

REIN CONTROL. A combination of two unidirectional rate sensitive channels in the manner of two reins, each of which represents change of a different polarity. The system senses the polarity of the change from the spatial location of the channel, although the message in each may have similar dynamic form. (MC)

*R-M FUNCTION. A function of the brain which responds to a change in a variable from rest to motion. A hierarchial construct of three unidirectionally rate sensitive channels, two of these summing in rein control fashion; the output of the sum is another URS channel. (MC)

RULE OF INFERENCE. See axiomatic theory. (MAA)

SEMANTIC RULE. See generative grammar. (IGM & AML)

SENSITIVITY. In visual psychophysics, is the reciprocal of the light intensity required to elicit a criterion response, often a threshold response. The intensity variable is usually at the threshold of visibility, but other criteria (e.g., brightness matching to specify spectral sensitivity) can also be used. (RMB)

*SENTIC CYCLES. A succession of sentic states which are experienced in the course of programmed sequences of expressive actons. In sentic cycles, sentic states are switched through presentic control in response to verbal or other instruction. Sentic cycles usually consist of 8 to 10 sentic states and last approximately half an hour. (MC)

*SENTIC STATE. A particular state of emotion or feeling as a brain algorithm; does not refer to sensory feeling of inputs, or sensory perception. (MC)

SEQUENTIAL MACHINE. A system M specified by a quintuple (Q,X,Y,δ,β) where Q is a set of states, X is a set of inputs, Y is a set of outputs, and $\delta:Q \times X \to Q$ and $\beta:Q \to Y$ are mappings or some specified transformations, such that if M is in state q of Q and receives input x of X at time t, then its output at that time is $\beta(q)$ in Y, and at time $t + 1$ its state will have changed to $\delta(q,x)$ in Q. (MAA)

SHORT-TERM VISUAL STORAGE. Maintenance of a decaying neural representation of a brief stimulus from which information may be extracted. It is generally of the order of 250 msec. (RNH)

SURFACE STRUCTURE. See generative grammar. (IGM & AML)

SURROUND INHIBITION. Diminution of neural response by response of neighboring units. (RML)

TEMPORAL INTEGRATION. A combination of effects when two or more stimuli are presented sufficiently close together in time. (RNH)

THRESHOLD. See McCulloch-Pitts neuron. (MAA)

THRESHOLD LOGIC UNIT. A McCulloch-Pitts neuron ($q.v.$). (MAA)

TOTE HIERARCHY. A scheme proposed by Miller, Galanter and Pribam in reaction to stimulus-response theories of behavior. It introduces programs into psychology via a hierarchy of feedback schemes called TOTE units because of their common scheme "*T*est, *O*perate if discrepancy exists, *T*est, *E*xit if discrepancy has been removed." (MAA)

TRACT. A bundle of nerve fibers in the central nervous system that have similar connectivities. (JCE)

TRANSFORMATIONAL COMPONENT. See generative grammar. (IGM & AML)

TRANSFORMATIONAL GRAMMAR. A device for explicit, precise description of languages which represents the syntactic regularities of a language by a set of base rules (for forming deep phrase structures) and a set of grammatical transformations (for converting deep structures into surface phrase structures. (PSP)

TRANSFORMATIONAL RULES. See generative grammer. (IGM & AML)

TREE, LABELLED. See generative grammar (IGM & AML)

TROLAND. Is a unit of retinal illumination equal to 2.5 d^2 millilamberts, where d is the diameter of the pupil of the eye in millimeters. The millilambert is a unit of stimulus luminance (intensity per unit project area of an extended source). Good interior illumination will cause a white piece of paper to have a luminance of about 50 millilamberts. (RMB)

TURING MACHINE. A device which consists of a control box containing a finite program, and a tape-scanner-printer-mover whereby it can interact with an indefinitely extendable tape, divided lengthwise into squares. It is believed that for every effective procedure for transforming strings of symbols there exists a program which will enable a Turing machine to carry out the transformation on any string of symbols presented one symbol per square upon its tape. (MAA)

UNIDIRECTIONAL RATE SENSITIVITY. Asymmetric, dynamic behavior of a biologic channel of communication and control which allows the channel to respond more readily to changes in a variable for one direction of change than the other. One of the results of this dynamic asymmetry is a DC shift with repetitive stimulation. (MC)

VERB PHRASE. That grammatical category containing as its members all sequences consisting of a verb and its complements (e.g., direct object, indirect object, prepositional phrase adjuncts, etc.) or of an adjective plus its complements. (PSP)

VISUAL MASKING. Interference in the perception of a visual stimulus which comes about when it is paired with another stimulus. Temporal separation between the stimuli shows both proactive and retroactive interference effects. Current research has made it evident that several different kinds of masking phenomena may be discerned which appear to be brought about by different neural mechanisms. (PHS)

VISUAL NOISE. A randomly patterned stimulus used to degrade other stimuli. Frequently used in a background masking context. (RNH)

VISUAL PERSISTENCE. Judgement by a perceiver that some excitation persists after the physical energy in the stimulus has terminated. It is this persistence on which short-term visual storage is based. (RNH)

* Definition specifically used in this volume.

INDICES

Author Index

Abramson, A., 110
Adey, W. R., 231–234, 236, 237
Adkins, R. J., 233
Adrian, E. D., 210
Albe-Fessard, D., 234
Alpern, M., 141, 145
Amassian, V. E., 232, 234
Andersen, P., 280
Arbib, M. A., 3, 4, 8, 10, 11, 13
Ariens, E. J., 274
Armstrong, D. M., 256, 257
Assanuma, H., 234, 237–240
Aschoff, J. C., 233
Attneave, F., 209, 210, 212, 213
Averbach, M., 130

Barlow, H. B., 14, 207, 209, 212, 215, 217–221
Bard, P., 232, 236
Barzdin, Y. M., 5
Battersby, W. S., 174
Bender, D., 141
Benton, A. L., 53
Beurle, R. L., 40
Bever, T., 69, 70
Bishop, P. O., 147, 148
Blum, M., 294
Blumenthal, A., 69
Boldrey, E., 231, 233
Boole, G., 222
Boycott, B. B., 288
Boynton, R. M., 142–143, 145, 155

Broadbent, D. E., 90, 108
Brodal, A., 232, 259
Brooks, V. B., 231, 240
Bryden, M. P., 108
Burns, B. D., 233
Buser, P., 233–235

Caianiello, E., 293
Cajal, R. Y., 216
Calhoun, J. B., 307
Cataldo, M., 128
Chaney, R. B., 108
Chistovich, L. A., 101
Chomsky, N., 54, 66, 68, 74–76, 98, 103, 105
Clynes, M., 179, 183, 185
Coffey, J. L., 99
Cole, K. S., 280
Coleman, E., 69
Collins, J. F., 141
Colonnier, M., 239, 249
Condouris, G. A., 280
Cooley, J. W., 282, 284
Cooper, F. S., 98, 102
Coriell, A. S., 130
Craik, K., 210
Csillag-Kalmar, 72
Culbertson, J. T., 319, 320

Da Fonseca, J. S., 294, 305
Dainoff, M., 125
Darwin, C., 183

361

Subject Index